The B
Guide to 2000 British and European Carp Waters

Compiled by
Kevin Maddocks
and
Peter Mohan

ACKNOWLEDGEMENTS

We are especially grateful to Ann Pillinger, who deciphered all of PM's dreadful handwriting and entered over 500 new waters in her computer, Roberto Ripamonti, who supplied us with the complete new section on Italy and Norman Smith, from Spain, who compiled and listed all the Spanish waters.

We should also like to thank all those who have written in with corrections and amendments from the last edition and those whom we hope will send us the same type of information on the current edition.

* County Maps
Please note that these maps are not to scale, nor are the locations indicated the exact geographical position of the place concerned. They are only intended to be a rough guide when the reader does not have a proper map to hand.

** A
Waters which have the symbol beside them have some form of accommodation with them, and so are particularly suitable for holidays: many of them for families.

Cover picture: Sunset at Withy Pool.

Withy Pool, Bedford Road, Henlow Camp,
Beds, SG16 6 EA. England.

ISBN 0 947674 46 2

Introduction

It has been said that the last thing left to do in carp fishing is to publish a list of carp waters and their locations, and this is what Beekay International have tried to do with this book. We feel that the publication of this material ushers in a new era in carp fishing; one which is long overdue. The time has passed for one of the major factors in carp fishing to be the excessive secrecy which was a characteristic of the sport in past years.

In 1969, when the British Carp Study Group, the world's first large national organisation for carp anglers was founded by Peter Mohan, there were probably about 250 specialist carp anglers in the whole country; now there are reliably estimated to be around 50,000, many of whom demand every type of information about baits, methods and rigs, and also about locations of carp waters.

Secrecy

The older and more secretive carp anglers, who don't like the idea of a book of this kind, should remember that they are very much in the minority;most of today's carp anglers welcome a book of this sort. We have been very careful to omit all waters we know to be 'secret'; we have left out any waters, club or otherwise, where there are 'no publicity' rules; and we have omitted all waters where membership cannot be obtained. We even asked many carp anglers which waters they wanted to be left out of the book, and we did not include those waters!

Most of the waters listed are those which anyone can fish, and which were already known to many anglers. We don't feel that a listing in this book will substantially increase the number fishing any particular water; in fact, the number fishing your water may actually be reduced when readers learn about other waters from this book and go to fish them, thus 'spreading the load' better on waters throughout the country.

We are not in the business of giving away anglers' secrets and this has been carefully avoided in the book as far as possible.This book will have its critics, but we feel that like anything new it has now been accepted and has become as natural a part of the carp scene as any book on carp methods and tactics, and that all carp anglers will want to own a copy. Obviously, the book will be particularly helpful to the many thousands of anglers who take up specialist carp fishing every year, but we feel it will also be especially helpful to more experienced carp anglers who wish to try other waters, and we are sure that it will be of great help to the many who write to well known carp anglers regularly asking them for the names of waters they can fish whilst they are on holiday in different parts of the country.

Carp Waters

It must be noted by readers that many of the waters listed in this book are not really 'carp waters', if this is taken to mean waters containing mainly, or only, carp. In fact there are very few waters in the country which contain only carp, or where carp are very much in the majority. Most waters contain only some carp, and so many of these have been included in this book. We have listed many waters which contain few carp, because some carp anglers prefer to fish this type of water in the hope of big carp from an unrecognised water. So please don't expect most of the lakes to be packed with carp; they often aren't.

Quite a few of those 'secret' and 'no publicity' lakes which we have not been able to list in this book may come under the category of waters which contain mainly carp, and often big ones - which is the reason those who control the waters of this kind want to keep them quiet!

Organisation of the book

Some angling guides we have examined are so complex that they are difficult to use, and to avoid this we kept the layout of the book as simple as possible. The waters are classified into counties,whch are arranged in alphabetical order, and the waters under each county name are also arranged in alphabetical order, with an index at the back of the book. The categories are listed for each water, and there are no abbreviations so there is nothing to look up; all the information you will need will be under the entry for the venue concerned.

We don't feel it appropriate for a book of this kind to include instructional articles or 'tips' on carp fishing. If you want this kind of material, obtain copies of a carp magazine, or we can strongly recommend the following books also published by BK International: *Carp Fever* by Kevin Maddocks, Carp: *Successful Angling Series* by Rob Maylin, and *Carp Sense* by Jim Gibbinson. There are also three other books in this series; *The Beekay Guide to Carp Fishing, The Beekay Guide to Carp Rigs* and *The Beekay Guide to Carp Baits.* All the information about baits, methods, tackle, flavours, bait recipes and rigs will be found in these books.Beekay also publish a large range of carp videos under the Clean River label.

Research

Readers (and reviewers!) should take careful note of the fact that it is absolutely impossible for a guide of this kind to be completely accurate.

The present revision took six months work, followed by three months to prepare and print the book. During this time, it is inevitable that many of the details listed have changed; in fact, we were making' corrections of corrections' right up to the last minute, but it was obviously impossible to make corrections after the book had gone to print - and it takes three months at least to print a book, during which time some of the information in the book is obviously out of date, as waters change hands, or owners change fishing costs.

In addition, in January this year we wrote over 300 letters to people many of whom controlled waters listed in this book and only 150 replies were received - had the other 150 answered our letter, the book would undoubtedly be even more accurate.

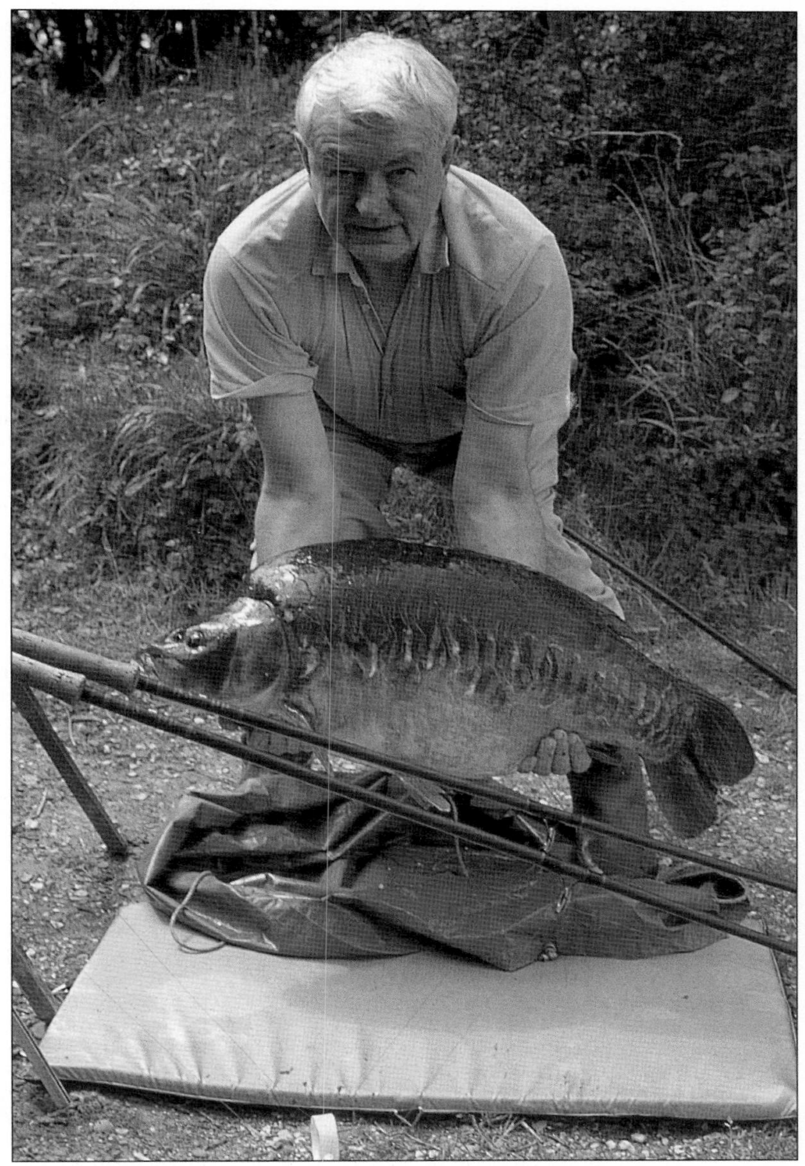

Peter Mohan with a lovely mirror of 33 1/2 pounds.

Even some of our critics were of little help; they told us where we were wrong, but many didn't bother to send us the correct information, so that we could put it right!

If you can help, please contact us as soon as possible, so that we can make further corrections for the next edition in two years time.

Because of the obvious problems mentioned above, the Publishers can take no responsiblity for any mistakes or omissions which may have occurred - all of our information is published in good faith, but it would have taken us many years to visit all the waters listed, in which case the book would never have been published, and some of the informaton supplied by others, may not necessarily be accurate.

We have done our best to make the information as accurate as possible, but had we taken any longer to check it even more carefully, more details would have become out of date!

Some of the categories such as whether a water is easy, moderate or difficult are subjective, and some anglers may not agree with us; we can only enter in what our judgement is correct.

We shall be happy to hear from readers if they have any criticism of the information provided, and especially if they would like to add any waters to the book which they think should be included. Just write to Beekay International at the address given at the beginning of the book, if you wish to comment on any of the information given, or to add anything to the new edition.

Information

Please note the book is a 'guide' to carp waters. Exactly the same information is not included for every water, and any omissions are intentional. If you find that categories are omitted from some of the waters this was simply because we were not able to obtain the information in the case of that water to enable us to complete the category. If there was information which we were unable to obtain or which we weren't sure about, we simply left out that category.

In some cases we were able to find out very little about a water, but as long as we were able to give a rough idea of where it was, that it existed, and that it contained some carp, and that we could indicate in some way in which you could obtain permission to fish, then we thought it better to include the venue, and leave it to you to find out the rest of the information yourselves.

Revision

It is our intention to revise and up-date the book every two years, or sooner, so any information you can provide for future editions will be gratefully received by the Publishers, and will enable us to keep this guide up to date. (Please use the form at the back of this guide.)

Well-known Waters

Some readers may be surprised to find some of the well-known carp waters omitted from the list. As we have already said, we can see no point in listing waters which you cannot fish and other well-known waters have a publicity ban; there would be no point in including them, as this would only cause trouble for those lucky enough to be able to fish there. For this reason, some of the better known lakes have been left out.

Day Ticket Waters

In many cases, you can get permission to fish these waters in advance at the address given; if you can't, it might be worth going to the water and fishing. In many cases, there are bailiffs who will collect your money on the spot, although sometimes you may have to pay more if you buy a permit on the bank.

If it is stated that you must obtain a ticket in advance, it is advisable to do so, or you may be banned from fishing the water.

Club Waters

Clubs have some of the best carp waters in the country, but the carp anglers may well have to share the water with non-carp anglers. It pays to try to get on with other anglers, whatever you may think of them. If you upset them too much, you may well find that the clubs start to ban carp anglers; this has already happened in some cases. We are in a minority on waters of this kind, so we should be careful how we behave.

We are sorry that so few good club carp waters are included in this guide. We know of many good club waters but it has not been found possible to include them because most of the clubs seem to be very shy of publicity.

To give some idea of the problems of compiling a guide of this kind, we wrote to more than 100 of the major clubs which we know have good carp fisheries, most containing carp of over 20lbs; some of these were clubs, which advertise in the angling press for more members from time to time.

Less than 10% replied.

Syndicate Waters

Most syndicate waters have not been included because in many cases it is impossible to obtain membership. Those that are included are on the request of those in charge of the water. We have not put syndicate waters in without permission, and since these are always on private property readers should not go to these waters without permission. We know of a number of cases where anglers have lost their chance of getting into a syndicate water by walking round that water before being given permission to do so! Syndicate water locations are deliberately omitted to avoid unwelcome visitors. Please remember that a syndicate leader is under no obligation to offer membership to anyone; he is likely to be very choosy.

Using the Information Contained in this book

Please remember to use this book as the 'guide' it is intended to be. Read the information on the water concerned and then try and find out as much more about it as you can, which will help you to be successful with your fishing here.

Don't expect every bit of information to be exactly accurate, although, as we have already said, we have tried to be as careful as possible about accuracy. However, waters change, often rapidly, and what was the best bait or method at the time of compilation may not be so by the time you get to the water. This applies to prices, of course, which may be altered at any time. It may even apply to the ownership or control of the water, which may have changed during the compilation or printing of this book, which has taken about a year. So please don't blame us if you go to a water

Some lines are cheap...

Some lines are expensive...

listed and find you can't fish it because control or other circumstances have changed since we listed it; just let us know how the circumstances have changed so that we can include the altered information in our next revision of this book. Club Secretaries change frequently, for example; those we have included were correct when we went to press.

Categories

Our categories are: Carp Only; Carp Water; Mixed Fishery; Few Carp. These are all self-explanatory, except perhaps the 'Carp Water' category, which in our judgement means that the water contains mainly carp.

BK Ratings

Our ratings are: Very Easy; Easy; Moderate; Fairly Hard; Difficult; Very Difficult; Super-Difficult.

As we have said earlier, these ratings are only our opinion; if you disagree, please let us know.

Carp Anglers' Behaviour

We do feel that a note in connection with this subject is appropriate in a book of this kind, especially as many people who control waters have told us that the behaviour of some carp anglers is giving cause for concern.

Do not leave litter of any kind - take it home with you, and be especially careful not to leave monofilament nylon line at the water side; it can damage birds and animals. Leave the bank clean and tidy, and do nothing in any way to upset or annoy other anglers, those who own the waters, or those who may visit them. At a time when angling is under attack by many people, most of whom know nothing about the subject, be conservation conscious, and try to be a good example of an angler. Do not harm waterbirds, either directly or indirectly, keep to bye-laws, especially those which have been introduced in connection with the use of lead weights, shut all gates and do nothing to damage the banks or vegetation on the waters you fish.

Long-stay carp fishing is already causing carp anglers to be banned from some waters; if the 'float angler' can never get a place to fish because all the swims are occupied by carp anglers who live in bivvies and hardly ever leave the water, which is happening in some places, it won't be long before those who control waters start to ban this type of fishing. You have only yourself to blame if this happens. There are others to consider apart from yourself; others who have as much right to be on the water as you have, and if you spoil their fishing, they may soon be at a club meeting voting out your type of fishing!

Leaving baits out for long priods whilst you are away is another thing which has been getting carp anglers a bad name in some quarters; all of these points will only give extra help to those who are against angling, and we would urge our readers to avoid these bad aspects of modern carp fishing.

Rod Licences

It is an offence not to have the appropriate rod licences, and you may also break the rules of the water you are fishing if you don't obtain them. Even if you are one of those people who don't approve of rod licences you will certainly find that for the sake of a few

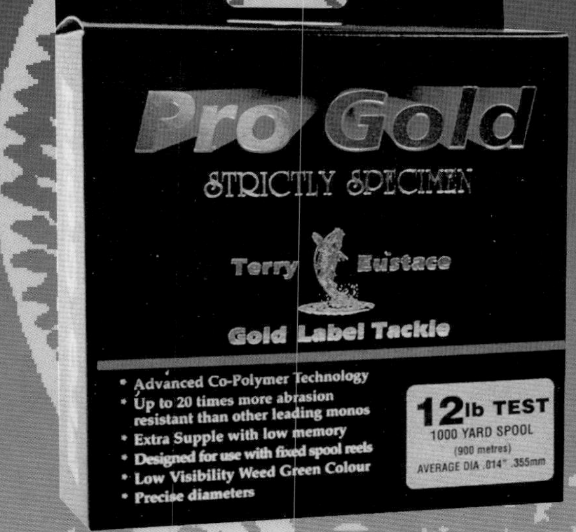

"Confidence puts more fish on the bank than any specialist tackle or bait. 'Pro-Gold' lines by Gold Label Tackle simply double that confidence.
Brilliant for abrasion resistance castability and wet knot strength in all circumstances."
JOHN BAKER

"I thought I was happy with the line I have been using for the last five years. I didn't think anything could change my mind...until I tried the new Pro-Gold from Gold Label...This line will revolutionise the specimen line market. It looks like Terry is on to another winner here."
DES TAYLOR

is priceless

For further details, see inside back cover.

for inclusion in the next issue of this Guide, there is no charge for any insertion, although you may also take advertising space if you wish to do so - rates on application. You can ensure the opportunity to advertise by returning the advertisement enquiry form at the back of this guide. You will be contacted at the right time prior to production of the next edition.

We hope later editions of the 'BK Guide to Carp Waters' will eventually list every carp water in the country which can be fished by the general angling public; with your co-operation we are sure this can be achieved.

Good fishing, and we hope you enjoy your time spent in the beautiful British countryside - or even on the slightly less attractive town waters!

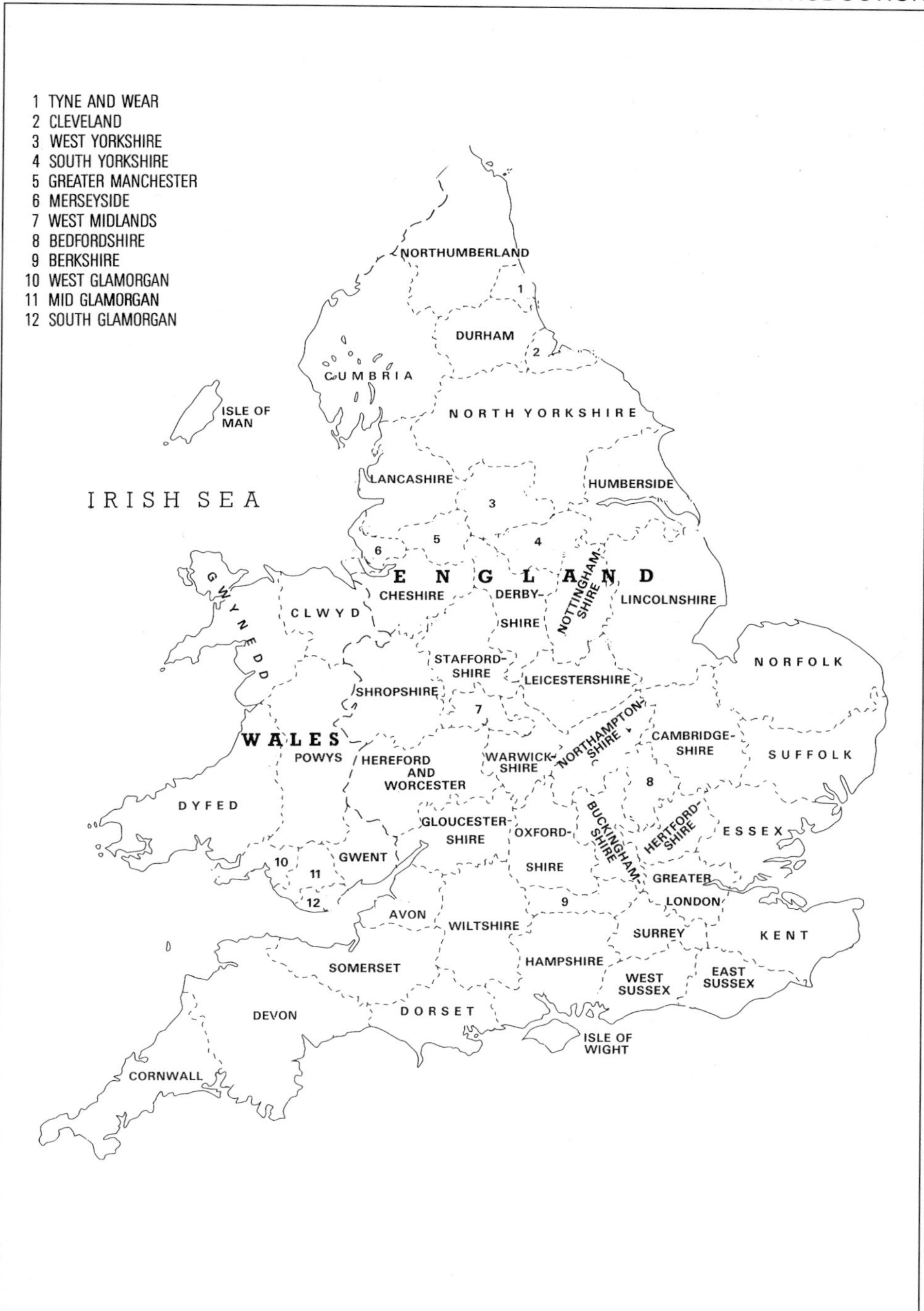
1 TYNE AND WEAR
2 CLEVELAND
3 WEST YORKSHIRE
4 SOUTH YORKSHIRE
5 GREATER MANCHESTER
6 MERSEYSIDE
7 WEST MIDLANDS
8 BEDFORDSHIRE
9 BERKSHIRE
10 WEST GLAMORGAN
11 MID GLAMORGAN
12 SOUTH GLAMORGAN
NORTHUMBERLAND
DURHAM
CUMBRIA
ISLE OF MAN
NORTH YORKSHIRE
IRISH SEA
LANCASHIRE
HUMBERSIDE
ENGLAND
GWYNEDD
CLWYD
CHESHIRE
DERBY-SHIRE
NOTTINGHAM-SHIRE
LINCOLNSHIRE
NORFOLK
STAFFORD-SHIRE
LEICESTERSHIRE
SHROPSHIRE
WALES
POWYS
HEREFORD AND WORCESTER
WARWICK-SHIRE
NORTHAMPTON-SHIRE
CAMBRIDGE-SHIRE
SUFFOLK
DYFED
GLOUCESTER-SHIRE
OXFORD-SHIRE
BUCKINGHAM-SHIRE
HERTFORD-SHIRE
ESSEX
GWENT
GREATER LONDON
AVON
WILTSHIRE
SURREY
KENT
SOMERSET
HAMPSHIRE
WEST SUSSEX
EAST SUSSEX
DEVON
DORSET
ISLE OF WIGHT
CORNWALL

5 LAKES HEAVILY STOCKED WITH CARP to 24LBS,

.....AND ALL JUST A STONES THROW

CATFISH to 22lbs, TENCH, BREAM, ROACH AND
ALLS
OARSE
RY
Top class cabaret nightly in our very exclusive club, childrens entertainment programme, a superb heated swimming pool complex with spa-bath, sauna and solarium. Restaurant, take-away, shop and launderette are all part of the amenities which we hope will ensure your family have a holiday to remember. Bait and Tackle are available in our excellent on site Tackle Lodge so all aspects of fishing are catered for.
AA
BRITISH GRADED HOLIDAY PARKS
ROSE AWARD
CARAVAN HOLIDAY PARK
1997
FROM YOUR HOLIDAY ACCOMMODATION

CONTENTS

The county designations used in this book are those used since the boundary changes in 1974.

This means, for example, that there is now an East Sussex and a West Sussex, and that counties such as 'Middlesex' (now Greater London) and 'Worcestershire' (now Hereford and Worcester), no longer exist.

We started this revision in the summer of 1996. We understand that in 1997 the counties are changing yet again, so we suggest you check adjacent areas to find out if waters are now in a different county. The waters in Ireland are all in the Irish Republic - we have not been able to track down any waters containing carp in Northern Ireland.

AVON

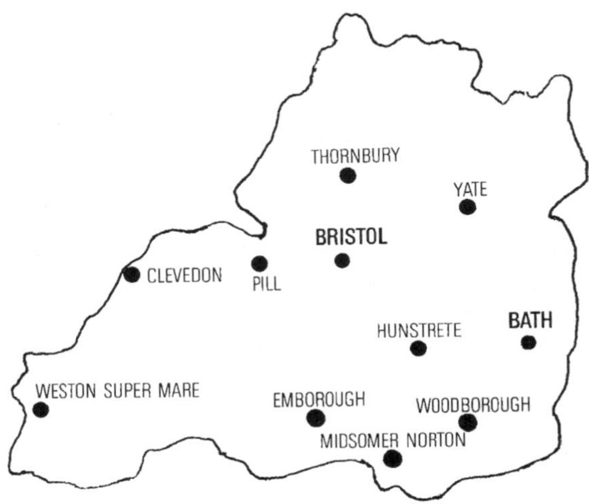

Bitterwell Lake

Location: Coalpit Heath, north Bristol
Type and Size: Two acre pit
How to Find: About one mile from recreation ground at Coalpit Heath
Carp Stock: Heavily stocked, many small mirrors but occasional 20 caught
Category: Mixed Fishery
Other Species: Rudd, roach, tench, eels, small bream
Permits: Caravan on site Tel: 01454 778960
Cost: £2.50 per rod per day (concessions)
Baits/Methods: Normal carp methods and bait plus float fishing
Control: Council day and season ticket (Bristol Corporation)
Restrictions: No night fishing although occasional night fishing permission can be obtained. No loose feeding. Barbless hooks. No nuts.
E/A: Wessex
BK Rating: Moderate
Comments: Hard fished, 'town' water, often shoulder to shoulder at weekends Tackle shop on site.

Emborough Pond

Location: Ston Easton, near Midsomer Norton
Type and Size: Six acre lake
How to Find: Off the A37 south of Bristol
Carp Stock: Some carp, mostly small commons
Category: Few Carp
Other Species: General coarse fish
Permits: Day tickets on bank, information from I. Crudgington, 37 Broad Street, Bath (tackle shop). Tel: 01225 466325
Cost: On application
Control: Knowle Angling Centre
E/A Wessex
Comments: 'Public' lake in attractive surroundings

Fishponds Lido

Location: Alcove Road, off Fishponds Road in the City of Bristol
Type and Size: Deep old pit of about an acre or less
How to Find: From the centre of Bristol find Fishponds Road and Alcove Road is less than a mile from the City Centre on the right. A path leads down to the lake.
Carp Stock: Probably about 60 carp which were put in, in two stockings. Fish from the earlier stocking have reached upper double figure size and some 20s.
Category: Mixed Fishery
Other Species: Roach, tench and perch
Permits: Season tickets from Fishponds Lido Angling Club, with a limited membership and a waiting list. Details and cost from Burt Elson, Tel: 01454 250407.
Restrictions: No night fishing
Control: Club
E/A Wessex
BK Rating: Moderate
Comments: A town water surrounded by houses and with a floating restaurant on it yet the water contains 20lb carp, which shows these can be caught within a city.

Ham Green Lake

Location: Behind Ham Green Hospital, Pill, near Bristol
Type and Size: Dammed estate lake in two parts, about an acre each
How to Find: Take the A369 Bristol/Portishead road and turn right, signposted 'Ham Green and Pill'. Turn first right to Ham Green Hospital and continue down hill. Lake will be seen on the right.
Carp Stock: Not large numbers, perhaps 50 fish in both lakes. Commons to about 11lbs. Mirrors to about 16lbs. A well authenticated fish of 20lbs was caught in 1991.
Category: Mixed Fishery
Other Species: Roach, rudd, tench, pike, eels
Permits: On bank or Veals Tackle, Old Market, Bristol
Cost: On application
Control: Syndicate - Mr R Barnes, Withywood, Bristol
Baits/Methods: Normal carp methods and baits. Some surface fishing
BK Rating: Fairly Hard
E/A: Wessex
Comments: Heavily weeded and full of lilies. Upper part best.

Henleaze Lake

Location: Henleaze, Bristol, near the Downs
Type and Size: 3 acre town lake, used by a swimming club
Carp Stock: Singles and doubles to 19lbs
Category: Mixed Fishery
Other Species: Pike, perch, roach, tench and crucians
Permits: Waiting list: Tel: 01179 623748
BK Rating: Easy
E/A: Wessex

Hunstrete Lake

Location: Village of Hustrete, near Bath
Type and Size: Dammed estate lake of about 5 acres
How to Find: Take the main A4 Bath to Bristol road, and then the left fork (A368) at traffic lights at Newton St Loe. After about 2 miles turn right towards Hunstrete and there is a path to the lake on the left, just before the village.
Carp Stock: Probably only about 20-30 fish, most of which are doubles. Two twenties reported caught in 1985. There might be as many as four 20's in the lake.
Category: Mixed Fishing
Other Species: Tench, roach, bream
Permits: Syndicate: Tel: 01934 632471
Restrictions: No night fishing
Control: Club
BK Rating: Easy
Baits/Methods: Advanced carp fishing rigs and baits necessary
E/A: Wessex
Comments: This is the lake named by Dick Walker in his literature as 'Lackey's Leap'. Fishing here with 'BB' Dick hooked one of the original commons, which now seem to have died out, and played it on very light tackle for an hour and 55 minutes, only to find it had the hook in its mouth and the line looped round a spine of the dorsal fin, which is perhaps why it fought so hard. Dick thought it was a 30, and the British record was then 26lbs; the fish actually weighed only 9 3/4 lbs. There is a small syndicate on this water, details from the secretary.

Linear Fisheries Oxford

MANOR FARM
LAKE 30LB 2OZ

Hutton Pond

Location: Hutton Moor Road, Weston-Super-Mare
Type and Size: Ballast pit of about 1 1/2 acres
How to Find: Turn off the M5 motorway at the Weston-Super-Mare exit and after about a mile find Hutton Moor Road on the left, shortly after the left hand Banwell turn. The pond will be found on the left after about 600 yards.
Carp Stock: A small number of mirrors most of which are lower doubles and are now quite old. Best known authenticated carp caught is 18 1/4 lbs.
Category: Few Carp
Other Species: Bream, roach, rudd, tench
Permits: Enquire locally
BK Rating: Difficult, as there are not many carp
Baits/Methods: Good specialist methods needed as these fish have been caught quite a lot over the years. Some may still be taken on floating crust after dark or in the early morning. Normal carp boilies etc best on the bottom. Bream a problem on soft baits, hard boilies such as KM Boilies work well
E/A: Wessex
Comments: Not a very pleasant little place, with a road on one side, a railway line across the north end, and a 'factory' on the opposite side to the road. This bank is out of bounds as the 'factory' is a Government institution of some kind. The lake is long and narrow and nearly all carp are caught very close to the reeds on the 'factory' side; in fact; it is considered to be a waste of time anywhere but within a metre of this farther reed hedge

Leigh Farm **A**

Location: Pensford, Bristol, BS18 4BQ - between Bristol and Bath
Type and Size: Several small ponds
Carp Stock: Well stocked with carp to 10 lbs
Category: Mixed Fishery
Other Species: Tench
Permits: No day tickets, but some pre-booked parties may fish during the week
Cost: On application. Some free fishing to those who stay
Control: Tel: 01761 490281
Restrictions: Fishing permitted from stages only. No boilies or grroundbait. No night fishing; barbless hooks
BK Rating: Moderate
E/A: Wessex
Comments: Self-catering accommodation in cottages and bungalows - request details

THE BEEKAY GUIDE TO 2000 BRITISH & EUROPEAN CARP WATERS

Is YOUR Water listed? If so, are the details correct?
If you spot omissions, inaccuracies, or know of any changes, please let us know by filling in the Waters Questionnaire at the back of this guide and return it to us at:

Beekay International
Withy Pool
Henlow Camp
Bedfordshire
SG16 6EA

Kevin Maddocks

Carp Rods

Challenger™, Exocet™ and Silurus™ are registered European Trade Marks

Newton Park

Location: Newton St Loe, near Bath
Type and Size: 3 1/2 acre shallow lake
Carp Stock: Stocked with 1,250lbs of carp - all small - from 4oz to 10lbs
Category: Carp Water
Other Species: Roach and perch
Permits: A members only water of Bathampton AA - tickets from local tackle shops. Secretary: D Crookes, 25 Otago Terrace, Larkhall, Bath.
Control: Club. Tel: 01275 343928
Restrictions: Barbless hooks;no keepnets; no night fishing
BK Rating: Very Easy
E/A: Wessex
Comments: Cost is £2.50 per day to club members only. £16 per season. Concessions.

Tanhouse Farm

Location: Chipping Sodbury, near Bristol
Type and Size: Old 5 acre stone quarry
Carp Stock: Well stocked with carp to mid-doubles
Category: Mixed Fishery
Other Species: General coarse fish
Permits: Mrs James, Tanhouse Farm
Cost:: About £4 per day. Season tickets
Control: Tel: 01454 228280
Restrictions: No boilies or cat/dog foods
BK Rating: Moderate
E/A: Severn Trent
Comments: Touring caravans welcome. Toilet and washroom at farm.

Woodborough Park Lake

Location: Woodborough Court near Midsomer Norton
Type and Size: Dammed estate lake of about 2 acres
How to Find: Take the A367 Radstock road from Bath, and about two miles before Radstock you will see a left turn to Woodborough Court. Cars must be left in the car park on the right and it is about half a mile walk across fields to the lake.
Carp Stock: Well stocked with mirrors many of which are under 10lbs, but there are some doubles and the best reported is about 15lbs.
Category: Mixed Fishery
Other Species: Tench, roach, and perch
Permits: This lake is on the same ticket as Hunstrete Lake, Bathampton Angling Association. Open membership from the General Secretary Dave Crookes, 25 Otago Terrace, Larkhall, Bath, Avon Tel: 01275 343928. In addition, only a few tickets are issued per day, and these must be obtained at a small extra cost from Crudgington Fishing Tackle, Bath or from Veals Fishing Tackle, Old Market, Bristol.
Cost: Approximately £20 per season plus a small daily payment
Restrictions: No night fishing; the dam is out of bounds
BK Rating: Easy
Baits/Methods: Normal carp fishing baits and methods
E/A: Wessex
Comments: A very pleasant little water if you don't mind the walk. Since tickets are limited to four a day it can never get crowded. Bathampton AA now has another newly dug pond containing carp near Hunstrete.

BEDFORDSHIRE

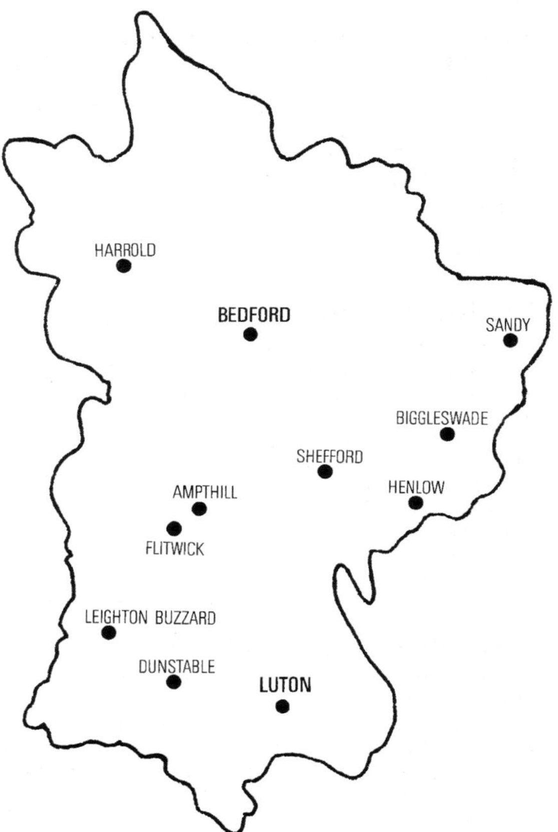

Airman Pit

Location: On the A600 Bedford road, between Withy Pool and Shefford
Type and Size: Brick pit of about 3½ acres
How to Find: On the left hand side of the main A600 Hitchin to Bedford road between Kevin Maddocks' Withy Pool and the village of Shefford, next to the Airman pub
Carp Stock: Well stocked with small carp, a few doubles and one or two twenties
Category: Carp Water
Other Species: Roach, rudd, tench, pike, catfish, perch
Permits: Seasonal from Shefford and District AA. Secretary: Mrs P Leath, 3 Ivel Close, Shefford. Tel: 01462 812323; or from Chris's Tackle Box, Biggleswade, Beds
Cost: £28 per season. Concessions available.
Control: Club
E/A: Anglian
BK Rating: Easy
Comments: There is another pit containing many carp on the same ticket

Ampthill Reservoir

Location: Off the A 507 at Ampthill
Type and Size: Small pool
Carp Stock: Well stocked with small carp - a few to 20 lbs
Category: Mixed Fishery
Other Species: Tench, roach, rudd, crucians and perch
Permits: Local tackle shops - no day tickets
Cost: £22.50 per season; £8.50 juniors and O.A.P's
Control: Ampthill D.A.F.P.S. Tel: 01525 403293
BK Rating: Not known
E/A: Anglian

Arlesey Lake

Location: Church End, Arlesey, near Hitchin
Type and Size: Very deep, old brick pit of about 12 acres
How to Find: Turn right going north on the A600 (Hitchin to Bedford road) at Henlow Camp, then right again at A507 junction - lake is alongside railway line on left hand side
Carp Stock: Plenty of upper doubles and some good twenties
Category: Mixed Fishery
Other Species: Perch, tench, roach, pike, catfish
Permits: D Beatham, Etonbury Farm, Stotfold Road, Arlesey SG16 6XB. Tel: 01462 731709
Cost: On application
Control: Syndicate
BK Rating: Moderate
E/A: Anglian
Comments: Famous as the lake where the late Richard Walker invented the Arlesey Bomb for fishing for the big perch at long range in 40ft of water. The lake is now partially filled in and the future of the lake as a fishery is unsure.

Beckerings Park Farm Reservoir

Location: Steppingly, near Flitwick, just to the left of the A418 Flitwick - Millbrook Road
Type and Size: 5 acre irrigation reservoir
Carp Stock: Stocked in 1990 with 25 doubles including 7 carp over 20lbs
Category: Mixed Fishery
Other Species: Tench, roach, and bream
Permits: Members only water of Luton and District AC. Secretary: G Buss, 1 Easthill Road, Houghton Regis, Dunstable, Beds LU5 5EQ. Permits can be obtained from local tackle shops, especially Leslie's of Luton. About £20 per season. Concessions.
Control: Club. Tel: 01582 28114
Restrictions: Members Only
BK Rating: Moderate
E/A: Anglian

Bedford Boating Lake

Location: Alongside the River Great Ouse, Bedford Embankment
Type and Size: Public town lake of bout 2 acres
Carp Stock: Occasional carp reported, including a 20lb common in July 1991
Category: Few Carp
Other Species: Roach, dace, bream, perch and pike
Permits: None necessary - free fishing. Anglian licence required

BK Rating: Difficult
E/A: Anglian
Comments: Busy town boating lake not known for its carp, but it does contain one or two good fish; lots of people and water birds. In August 1991 a famous match angler caught a 4lb terrapin here, which bit its captor - so anything could happen in this public lake.

Beeston Waters, River Ivel

Location: Sandy
Type and Size: Narrow river
Carp Stock: Plenty of carp to 20 lbs
Category: Mixed Fishery
Other Species: Chub, roach, bream, barbel and pike
Permits: In advance only from local tackle shops
Cost: £25 per season; concessions
Control: Biggleswade and Hitchin D.A.A. Tel: 01767 314902
BK Rating: Difficult
Baits/Methods: Boilies are the best bait
E/A: Anglian
Comments: Open June 16th to March 14th

Blue Lagoon

Location: On the Beds/Herts border near Arlesey
Type and Size: 60 foot deep chalk pit of over 30 acres
Carp Stock: Not many carp, but there are some big ones - a 37lb leather was caught in 1989 and at least one other 30 in 1990
Category: Few Carp
Other Species: Big pike, tench, bream, rudd, roach, perch and chub
Permits: 24 hour day tickets on bank, and also season tickets
Cost: Day tickets about £3 per day
BK Rating: Difficult
E/A: Anglian
Comments: A true big fish water, with most fish caught in shallow water close in.

Blunham L-Shaped Lake

Location: Blunham, between Sandy on the A1 and Bedford (A603)
Type and Size: Long, narrow gravel pit of 5 acres
How to Find: Turn off the A1 at Sandy and go to Blunham
Carp Stock: Quite well stocked to upper twenties
Category: Mixed Fishery
Other Species: Tench, roach, rudd, bream, perch
Permits: Season tickets from Blunham Angling Club, and local tackle shops
Cost: £20 per season
Control: Club - Secretary: G Palmer, Tel: 012302 3959
BK Rating: Difficult
E/A: Anglian

Blunham Pits

Location: Blunham, just off the A1 at Sandy, near Biggleswade
Type and Size: 2 lakes of 6 and 7 acres, both gravel pits, and a stretch of the River Ivel
How to Find: Turn off the A1 at Sandy, and the lakes will be seen near Blunham
Carp Stock: Muddy Lake - good head of doubles and a few twenties to over 30lbs Clear Lake - good head of doubles and a few twenties
Category: Muddy - Carp Water; Clear - Mixed Fishery

Other Species: Tench, roach, rudd, pike and perch
Permits: Often vacancies from Mr Twell, Maperton Lodge, Station Road, Raunds, Northants. Tel: 01903 622007
Cost: Approximately £45 per person
Control: Syndicate - try 01582 410277
BK Rating: Moderate
E/A: Anglian
Comments: Plenty of good carp in the River Ivel as well as in the pits

Briarwood Fishery

Location: Harlington, near Ampthill
Type and Size: 2 1/2 acre pretty 100 year old clay pits, with lilies and an island
How to Find: Come off the M1 at the Toddington junction (12) and turn towards Flitwick and Ampthill on the A5120. The fishery is sign posted on the right after 1/2 mile
Carp Stock: Well stocked with carp to 30 lbs
Category: Mixed Fishery
Other Species: Pike, tench, roach, rudd, perch and bream
Permits: On bank
Cost: £5 per day
Control: Private. Tel: 01525 872201
Restrictions: Night fishing by arrangement only at £10 per night
BK Rating: Moderate
Baits/Methods: Boilies and luncheon meat
E/A: Thames
Comments: This is an attractive fishery of two lakes joined by a channel, in the owner's garden

Broom Lake

Location: Between Shefford and Sandy on the A 658 road
Type and Size: Matured gravel pit of about 8 acres
Carp Stock: Carp to about 10 lbs
Category: Mixed Fishery
Other Species: Roach, bream, crucians, rudd, tench and perch
Permits: In advance only from local tackle shops
Cost: £26 per season; reductions for juniors, O.A.P's and disabled
Control: Shefford and District A.A. Tel: 01462 812323
Restrictions: No night fishing
BK Rating: Moderate
E/A: Anglian

Brogborough No.1 pit

Location: Ridgemont, near Ampthill
Type and Size: 15 acre brick pit
Carp Stock: Carp to upper twenties
Category: Mixed Fishery
Other Species: Big bream and other coarse fish
Permits: Tel: 01525 713626
Cost: Not known
Control: Ampthill A.C.
BK Rating: Difficult
E/A: Anglian

Elstow Pits

Location: Just off the A6 at Elstow near Bedford
Type and Size: Brick pit of 30 acres plus, Elstow No.2 is 25 acres
How to Find: The pit will be seen on the right hand side of the A6 road going south from Bedford, near the village of Elstow
Carp Stock: Well stocked with carp to 45lbs, with plenty of good doubles and 20's
Category: Carp Water
Other Species: Roach, rudd, tench, bream, pike

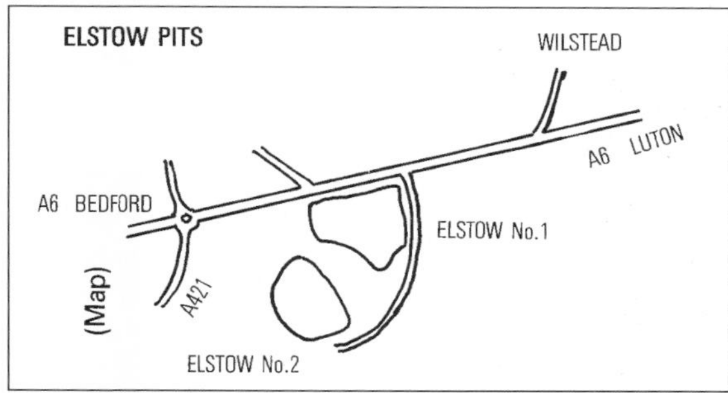

Permits: Syndicate only from Linear Fisheries, Bedford 10a Rackstraw Grove, Old Farm Park, Milton Keynes MK7 8PZ
Cost: £400 per season
Control: Linear Fisheries, Bedford. Tel: 01908 645135/647320
BK Rating: Moderate
Restrictions: No day tickets - season (syndicate in advance only). Rotas
E/A: Anglian
Comments: One of the best thirties waters. A big water with good carp fishing, although the fish can be hard to find. Normal carp fishing methods and baits. Regulars estimate there are 50-100 twenties in this lake, and fifty thirties. Best caught so far 45 3/4 lbs. in 1996. There is a second large pit on the site, which is included in the membership. This contains a small number (perhaps only 20) really big fish, most

Pit One at Elstow holds a large head of big carp like this fine 32 pounder of which are 20's, and thirties, with several forties caught in 1996. Separate membership for Pit 2 at about £150 per season.

Elstow No 2 Pit

Location: On the right hand side of the A6 Bedford - Luton road, 1 mile from Bedford

Type and Size: 25 acre brick pit

Carp Stock: 10 different thirties, and a 42 pounder was caught in 1995

Elstow No. 2 is the home of this fabulous 41 1/2 pounder known as 'The Mother'.

Category: Carp Water

Other Species: Rudd

Permits: From Linear Fisheries, 10a Rackstraw Grove, Old Farm Park, Milton Keynes. MK7 8PZ Tel: 01908 645135/ 647320

Cost: About £140 per season

Control: Linear Fisheries, Bedford.

BK Rating: Very difficult

E/A: Anglian

Comments: Open all year. Not many carp, but some very big ones. Syndicate membership includes waiting list for Elstow Pit One, which contains over thirty 30's and several 40's

Felmersham Gravel Pits

Location: Felmersham, off the A6 between Bedford and Rushden, and about 7 miles north of Bedford

Type and Stock: Two quite large gravel pits

Carp Stock: Well stocked with carp to about 10lbs

Category: Mixed Fishery

Other Species: Tench

Permits: Luton and District AA, Secretary: S R Branch, 3 Holmbrook Avenue, Luton, Beds, Members only

Cost: About £12.50 per season

Control: Club. Tel: 01582 28114

BK Rating: Moderate

E/A: Anglian

Fingers Lake

Location: In the town of Bedford, off Goldington Road, next to Priory Lake
Type and Size: Lake of about 5 acres
Carp Stock: Some carp to 24lbs
Category: Few Carp
Other Species: Tench to 7lbs, bream, roach, rudd, and pike
Permits: Day tickets on bank at £2 for adults; £1 for under 12's. Season tickets £5 for OAP's; cost includes the larger Priory Lake
Control: North Beds Borough Council. Tel: 01234 21182
Restrictions: No night fishing; fishing from pegged swims only
BK Rating: Moderate
E/A: Anglian

Green Lagoon

Location: Beds/Herts border near Arlesey
Type and Size: Three acre chalk pit, up to 30ft deep
Carp Stock: Fairly well stocked with carp to low twenties
Category: Mixed Fishery
Other Species: Large bream, tench, perch, pike and roach
Permits: 24 hour day ticket on bank; season tickets
Cost: About £3 per day
BK Rating: Moderate
E/A: Anglian
Comments: Heavily fished, with difficult access

Harrold - Odell Country Park

Location: 10 miles north west of Bedford
Type and Size: Matured gravel pit of about 7 acres
How to Find: The Country Park is signposted (5 miles) to the left of the A6 between Bedford and Rushden, shortly after the Falcon Inn
Carp Stock: Some carp, numbers and size not known
Category: Mixed Fishery
Other Species: Pike, roach, rudd,perch,tench and bream
Permits: The water is controlled by Harrold Working Mens AC: Tel: 01933 55696 (Cliff Roberts)
Control: Club
Restrictions: Members only. Probably no night fishing
E/A: Anglian
Comments: A pleasant lake, but in a busy country park with Nature Reserve. Details, refreshments etc on site. There is another much larger lake opposite, where there are certainly fish, and possibly carp, and we understand that there may later be public fishing in this one also. For information contact Bedfordshire Leisure Services Dept, Beds County Council, County Hall, Cauldwell Street, Bedford. Tel: 01234 63222.

Houghton Regis Quarry

Location: Houghton Road, Dunstable
Type and Size: 11 acre chalk pit
How to Find: At the end of the main street in Dunstable going towards Leighton Buzzard turn right at the roundabout towards Houghton Regis,and the pit is on the left.
Carp Stock: About 200 carp; the best caught to date is 23lbs, plenty of low doubles, but most fish between 9 and 11lbs.
Category: Mixed Fishery

Other Species: Roach, bream, tench and pike
Permits: Members only, Dunstable and District AC. Enquire in local tackle shops
Cost: Low cost for season tickets
Control: Club. Peter Garner. Tel: 01582 472067
Restrictions: Special permission needed for night fishing; members only
BK Rating: Moderate
E/A: Thames

Jones's Pit

Location: Close to the A5 at Heath and Reach, between Dunstable and Bletchley
Type and Size: Two clay pits, of 8 acres and 1 acre
Carp Stock: Quite heavily stocked, mainly with doubles, with the occasional 20. Only a few carp in the small lake.
Category: Mixed Fishery
Other Species: Catfish to 27lbs, roach, bream, pike and big crucians
Permits: Season ticket water of Leisure Sport Angling, Thorpe Park, Staines Road, Chertsey, Surrey. Tel: 01932 564872
Cost: About £32 per season, concessions £16
BK Rating: Moderate
E/A: Anglian
Comments: A famous catfish water, but with plenty of carp

Kempston Hardwick

Location: Kempston Hardwick village, near Bedford
Type and Size: 4 pits, about 30 acres
How to Find: Take the Ampthill Road from Bedford, and the lake is opposite the Chimney Corner public house in Kempston Hardwick
Carp Stock: This is a recently stocked water with a reasonable head of carp to lower doubles. Carp are reported to be growing well. Carp to 20lbs plus
Category: Mixed Fishery
Other Species: Tench, roach, bream, perch and pike
Permits: Enquire locally, or tackle shops in Bedford
Control: Not known at time of going to press
BK Rating: Moderate
E/A: Anglian
Comments: Also Brogborough Lake, carp to 24lbs

Lakeside Farm

Location: Cublington, near Leighton Buzzard
Type and Size: 2 acre man-made lake
How to Find: At Wing on the A418 Leighton Buzzard to Aylesbury road, turn right towards Whitchurch, and the fishery is on the right in 3 miles
Carp Stock: Well stocked with carp to lower doubles
Category: Mixed Fishery
Other Species: Crucians, roach, rudd, perch, tench and gudgeon
Permits: From the lodge by car park
Cost: £4 per day; £2.50 juniors and O.A.P's £2.50 and £1.50 after midday
Control: Private. Tel: 01296 682201
Restrictions: No boilies, nuts or bloodworm
BK Rating: Not known
E/A: Anglian
Comments: Closed Monday to Thursday in winter

Oldfield

Location: Arlesey, near Hitchin, alongside A507
Type and Size: Two gravel pits of 6 and 4 acres in quiet countryside
Carp Stock: Very heavily stocked with good looking fish to mid-twenties
Category: Mixed Fishery
Other Species: Bream, tench, roach, rudd and perch
Permits: Syndicate membership, enquire locally
Control: Private
BK Rating: Very Easy
E/A: Anglian
Comments: The main lake has been the setting for several carp videos, including Carp Fever 1 and Carp from the Start 1, featuring Kevin Maddocks who caught many good fish here.

Priory Lake

Location: In the town of Bedford, off Goldington Road
Type and Size: 64 acre town lake, with a Visitors Centre and water sports
Carp Stock: Small number of carp to over 20lbs
Category: Few Carp
Other Species: Roach, perch, crucians and pike to 28lbs
Permits: Day tickets on bank
Cost: £2; £1 for under 12's. £5 per season for OAP's; also includes the smaller Fingers Lake
Control: Tel: 01234 211182; North Bedfordshire Borough Council
Restrictions: No night fishing. Fishing only from pegged swims. No live bait; no spinning
BK Rating: Very Difficult
E/A: Anglian
Comments: Toilet

Rackley Hills Pit

Location: Near the centre of Leighton Buzzard; Grovebury Road
Type and Size: Working sand pit of about 8 acres
How to Find: In Leighton Buzzard
Carp Stock: Small number of carp to 20lbs plus
Category: Few Carp
Other Species: Catfish to 35lbs
Permits: Seasonal from Leighton Buzzard Angling Club and selected tackle shops in the area. Secretary: B Smalley, 3 Isis Walk, Leighton Buzzard, Beds. Tel: 01525 852227
Cost: £20 per season. Joint husband and wife £23. Juniors: £4. Senior Citizens: £3
Control: Club
BK Rating: Very Difficult, very few fish
Restrictions: Night fishing reserved for a selected few only
E/A: Anglian

Radwell Complex

Location: Between Milton Ernest and Sharnbrook
Type and Size: 4 pits, two of which are quite large
How to Find: These lakes can be seen from the A6, on the left hand side between Bedford and Rushden. Access is from a lane near the Swan public house in Radwell. To reach this village take a left turn just before the Swan
Carp Stock: All the pits contain carp to about 10lbs

Category: Mixed Fishery
Other Species: Tench, bream, roach, perch and pike
Permits: Vauxhall Motors AC. Season tickets from Leslie's of Luton, 89 Park Street, Luton. Tel: 01582 419489
Restrictions: Members only - no day tickets
Control: Club
BK Rating: Moderate
E/A: Anglian

Stanford Pit

Location: Stanford, near Shefford
Type and Size: 1/2 acre pool with island
How to Find: Turn right off the B 658 Shefford to Biggleswade road at the Green Man pub - the lake is on the right in woodland
Carp Stock: Stocked with carp to doubles
Category: Mixed Fishery
Other Species: Perch, roach, rudd, bream and gudgeon
Permits: In advance only from local tackle shops
Cost: £26 per season; reduced prices for juniors, O.A.P's and disabled Price includes other club waters
Control: Shefford D.A.A. Tel: 01462 812323
BK Rating: Moderate
E/A: Anglian

Tingrith Manor Lake

Location: Village of Tingrith, near Toddington, Dunstable
How to Find: Leave the M1 at Toddington (junction 12) and take the road sign posted 'Tingrith'
Type and Size: Estate lake of 5 acres

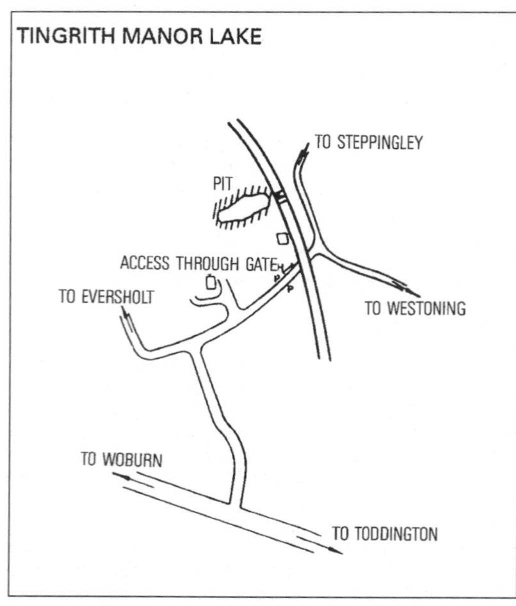

Carp Stock: Well stocked with commons to 10lbs. There are a few mirrors to upper doubles
Category: Mixed Fishery
Other Species: Perch, roach, rudd, pike and catfish
Permits: Vauxhall Motors Angling Club. Season tickets from Leslie's Fishing Tackle, Luton. Secretary: B Matthews, 88 Langford Drive, Luton, Beds. Tel: 01582 419489
Cost: On application
Control: Club
BK Rating: Moderate
E/A: Anglian
Baits/Methods: Normal carp fishing methods and baits; floating baits sometimes work well

Water End Fishery

Location: Maulden, near Ampthill
Type and Size: Three 'canals' - about an acre of water
How to Find: Going south on the A6 from Bedford, turn right at Clophill (before roundabout)
Carp Stock: Canal No.1 holds carp to about 18lbs
Category: Mixed Fishery
Other Species: Roach, rudd, bream, tench, dace, chub, orfe and crucians
Permits: On bank
Cost: £5 per day
Control: Robert Hinds Tel: 01525 403310. Mobile 0850 406866
Restrictions: No boilies, barbless hooks only
BK Rating: Moderate
E/A: Anglian
Comments: Mainly used for match fishing. Toilets

Willington Lake

Location: Near Great Barford Bridge, on the lane leading to Willington
Type and Size: Gravel pit of about eight acres, dug in 1984
Carp Stock: Restocked in 1990, with mostly mid-doubles to about 20lbs
Category: Mixed Fishery
Other Species: Big bream and pike; most other species
Permits: Shefford and District AA. Secretary: Mrs P Leath, 3 Ivel Close, Shefford. Tel: 01462 812323, or from Chris's Tackle Box, Biggleswade.
Cost: About £24 a season
Restrictions: Club members only - no day tickets
BK Rating: Easy
Comments: On the same ticket as Airman Pit

Withy Pool

Location: Bedford Road (A600), Henlow Camp, Beds SG16 6EA
Type and Size: Clay pit of 3 acres and man-made lake of 1/2 acre
Carp Stock: At least four carp over 40lbs plus, 15 or so over 30lbs, and a small head of younger, stock fish. Small lake holds carp to 19lbs
How to Find: Take the A600 Hitchin to Bedford Road going north, and the lake is on the left about 300 yards after the roundabout at Lower Stondon, about 4 miles from Hitchin
Category: Carp Water
Other Species: Main lake; catfish to 61lbs (current British record), grass carp to 26lbs, golden orfe to 6lbs, koi carp to mid-twenties, plus roach and perch to nearly 3 lbs. Small lake: catfish to mid - doubles, bream to 6 lbs plus numerous other species including exotics

Withy Pool boasts one of the greatest densities of big fish to be found anywhere in England. Virtually every carp caught is over 30lbs, like this '37' caught by fishery owner Kevin Maddocks

Cost: Main Lake: Monday to Thursday £40 per 24 hours, weekend tickets (Friday, Saturday, and Sunday) £140, Weekly ticket £280. Small lake: £15 per 24 hours, £45 weekend (Friday, Saturday and Sunday) and £90 per week

Permits: Bookings in advance only, Tel: 01462 816960

Restrictions: Maximum of 5 anglers on main lake and maximum of 3 anglers on small pool. Main lake has area of no fishing. Very few other restrictions - copy of rules available on request

Control: Private: contact Kevin Maddocks at the above address. Tel: 01462 816960

BK Rating: Main lake - Fairly Hard, small lake - Easy

E/A: Anglian

Comments: Brand new building incorporating separate ladies and gents toilets and shower. Angler's hut incorporating fridge freezer, cooker, microwave etc. The main lake is a 100 year old clay pit which varies in depth from 4 to 30 feet. It contained 20lb carp in the '50's. Dick Walker fished it and Jack Hilton caught his first doubles from the water, which was formerly known as Cafe Pool and Maylin's Pool. Since Kevin and Brenda Maddocks bought the property in 1985 it has become one of the best known small fisheries in the country for big carp - a fish under 30lbs from the main lake is rare. The lake record currently stands at 44 lbs. and gets beaten every year.
N.B. Withy Pool is a highly exclusive day-ticket water run in a very professional manner. Day-ticket anglers can enjoy beautiful, private surroundings with generous facilities, and the opportunity to fish a lake boasting the highest density of big carp in this country.

Stuart Mead with one of Withy Pool's 40's, taken on KM's Strawberry Oil Palatant boilies

Another '40' from Withy Pool this time a 41-14 caught by day ticket angler, John Scott.

Woburn Sands

Location: Woburn Sands village, near Woburn
Type and Size: Brick pit of 10 acres
How to Find: Take the A5 from Dunstable going north and turn off at Hockcliffe to Woburn Sands. Entrance is off the B557 road
Carp Stock: About 40 carp to 20lbs plus
Category: Mixed Fishery
Other Species: Roach, bream, tench, rudd, pike, catfish
Permits: Vauxhall Motors Angling Club. Season tickets only from Leslie's Tackle Shop. Luton. Secretary: B Matthews, 88 Langford Drive, Luton, Beds Tel: 01582 419489

Cost: About £15 per season
Control: Club
BK Rating: Fairly Difficult
E/A: Anglian

Woburn Sands Syndicate

Location: Woburn Sands
Type and Size: 2 acre disused brick pit
Carp Stock: About 40 doubles and a few low twenties
Category: Carp Water
Other Species: Catfish and roach
Permits: Syndicate only. Tel: 01908 645135
Cost: On application
BK Rating: Moderate - the owner says that it's easy for good carp anglers, and difficult for those who are not so good! (I've only fished it once, and I had a blank, which shows what a useless carp angler I am! P.M.).
Restrictions: No long stay fishing
Control: Private
E/A: Anglian
Commentss: A very pretty water, secluded and well protected; private property - do not visit without permission. Ideal for 'old fashioned' methods, such as stalking and float fishing.

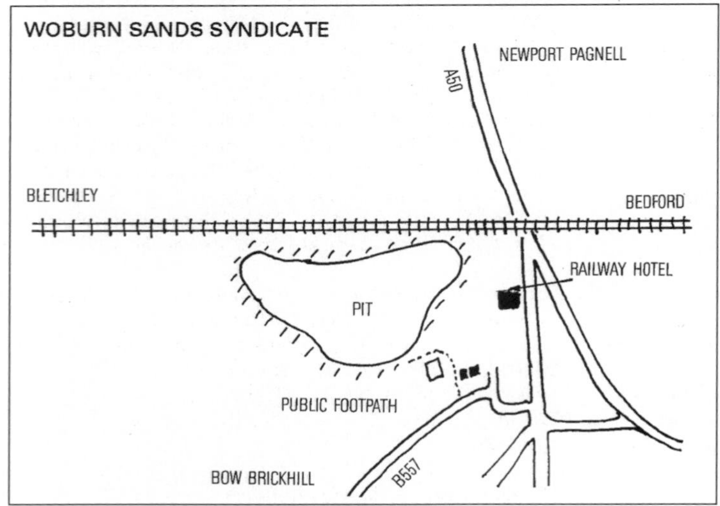

BERKSHIRE

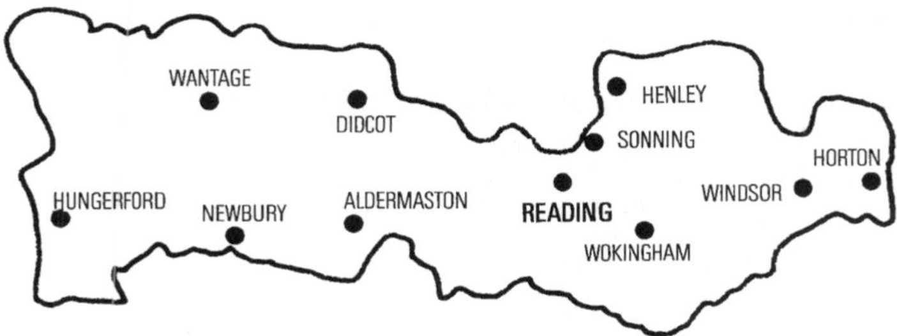

Aldermaston

Location: Paices Hill, Aldermaston, near Reading
Type and Size: 7 lakes of an acre or less, and one lake, No 6, of 3.8 acres. Gravel pits
How to Find: Take the M4 to the Theale turn off, and then A340 to Aldermaston. After Aldermaston the entrance is at the top of the hill on the right after the village.
Carp Stock: The Leisure Sport Guide describes the carp as 'numerous' in Lake 6, but only to about 8lbs. Some doubles were introduced into Lakes 2 and 3 in 1982-83, and best reported to date is 25lbs.
Category: Lake 6 - Carp Water. Other lakes are Mixed Fisheries
Permits: This is an LSAC Group Water. Season tickets and day tickets. Apply to Leisure Sport for an application firm. Thorpe Park, Staines Road, Chertsey, Surrey. Tel: 01932 564572 Fax: 01932 566 367. A limited number of Group Water Permits are issued for all 25 venues. Two passport photographs required to be sent with the application form.
Cost: £26 per season; juniors/OAP/disables - £13; Coverall Permits (25 venues) - £56 (juniors/OAP/disabled - £28).
Restrictions: Usual rules - no camping, no fires, no radios. Night fishing allowed. Carp over 3lbs must not be retained.
BK Rating: Lake 6 - Easy; others - Moderate
Control: Leisure Sport.
E/A: Thames

Brimpton Lakes

Location: Shalford Bridge, near Aldermaston
Type and Size: Two large gravel pits
How to Find: Off the Brimpton - Woolhampton Road
Carp Stock: Well stocked with carp, many of which are doubles
Category: Mixed Fishery
Permits: Reading and District AA. Secretary: D Capon, 61 Thame Road, Haddenham, Bucks HP17 8EP.
BK Rating: Moderate
Control: Club
E/A: Thames

Burghfield

Location: Pengewood Road, Pengewood, Burghfield
Type and Size: Lake 1 - 94 acres; Lake 2 5 acres; Lake 3 - 3 acres. Gravel pits
How to Find: Off the A4 from Reading to Southcote; Burghfield Road and the canal
Carp Stock: Carp to over 30lbs reported
Category: Few Carp
Other Species: General coarse fish
Permits: Leisure Sport Angling, Staines Road, Chertsey, Surrey. Tel: 01932 564872
Cost: £26 Concessions £13
BK Rating: Difficult
Control: Leisure Sport Angling Club
Restrictions: No bright lights
E/A: Thames
Comments: Night fishing is allowed. River fishing on the River Kennet incuded

Child Beale Fishery

Location: Child Beale Park, Pangbourne - off the A329
Type and Size: 10 acre lake
Carp Stock: Some carp to over 30 lbs
Category: Mixed Fishery
Other Species: Roach, tench, bream, pike, perch, golden orfe and koi
Permits: On bank
Cost: About £5 per day
Control: Tel: 01256 466343
Restrictions: No night fishing
BK Rating: Difficult
E/A: Thames

Countryside Club

Location: Reading
Type and Size: Some lake carp fishing, details not known
Carp Stock: Well stocked with carp
Category: Mixed Fishery
Other Species: General coarse fish
Permits: Countryside, 109 Upper Woodcote Road, Caversham Heights, Reading.
Control: Private
BK Rating: Not known
E/A: Thames

Horton Lake

Location: Stanwell Road, Horton, near Slough, Berks. Tel: 01753 684458
Type and Size: Church Lake - 14 acres; Boat Pool - 6 acres; former gravel pits
How to Find: Take junction 14 off the M25 and take the Poyle/Datchet road, and after roundabout take the first road on the left (Stanwell Road); the Horton Fishery entrance is on the left in one mile.
Carp Stock: Church Lake was well stocked with very big carp to 49lbs. There were already carp in this lake, a former trout fishery, but in 1991 when Longfield (Staines), a famous carp water, was closed and netted 57 big carp, all of which were twenties and thirties, with some doubles

and two forties, were transferred to Church Lake, Horton. At the time of going to press (July '97), the fishery was closed due to many big carp deaths which included at least three 40's

Category: Mixed Fishery
Other Species: Grass carp to 28lbs, bream to 11 ½ lbs, tench to 8 ¾ lbs, pike, roach, perch and eels
Permits: Leisure Sport Angling, Thorpe Park, Staines Road, Chertsey, Surrey KT16 8PN. Tel: 01932 564872. This is an LSA 'Special Venue' and tickets may be hard to obtain.
Cost: £400 per season. Waiting list for syndicate.
Restrictions: Two rods only; 7 days stay only - after that you must leave for at least 24 hours. Members wishing to leave the fishery between 7am and 8pm are only allowed a 90 minute absence; no keepnets or sacks; no guests; 50 anglers only.
BK Rating: Difficult
E/A: Thames
Comments: There is a fisherman's lodge at Church Lake, open 24 hours a day, and two toilets in the car park. LSA rules and their bailiffs are very strict, and if you break the rules you will lose your membership.

Kennet & Avon Canal

Location: Lower Denford, near Hungerford
Type and Size: 3 mile stretch of canal; The Marsh and Church best for carp
Carp Stock: Carp to 20lbs
Category: Mixed Fishery
Other Species: Tench, roach, bream, perch and pike
Permits: In advance only
Cost: £2 per day
Control: Tel: 01635 43186
Restrictions: No night fishing
BK Rating: Difficult
E/A: Thames
Comments: Boat traffic a problem in summer

Longmoor Lake

Location: California Country Park, Nine Mile Ride, Finchampstead, Wokingham
Type and Size: 6 acre lake
Carp Stock: Well stocked with carp to mid-twenties
Category: Mixed Fishery
Other Species: Pike, tench, perch, roach, rudd
Permits: Day and season tickets sold on lakeside
Cost: Adult day - £3. Adult Season - £20
Baits/Methods: Normal carp fishing bait and methods
Control: Council (Wokingham District Council). Tel: 01734 730028
Restrictions: No nut baits, barbless hooks, night fishing through a syndicate only, no fishing on paved frontage.
BK Rating: Moderate
E/A: Thames
Comments: Plenty of good carp averaging 15lb in this picturesque lake with several islands and lily beds.

Mill Pond

Location: Off the A329 at Wild Ridings Tavern, in the town of Bracknell
Type and Size: 6 acre park lake
Carp Stock: Carp to 20 lbs
Category: Mixed Fishery
Other Species: Roach, tench, bream, rudd, pike, crucians and gudgeon
Permits: On bank
Cost: £2 per day; £1 juniors and O.A.P's
Control: Bracknell Angling Centre. Tel: 01344 425130
Restrictions: No barbed hooks, floating baits or keepnets
BK Rating: Moderate
Baits/Methods: Boilies are best for carp
E/A: Thames
Comments: Open June 1st to March 31st. Toilet and cafe

Priory Water

Location: Near Windsor
Type and Size: Several gravel pits
How to Find: Just off the Wraysbury junction of the M25
Carp Stock: Priory - some good carp; Hythe Lagoon - some carp; Watts Pool - some carp
Category: Mixed Fisheries
Other Species: Mixed coarse fish
Permits: Peter Howes. Tel: 01256 466343
Cost: On application - about £12 per annum
BK Rating: Insufficient information
Control: Not known - try local tackle shops
E/A: Thames
Comments: Priory also used for sailing.

Pondwood Farm

Location: Smewins Lane, White Waltham
Type and Size: Two lakes of an acre each
Carp Stock: Well stocked with carp to over 20 lbs
Category: Mixed Fishery
Other Species: Roach, rudd, tench and perch
Permits: On bank
Cost: About £10 per day
Control: Tel: 01734 345299
Restrictions: No keepnets or barbed hooks
BK Rating: Moderate
E/A: Thames
Comments: Probably open all year

Sonning Eye Pit

Location: Off the A4155 Reading - Henley road at Sonning
Type and Size: Huge gravel pit
Carp Stock: Not many carp but said to be some big fish up to 40lbs
Category: Few Carp
Permits: Reading and District Angling Association. Secretary: D Capon, 61 Thame Road, Haddenham, Bucks HP17 8EP.

BK Rating: Very Difficult
Restrictions: No night fishing
Control: Club
E/A: Thames

Savernake Pond

Location: In Bracknell, off the B 3430
Type and Size: 2 acre attractive pond
Carp Stock: Some carp to about 8 lbs
Category: Mixed Fishery
Other Species: Rudd, crucians, goldfish, roach and big grass carp
Permits: In advance only from Bracknell Angling Centre, 2a Fowlers Lane, Bracknell
Cost: £2 per day
Control: Tel: 01344 425130
Restrictions: No night fishing
BK Rating: Moderate
E/A: Thames

South Hill Park

Location: Bracknell
Type and Size: 2 acre park lake
Carp Stock: Some carp to 10 lbs
Category: Mixed Fishery
Other Species: Bream, tench and roach
Permits: Bracknell Angling Centre in advance only
Cost: £2 per day, £1 for juniors and OAP's
Control: Bracknell Herons A/C. Tel: 01344 425130
Restrictions: No night fishing, barbed hooks, keepnets or floating baits
BK Rating: Not known
E/A: Thames
Comments: Open June 1st to March 31st. Toilets, pub 50 metres away

South Lake/Redlands Lake

Location: Woodley, Reading
Type and Size: Lake of 50 acres
How to Find: Fairwater Road, behind the Thatchers public house
Carp Stock: Well stocked with carp to 25lb
Category: Mixed Fishery
Other Species: Tench, roach, and bream
Permits: Mr Williams, South Lake Angling Society, 24 Duncan Road, Woodley, Reading
BK Rating: Moderate
E/A: Thames
Restrictions: Only open to those living within 3 miles of Woodley.

The Old Mill

Location: Aldermaston
Type and Size: Small lake in grounds of mill, with 1 mile of the River Kennet
Carp Stock: Carp to 30 lbs in lake
Category: Mixed Fishery

Other Species: Bream, tench and roach
Permits: At mill or on the bank
Cost: About £8 per day
Control: Mr R Arlott. Tel: 01734 712365
BK Rating: Not known
E/A: Southern
Comments: Fine river fishing in the Kennet included - big roach, dace, pike, chub, perch, barbel and eels. Weirpools.

White Swan Lake

Location: Dinton Pastures Country Park, Davis Street, Hurst, Wokingham
Type and Size: Open gravel pit of about 24 acres
Carp Stock: Well stocked with carp to upper twenties
Category: Mixed Fishery
Other Species: Pike, tench, perch, roach, rudd, chub, bream
Permits: Day and seaon tickets sold on lakeside
Cost: Adult Day - £4. Adult Season - £25. Night syndicate £75.
Baits/Methods: Normal carp fishing bait and methods
Control: Council (Wokingham District Council) Tel:01734 342016
Restrictions: No nut baits, night fishing through a syndicate only
BK Rating: Moderate to hard
E/A: Thames
Comments: Well stocked with carp, also holds tench to over 11lbs and pike to 34lb. Toilet. Disabled access.

BUCKINGHAMSHIRE

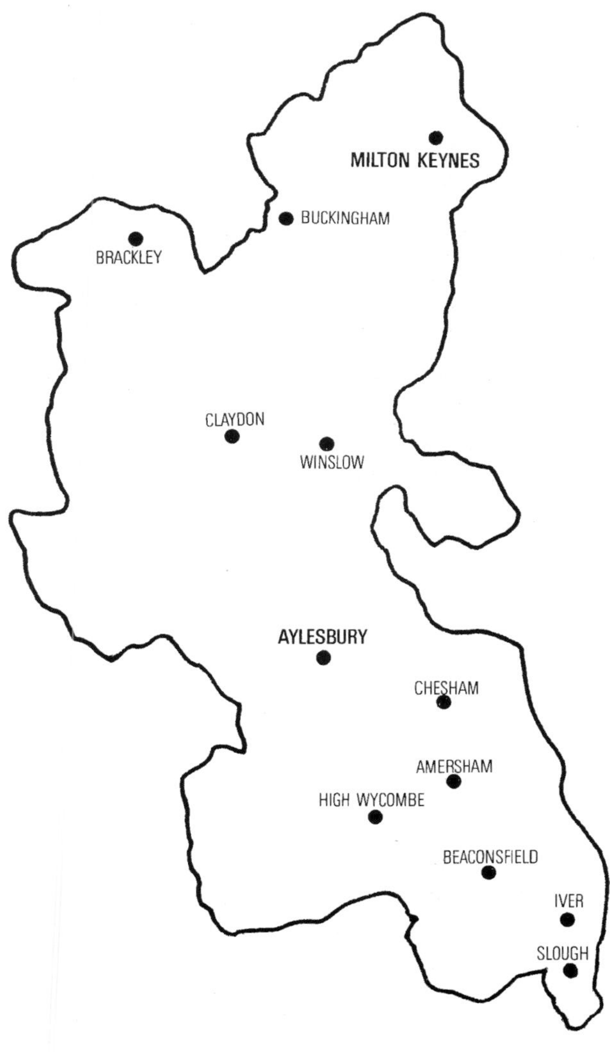

Amerden Pool

Location: Amerden Grove, near Slough
Type and Size: Small lake
How to Find: Take the Taplow road from Slough and pass the Dumbell pub on your right. In 150yds turn left at the garage, go under railway bridge, past sailing club, turn right and first right again, then follow track to lake.
Carp Stock: A small number of carp to 16lbs
Category: Few Carp
Other Species: Crucians, tench, rudd, roach and perch
Permits: Boyer Leisure, Trout Road, West Drayton, Middlesex UB7 7DS. Tel: 01895 444707.
Cost: £35 per season. Concessions £20.
Control: Boyer Leisure
Restrictions: Barbless hooks; no keepnets or carp sacks; do not go through the house entrance; do not disturb livestock on the farmland.
BK Rating: Difficult
E/A: Thames
Comments: Open for 10 months of the year.

Aylesbury Arm Canal

Location: Just outside Aylesbury
Type and Size: Narrow disused canal
Carp Stock: Well stocked with carp to doubles
Category: Mixed Fishery
Permits: John MacDonald. Tel: 01296 29983
Control: Club; Aylesbury DAF
BK Rating: Moderate
E/A: Thames

Black Park

Location: Town of Iver
Type and Size: Park lake of about 7 acres
Carp Stock: Small number of carp to 28lbs
Category: Few Carp
Other Species: Pike and bream
Permits: Free fishing
Control: Council
BK Rating: Difficult
E/A: Thames
Comments: Refeshments etc. available on site

Bowlers

Location: A stretch of the Grand Union Canal in Milton Keynes; good fishing between bridge 90 and 91 at Woughton Park; access from the Simpson roundabout or Netterfield roundabout
Type and Size: Shallow canal with some boat traffic
Carp Stock: Some carp to 20lbs
Category: Mixed Fishery
Other Species: Bream, roach, perch, and gudgeon
Permits: Day tickets on bank
Cost: £3 for adults; £1.50 for juniors, OAP's and the disabled; tickets in

advance from K Osborne, 7 Gilpin Way, Olney, Bucks. Tel: 01908 713414

Control: Milton Keynes AA
Restrictions: Fishing from towpath only
BK Rating: Difficult
E/A: Anglian

Calves Lane Lake

Location: Love Hill Lane, off the B470 near Iver
Type and Size: Small lake - 1 ½ acres
Carp Stock: Stocked in 1990 with 250 carp to 7lbs
Category: Mixed Fishery
Other Species: Roach, tench, perch, and pike
Permits: Boyer Leisure
Cost: £30 per season; £20 juniors, OAP's and disabled
Control: Boyer Leisure
Restrictions: Unhooking mats compulsory
BK Rating: Moderate
E/A: Thames

Claydon Lake

Location: Middle Claydon, Winslow, near Leighton Buzzard
Type and Size: Estate lake of about 3 acres
How to Find: Take the A413 from Buckingham, and turn right to Middle Claydon just before the village of Winslow
Carp Stock: Very heavily stocked with carp of 5-10lbs, with some doubles up to 20lbs. Mostly commons
Category: Mixed Fishery
Other Species: Roach, rudd, bream, pike and very large catfish and zander
Permits: Season tickets for members only; Leighton Buzzard Angling Club, B Smalley, 3 Isis Walk, Leighton Buzzard, Beds. Tel: 01525 852227 or from Jim Brennan on the bank.
Cost: £25 adult, £30 husband and wife
Control: Club
BK Rating: Easy
Restrictions: No night fishing
E/A: Anglian
Comments: This lake is on an estate with a house once lived in by Florence Nightingale. It is a shallow, very open water. Cars must be parked by the roadside and it is more than half a mile's walk across a field to the lake. The water is famous for its catfish of over 30lbs, but there are plenty of carp also. The Leighton Buzzard Club has a number of other carp waters on the same ticket. An excellent water to gain experience on.

College Farm Lake

Location: Just outside the attractive village of Aynho, near the railway line off the B4031 Aynho to Deddington Road.
Type and Size: 2 acre lake
Carp Stock: Well stocked with carp to doubles
Category: Carp Water
Other Species: Some other coarse fish and trout

Permits: From bailiff
Cost: About £4 per day
BK Rating: Easy
E/A: Severn Trent
Comments: Open all year

Common Pond

Location: Common near Gerrards Cross
Type and Size: One acre common land pond
Carp Stock: Fairly well stocked with carp including some doubles up to about 20lbs
Category: Mixed Fishery
Other Species: Roach and tench
Permits: Free fishing
Control: Local council
BK Rating: Easy
E/A: Thames

Furzton Lake

Location: Chaffron Way, Furzton, Milton Keynes
Type and Size: 40 acre man-made lake
How to Find: From juntion 14 of the M1, take the A509 and turn right at the first roundabout. Follow this road (H5 Portway) for 6 miles to Watling Street roundabout, turn left and take the first right; then turn right at the second roundabout into Chaffron Way.
Carp Stock: Stocked in 1990 with about 1,400 carp, mirrors and commons, between 4lb and 14lb
Category: Mixed Fishery
Other Species: Tench, rudd and perch
Permits: Day tickets from bailiff on bank
Control: Milton Keynes AA - membership from local tackle shops or from K Osborne, 7 Gilpin Way, Olney, Bucks. Tel: 01234 713144
Restrictions: No fixed leads
BK Rating: Easy
E/A: Anglian
Comments: A new water, first opened in the 1990-91 season. Some areas out of bounds. Housing estate along one side.

Gallows Pool

Location: Grendon Underwood, near Buckingham
Type and Size: Half acre pool with islands
Carp Stock: Well stocked with carp to lower doubles
Category: Mixed fishery
Other Species: Tentch, chub, perch, roach, rudd, crucians, bream, dace, gudgeon and trout
Permits: In advance only from ticket office on site
Cost: £3 per day. Lake can be booked for matches
Restrictions: No night fishing; no keepnets; barbless hooks
BK Rating: Easy
E/A: Thames
Comments: Open all year

Gayhurst Lakes

Location: Gayhurst Estate, near Newport Pagnell

Type and Size: Two pretty stream-fed estate lakes of 2 acres and one acre, both on the same stream, which runs from the larger lake to the small one

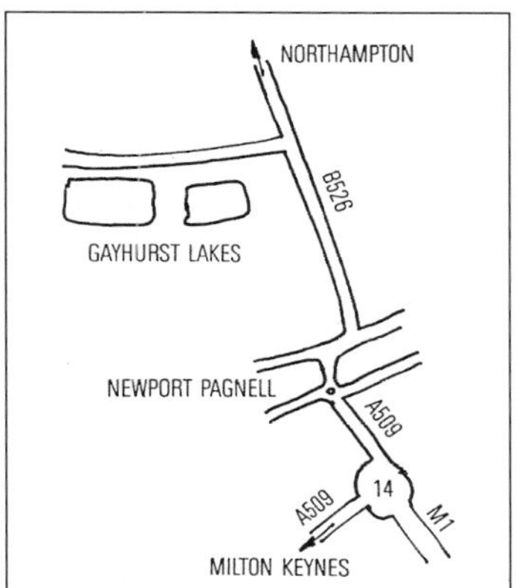

Carp Stock: The upper (larger) lake is very heavily stocked with carp to over 20lbs, although most are betwen 3lbs and 12lbs.

Category: Carp Water

Other Species: Bream, roach, and perch. Some pike in lower lake

Permits: Private syndicate water of Linear Fisheries, Bedford, 10a Rackstraw Grove, Old Farm Park, Milton Keynes, MK7 8PZ. Tel: 01908 645135/01234 212066

Cost: About £60 per season, and a £10 entry fee for Gayhurst Lakes. Enquire from the Secretary for prices and details of other Linear waters.

Baits/Methods Standard carp fishing methods; sweetcorn, luncheon meat and boilies all doing well

Control: Linear Fisheries, Bedford

Restrictions: Syndicate only - no day tickets. Membership in advance only. Alternate Saturday and Sunday rota to avoid weekend overcrowding. Small exclusive syndicate with limited membership, but vacancies at present

BK Rating: East to Moderate

E/A: Anglian

Comments: The lakes are on a beautiful and peaceful private estate in the grounds of a large mansion, and are surrounded by trees and bushes. Three carp of over 20lbs were reported from the water in the 1990 to 91 season, with a good number of doubles. Mirrors and commons. Frequent vacancies.

Grand Union Canal

Location: Globe Bridge (111) to Sandy Bridge (110)

Type and Size: 12 metre wide canal

How to find: Near Great Brickhill, off A 4146 Leighton Buzzard to Bletchley road

Carp Stock: Well stocked with carp to upper doubles

Category: Mixed Fishery
Other Species: Roach, small bream and perch
Permits: On bank
Cost: £3 per day; 50p for juniors and O.A.P's £18 per season
Control: Luton A.C. Tel: 01582 28114
Restrictions: No night fishing
BK Rating: Difficult
E/A: Thames
Comments: Disabled access

Grand Union Canal

Location: Slapton Lock, off the B486 near Leighton Buzzard, between bridges 118 and 120
Type and Size: Narrow canal
Carp Stock: Quite well stocked with carp to 20 lbs
Category: Mixed Fishery
Other Species: Bream, roach, perch and tench
Permits: On bank
Cost: £3 per day; 50p for juniors and O.A.P's £15 per season; £4.50 concessions
Control: Luton A.C. Tel: 01582 28114
Restrictions: No fishing below power lines
BK Rating: Moderate
E/A: Thames

Great Ouse

Location: Lavendon Mill, off the B565 between Olney and Turvey
Type and Size: Wide river with weir
Carp Stock: Some carp to mid - twenties
Category: Few carp
Other Species: Bream, tench,roach, perch, pike,chub and barbel
Permits: In advance from local tackle shops
Cost: £15 per season; £4.50 juniors; O.A.P's and disabled
Control: Luton A.C. Tel: 01582 28114
BK Rating: Difficult
E/A: Anglian

Hyde Lane Reservoir

Location: Hyde Lane, Buckingham
Type and Size: Reservoir of about 40 acres
How to Find: Near Buckingham
Carp Stock: Not many carp, but some big fish to over 30 pounds
Category: Mixed Fishery
Other Species: A few catfish to over 25 pounds
Permits: Season tickets from local tackle shops
Cost: On application
Control: Club
BK Rating: Difficult
E/A: Anglian

Lodge Lake

Location: Dansteed Way, Great Holm, Milton Keynes
Type and Size: Eight acre man-made lake divided by a central island
How to Find: Turn off the M1 at junction 14 and take the A509 to the first roundabout. Turn right into Portway and right again at the second roundabout into Brickhill Street. The left turn at the next roundabout will bring you into Dansteed Way and the lake will be seen on the left. Parking to the left of the lake in Bradwell Road.
Carp Stock: Very well stocked with about 1,500 carp to 22lbs - mirrors, commons and leathers
Category: Mixed Fishery
Other Species: Golden koi, crucians, roach, perch, bream, rudd and tench
Permits: Members only water of Milton Keynes AA (no day tickets). Membership open to all. Permits from local tackle shops or the Secretary. 11 Gilpin Way, Olney, Bucks. Tel: 01908 378942
Control: Club
BK Rating: Easy
Baits/Methods: Usual carp fishing methods, although no fixed leads are allowed
E/A: Anglian
Comments: Some areas are out of bounds and so cannot be fished

Loughton Lodge Lake

Location: National Badminton Centre, Bradwell Road, Milton Keynes
Type and Size: 20 acre lake
Carp Stock: Carp to over 20 lbs
Category: Mixed Fishery
Other Species Crucians, roach, tench and some bream
Permits: On bank
Cost: About £4 per day; £25 per season. Concessions
Control: Milton Keynes A.A. Tel: 01908 374400
BK Rating: Not known
E/A: Anglian

Newport Pagnell Gravel Pits

Location: Newport Pagnell, off the Bedford Road
Type and Size: Eight small pits
Carp Stock: Most of the lakes contain carp, up to 20lbs in some of them
Category: Mixed Fishery
Other Species: Tench, pike, roach, perch, and bream
Permits: Newport Pagnell Fishing Association. Secretary: R D Dorrill, 7 Bury Street, Newport Pagnell. Tel: 01909 610639
Cost: About £15 per season
BK Rating: Moderate
E/A: Anglian

Snowberry Lake

Location: Bletchley, near Milton Keynes, just off the A5
Type and Size: Attractive 3 acre lake
Carp Stock: Well stocked with carp to upper twenties
Other Species: Tench, zander, roach, bream and crucians
Permits: Fourways Fisheries, Poplars Nursery, Harlington Road, Toddington,

	Dunstable LU5 6HE. Tel: 015255 5590
Cost:	£175 per season
Restrictions:	No day tickets
BK Rating:	Moderate
E/A:	Anglian
Comments:	A very pleasant water, once controlled by the late Richard Walker.

Teardrops

Location:	Loughton Lakes, Milton Keynes - behind the Milton Keynes Bowl
Type and Size:	Three lakes of about two acres each
Carp Stock:	Heavily stocked with small carp
Category:	Mixed Fishery
Other Species:	Roach, bream, perch, tench, chub and catfish
Permits:	£3 per day on bank
Control:	Tel: 01908 664005
BK Rating:	Easy
E/A:	Anglian

Tiddenfoot Pit

Location:	On the Leighton Buzzard ring road, Mentmore Road
Type and Size:	Sand pit of 10 acres
How to Find:	Near the town of Leighton Buzzard
Carp Stock:	A small number of carp to about 24lbs
Category:	Few Carp
Other Species:	Catfish, bream, pike, roach, perch
Permits:	Leighton Buzzard Angling Club. Secretary: B Smalley, 3 Isis Walk, Leighton Buzzard, Beds. Tel: 01525 852227
Cost:	£20 per season. Joint husband and wife £23
Control:	Club
BK Rating:	Moderate
E/A:	Anglian

Weston Tervell Reservoir

Location:	Holton, Prestwood, near Great Missenden
Type and Size:	15 acre reservoir
Carp Stock:	About 30 original fish up to 32lbs. Recently stocked with about 200 carp, sizes not known
Category:	Mixed Fishery
Other Species:	Usual coarse fish
Permits:	Day time season tickets from Prestwood and District AC; enquire locally
Cost:	£24 joining fee and £18 extra for night fishing
Restrictions:	Lots...but our informant doesn't say what they are!
BK Rating:	Difficult
E/A:	Thames
Comments:	In or very near the reeds said to be the best area for carp

Wolverton Lakes

Location:	Stratford Road, Wolverton, Milton Keynes
Type and Size:	Two small man-made lakes of about one acre
Carp Stock:	About 100 mirrors and commons to 6lbs
Category:	Mixed Fishery

The Catfish Conservation Group

Joining the **C.C.G.** offers the following benefits to all members:

- Three copies of our newsletter *Silurus*
- Our high quality colour magazine *Whiskers*
- The opportunity to fish **Adams Pool**, our very own specialist cat water
- Continental tackle hire for those European monsters
- The combined knowledge of some of the top catfish anglers in the country
- Exclusive **C.C.G.** products, including Tee shirts, Sweat shirts, Badges, Stickers, Mugs, Key Fobs and Lighters
- Specialist catfish hooks and floats available to purchase
- Our very own Video, *Catfish & How to Catch Them*
- Free advice on stocking catfish and maintaining specialist cat fisheries

For information about the Catfish Conservation Group write to:

The C.C.G. Secretary,
The Retreat,
Heath Lane,
Ewshot,
Surrey, GU10 5AW

If you wish to join, send £11 subscription for one year's membership to include *Whiskers* colour magazine and at least two copies of *Silurus* newsletter

For a list of waters containing catfish turn to the back of this guide.

Other Species:	Crucians, tench, roach, perch
Permits:	Members only water of Milton Keynes Angling Association (no day tickets). Membership is open to all - permits from local tackle shops or from the Secretary, 107 Baccara Grove, Bletchley, Milton Keynes
Control:	Club. Tel: 01234 713144
Restrictions:	Members only
E/A:	Easy
Comments:	Small fish carp water, suitable for the non-carp specialist. Car park is at Wolverton Mill, opposite the footpath to the lakes

CAMBRIDGESHIRE

Ashmire Carp Syndicate

Location: Earith, near Cambridge
Type and Size: 15 acre attractive lake
Carp Stock: Well stocked with many doubles and twenties to 30 lbs
Category: Carp Water
Other Species: Pike to over 25 lbs and some other species
Permits: Owner Ron Middleton. Tel: 01487 740943
Cost: £300 per season
Restrictions: Carp anglers aged 21 and over only. Limited to 50 members
BK Rating: Moderate
E/A: Anglian
Comments: Specialist carp water controlled by a well known carp angler. Not heavily fished. Few carp below 10 lbs

Barway Lake

Location: Barway, near Ely
Type and Size: 5 acre lake
Carp Stock: Well stocked with carp to 20lbs
Category: Mixed Fishery
Other Species: Tench, roach and crucians

Permits: P S and J M Randall. Tel: 01353 720052
Cost: Day tickets on application; 6am to dusk only
Control: Private
BK Rating: Not known
Restrictions: No night fishing
E/A: Anglian

Brackhill Lake

Location: Earith between Huntingdon and Ely
Type and Size: 3 gravel pits
Carp Stock: Brackhill Lake said to contain 'a few' carp, has some to double figures. This complex is being developed as a carp fishery
Category: Few Carp
Other Species: Roach, perch, rudd, tench and bream
Permits: Enquire locally
Control: Private (ex A.R.C.)
BK Rating: Difficult
Restrictions: No night fishing
E/A: Anglian

Burnside Lake

Location: Old Blue Circle Cement Works, Coldhams Lane, Cambridge
Type and Size: 10 acre chalk quarry
Carp Stock: About 200 carp, between 7lbs and 15lbs
Category: Mixed Fishery
Other Species: Roach, rudd, bream, perch, chub and pike
Permits: Season tickets only from Cherry Hinton AC. Secretary: Mr Hobson, 25 Ivory Close, Cherry Hinton, Cambridgeshire
Cost: £15 per season
Control: Club
Restrictions: No day tickets
BK Rating: Moderate
E/A: Anglian
Comments: The average depth of this quarry is about 25ft, with some areas 35ft deep. Most carp are caught in the margins or on floating or suspended baits because of the great depth

Burwell Lode

Location: Cock-Up Bridge, Burwell, near Cambridge
Type and Stock: Narrow drain-type river, a tributary of the River Cam
Carp Stock: Stocked in the winter of 1991 with about 400 carp to 15lbs, mostly very small and transferred from a local pit
Category: Mixed Fishery
Other Species: Tench, bream, rudd, roach and perch
Permits: Enquire in local tackle shops
Control: Cambridge FPAS
BK Rating: Not known
E/A: Anglian
Comments: Let's hope your fishing here is not like the name of the bridge where the fish were put in!

Chawston Lake

Location: Chawston, near St Neots
Type and Size: Gravel pit of about 8 - 10 acres
How to Find: One mile off A1 near St Neots

Carp Stock: Quite well stocked with carp to 19-20lbs. Most are doubles of 10 -14lbs
Category: Mixed Fishery
Other Species: General coarse fish
Permits: Chawston AC - tackle shop in St Neots
Cost: On application
BK Rating: Moderate
Control: Club
E/A: Anglian
Comments: Fish to around 20lbs

Chesterford Fisheries

Location: Great Chesterford, Saffron Walden
Type and Size: 3 lakes - 7 acres, 2 of 3 acres. Mature gravel pits
How to Find: Off M11, junction 9
Carp Stock: Chesterford Lake (7 acres) - 100 carp to 30lbs plus; Borough Lake - 40 fish, doubles and twenties; Ickleton Lake - 100 plus doubles up to 18lbs, 3 thirties
Category: Mixed Fisheries
Other Species: Big perch, roach, tench, pike
Permits: Season tickets only from Paul Elsegood, 2 Wentfords Cottages, Clare Road, Poslingford, Sudbury, Suffolk. Tel: 01787 277468
Cost: £125
Control: Private
Restrictions: Fishing up to 10.30pm; and after 3am. No sacking
BK Rating: Chesterford - Difficult for big fish. Borough - Difficult. Ickleton - Moderate
E/A: Anglian
Comments: Do not visit water until you have contacted the owner. Tickets in advance only. No day tickets.Guest tickets for members. Cooking hut. Toilets

Clearwaters Coarse Fishery

Location: Near Earith, which is not far from St Ives
Type and Size: 13 acre lake, matured gravel pit
Carp Stock: Well stocked with carp to about 20lbs
Category: Carp Water
Other Species: Some other coarse fish, including tench
Permits: Season tickets in advance only - for details telephone 01582 853307 between 6pm and 9pm
Control: Private
BK Rating: Moderate
E/A: Anglian

Decoy Lake

Location: Decoy Farm, Eastrea, Whittlesey, Peterborough
Type and Size: Gravel pit of about 3½ acres
How to Find: From Peterborough take the A605 to Whittlesey. Follow A605 towards March for 1½ miles, turn left opposite some white silos
Carp Stock: 11,000 small carp, up to 4lbs!
Category: Mixed Fishery
Other Species: Bream,tench, rudd, few roach
Permits: Club bookings and matches only; 10, 22 or 32 anglers only. From Peter Band on 01733 202230, or Tony Hudson on 01733 203428
Cost: Approx £5 per peg for 6 hours fishing
BK Rating: Easy
Control: Private

Restrictions: Barbless hooks; keepnets supplied. No children. No night fishing
E/A: Anglian
Comments: Spring fed water, specially stocked for match fishing. The 11,000 commons and mirrors were stocked at 7oz - 1lb, and some weigh 4lbs, after 6 months! No individual fishing - block bookings only. Enormous catches are routine. England International Ian Heaps, who regularly fishes the waters, says that he considers this the match fishing of the future, as heavily stocked carp match waters provide more sport for all. Something a bit different for our Guide - nearly 4,000 carp per acre!

Dickersons Pit

Location: Milton Pits, Milton Road, Cambridge
Type and Size: Large matured gravel pit
Carp Stock: Well stocked with cap to over 20lbs
Category: Mixed Fishery
Other Species: Pike, tench, rudd
Permits: Try Cooper Brothers Tackle Shop, Milton Road, Cambridge for permits and information
Cost: About £10 per person
Control: Histon AC
Restrictions: Most of this pit has recently been designated a 'Nature Reserve' , and, as so often in these cases, has been closed to anglers, most of whom are true nature lovers! However, the small pit attached to the main one by a narrow stretch of water, remains open, and other pits on the site, including Todds Pit, which also contains carp, are still in the control of Histon AS - Secretary: R Cooper, 236 Histon Road, Cottenham, Cambridge (members only)

Earith Lakes

Location: Holme Fen Drove, Earith, near St Ives
Type and Size: Originally an 18 acre matured gravel pit, now divided into two parts
Carp Stock: Larger lake (11 acres) - several hundred to 31lbs; smaller lake (7acres) - heavily stocked with small carp to low twenties
Category: Carp Water (both lakes)
Other Species: Perch, rudd, roach,chub, tench and pike
Permits: From the owner, Ken McLennan, on site. Tel: 01487 740301
Cost: Both lakes - syndicate at £120 per year
BK Rating: Moderate for both waters
Control: Private
Restrictions: No sacks. No tiger nuts or peanuts
E/A: Anglian
Comments: This is a very pleasant carp fishery, very well stocked with large numbers of good carp. There is also an 18 acre coarse fishery and a 36 acre trout lake on this site - details from the owner.

Eaton Socon Lake

Location: Eaton Socon, near St Neots
Carp Stock: Well stocked with carp to 20lbs
Category: Mixed Fishery
Other Species: Tench, rudd, and bream
Permits: Hitchin and District AC, L G Day, 14 Thatchers End, Hitchin, Herts or from local tackle shops
Cost: Members only - season ticket at about £20
Control: Club

BK Rating: Moderate
E/A: Anglian

Eldernell Lake

Location: Coates, near Whittlesey
Type and Size: Attractive Fenland 'bagging up' lake
How to Find: Eldernell Lane, off the A 605 Peterborough to March road
Carp Stock: Very heavily stocked with carp to 10 lbs
Category: Mixed Fishery
Other Species: Tench, rudd and roach
Permits: On bank
Cost: About £8 per day; £5 for the evening
Control: Frank Vaira
Restrictions: No boilies or hemp
BK Rating: Very Easy
E/A: Anglian
Comments: Probably open all year

Fen Drayton Complex

Location: Fen Drayton, between Cambridge and Huntingdon
Type and Size: Gravel pits - Drayton Fen quite large
How to Find: Off the A604 Cambridge - Huntingdon Road
Carp Stock: Some large carp
Category: Few carp
Others Species: General coarse fish including zander
Permits: Head Bailiff: Neil Prior. Tel: 01954 303345 (evenings)
Cost: On application
BK Rating: Moderate
Control: Private
Restrictions: None
E/A: Anglian
Comments: Also board sailing on this lake

Fen Drayton Lake

Location: Fen Drayton, near Fenstanton
Type and Size: 30 acre gravel pit
How to Find: Fen Drayton between Huntingdon and Cambridge
Carp Stock: Very few fish to 30lbs plus
Category: Few Carp
Other Species: Mixed coarse fish
Permits: Enquire locally
BK Rating: Very Difficult
Restrictions: None
E/A: Anglian
Comments: Sailing and windsurfing also take place on this pit

Fenland Fisheries

Location: Earith, near Huntingdon
Type and Size: Seven acre gravel pit and 2 acre lake
Carp Stock: Well stocked with carp to 20lbs
Category: Mixed Fishery
Other Species: Koi, grass carp, roach, tench, perch and trout
Permits: Day tickets, booked in advance from Fish Farm, Meadow Drive, Earith. Tel: 01487 841858
Cost: £6

Restrictions: No night fishing; no keepnets; barbless hooks only
BK Rating: Not known
E/A: Anglian
Comments: Limited number of anglers each day. Toilets and refreshments on site

Fourways Fishing Club

Location: Baston, near Peterborough
Type and Size: Lake of 5½ acres
Carp Stock: Well stocked with carp to 26lbs
Category: Mixed Fishery
Other Species: Tench and roach
Permits: £80 a season. Tel: 01406 380473/380557
Restrictions: No day tickets; season tickets only
BK Rating: Moderate
E/A: Anglian

Gerards Carp Lake

Location: Woodgate Lane, Maxey, Peterborough. Tel: 01945 780309
Type and Size: 6 acre pit
Carp Stock: Heavily stocked with carp to 20lbs
Category: Carp Water

Other Species: Some coarse fish
Permits: Day tickets on bank - about £5
Control: Private
BK Rating: Easy
E/A: Anglian
Comments: No fishing after 9pm

Hatton Park Pool

Location: Longstanton, near Cambridge
Type and Size: Gravel pit of 1½ acres
How to Find: In the middle of a field on the east side of Station Road, 300 yards outside Longstanton
Carp Stock: Stocked in 1982 with 15 carp to 10lbs that have since bred
Category: Carp Water
Other Species: Tench to 6lbs, plus rudd
Permits: Free
BK Rating: Moderate
E/A: Anglian

Hinchingbrooke Country Park

Location: Off the A1 near Huntingdon - the road to the lake is signposted
Type and Size: Fifty acre lake
Carp Stock: Well stocked with carp to 25lbs
Category: Mixed Fishery
Other Species: Roach, bream, perch, tench, pike, chub and eels
Permits: Day tickets from Tim's Tackle, 88 High Street, Huntingdon
Cost: £2 adults; £1 for juniors and OAP's
Control: 01480 450039
BK Rating: Moderate
E/A: Anglian
Comments: Food and drinks available; toilets

Holme Fen Fishing

Location: Earith, near Chatteris
Type and Size: Five small lakes
How to Find: Off the B1050 Somersham to Earith road. Turn left into Holme Fen Drove
Carp Stock: Well stocked with carp to 20 lbs; many doubles
Category: Mixed Fishery
Other Species: Bream to 12 lbs, tench, roach, rudd and crucians
Permits: On bank
Cost: Day ticket £4 one rod, £6 two rods
Control: Del Maginn. Tel: 01354 695559
Restrictions: No boilies, barbless hooks only. Fishing 6 a.m. to 9 p.m.
BK Rating: Moderate
E/A: Anglian

Lakeside A

Location: Biggs Road, Walsoken, between Wisbech and King's Lynn
Type and Size: Small lake in the grounds of an hotel; also a pond for children's fishing
Carp Stock: Well stocked with carp averaging upper singles
Category: Mixed Fishery
Other Species: Tench, bream, roach and perch
Permits: On bank
Cost: £5 for 8 hours; £3 for 4 hours
Control: Tel: 01945 584435
Restrictions: No boilies or nuts
BK Rating: Moderate
E/A: Anglian
Comments: Platforms for anglers; section for the disabled. Accommodation in hotel, self-catering and touring caravans

Lees Brook

Location: Berry Lane, Godmanchester, near Huntingdon
Type and Size: Small river, tributary of the Great Ouse
Carp Stock: Some carp to about 10lbs
Category: Few carp
Other Species: Chub, bream, roach, dace, perch, and gudgeon
Permits: In advance from Stanjay Fishing Tackle, Godmanchester. Tel: 01480 453303
Control: Godmanchester AC
Restrictions: More than half of the bank is private
BK Rating: Difficult
E/A: Anglian

Lily Park Lakes

Location: Earith
Type and Size: Four gravel pits, one large
How to Find: Off the A 142 between Earith and Colne
Carp Stock: Some carp to mid - twenties
Category: Mixed Fishery
Other Species: Tench, rudd, bream and pike
Permits: In advance from local tackle shops
Cost: Season tickets about £50. About £5 per day
Control: Private. Tel: 01223 461361
Restrictions: No nuts
BK Rating: Not known
E/A: Anglian

Little Paxton Fishery

Location: Near St Neots
Type and Size: Gravel pits, 4 lakes, total about 30 acres
How to Find: Take the A1 north from London. After the A45 turn off, take the left turn marked 'St Neots - Little Paxton', B1041.Turn left at the signpost marked 'Paxton Quarry' and continue for 600 yards to car park
Carp Stock: All lakes have some large carp to 20lbs. The car park lake has been stocked with carp to 20lbs
Category: Mixed Fishery
Other Species: Bream, tench, roach, rudd, perch and pike
Permits: Day tickets on bank. At weekends ONLY anglers may fish from 8am before obtaining tickets and the bailiff will sell them later on the bank. Season tickets from Fishery Manager, Little Paxton. Laurie Bowden. Tel: 01480 476088
Cost: Day tickets: £2 (juniors/OAP/evenings £1). Season tickets: £25. Limited night fishing at £25 extra
BK Rating: Moderate
Restrictions: No night fishing. Open daily 7.30am until sunset. Season and advance day ticket holders may fish from sunrise till dark. No sacking.
Baits/Methods: Normal modern carp methods and baits
E/A: Anglian
Comments: Commercial fishery. Season ticket holders may night fish for carp by arrangement with the fishery manager. Do not go to the works area. Park only in the car park.

Long Reach

Location: Off St Ives by-pass
Type and Size: 20 acre gravel pit
How to Find: Take A604 towards Cambridge, St Ives turning (B1040; St Ives by-pass), lake on right by third roundabout
Carp Stock: Lightly stocked to 36lbs plus
Category: Few Carp
Other Species: General coarse fish
Permits: Enquire locally
BK Rating: Difficult
Control: Private
Restrictions: None
E/A: Anglian
Comments: Water ski-ing on this lake during the day. A good venue for the pioneering type angler - full potential unknown

Milton Lake

Location: Near Cambridge
Type and Size: Large lake
Carp Stock: Stocked with carp to over 20lbs
Category: Mixed Fishery
Other Species: Most coarse fish
Permits: Try local tackle shops
Control: Club - possibly Cambridge AS
Cost: £1 per day
BK Rating: Difficult
E/A: Anglian

Milton Pits

Location: Old School Lane, Milton, Cambridge
Type and Size: 4 acre gravel pit
How to Find: Take the A45 north to Cambridge to Milton village. Take the High Street, turn into Coles Road and Old School Lane
Carp Stock: Well stocked with carp to 20lbs
Category: Mixed Fishery
Other Species: General coarse fish
Permits: Cooper Brothers Tackle Shop, Milton Road, Cambridge, in advance only
Cost: Approximately £10 per season, no day tickets
BK Rating: Moderate
Control: Histon Angling Club
Restrictions: None
E/A: Anglian
Comments: Pleasant lake run by club

North House Lake

Location: The North House, Great North Road, Wyboston, near St Neots
Type and Size: Gravel pit of 5 acres
How to Find: Can be seen from the A1 at Wyboston
Carp Stock: Quite well stocked - 40 - 60 fish to 23lbs. Average 14lbs
Category: Mixed Fishery
Other Species: Crucians, tench, and rudd
Permits: Luton AC or Leslie's of Luton, 89 Park Steet, Luton, Beds. Tel: 01582 453542
Cost: Approximately £7.50 per season
BK Rating: Moderate
Control: Club. Tel: 01582 28114
E/A: Anglian
Comments: Pear-shaped open gravel pit. Luton Angling Club, D Bacon, 18 The Hedgerows, Parkside, Furzton, Milton Keynes MK14 1BP. No night fishing

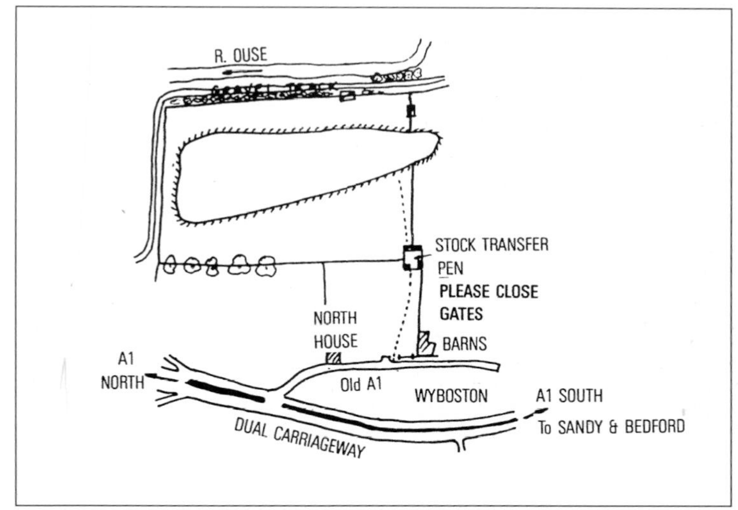

Offford Weirpool

Location: Offord, near Huntingdon
Type and Size: Very large millpool of the River Great Ouse
How to Find: At Buckden turn off the A1 towards Offord. The pool can been seen in about two miles, with a car park on the right
Carp Stock: Quite a number of doubles to nearly 30lbs
Category: Mixed Fishery
Other Species: Pike, chub, roach, and bream
Permits: Day tickets on bank
Cost: £3 per day; OAP's and juniors £1; season tickets £15 and £5
Control: Offord and Buckden AC
Baits/Methods Legered luncheon meat and floaters work well
BK Rating: Moderate
E/A: Anglian

Paxton Lake

Location: Great Paxton, near St. Neots
Type and Size: Medium sized lake
Carp Stock: Well stocked with carp, said to go to 30lbs
Category: Mixed Fishery
Other Species: Tench, chub, bream and roach
Permits: Day tickets on bank from bailiffs, or the Secretary, St. Neots and District, Watling, 43 Shakespear Road, Eaton Socon, Cambs PE19 3HG
Cost: About £1 per day; £4 per week; £9.40 per season - includes fishing on the Great Ouse
Control: Club
BK Rating: Not known
E/A: Anglian

Pisces Caravan Park and Fishery

Location: Bedford Bank, Welney, Wisbech, PE14 9TB. Tel: 01354 610527
Type and Size: Lakes of 4 acres and 2 acres
Carp Stock: Larger lake well stocked with carp to about 15lbs. Smaller lake contains crucian carp
Category: Mixed Fishery
Other Species: Bream, roach, rudd, perch, pike; some tench in smaller lake
Permits: No day tickets. Fishing is free, and is for residents only
Control: Pisces Caravan Park - private
BK Rating: Not known
Restrictions: Barbless hooks only. No keepnets. No groundbait. No boilies to be thrown in the lake
E/A: Anglian
Comments: Catches listed includes pike to over 30lbs, bream to 11lbs 6ozs, tench to over 8lbs, perch to 2lbs, rudd to 3lbs 11ozs, roach to 2 1/2 lbs. and an eel of 2 1/2 lbs. There are 16 letting caravans round the lake, and the rivers Bedford and Delph run alongside the Park - fishing free in the River Bedford, local tickets for the Delph.There is also a new trout lake on the site, with a small charge for the fishing. Rod licenses and bait on site.

Randalls Lake

Location: Barway, south of Ely
Type and Size: Small lake with two large islands
How to Find: Take the A142 from Ely towards Soham. Go into Barway and take the right fork, when the lake is signposted
Carp Stock: Well stocked with carp to doubles

Category: Mixed Fishery
Other Species: Crucians, rudd, roach, bream, tench, pike, chub, small zander and eels
Permits: On bank at £3.50 per day
Restrictions: No night fishing; fishing is 6am till dusk in summer, and 8am to dusk in winter
BK Rating: Not known
E/A: Anglian
Comments: Toilets and car park; river on one side

Sibson Fisheries

Location: On A1 between Peterborough and Stamford
Type and Size: Three lakes
How to Find: Turn left off A1 southbound at Stibbington, top of hill, turn left, follow road to chicken farm, turn right down gravel track
Carp Stock: Recently stocked with many 10 - 15 lb carp. Biggest fish (1996) was 29 lbs
Category: Mixed Fishery
Other Species: General coarse fish
Permits: On bank
Cost: £6 for day ticket; £70 - season ticket
Control: Tel: 01780 782621; Fax 01780 783694
BK Rating: Not known
Baits/Methods: Use maggots and sweetcorn. Boilies banned on 2 and 3 lakes
E/A: Anglian
Comments: No accommodation available through club. Pub approx. 1 mile away. Cross Keys, Wansford 01780 782266 B & B cost approx. £25 p.p.n. Open June 1st to March 31st

Silver Street Mill

Location: Cambridge
Type and Size: Large millpool on the River Cam
How to Find: Silver Street or Queen's Road, Cambridge, close to the colleges
Carp Stock: Some carp to doubles
Category: Few Carp
Other Species: Chub, roach, and dace
Permits: Free fishing
BK Rating: Difficult
E/A: Anglian
Comments: Very heavy boat traffic in summer; many punts

Soham By-Pass Lake

Location: Soham, near Cambridge
Type and Size: Small gravel pit
Carp Stock: Well stocked with small carp, mostly commons, to doubles
Category: Mixed Fishery
Other Species: Crucians and rudd
Permits: Enquire from tackle shops in Cambridge
BK Rating: Not known, but very heavy catches of small carp are reported
E/A: Anglian

St Ives Complex

Location: Fen Drayton, near St Ives
Type and Size: Several gravel pits
How to Find: Near St Ives
Carp Stock: Trior Lake contains some carp; St Ives Lagoon - a few large carp; Anderson's Lake - good carp

Category: Mixed Fisheries
Other Species: General coarse fish
Permits: Site Warden: Bernard Hunt. Tel: 01480 86444 (day); Tel 01480 212815 (evenings)
Cost: Day tickets on application
BK Rating: Not known
Control: Private
E/A: Anglian
Comments: Lowry's also contain some carp. Little known about this fishery

The Stew Pond

Location: St Neots
Type and Size: Pit of about 1 1/2 acres
How to Find: The pit is in the Wyboston Complex just of the A1
Carp Stock: Many carp up to 20lbs, with some bigger ones up to 18lbs
Category: Carp Water
Other Species: General coarse fish
Permits: Day tickets from the Club House on the golf course next to the pit
Cost: Approximately £2 per day
Control: Private
BK Rating: Moderate
E/A: Anglian
Comments: Night fishing allowed

Turk's Head Lake

Location: Hunter's Fen pub, Smithy Fen, Cottenham
Type and Size: Horseshoe - shaped canal type pond
Carp Stock: Well stocked with carp to 20 lbs
Category: Mixed Fishery
Other Species: Tench, crucians, roach, bream, rudd and eels
Permits: On bank
Cost: About £4 per day
Control: Tel: 01954 250687
Restrictions: No night fishing; barbless hooks
BK Rating: Moderate
E/A: Anglian
Comments: Toilets

Werrington Lake

Location: Werrington, near Peterborough
Type and Size: Medium sized pits
Carp Stock: Very well stocked with carp to over 20lbs
Category: Carp Water
Other Species: Some tench, roach, and catfish
Permits: Seasonal - information and details Tel: 01733 570266
Cost: On application
Control: Private
BK Rating: Moderate
E/A: Anglian

Wimblington Mere

Location: Wimblington, near Wisbech
Type and Size: Small gravel pit
How to Find: Just off the B1098 between Chatteris and Wisbech
Carp Stock: Some carp, numbers and sizes unknown, but a schoolboy had a 21 1/4 lb

CARP VIDEOS

CARP RIGS - Underwater- Kevin Maddocks	£13.99
WITHY POOL : Carp Water Supreme - Kevin Maddocks	£13.99
PRACTICAL CARPING 1: Julian Cundiff	£13.99
PRACTICAL CARPING 2: Julian Cundiff	£13.99
PRACTICAL CARPING 3: Julian Cundiff	£13.99
PRACTICAL CARPING 4: Julian Cundiff	£13.99
BIG CARP CHALLENGE 1: Mid Northants - Alan Taylor	£13.99
BIG CARP CHALLENGE 2: Horton - Alan Taylor	£13.99
FRENCH CARPING : An Introduction - Alan Taylor	£13.99
FRENCH CARPING 1: River Seine - Marc Ponsot & Friends	£13.99
FRENCH CARPING 2: Ton-Up, Lac Du Der - A. Taylor & Friends	£13.99
FRENCH CARPING 3: Chantecoq Facts - A. Taylor & Kevin Maddocks	£13.99
FRENCH CARPING 4: Big Carp, Orient - Kevin Maddocks	£13.99
FRENCH CARPING 5: Successful Failure - P. Regent & K. Bishop	£13.99
CARP FEVER 1: The Carp Revolution - Kevin Maddocks	£12.99
CARP FEVER 2: Rigs & Baits - Kevin Maddocks	£12.99
CARP FEVER 3: Baits & Rigs - Kevin Maddocks	£12.99
CARP FEVER 4: Off The Top & Down Below - Kevin Maddocks	£14.99
COLD - WATER CARPING: Kevin Maddocks	£13.99
ITALY : Basic Carping - Kevin Maddocks	£13.99
ITALY : Advanced Carping - Kevin Maddocks	£13.99
LONG RANGE CARPING: Phil Hyde & Clive Gibbins	£13.99
CARP TEACH - IN : Andy Little & Friends	£13.99
CARP FISHING: (Cuttle Mill) - Des Taylor	£13.99
STALKING CARP : (On Floaters) - Des Taylor	£13.99
EURO CARP QUEST 1: Fishabil - Kevin Maddocks	£12.99
EURO CARP QUEST 2: Brive - Kevin Maddocks	£12.99

BEST SELLERS

EXPEDITION BELUGA : (Sturgeon To 273lbs) - Kevin Maddocks	£13.99
CATFISH TOUR OF EUROPE: (Double Pack 2 x 60mins) - Kevin Maddocks	£19.99
BIG CATS OF THE VOLGA : Kevin Maddocks	£12.99
TENCH FISHING: David Maddocks	£13.99

All these videos can be purchased or ordered via your local tackle shop if you find this not possible, you can obtain them direct from Beekay - simply add £1 per item for P+P

**Withy Pool, Henlow Camp,
Beds, SG16 6EA.
Tel: 01462 816960
Fax: 01462 817253**

here in 1987, reported in Angling Times
Category: Mixed Fishery
Other Species: Crucians, rudd, roach, tench, bream
Permits: Head Bailiff Keith Bradshaw. Tel: 01354 740350 (evenings)
Cost: On application - about £15 per season
BK Rating: Moderate
Control: Private
Restrictions: No cereal groundbaits; no keepnets
E/A: Anglian
Comments: On the same site as Browns Water, containing carp, and Honey Pond with some carp and tench.The 21¼ was caught on slow sinking flake

Woburn Close Lake — A

Location: Hemingford Grey, St Ives
Type and Size: Gravel pit of 3 acres
Carp Stock: Very heavily stocked with about 2,000 carp. Average size is about 8lbs and the best fish is about 17lbs
Category: Carp Water
Permits: Fishing can only be obtained by renting a holiday on the property. All information and bookings from: Jim Eggett, Woburn Close, Meadow Lane, Hemingford Grey, St Ives, Cambridgeshire. Tel: 01480 62623.
Cost: On application
Control: Private
Restrictions: No night fishing
BK Rating: Very Easy
E/A: Anglian

Woolpack Fishery

Location: Godmanchester, on the main road north of Hilton, near St Ives
Type and Size: 8 lakes
Carp Stock: Quite well stocked with carp which range from 12lbs to 30lbs
Other Species: Tench, roach, rudd, bream to 14lbs, pike to 30lbs, perch
Category: Mixed Fishery
Permits: At the time of going to press the control of this water was changing - visit lake for further details
Cost: £50 per season; £25 OAP's; day tickets £3 in advance. £5 on bank
Control: Stan Jay Fishing Tackle, 7 Old Court Hall, Godmanchester, Huntingdon. Tel: 01480 453303. SAE for details
Restrictions: No peanuts to be used
BK Rating: Moderate
E/A: Anglian

CHESHIRE

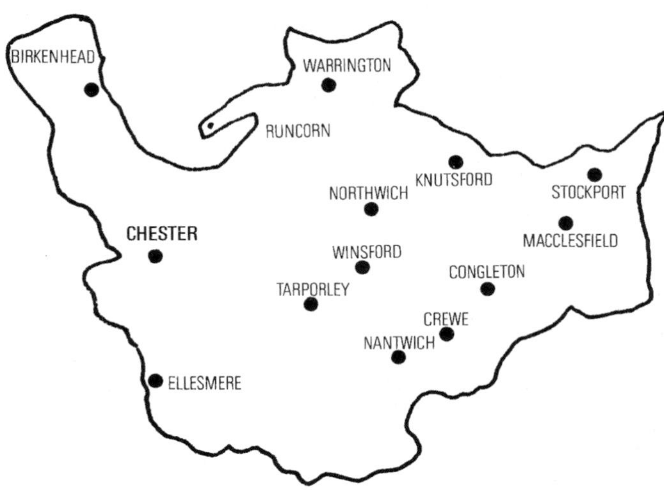

Acker's Pit

Location: Acker's Lane, Stockton Heath, near Warrington
Type and Size: Small mill dam
Carp Stock: Carp to doubles
Category: Mixed Fishery
Other Species: Roach, tench, bream, perch and pike
Permits: In advance only
Cost: £20 per season, plus £10 joining fee. Reduced prices for ladies and juniors
Control: Warrington A.A. Tel: 01928 716238
Restrictions: No night fishing; no keepnets; barbless hooks
BK Rating: Moderate
E/A: North West

Antrobus Lakes

Location: Off the A 559 golf course near Lymm
Type and Size: Five small pools
Carp Stock: The largest pool holds carp to about 10 lbs
Category: Mixed Fishery
Other Species: Roach, rudd, bream, tench, crucians, perch, barbel, chub, dace and grass carp
Permits: In advance only from local tackle shops
Cost: £24 per season, plus £12 joining fee; reduced prices for juniors, O.A.P's and ladies. Includes many other club waters
Control: Lymm A.C. Tel: 01925 411774
Restrictions: No keepnets; barbless hooks
BK Rating: Not known
E/A: North West

Astle Pool

Location: Astle Hall, Chelford, near Knutsford - Peover Lane, off the A537
Type and Size: 5 acre lake
Carp Stock: Some carp to 15 lbs
Category: Mixed Fishery
Other Species: Roach, crucians, bream, tench and pike
Permits: From local tackle shops
Cost: £20 per season, plus £20 joining fee. Some concessions for juniors and ladies
Control: Warrington A.A. Tel: 01928 716238
BK Rating: Moderate
E/A: North West
Comments: Attractive, weedy, shallow lake, with a 'waterfall' outlet

Ashenhurst Lakes

Location: Blackely, Manchester
Type and Size: Two lakes of about three-quarters of an acre each
Carp Stock: Very heavily stocked with carp to about 16lbs, though most are singles
Category: Carp Water
Other Species: Roach and a few grass carp
Permits: Club season tickets, very hard to obtain - try local tackle shops
Control: Broughton Angling Club. G Guy, 27 Geralds Road, Salford M6 6DW, who may be able to help with membership
Baits/Methods: Floaters and all other methods successful
BK Rating: Very Easy
E/A: North West
Comments: A very pleasant and attractive venue, which explains why it is so hard to obtain membership
Restrictions: No night fishing; members only. Advertised for sale in 1990

Billinge Green

Location: Off the A556, south of Northwich, near Davenham
Type and Size: Small pool
Carp Stock: Well stocked with carp to doubles
Category: Mixed Fishery
Other Species: Roach, bream, perch and tench
Permits: Northwich AA, PO Box 18, Northwich CW9 5SE
Control: Club
BK Rating: Moderate
Restrictions: Members only
E/A: North West

Blakemere

Location: Off the junction of the Shrewsbury/Whitchurch roads, about one mile from town centre of Ellesmere; park the car at the junction and walk 200 yards along canal towpath to lake
Type and Size: Lake of about 7 acres
Carp Stock: Carp to doubles
Category: Mixed Fishery
Other Species: Roach, bream, tench, perch and pike
Permits: Ellesmere AC
Control: Club
BK Rating: Not known
E/A: North West

Bosley Reservoir

Location: Bosley, near Macclesfield
Type and Size: Huge reservoir of 90 acres
Carp Stock: Carp were stocked in 1964. There are not many, but one thirty has been reported
Category: Few Carp
Other Species: General coarse fish
Permits: Prince Albert AS, season tickets only. Secretary: C Clarke, 2 Avon Close, Upton, Macclesfield, Cheshire
Cost: Around £35 entry fee and £35 per season
Control: Club. Members only
BK Rating: Very Difficult
E/A: North West

Bream Hole

Location: Marsh lane, Nantwich, off the A534 Wrexham Road
Type and Size: Wide opening on the Shropshire Union Canal. The lane crosses the canal and the 'hole' can be seen opposite the towpath side
Carp Stock: Some carp to doubles
Category: Probably Few Carp
Other Species: Bream, hybrids, roach, eels, ruffe and gudgeon
Permits: On bank at £3 per day, and £1.50 for juniors and OAP's
Restrictions: None known, but there is quite a lot of boat traffic in the summer
BK Rating: Difficult
E/A: North West

Brereton Pool

Location: Off the A54 near Congleton
Type and Size: Sand pit of 14 acres; a very attractive water
Carp Stock: Some carp to over 20lbs
Category: Mixed Fishery
Other Species: Roach, bream and big pike
Permits: £3 per day on the bank
Control: Wheelock AS. Tel: 01477 534115
Restrictions: No night fishing unless you are a club member; over half the bank has no fishing. Leave the car park by 9.30pm, or your car will be locked in for the night!
BK Rating: Difficult
E/A: North West
Comments: No close season; toilets and Ranger's hut on bank

Brereton Quarry

Location: Holmes Chapel, off the A54
Type and Size: Large quarry
Carp Stock: Some big carp
Category: Mixed Fishery
Other Species: Bream, pike and most other coarse fish
Permits: £2 per day on bank. Tel: 01477 534115
Control: Wheelock AC; details from Dave's of Middlewich, 67 Wheelock Street, Middlewich CW10 9AB. Tel: 0606 833853
BK Rating: Difficult
E/A: North West

Bridgewater Canal

Location: Broadheath Bridge to Preston Brook
Type and Size: Canal some miles in length
Carp Stock: Well stocked with carp to 17lbs
Category: Mixed Fishery
Other Species: General coarse fish
Permits: Warrington Anglers. Secretary: Frank Lythgoe, P O Box 71, Warrington, WA1 1LR. Tel: 01928 716238
Control: Club
BK Rating: Moderate
E/A: North West
Comments: Carp have been growing well in this part of the canal and many are now caught in matches. There is some good carp fishing here as a change from lakes, and it should be noted that Warrington Anglers have several carp waters mentioned in this book, all on the same ticket

Brookside Carp Fishery

Location: Betley, south east of Crewe
Type and Size: One acre pool, up to 15 feet in depth
How to Find: From Junction 16 of the M6, take the A500 towards Crewe. At the first roundabout go straight on towards Nantwich, and at the next roundabout turn left towards Keele, and you will fnd Betley in three miles. Opposite the Swan Inn, turn left, and you will see the fishery on the left in about half a mile
Carp Stock: Very well stocked with carp to 20lbs
Category: Carp Water
Other Species: Roach
Permits: On bank at £4 per rod
Control: Dave Barratt. Tel: 01270 820528/820271
Baits/Methods: Luncheon meat and sweetcorn; floaters do well in hot weather
Restrictions: Barbless hooks only; no boilies or nuts; no keepnets or sacks; micromesh landing nets only; no groundbaiting before fishing; no night fishing - 7.30am till dusk only
BK Rating: Moderate
E/A: North West
Comments: With all these bans, I sometimes wonder whether fishery owners want their fish caught! There is also a trout pool next to the coarse lake. Refreshments and tackle shop. Trout fishing

Budworth Mere

Location: Near Great Budworth, off the B5075, north of Northwich
Type and Size: Large lake
Carp Stock: Well stocked with carp to about 20lbs
Category: Mixed Fishery
Other Species: Tench, roach, rudd, bream, perch and pike
Permits: Northwich AA, PO Box 18, Northwich, CW9 5SE
Control: Club. Try Scotts Tackle. Tel: 01606 46543
Restrictions: Members only
BK Rating: Not known
E/A: North West

Burton Mere

Location: Burton, off the A54 Chester to Hoylake Road - in Burton, turn right into Puddington Lane, then take the first right to the lakes
Type and Size: Two small man-made lakes

Category: Mixed Fishery
Other Species: Roach, rudd, perch, bream, crucians, tench, chub, catfish and trout
Permits: Day tickets from the lodge on site. Tel: 0151 2530115
Cost: £4 per day; £2.50 per evening, from 5pm
Control: Private
Baits/Methods: Float fishing works well, with standard baits
BK Rating: Moderate
Restrictions: No keepnets; no groundbaiting
E/A: Welsh
Comments: The larger lake is day ticket, and the smaller one is a members only carp fishery. No close season on the day ticket water, as rainbow trout are stocked in March, but worm fishing only is allowed in the coarse fish close season

Canal Pit

Location: Whatcroft, off the A530 south of Northwich
Type and Size: Small pit
Carp Stock: Some carp to doubles
Category: Mixed Fishery
Other Species: Usual coarse fish
Permits: Northwich AA, PO Box 18, Northwich CW9 5SE; Scotts Tackle, Northwich. Tel: 01606 46543
Control: Club
Restrictions: Members only
BK Rating: Not known
E/A: North West

Capesthorne Hall Garden Pool

Location: Capesthorne Estate, Siddington, near Macclesfield
Type and Size: Estate lake of 7 acres
How to Find: The estate is just off the A34, 3 miles from Macclesfield, and 6 miles from Knutsford and Wilmslow
Carp Stock: The lake is well stocked with carp under 10lbs, and there are about 60 doubles, of which 6 are twenties - best 28lbs
Category: Mixed Fishery
Other Species: Tench, crucians, perch, roach, rudd, pike and gudgeon
Permits: Season tickets from Stoke-on-Trent AS. Secretary: Mr A Perkins, Muirshearlich, Fowrlers Lane, Lightoaks, Stoke - on - Trent ST2 7NB. Enclose SAE. Members only, some guest tickets.
Baits/Methods: All methods and baits. Float fishing works well near lilies and bushes; surface fishing very successful in summer
Control: Club
BK Rating: North West
Comments: Stocked with mirror carp in 1958 and 1963. Good spawning and carp spawned in 1976 now up to 20lbs

Central Lake

Location: Public park in Wallasey, near Birkenhead, on the Wirral
Type and Size: Four acre boating lake with an island
Carp Stock: Well stocked with carp to doubles
Category: Mixed Fishery
Other Species: Crucians, roach, rudd and small tench
Permits: In advance from local tackle shops
Cost: £1 per day; £4 per year

Control: Association of Wirral Angling Clubs
BK Rating: Moderate
E/A: North West

Cheshire Fishing

Location: Tattenhall, near Chester
Type and Size: Three small lakes
How to Find: From Chester take the A41 Whitchurch Road. The Tattenhall turn is on the left in about 8 miles. At the T-junction in Tattenhall, turn left towards Burwardsley. In 1½ miles you wil see a 'Cheshire Fishing' sign on the left
Carp Stock: Lakes 1 and 2 well stocked with carp to 20lbs; Lake 3, the smallest contains many small carp
Category: Mixed Fishery
Other Species: Bream, tench, roach
Permits: On site - match bookings in advance
Cost: £6.50 per day per rod, dawn to dusk only; 34 for a 5 hour ticket, extra rods £1 each
Control: Private. Tel: 01829 70041
Restrictions: No night fishing; all fish over 1lb to be returned immediately; barbless hooks only
Baits/Methods Most baits and methods, though most carp are taken on boilies
BK Rating: Moderate
Comments: There are also two trout lakes on the same site

Cicely Mill Pool

Location: Knutsford
Type and Size: Small mere of about 3 acres
Carp Stock: Not many carp, but some to low doubles
Category: Few Carp
Permits: Warrington Anglers. Secretary: Mr Jackson, 23 Nora Street, Warrington
Control: Club. Members only Tel: 01928 716238
BK Rating: Difficult
E/A: North West
Comments: No night fishing; no keepnets. About £25 per season

Crabmill Flash

Location: Moston near Sandbach
Type and Size: Estate lake of about 10 acres
Carp Stock: Plenty of doubles and about twenty 20's with the best fish over 30lbs
Category: Carp Water
Permits: Season tickets from Wheelock Angling Society, and local tackle shops
Control: Club
BK Rating: Moderate
E/A: North West
Comments: Long, narrow canal-like lake, about ¼ mile long. Good twenties water

Crosemere

Location: About 3 miles from Ellesmere on the main Shrewsbury Road; parking down lane about half a mile past the lake
Type and Size: Large Cheshire mere
Carp Stock: Some carp to doubles
Cateory: Few Carp
Other Species: Roach, bream, perch, tench and pike
Permits: Ellesmere AC

Control: Club
BK Rating: Very Difficult
E/A: North West
Comments: As this area is an S.S.S.I., great care must be taken to observe rules and signs, and to keep to marked paths. No cutting of undergrowth etc

Doddlespool Farm Lake A

Location: Betley, near Crewe
Type and Size: Attractive woodland pool of an acre
Carp Stock: Well stocked with carp to 20 lbs
Category: Mixed Fishery
Other Species: Roach, perch, tench and bream
Permits: On site
Cost: About £4 per day
Control: Tel: 01270 820216
Restrictions: No night fishing
BK Rating: Not known
E/A: Severn Trent
Comments: Bed and breakfast accommodation. Probably open all year

Dovemere, Sandmere and Woodlands

Location: Allostock, near Knutsford
Type and Size: 3 lake complex, lakes dug to provide material for the motorway. Dovemere - 17 acres; Sandmere - 15 acres; Woodlands - 10 acres
How to Find: Lakes are alongside the M6 at Allostock
Carp Stock: Well stocked with mostly carp doubles
Category: Carp Water
Other Species: Mixed coarse fish
Permits: Season tickets only from Prince Albert Angling Society. Secretary: C Clarke, 2 Avon Close, Macclesfield, Cheshire
Cost: Avour £35 entry fee plus £35 annual subscription
Control: Club
BK Rating: Generally Easy, waters may vary
E/A: North West

Egerton Lakes

Location: Fruit Farm, Bickerton Lane, Cholmondeley castle
Type and Size: 3 acre lake
Carp Stock: Well stocked with carp to 25 lbs
Category: Mixed Fishery
Other Species: Roach, rudd, crucians, bream and trout
Permits: On bank
Cost: About £5 per day
Control: Egerton Fruit Farm. Tel: 01270 627232
Restrictions: No tiger nuts or peanuts
BK Rating: Moderate
E/A: North West

Founders Pool

Location: Near Warrington
Type and Size: Small pond of 1 acre
Carp Stock: Well stocked with carp to doubles
Category: Mixed Fishery
Other Species: Roach and perch
Permits: Members only water of Lymm AC. Tel: 01925 411774

Cost: £23 per season, and a joinlng fee of £13
Restrictions: No night fishing; members only
BK Rating: Easy
E/A: North West

Gale Green Farm Fishery

Location: Gale Green Farm, off the A54 near Winsford
Type and Size: Four acre lake
Carp Stock: Well stocked with carp, mostly between 16lbs and 28lbs; commons and mirrors
Category: Mixed Fishery
Other Species: Pike, tench, roach, rudd, bream, chub, perch and eels
Permits: Must be obtained from the farm by the car park before fishing
Cost: £3.75 per day; £2.75 for summer evening tickets
Control: Tel: 01606 552151
Restrictions: Night fishing for club members only; difficult footpath to dense, wooded valley
BK Rating: Moderate
E/A: North West

Godwins Pool

Location: Near Congleton
Type and Size: Small pool
Carp Stock: Some carp to about 20lbs
Category: Mixed Fishery
Other Species: Tench and most other coarse fish
Permits: Congleton Anglers Society. Secretary: Mrs N Bours, 8 Norfolk Road, Congleton. Tel: 01260 277284
Cost: Membership (to include other waters) costs £20 per season plus a £5 entry fee
Control: Club
BK Rating: Moderate
E/A: North West

Grey Mist Mere

Location: Woolston, near Warrington
Type and Size: Mere of about 10 acres
Carp Stock: Very well stocked with carp. Plenty of doubles with a few low twenties, best fish 21lbs
Category: Carp Water
Other Species: General coarse fish
Permits: Warrington Anglers, season tickets only. Secretary: Mr J S Jackson, 23 Nora Street, Warrington. About £25 per season
Control: Club. Tel: 01928 716238
BK Rating: Moderate
E/A: North West
Comments: A well known carp water, very good for doubles. Open 1st May to end of February

Grimesditch Pool

Location: Stretton, near Warrington
Type and Size: Small pool of one acre
How to Find: Stretton is near junction 10 of the M56 motorway
Carp Stock: Not many carp, to about 10lbs
Category: Few Carp

Permits: Lymm Angling Club. Tel: 01925 411774.Season tickets
Control: Club
BK Rating: Difficult
E/A: North West
Comments: It should be noted here that Lymm Angling Club has several carp waters on the same ticket. About £3 per day from Milestone Pub by fishery entrance

Hack Green Lake

Location: Hack Green, 3 miles from Nantwich
Type and Size: Man-made lake of 2 acres
Carp Stock: Well stocked with carp (in 1986) to doubles
Category: Mixed Fishery
Other Species: Tench, roach and bream
Permits: See below
BK Rating: Moderate
E/A: North West
Comments: This water was advertised for sale, within a 4 1/2 acre site, in March 1991 so you will need to enquire at local tackle shops to find out who controls it now. The agents were Wright-Manley. Tel: Tarporley (01829) 732151

King George V Pool

Location: Altrincham
Type and Size: Small, shallow lake of about 3 acres
How to Find: Altrincham is near Sale on the SW outskirts of Manchester.Take the Manchester - Northwich road
Carp Stock: Well stocked mainly with small carp, but there are fish to upper double figure size with the odd 20
Category: Carp Water
Permits: Day tickets from bailiff on bank - about £2 per day
Control: Trafford Metropolitan Council
BK Rating: Easy
E/A: North West

Little Budworth

Location: Little Budworth, near Tarporley
Type and Size: 5 acre lake
Carp Stock: Some carp to doubles
Category: Mixed Fishery
Other Species: Tench, bream, roach, and small perch
Permits: Tarporley and district A.C. Mr MJ Clays, 58 Churchill Drive, Tarporley CW6 OBZ; members only
Control: Club
Restrictions: Membership is restricted to those living within a 5 mile radius of Tarporley
BK Rating: Not known
E/A: North West

Little Mill

Location: Near Tarporley
Type and Size: Mill pool of just over 3 acres
Carp Stock: Carp to over 20lbs
Category: Mixed Fishery
Other Species: Tench, perch, bream, roach and a few crucians
Permits: Tarporley and district A.C. Mr MJ Clays, 58 Churchill Drive, Tarporley

	CW6 OBZ; members only
Control:	Club
Restrictions:	Membership is restricted to those living within a 5 miles radius of Tarporley
BK Rating:	Difficult
E/A:	North West

Lymm Dam

Location:	Near the village of Lymm, near Warrington, Manchester
Type and Size:	15 acre lake
How to Find:	Go through Lymm onto the A56 and the lake will be seen on the right
Carp Stock:	There are not thought to be many carp but there are some very big ones. Largest known caught recently was 27lbs, but we know of a least one thirty caught a long time ago, and there are rumours of even bigger fish
Category:	Few Carp
Other Species:	Bream, roach, pike and a few catfish
Permits:	Day tickets from bailiffs on the bank
Cost:	About £2.50 per day
BK Rating:	Moderate
Baits/Methods:	Advanced carp fishing methods needed; high protein boilies
Control:	Lymm Angling Club, which has a number of other good carp waters. Tel: 01925 264893
E/A:	North West
Comments:	This is known mainly as a match water, but there are some big fish of most species, and probably some very big carp, which are hard to find in this large water. Uncontrollable fish are occasionally hooked and lost - thought to be big catfish. Toilet

Macclesfield Canal

Location:	Kidsgrove and Congleton lengths especially good
Type and Size:	Some miles of a narrow canal
Carp Stock:	Plenty of carp to about 5lbs, with possibly some bigger fish present
Category:	Mixed Fishery
Other Species:	Bream, roach, tench and pike
Permits:	Local angling clubs - try tackle shops in Congleton and Kidsgrove
Control:	Club
BK Rating:	Easy
E/A:	North West
Comments:	No close season

Marbury Mere

Location:	Marbury
Type and Size:	Mere of 30 acres
Carp Stock:	Only a small number of carp, but some are upper 20's
Other Species:	General coarse fish
Permits:	Season tickets only. Prince Albert AS. Secretary: C Clarke, 2 Avon Close, Macclesfield, Cheshire
Cost:	About £35 entry fee plus £35 per season
Control:	Club
BK Rating:	Difficult
E/A:	North West
Comments:	All Prince Albert club waters are members only. This is one of the largest clubs in the country with a fine selection of waters

Mobberley Pool

Location: Small Lane, Mobberley, near Altrincham
Type and Size: Small pool of less than an acre
How to Find: Mobberley is near Knutsford on the B5085 road from Knutsford to Alderley Edge, south of Manchester
Carp Stock: Well stocked with small carp to lower double figure size
Category: Mixed Fishery
Permits: Altrincham AS. A Lea, 37 Crossgates Avenue, Sharston, Manchester
Control: Club
BK Rating: Easy
E/A: North West

Moreton Fisheries

Location: On the A 34 at Astbury, near Congleton
Type and Size: Two lakes of 7 acres and 1 acre
Carp Stock: Carp to doubles
Category: Mixed Fishery
Other Species: Bream, roach, rudd and tench
Permits: On site
Cost: Up to £5 per day, depending on which lake fished. Concessions
Control: Tel: 01260 299496
BK Rating: Not known
E/A: North West

Moreton Mere

Location: Off the A553 at Moreton, Hoylake, Wirral
Type and Size: Three acre lake, very recently dug
Carp Stock: Well stocked with small carp of around 2lbs, with a few low doubles
Category: Mixed FIshery
Other Species: Roach, rudd, bream, perch and grass carp
Permits: Day tickets on bank
Cost: £3 per day; concessionary rates. Annual £15
Control: Tel: 0151 645 7211
Restrictions: No night fishing; no keepnets
BK Rating: Not known
E/A: North West

Moss and Mossbank Pools

Location: Lymm, near Manchester
Type and Size: Two small ponds
Carp Stock: Well stocked with carp to about 10lbs
Category: Carp Water
Other Species: Crucians and grass carp (these are not really carp at all - Latin name: *Ctenopharyngodon Idella* !)
Permits: Members only water of Lymm. A.A. Tel: 01925 411744
Restrictions: No day tickets; no night fishing
BK Rating: Easy
E/A: North West

Ocean Pool

Location: Winsford
Type and Size: Medium sized lake
How to Find: Winsford is south of Northwich on the A54 Chester to Congleton Road
Carp Stock: Small number of carp to mid-twenties
Category: Few Carp

Other Species: General coarse fish
Permits: Winsford and District Angling Association, J Bailey, 22 Plover Road, Winsford
Control: Club
BK Rating: Easy
E/A: North West

Oulton Mill

Location: Near Tarporley
Type and Size: 4 acre mill lake
Carp Stock: Very well stocked wtih carp to 20lbs
Category: Carp Water
Other Species: A few tench and roach
Permits: Tarporley and District AC - M J Clays, 58 Churchill Drive, Tarporley
Cost: Season tickets at £60 per season, open to all
Control: Club
BK Rating: Moderate
E/A: North West
Comments: Some waters in the North West now have no close season

Petty Pool

Location: Sandiway, off the A556 to the south west of Northwich
Type and Size: Medium-size lake
Carp Stock: Some carp to doubles at least
Category: Mixed Fishery
Other Species: Usual coarse fish
Permits: Northwich AA, PO Box 18, Northwich CW9 5SE; Scotts Tackle, Northwich. Tel: 01606 46543
Control: Club
Restrictions: Members only
BK Rating: Not known
E/A: North West

Plex Flash

Location: Oakwood Lane, Moston, Sandbach
Carp Stock: Contains about 55 doubles to 18lbs 10ozs
Category: Mixed Fishery
Other Species: General coarse fish
Permits: Wheelock Angling Club, and local tackle shops
Control: Club. Tel: 01477 534115
BK Rating: Moderate
E/A: Noth West
Comments: Little is known about this water. Further details from Club Secretary

Poynton Pool

Location: South Park Drive, Poynton
Type and Size: 4 acre lake
Carp Stock: Quite well stocked wtih carp to over 20lbs
Category: Mixed fishery
Other Species: Roach, bream, crucians and pike
Permits: On bank
Cost: About £2 per day
Control: Stockport D.A.F. Tel: 0161 477 4536
Restrictions: One rod only; one bank; no night fishing; no keepnets
BK Rating: Not known

E/A: North West

Reddish Vale Mill Ponds

Location: Reddish Vale Road, Stockport, off the B6167 Manchester to Stockport Road
Type and Size: Two small ponds
Carp Size: Both ponds quite well stocked with carp to over 20lbs
Category: Mixed Fishery
Other Species: Bream, tench, roach, perch and small pike
Permits: On bank, or at the site Visitors Centre
Cost: £2 per day; £3 for two rods; season tickets £15 and £5 for children under 15 and OAP's
Control: Teme Valley Countryside Warden Service
Baits/Methods: Boilies best for carp
Restrictions: No night fishing (dawn till dusk only); floating crust is banned; live baits banned; keepnets only allowed in matches
BK Rating: Not known
E/A: North West

Redesmere

Location: Capesthorne Estate, Siddington, Macclesfield
Type and Size: Estate mere of 40 acres
How to Find: The lake is just off the A34 Alderley Edge to Congleton Road
Carp Stock: There are reliably estimated to be about 150 doubles in the lake, of which 45 fish are over 20lbs.There are 6 thirties, a common of 33lbs 6ozs, and a mirror of 32lbs. Water was stocked with 150 fingerlings in 1958, and in 1963 a further 100 fish were stocked. Small number of carp including some doubles have been put in since
Category: Mixed Fishery
Other Species: Large bream, pike, tench, crucians, roach and perch
Permits: Season tickets from Stoke-on-Trent Angling Society. Mr A Perkins, Muirshearlich, Fowlers Lane, Light Oaks, Stoke-on-Trent, ST2 7NB. Enclose SAE. Members only, some guest tickets allowed
Baits/Methods Normal carp fishing baits and methods
Control: Club. Bailiff: Mrs E Shapley. Tel: Wilmslow 520061
BK Rating: Difficult
E/A: North West
Comments: This is one of the best big fish carp waters in the north west, but due to its large size it is not an easy water to succeed on. It has the potential to produce even bigger fish than at present. 48 hours only allowed in one swim. £50 per year plus entry fee

Rhodes Lodges

Location: Middleton, near Manchester
Type and Size: Old mill pits - one of 5 acres and four smaller ones
Carp Stock: Very well stocked wtih small carp, with some double figure mirrors and commons to about 15lbs
Category: Carp Water
Other Species: Some roach and perch
Permits: Day tickets on site at £1.45; 70p for OAP's, juniors and the unemployed
Control: Private. Tel: 0161 654 8278
Restrictions: No night fishing; no season tickets; no sacks
BK Rating: Moderate
E/A: North West
Comments: Heavily fished, crowded water open to all

River Weaver

Location: Rises near Macclesfield and flows through Northwich to the Mersey
Type and Size: Short river
How to Find: Northwich area
Carp Stock: 100lb catches in a day reported, of carp to 5lbs and up to 9lbs
Category: Mixed Fishery
Other Species: General coarse fish
Permits: On bank
Cost: £2
BK Rating: Easy when carp are located
Control: Club
E/A: North West
Comments: Fish caught on match tackle - waggler and double maggot. Best area is the Marina where the A54 crosses the river south of Winsford. Above Vale Royal locks also said to be good. For information try Northwich AA, R Hankey, PO Box 18, Northwich - tickets supplied

Rode Pool

Location: Townsend Lane, Rode Heath, near Sandbach
Type and Size: Narrow lake a mile long
Carp Stock: Some carp to doubles; several thirties reported
Category: Mixed Fishery
Other Species: Crucians, bream, tench, pike, roach, rudd and perch
Permits: On bank
Cost: £3 per day
Control: Tel: 01270 883624
Restrictions: No night fishing; no nuts; barbless hooks
BK Rating: Difficult
E/A: North West

Roman Lake

Location: Near Marple
Type and Size: 10 acre lake, with islands and gravel bars
Carp Stock: Well stocked with many low doubles, up to just over 20lbs
Category: Carp Water
Other Species: Roach and tench
Permits: Day tickets from bailiff at the water
Cost: About £4 per day
Control: Private - B Sewart. Tel: 0161 4272039
Restrictions: Barbless hooks only; no night fishing; no multiple baits; no fishing on one side. No fixed leads
BK Rating: Difficult
E/A: North West
Comments: A hard fished carp water, which is now quite difficult because the fish are well educated. Toilet

Runcorn Park Lake

Location: Norton Priory Recreation Centre, Runcorn
Type and Size: Small lake
Carp Stock: Well stocked with carp to upper doubles
Category: Mixed Fishery
Other Species: Pike, roach and perch
Permits: On bank
Cost: About £2 per day
Control: I.C.I.Weston A.C. Tel: 01928 578139

BK Rating: Not known
E/A: North West

Sale Water Park

Location: Rifle Road, Sale
Type and Size: Lake excavated to provide material to build the motorway, 55 acres
How to Find: Come off the M63 at junction 8
Carp Stock: Stocked with mirror carp in 1978, two years after the lake was completed. Numbers not known but there are now a reasonable head of carp mostly between 4 and 12lb, with some upper doubles and one or two lower twenties
Category: Mixed Fishery
Other Species: Catfish, grass carp, pike, eels, roach, perch, bream and tench
Permits: About £2 per day from office on site, or £3 from bailiff on bank during the weekends; EXTRA ON BANK HOLIDAYS AND AT WEEKENDS. Season tickets: Adults £15; Junior £5
Control: Mersey Valley Joint Committee. Tel: 0161 969 7063
BK Rating: Easy
Restrictions: Fishing 8am till sunset only, unless special night permit obtained
Baits/Methods: Legering with boilies best method
E/A: North West
Comments: Water is 80 feet deep in places and the very deep areas would not be likely to produce carp. This water is only 4½ miles from Manchester City Centre

Shakerley Mere

Location: Allostock, near Northwich
Type and Size: Large mere of 17 acres
How to Find: Just off the M6 near Northwich
Carp Stock: Some carp to over 20lbs
Category: Mixed Fishery
Other Species: Tench, roach, perch, bream
Permits: Day tickets on bank
Cost: £3
Control: Club. Tel: 01925 264893
BK Rating: Insufficient informaton
E/A: North West
Comments: Formerly Council controlled. Local tackle shops have details

Springwood Pool

Location: Mobberley, near Knutsford
Type and Size: Small pool
Carp Stock: Well stocked with carp to doubles
Category: Mixed Fishery
Other Species: Most common coarse fish
Permits: Congleton Anglers' Society. Secretary: Mr N Bours, 8 Norfolk Road, Congleton. Tel: 01260 277284
Cost: Membership costs £20 per season, with a £5 entry fee
Control: Club
BK Rating: Moderate
E/A: North West

Please support the AGA see Ad on page 167.

Statham Pool

Location: Lymm, near Warrington
Type and Size: Small pond
Carp Stock: Well stocked with carp to doubles
Category: Mixed Fishery
Other Species: Roach, bream, tench and perch
Permits: Day tickets from bailiff on bank - enquire local tackle shops for details
Control: Club - name not known - possibly Lymm AA?
Restrictions: No night fishing
BK Rating: Moderate
E/A: North West

Stock Pool

Location: Capesthorne Estate, Siddington, Macclesfield
Type and Size: Estate stock pond of 1acre
Carp Stock: This water is well stocked with small carp and is ideal for youngsters or beginners
Permits: Day tickets can be booked in advance from the bailiff: Mr A Bradley. Tel: 01625 861584, or on bank at £6 per day; £4 for a half day
BK Rating: Easy

Taxmere

Location: Near Sandbach
Type and Size: Medium sized lake
Carp Stock: Some carp, numbers and sizes not known
Category: Mixed Fishery
Other Species: Bream, roach, tench, perch and pike
Permits: Day tickets from I F McDonald, 49 Welles Street, Sandbach
Control: Club
BK Rating: Moderate
E/A: Severn-Trent

Tegg's Nose Reservoir

Location: Sutton Lane End, Langley, near Macclesfield
Type and Size: Small attractive reservoir
Carp Stock: Carp to over 20 lbs
Category: Mixed Fishery
Other Species: Tench, roach, bream, crucians and perch
Permits: In advance only from Barlow's Tackle, Bond St, Macclesfield
Cost: £3 per day
Control: Tel: 01625 619935 - Macclesfield Waltonians
Restrictions: No night fishing; one rod only
BK Rating: Moderate
E/A: North West

Tetton Lake

Location: Near Middlewich, off A533 near Elworth
Type and Size: Three acre lake
Carp Stock: Well stocked with carp to 20lbs
Category: Mixed Fishery
Other Species: Tench, bream and roach
Permits: An Association of local angling clubs - try local tackle shops for details
Control: An Association of Middlewich AS, Middlewich British Legion and Middlewich Big Lock AC. Permits also include river fishing and 8 miles of two local canals. Dave's of Middlewich. Tel: 01606 833853

BK Rating: Moderate
E/A: North West

Thorneycroft Hall Lakes

Location: Henbury, near Macclesfield
Type and Size: 2 lakes; Lower - 6 acres, Top - 12 acres
Carp Stock: Lower Lake - well stocked with plenty of small carp to 20lbs. Top Lake - not many carp but some good ones to 19lbs
Category: Lower - Carp Water. Top - Few Carp
Other Species: Mixed coarse fish
Permits: Prince Albert Angling Society, season tickets only. Secretary: C. Clarke, 2 Avon Close, Macclesfield
Cost: About £35 entry fee plus £35 per season
Control: Club
BK Rating: Lower - Easy to Moderate. Top - Difficult
E/A: North West

Town Park Lane

Location: Housing estate on the outskirts of Runcorn; take the road to Castelfields and Norton Sports Centre - the lake is near the car park
Type and Size: Man-made lake of about 3 acres with an island
Carp Stock: Some carp to doubles
Category: Mixed Fishery
Other Species: Bream, pike, roach, perch, tench and gudgeon
Permits: Day tickets on bank
Cost: 15 pence! Possibly a little more in 1997
Control: Council
BK Rating: Moderate
E/A: North West

Village Pool

Location: Whitley, Near Warrington
Type and Size: Village pond of about 1/2 acre
How to Find: The pond is in the centre of the village of Whitley. Come off the M56 motorway at junction 10 and from Stretton take the A559 south of Whitley
Carp Stock: Quite well stocked with carp, most of which are mid-doubles to about 21lbs
Category: Mixed Fishery
Other Species: Usual coarse fish
Permits: Lymm Angling Club. Tel: 01925 411744
Control: Club
BK Rating: Moderate
Baits/Methods: Normal carp fishing methods
E/A: North West

Walpool Lodge

Location: Gawsworth, near Macclesfield
Type and Size: Three lakes
How to Find: Take the A536 south from Macclesfield, and in about 2 miles follow the signs to Gawsworth Hall, pass the gates and the car park is about 100 yards from the pool
Carp Stock: Well stocked with carp to upper doubles
Category: Mixed Fishery
Other Species: Crucians, tench, bream, rudd, roach, perch and gudgeon

Permits: On bank
Cost: £3 for one rod; £5 for two rods
Control: John Birch. Tel: 01260 223442
Restrictions: Beans are banned; night fishing by special arrangement only
Baits/Methods: Legered boilies and luncheon meat. Surface fishing with floaters and crust
BK Rating: Moderate
E/A: North West
Comments: Open all year

Westgate Pool

Location: Near Lymm, west of Manchester
Type and Size: Tiny pond
Carp Stock: Well stocked with small carp - ideal for youngsters
Category: Mixed Fishery
Other Species: Rudd and tench
Permits: Members only water of Lymm Angling Club. Tel: 01925 411744
Control: Club
Restrictions: No night fishing
BK Rating: Easy
E/A: Severn-Trent

Whirley Pool

Location: Henbury, near Macclesfield
Type and Size: Small pit
Carp Stock: Said to be quite well stocked with small carp to mid-double figure size
Category: Mixed Fishery
Other Species: Usual coarse fish
Permits: Prince Albert Angling Society. Secretary: C Clarke, 2 Avon Close, Macclesfield
Cost: About £35 entry fee plus £35 annual subscription. Season tickets only
Control: Club
BK Rating: Thought to be Moderate
E/A: North West
Comments: It will be noticed that whilst the cost of joining Prince Albert Angling Society is high compared with many clubs, they have a number of very fine carp waters, all on the same ticket

Whitemere

Location: About one mile from the town of Ellesmere, on the Shrewsbury Road
Type and Size: Large lake
Carp Stock: Some carp to doubles
Category: Mixed Fishery
Other Species: Roach, bream, tench, perch and pike
Permits: Ellesmere AC
Control: Club
BK Rating: Difficult
E/A: North West
Comments: This mere is also used for sailing,and not all of the lake can be fished. It is also a Site of Special Scientific Interest (S.S.S.I.,) and care must be taken only to use marked paths, and to observe all rules and notices

Winterley Pool

Location: Winterley Farm, Wheelock, near Sandbach
Type and Size: Pleasant 8 acre lake, rather snaggy and surrounded by trees, and a new small pool
Carp Stock: Plenty of small carp to doubles, and a few 20's to about 25lbs

SANDBECK AS - FOTO: BARRY ORD CLARKE

Nick Payne, plater.

«...then I lacquer them once more to give the right finish.»

Tradition, Commitment & Craftsmanship: A job well done! Nick's job is to give Partridge fish hooks just the right coating and finish. Discerning carp fishers and other fishermen know what Partridge of Redditch stands for. That's why they consistently choose our products. If you put your heart into your rigs, you must try our hooks; we know you'll be satisfied! We offer many different hooks including the new Stronghold range, redesigned by Kevin Maddocks.

PARTRIDGE
OF REDDITCH
FINEST HANDMADE BRITISH FISH HOOKS

Partridge of Redditch Ltd. • Mount Pleasant, Redditch • Worcestershire, England B97 4JE.
Telephone: (01527) 541380. • Telefax: (01527) 546956.

Category: Mixed Fishery
Other Species: Usual coarse fish
Permits: Day tickets on bank
Cost: £4 per rod; £5 for 24 hours
Control: Private: Tel: 01270 582352
BK Rating: Moderate
E/A: North West

Woodlands Lake

Location: Allostock, near Knutsford, just off the M6
Type and Size: 10 acre lake, with two other lakes on site
Carp Stock: Not many carp, but most are doubles to about 20lbs
Permits: Prince Albert AS, J T Lovatt, 62 Beggerman's Lane, Knutsford or Queens Hotel, Waters Green, Macclesfield
Control: Club - season tickets only
Restrictions: No day tickets - check before night fishing
BK Rating: Fairly Hard
E/A: North West

CLEVELAND

Ascott Ponds

Location: Cleveland, North Yorkshire border
Type and Size: Three small lakes
Carp Stock: Well stocked with small carp
Category: Mixed Fishery
Other Species: Trout, tench, bream, dace, perch, gudgeon
Permits: D Speight, 10 Stainsby Gate, Thornaby, Cleveland. Members only
Control: Thornaby AA
BK Rating: Moderate
E/A: Northumbrian
Comments: Floating baits produce good results. Club has many other good fisheries

Charlton Ponds

Location: Billingham, north east of Middlesbrough
Type and Size: Eight acre town-type lake, with half acre pond next door
How to Find: Take the A1185 north of Middlesbrough to Billingham and go over two roundabouts to Central Avenue. At the next roundabout turn left into Cowpen Lane, then right into Hereford Terrace. The ponds are on the left, with a car park close to the Community Centre
Carp Stock: Well stocked with carp between 4lbs and about 10lbs
Category: Mixed Fishery
Other Species: Tench, eels, roach, and rudd. The small pond has crucians, roach, perch and tench only
Permits: Day tickets on bank
Cost: £1 for adults; 60p for juniors and OAP's. Season tickets £12 and £6
Control: Billingham Sportsman's AC
Restrictions: No night fishing; no keepnets; groundbait limited; no floating baits; one rod only (can we use hooks!?). No close season for larger lake
BK Rating: Not known
E/A: Northumbrian

Hartburn Brick Pit

Location: Hartburn Lane, Stockton - on - Tees
Type and Size: Small pit
Carp Stock: Some carp to doubles
Category: Mixed Fishery
Other Species: Crucians, bream, tench and roach
Permits: On site
Cost: About £3 per day
Control: Stockton Council Tel: 01642 588796 / 588789
BK Rating: Not known
E/A: Yorkshire
Comments: Open all year

Hemlington Lake

Location: Hemlington, near Middlesbrough
Type and Size: Large lake, much used for match fishing
Carp Stock: Well stocked with small carp
Category: Mixed Fishery
Other Species: Crucians, bream and roach
Permits: On bank at £1.50 per day
Control: Middlesbrough Council/Middlesbrough AC. Tel: 01642 596546
BK Rating: Easy
E/A: Northumbrian
Comments: No close season, best avoided at night! Try W P Adams Fishing Tackle, 42 Duke Street, Darlington. Tel: 01325 468069

Linear Fisheries Oxford

Hardwick Lakes
22lb 14oz

Hutton Rudby Ponds

Location: Near Middlesbrough
Type and Size: Small ponds
Carp Stock: Some carp
Category: Mixed Fishery
Other Species: Roach, perch and bream
Permits: Members only water of Middlesbrough AC - membership open to all from Redcar Angling Centre, Cleveland Angling Centre, Thornaby, Adams Tackle, Darlington and Middlesbrough and the Tackle Box, Billingham
Cost: £12 per season, with a £6 joining fee, to include other waters; juniors half price
Control: Club
Restrictions: No night fishing, members only
BK Rating: Not known
E/A: Northumbrian

Locke Park

Location: Off the B1085 road from Middlesbrough at Redcar
Type and Size: Small public park lake, surrounded by houses
Carp Stock: Well stocked with carp to just over 10lbs
Category: Mixed Fishery
Other Species: Bream, roach, and perch
Permits: Day tickets on the bank
Cost: £2; Juniors 55p. Permit needed for each rod. Season - £12
Control: Langborough Borough Council/Locke Park AC - Gordon Sanderson. Tel: 01642 477832
Restrictions: No night fishing; dawn till dusk only; no close season fishing
BK Rating: Not known
E/A: Northumbrian

New Marske Reservoir

Location: Near Middlesbrough
Type and Size: 10 acre reservoir
Carp Stock: Well stocked with carp to over 20lbs
Category: Mixed Fishery
Other Species: Bream, roach, tench and perch
Permits: Redcar Angling Centre, High Street, Middlesbrough
Cost: £2 per day
Control: Middlesbrough AC
Restrictions: No night fishing
BK Rating: Not known
E/A: Northumbrian
Comments: No close season

Priory Cottage Lake

Location: Guisborough, off the A171, opposite Butts Lane
Type and Size: One acre lake with islands
Carp Stock: Well stocked with carp to over 20lbs
Category: Mixed Fishery
Other Species: Bream, chub, roach, perch and rainbow trout
Permits: From the cottage by the lake; weekend tickets must be booked in advance. Tel: 01287 638816
Cost: £6.50 per day; £3.75 for juniors and OAP's
Restrictions: No night fishing; barbless hooks
BK Rating: Moderate
E/A: Northumbrian
Comments: No close season; fishing is dawn till dusk

Rossmere Park Lake

Location: Rossmere Way, Hartlepool
Type and Size: 2½ acre town park lake
Carp Stock: Well stocked with carp to doubles
Category: Mixed Fishery
Other Species: Bream, roach, tench and perch
Permits: On bank
Cost: About £2 per day; season tickets £10
Control: Hartlepool Borough Council. Tel: 01429 274844
Restrictions: No night fishing
BK Rating: Not known
E/A: Northumbrian
Comments: Disabled access. Open all year

CLWYD (Wales)

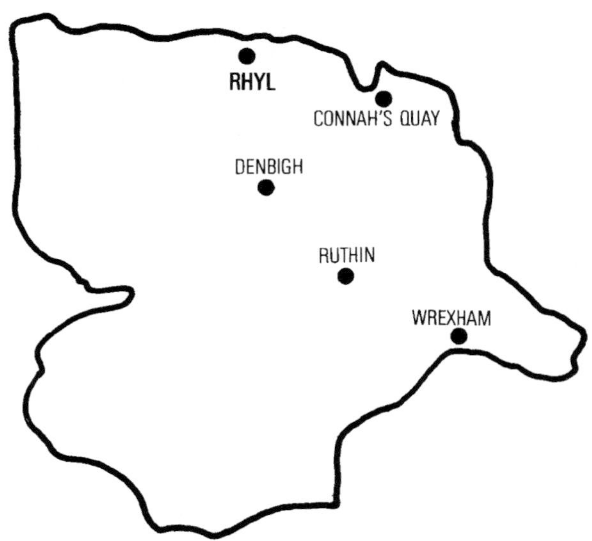

Argae Lake

Location: Moss Valley Park, Wrexham
Type and Size: Attractive 4 acre lake with island
Carp Stock: Well stocked with carp to over 20 lbs
Category: Mixed Fishery
Other Species: Roach, perch and dace
Permits: None
Cost: FREE FISHING
Control: Wrexham Borough Council
BK Rating: Not known
E/A: Welsh

Giler Arms — A

Location: On the A5 at the Giler Arms Hotel, Pentrefoelas, near Betwys-y-Coed, North Wales
Type and Size: Small pond with island
Carp Stock: Carp to doubles
Category: Mixed Fishery
Other Species: Roach and bream
Permits: From hotel
Cost: About £5 per day - free to hotel residents
Control: Giler Arms Hotel. Tel: 01690 770612
Restrictions: Some bait bans; barbless hooks; no keepnets
BK Rating: Moderate
E/A: Welsh
Comments: Probably open all year. Accommodation, food etc. in hotel

Llay Reservoir

Location: Llay, near Wrexham
Type and Size: Small reservoir
Carp Stock: Well stocked with carp to doubles
Category: Mixed Fishery
Other Species: Tench, rudd, perch and pike
Permits: Members only water of Llay AA. J Henshaw, 2 Queens Terrace, Mold Road, Cefn-y-Bedd, Wrexham, Wales; J Preston, 20 Mold Road Estate, Cworsyllt, Wrexham, Clwyd
Cost: About £10 per year
Restrictions: No cereal baits
BK Rating: Moderate
E/A: Welsh

Offa's Dyke

Location: Off the B 5010 near Llanfynydd
Type and Size: One acre pool
Carp Stock: Carp to 10 lbs
Category: Mixed Fishery
Other Species: Tench, roach, perch, rudd, bream and crucians
Permits: On bank
Cost: About £3 per day; concessions
Control: Tel: 01352 770296
Restrictions: No night fishing
BK Rating: Not known
E/A: Welsh

Padeswood Lake

Location: Padeswood, off the A5118 between Buckley and Mold
Type and Size: Two small lakes
Carp Stock: Heavily stocked with carp to 20lbs
Category: Carp Only
Permits: Day tickets from Deeside Fishing Tackle. Tel: 01244 813674
Cost: £3 per day for club members
Control: Connah's Quay DAC. P Ryan, 5 New Brighton Road, Sychdyn, Mold
Restrictions: You will need to join the club first
BK Rating: Easy; multiple catches of doubles reported, including commons to over 15lbs
E/A: Welsh
Comments: A new water opened in the summer of 1992; big catches on boilies

Ponky Pool

Location: Johnstown, Wrexham
Type and Size: 1½ acre pond
Carp Stock: Well stocked with carp to upper doubles
Category: Mixed Fishery
Other Species: Roach, tench and bream
Permits: Day tickets at low cost from Morris Tackle, Wrexham. Tel: 01978 364450
Control: Local club?
Restrictions: No night fishing
BK Rating: Moderate
E/A: Welsh
Comments: There might be a 20 or two in this pond

Sarn Mill Coarse Lakes

Location: Off the A 451 at Nannerton, near Mold
Type and Size: Two pools of about an acre each
Carp Stock: Well stocked with carp to 25 lbs
Category: Mixed Fishery
Other Species: Crucians, tench, roach and rudd
Permits: From lodge on site
Cost: About £4 per day
Control: Tel: 01352 720323
Restrictions: No night fishing
BK Rating: Not known
Baits/Methods: Boilies and luncheon meat are best baits
E/A: Welsh
Comments: Toilets. Disabled facilities

Swan Lake

Location: Near Connah's Quay, Deeside
Type and Size: 5 acre lake
Carp Stock: Well stocked with carp to 20lbs
Category: Mixed Fishery
Other Species: Tench and roach
Permits: Connahs Quay & Dist AC. P Ryan, 5 New Brighton Road, Sychdyn, Mold
Restrictions: Members only - no day tickets; no night fishing
Control: Club
BK Rating: Moderate
E/A: Welsh
Comments: Connahs Quay AC also has Wepre Park Lake in the area, which contains good carp; on the same ticket

Tan Llan

Location: Pontybodkin, off the A5104 near Ffrith
Type and Size: One and a half acre pool with islands
Carp Stock: Well stocked with commons to about 8lbs
Category: Mixed Fishery
Other Species: Ghost carp, crucians, roach, bream, tench, orfe, rudd, and perch
Permits: On the bank at £2 for adults; £1 for juniors; advance booking weekends
Control: Roger Roberts. Tel: 01352 770296
Restrictions: No night fishing
BK Rating: Moderate
E/A: Welsh

The Flash

Location: Gresford, Llay, near Wrexham
Type and Size: Small lake
Carp Stock: Some carp, numbers and sizes not known
Category: Mixed Fishery
Others Species: Tench, pike and rudd
Permits: Members only water of Llay AS - J Henshaw, 2 Queens Terrace, Mold Road, Cefn-y-Bedd, Wrexham
Cost: About £10 per year
Control: Club
E/A: Welsh

CORNWALL

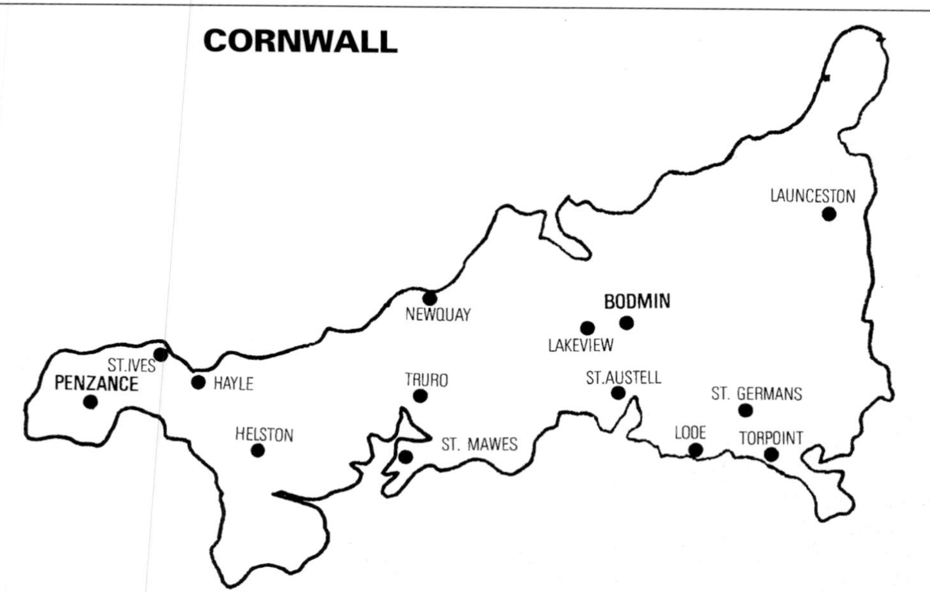

Amwalwhidden Farm

Location: Towednack, near Penzance
Type and Size: Four small lakes
Carp Stock: Well stocked with carp to over 20 lbs
Category: Mixed Fishery
Other Species: Perch, roach, tench, bream, golden tench, orfe, koi, crucians and gudgeon
Permits: On bank
Cost: About £4 per day; £5 for two rods. Reduction for juniors
Control: Tel: 01736 796961
BK Rating: Moderate
E/A: South West
Comments: Probably open all year

Avallon Holiday Park A

Location: Near Newquay
Type and Size: Small lake on dairy farm
Carp Stock: Well stocked with carp to doubles
Category: Mixed Fishery
Others Species: Bream, tench and roach
Permits: For information and permits Tel: 01502 501501
Control: Private
BK Rating: Not known
E/A: South West
Comments: This is a small site on a farm, with self-catering Norwegian Pine Lodges to rent for holidays with fishing; open all year - no close season

Bolingey Lake

Location: Penwartha Road, Bolingey, Perranporth TR6 ODH
Type and Size: Lake of 4 acres
How to Find: From Perranporth take the road towards Cos Hill, and turn right at

	the crossroads towards Bolingey. Pass the Post Office on your right and the Bolingey Inn, and the entrance to the lake will be seen on your left
Carp Stock:	Well stocked with carp to about 22lbs. 100 doubles
Category:	Mixed Fishery
Other Species:	Tench, roach, rudd, perch and trout
Permits:	From the site lodge
Cost:	£5 per day for 2 rods
Restrictions:	No night fishing. No keepnets or sacks. April to October
Control:	John Castle Tel: 01872 572388
BK Rating:	Very Easy
E/A:	South West
Comments:	Tackle and comprehensive range of bait and snacks and drinks on site. No close season. Carp tackle hired on site. Accommodation at an anglers pub - The Airways, St Mawgan. Tel: 01872 573904. (Voted one of Britain's top ten waters in Angling Times Yearbook!) Accommodation also at The Morgans Guesthouse, Perranporth. Tel: 01872 573904.B and B from £13. Atlantic View Hotel. Tel: 01872 573171

Bude Canal — A

Location:	From the sea at Bude
How to FInd:	Town of Bude
Type and Size:	Shallow old canal about 2 miles long and 2ft to 8ft deep
Carp Size:	Said to be fairly numerous, mostly to 10lbs. Commons to 20lbs caught in recent years by Gerry Savage
Category:	Mixed Fishery
Others Species:	Tench, roach, perch and big eels
Cost:	£1 day tickets, £5 for week from Tourist Information Centre, Bude. Hotels - The Globe, The Strand
Permits:	On the bank, or from tackle shops in Bude
Restrictions:	No fishing from 1st April to end of May. Barbless hooks
BK Rating:	Difficult
E/A:	South West
Baits/Methods	Normal carp tactics and baits
Control:	Club. Bude Canal Angling Association. Day tickets, P Braund, Wesley House, Leven Terrace, Bude. Tel: 01752 232804
Comments:	Clear weedy water, like many disused canals. Toilet

Bush Lakes

Location:	Notter Bridge pub car park, Saltash, near Liskeard
Type and Size:	Four small farm pools
Carp Stock:	Well stocked with carp to doubles
Category:	Mixed Fishery
Other Species:	Tench, bream, perch, rudd and roach
Permits:	On site
Cost:	About £5 per day
Control:	Tel: 01752 842148
Restrictions:	No boilies; barbless hooks
BK Rating:	Not known
E/A:	South West
Comments:	Said to be quiet and peaceful. Probably open all year

Bussow

Location:	Near St Ives
Type and Size:	Reservoir of 4 acres
How to Find:	Take the B3306 from St Ives. Turn left onto the B3311 and then right.

The entrance to the reservoir is then on the left
Carp Stock: Moderately stocked with carp to 16lbs
Category: Mixed Fishery
Other Species: Eels to 10lb, tench, bream, rudd and roach
Permits: Ken's Tackle, 9 Beachfield Court, The Promenade, Penzance. Tel: 01736 61969; Lanxon's Sports, 18 Causewayhead, Penzance Tel: 01736 62736; The Shirehorse Inn, Towendnack Road, Hessesveor, St Ives. Tel: 01736 796724; Newtown Angling Centre, Germoe. Tel: 01736 763721
Cost: Day £3.50, Concessions; Season £65, Concessions;
Control: Peninsula Coarse Fisheries. Tel: 01837 871565
E/A: South West
BK Rating: Moderate
Restrictions: No keepnets for carp. Barbless hooks requested. Permits must be obtained before fishing
Coments: No closed season

Choone Farm

Location: Choone Farm, St Buryan, Penzance. Tel: 01736 810220
Type and Size: Two small lakes
Carp Stock: Well stocked with carp to at least 10lbs
Category: Mixed Fishery
Other Species: Tench, rudd and perch
Permits: From Mr V B Care at the address above
Control: Private
Restrictions: No night fishing - open 7am to 8pm in summer
E/A: South West
Comments: No close season

Chyraise Lodge Hotel **A**

Location: Millpool, Goldsithney, Penzance TR20 9JD
Type and Size: Two large lakes 1/2 mile from hotel
How to Find: Just off the A394 between Helston and Marazion
Carp to Stock: Mixed Fishery
Other Species: Tench, bream, roach
Permits: From hotel. Tel: 01736 763485
Cost: On application
BK Rating: Insufficient informaton
Control: Private
E/A: South West
Comments: No close seaon. There are carp in some other waters in the Marazion area. Accommodation/holidays in hotel

College

Location: Near Falmouth
Type and Size: Reservoir of 38 acres
How to Find: Take the A38 from Falmouth to Penryn, then turn onto the B3291. A right turn will then take you into the car park
Carp Stock: The reservoir is well stocked with carp to 32lbs, with a good number in the 20-30lbs bracket. It was restocked in 1990 with 1850 carp to 15lbs and early 1991 with commons to 22lbs
Category: Mixed Fishery
Other Species: Tench to 8 1/2 lbs, bream to 8lbs 6ozs, eels to 7lbs, roach, rudd and perch
Permits: Day permits from the self service unit at Argal car park; Ken's Tackle, 9 Beachfield Court, The Promenade, Penzance. Tel: 01736 61969: Newtown Angling Centre, Germoe. Tel: 01736 76321. Season permits from the Ranger, Bob Evans, Little Argal Farm, Budock, Penryn, Cornwall.

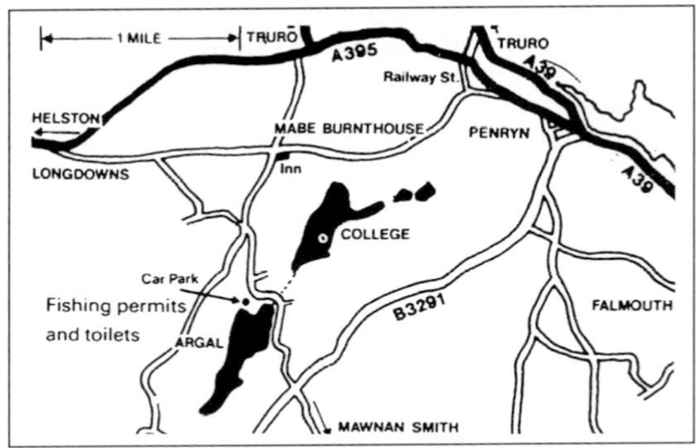

	Tel: 01326 72544
Cost:	Day £4 Concessions
Control:	Peninsula Coarse Fisheries. Tel: 01837 871565
E/A:	South West
BK Rating:	Moderate
Restrictions:	No cereal based groundbaits, except swimfeeders. No keepnets for carp. Barbless hooks requested. Permits must be obtained before fishing
Comments:	Mature and picturesque water with NO CLOSED SEASON. Night fishing is now allowed. Long casting is necessary to reach deep water from some areas. Long stay carp anglers generally do well

Crafthole

Location:	Village of Crafthole, near Torpoint
Type and Size:	Disused reservoir of 2 acres
How to Find:	Leave the A374, Plymouth to Liskeard Road, at Trerulefoot roundabout onto the A374, towards Torpoint. After Sheviock turn right to Crafthole. The pathway to the reservoir is almost opposite Crafthole Post Office
Carp Stock:	Very heavily stocked with carp to 22lbs
Category:	Carp Water
Other Species:	Tench
Permits:	Season tickets only
Cost:	Price on application
Control:	Peninsula Coarse Fisheries. Tel: 01837 871565
E/A:	South West
BK Rating:	Small Carp; Very Easy. Larger Carp: Easy
Restrictions:	Children under 16 must be accompanied by an adult. No cereal based groundbaits. No keepnets for carp. Barbless hooks requested. Permits must be obtained before fishing
Comments:	NO CLOSED SEASON. Very popular and attractive water, deep in a valley and surrounded by mature trees and hedgerows. Limited permits. Due to the rather long steep climb from the water, this venue is not recommended for the elderly or infirm

Dutson Water **A**

Location:	Lower Dutson Farm, Launceston
Type and Size:	Old clay pit, about an acre
How to Find:	Take the A388 road from Launceston to Barnstaple. Lower Dutson Farm is about two miles from Launceston
Carp Stock:	Fairly well stocked with carp to about 15lbs
Category:	Mixed Fishery

Other Species: Perch, rudd, tench crucians
Permits: From the farmer Mr E Broad at the farm. Tel: 01566 772607
Cost: £3 per day in advance; £6 on bank
Control: Private
Restrictions: No groundbaiting
BK Rating: Moderate
E/A: South West
Comments: Some weed and depths to about 10ft. Float fishing or legering methods can be used and luncheon meat and bread will catch carp. Many small rudd. There are sometimes caravans at the water and there is also a cottage to rent

Forda Holiday Lodges A

Location: Kilkhampton, near Bude
Type and Size: Tiny pond
How to Find: Near Bude on the north coast
Carp Stock: Some carp to double figures
Category: Mixed Fishery
Other Species: Bream, rudd, tench
Permits: On site. Tel: 0128 882413
Cost: On application
BK Rating: Not known
Control: Private
E/A: South West
Comments: No close season. Scandinavian style self-catering lodges for 4/5 people by lake. Near Tamar Lake and Bude Canal. Sandy beaches 10 minutes. Other accommodation: Tamar Lake Farm, near Bude. Stable and barn cottages and caravan. Tel: 0128 882426 for details and brochures

Gwinear Pool

Location: Near Newquay
Type and Size: 3 acre lake with islands
Carp Stock: Well stocked with carp to doubles
Category: Mixed Fishery
Other Species: Bream, tench, perch and roach
Permits: Day tickets on site - ticket machine
Cost: £4 Concessions
Control: Tel: 01637 830165
BK Rating: Not known
E/A: South West
Comments: No close season. No groundbait or nuts. No carp in keepnets

Lakeview Country Club A

Location: Old Coach Road, Lanivet, Bodmin. Tel: 01208 831079
Type and Size: Three lakes, dug in 1988; Carp lake 2 1/2 acres, stream-fed with island
How to Find: Where the A391 St Austell Road joins the A30 Bodmin by-pass, take the second exit at the roundabout, keeping in the outside lane, signposted 'Truro'. After 30 yards, turn right to Wheal Prosper, and in half a mile, turn left at the crossroads. Lakeview is in half a mile, on the right hand side.
Carp Stock: Carp to about 10lbs
Category: Mixed Fishery
Other Species: Roach, rudd, bream, tench, crucians and gudgeon
Permits: Day tickets from the Lodge, or on bank from Paul Pearce
Cost: £3 per day; juniors/OAP's £2 per day
Control: David and Barbara Daw, Lakeview Country Club

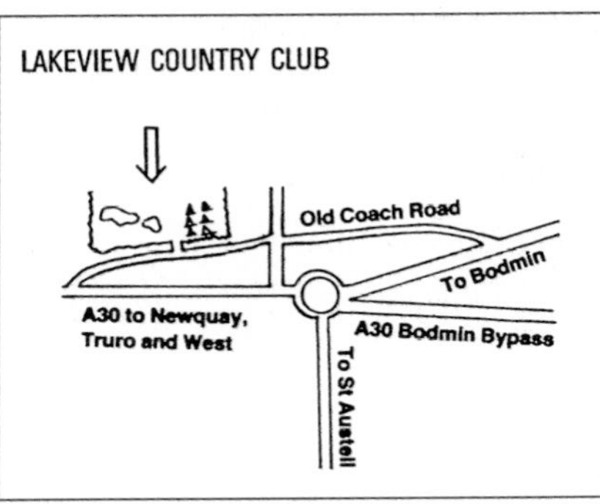

Restrictions: No boilies or nuts
Baits/Methods: Standard methods work well, with boilies, sweetcorn and luncheon meat
BK Rating: Moderate
E/A: South West
Comments: There are two other lakes at the club - Moorland Lake, which is small, and contains some mirrors to about 8lbs, and the 3 acre Wood Pool, which has some small carp; both contain other species. There are over 60 A-Frame Lodges (very popular with the children), and fabulous detached bungalows, each set well away from anyone else, many with dishwashers, spa baths, and en - suite shower, and all self catering, with an outside barbecue. The Country Club, close to the carp lake, has a heated indoor swimming pool, sauna, solarium, fitness room, snooker room, and a first class restaurant. There is a shop and just about every conceivable facility for a luxury holiday for the family at reasonable prices - and all within sight of the big carp being caught! Outside there are tennis courts, pitch and putt golf course, facilities for other sports, and an 18 hole golf course, a hotel, and sports centre was planned for 1993.This is one where we have been fortunate enough to stay, and we were very impressed with the fishing, the friendly but 'up-market' atmosphere of the country club, the pleasant surroundings and the beautiful detached bungalow, well away from others, and easily good enough for a permanent home. Lakeview is very strongly recommended, both for fishing and holidays; it is situated right in the centre of Cornwall, with easy access to both coasts, and is ideal for a day's fishing or for a long, luxurious family holiday

Langarth Pools

Location: 99 Polstain Road, Threemilestone, Truro.
Type and Size: Two three-quarter acre ponds
Carp Stock: Well stocked with carp to double figures
Category: Mixed Fishery
Other Species: Tench, roach, rudd, bream and perch
Permits: On site
Cost: £3 per day
Control: Private Tel: 01872 72578
BK Rating: Not known
E/A: South West
Comments: No close season; open 24 hours a day. Swims for the disabled

Mellonwatts Mill Fishery

Location: Pensagillas Farm, Grampound, Truro - on the main road from Grampound to Mevagissey. Tel: 0187 253232
Type and Size: 2 1/4 acre farm pond
Carp Stock: Well stocked with carp to doubles
Category: Mixed Fishery
Other Species: Crucians, tench, roach and rudd
Permits: From A W P Kent at the address above; self service permits in car park
Cost: £3 per day; £6 per night; £35 per season. Reduced prices for children and OAP's
Control: Private
BK Rating: Not known
E/A: South West
Coments: No close season. Camping, barbecues and picnic areas

Neets Valley Park

Location: Near Bude
Type and Size: Small lake
Carp Stock: Well stocked with carp
Category: Mixed Fishery
Other Species: Tench and rudd
Permits: Full details and permits from Russell Baker, 012888 395
Cost: £3.50 per day - half price for juniors
Control: Private
BK Rating: Not known
E/A: South West
Comments: This water was stocked in 1988, but had not been fished until 1991, so the potential is unknown. No close season

Polcoverack Farm A

Location: Near Penzance
Type and Size: Small lake
Carp Stock: Well stocked with carp to 15 lbs
Category: Mixed Fishery
Other Species: Tench
Permits: Free with accommodation
Cost: Enquire from owners
Control: Tel: 01326 280497
BK Rating: Not known
E/A: South West
Comments: Probably open all year. Self - catering cottages near beach and fishing village

Port Elliot Lake

Location: St. German's, near Plymouth
Type and Size: Attractive 2 acre lake
How to Find: From the A 38 take the B 3249 towards St. German's. Turn left just after the 30 m.p.h. signs
Carp Stock: Well stocked with doubles to over 20 lbs
Category: Mixed Fishery
Other Species: Tench, bream, roach, rudd, perch and eels
Permits: In advance from local tackle shops
Cost: £2 per day; £15 per season; £7.50 juniors and O.A.P's
Control: Plymouth D.C.A.C. Tel: 01752 783724
Restrictions: Barbless hooks
BK Rating: Moderate

E/A: South West

Porth — A

Location: Near St Mawgan Airfield, Newquay
Type and Size: Reservoir of 40 acres
How to Find: From Bodmin, leave the A30 at Indian Queens and join the A39 towards Wadebridge. At St Columb Major, turn left onto the A3059. Turn left at the water tower and the reservoir will be found on the left, after about three-quarters of a mile
Carp Stock: Moderately stocked with carp to 17lbs
Category: Mixed Fishery
Other Species: Tench to 10lbs, bream to 9lbs 2ozs, roach, perch, and rudd
Permits: Day or day and night permits from the self service unit at the car park: Ken's Tackle, 9 Beachfield Court, The Promenade, Penzance. Tel: 01736 61969: Newtown Angling Centre, Germoe. Tel: 01736 763721. Season permits from Mrs P Ford, The Bungalow, Porth Reservoir. Tel: 01637 879481
Cost: Day £4. Concessions. Season tickets £65. Concessions
Control: Peninsula Coarse Fisheries. Tel: 01837 871565
E/A: South West
BK Rating: Fairly Hard
Restrictions: No cereal based groundbaits except swimfeeders. No keepnets for carp. Barbless hooks requested. Permits must be obtained before fishing
Comments: NO CLOSED SEASON. Night fishing now allowed. Accommodation at White Lodge Hotel, Mawgan Porth Bay, Newquay. Tel: 01637 860512. Special holidays including fishing at reservoir, also fishing at Bolingey, Carnewas Farm, Frontier City, Lakeview, Meadowside Farm, Rosewater Lake - send for brochure

Rosewater Lake

Location: Hendravossan Farm, Rose, Truro. Tel: 01872 573992 / 573040
Type and Size: 1½ acre lake
Carp Stock: Well stocked with carp, numbers and sizes not known
Category: Mixed Fishery
Other Species: Crucians, tench, roach, rudd, perch and chub
Permits: From Mike or Andy Waters at the address above
Cost: Day - £3; evening - £1.50; second rod £1
Control: Private
Restrictions: Barbless hooks; no keepnets; no night fishing - open dawn till dusk only
BK Rating: Not known
E/A: South West
Comments: No close season. Bed and breakfast available at certain times of the year. Caravan Club. Send for brochure

Sharkey's Pit

Location: Strawberry Lane, Joppa, Hayle - one mile from Hayle Town Centre
Type and Size: 2½ acre lake
Carp Stock: Some carp to double figures
Category: Mixed Fishery
Other Species: Tench, crucians, roach, rudd, gudgeon, golden orfe
Permits: Self service at fishery
Cost: On application from Dave and Jenny Burn at the above address
Control: Private
Restrictions: No night fishing
BK Rating: Moderate

E/A: South West
Comments: No close season - fishing dawn to dusk

Shillamill Lakes — A

Location: Lanreath, Looe off the B3359
Type and Size: Four small dammed lakes
Carp Stock: Heavily stocked with commons and mirrors to 10lb. Some doubles and a few 20s to 25lbs reported
Category: Mixed Fishery
Other Species: Roach, rudd, tench, perch
Permits: Rick Pearce, Shillamill Lakes, Lanreath, Looe, Cornwall. Tel: 01503 220886. Day and week permit
Cost: Day tickets £3.50 for one rod. Weekly £12
Baits/Methods: Normal carp baits and methods
Control: Private commercial fishery, day and season tickets
Restrictions: Brolly camps must be booked in advance - night fishing by arrangement only
BK Rating: Easy
E/A: South West
Comments: Commercial fishery with caravans and accommodation in flats and cottages. No close season. Meals and bar snacks. Games room and TV in the Old Mill Country Club

St. Erth Fishery

Location: Little Mill Lane, St. Erth, near Penzance
Type and Size: 2½ acre lake
Carp Stock: Well stocked with carp to over 25 lbs
Category: Mixed Fishery
Other Species: Bream, tench, roach, perch, chub and crucians
Permits: In advance from local tackle shops and St. Erth Post Office
Cost: £3.50 per day; £2.50 ladies, juniors and O.A.P's
Control: Marazion A.C. Tel: 01736 65638
Restrictions: Night fishing by arrangement only
BK Rating: Not known
E/A: South West
Comments: Probably open all year

St Germans Lake

Location: St Germans, 1½ miles off the A38 between Saltash and Liskeard
Type and Size: Two acre lake
Carp Stock: Well stocked with carp to 20lbs
Category: Mixed Fishery
Other Species: Roach, rudd, perch, tench and bream
Permits: Members only - Plymouth AC
Cost: £3 per day
Control: Plymouth and District Coarse Angling Club
BK Rating: Moderate
E/A: South West
Comments: No close season

St Tinney Farm Holidays — A

Location: Otterham, near Penzance PL32 9TA. Tel: 0184 06274
Type and Size: Small farm lakes
Carp Stock: Well stocked with carp to doubles
Category: Mixed Fishery
Other Species: Tench, rudd, roach, bream, perch and trout

Permits: From St Tinney Farm
Control: Private
BK Rating: Not known
E/A: South West
Comments: Comfortable chalets to rent for self-catering holidays with fishing. 70 acre farm off the A39 coastal road in north Cornwall. Free colour brochure. No close season

Tindeen Fishery

Location: Bostrase, Goldsithney, Penzance. Tel: 01736 763486
Type and Size: Three small pools of about one acre each
Carp Stock: Some carp,numbers and sizes not known
Category: Either Few Carp or Mixed Fishery
Other Species: Tench, rudd, roach and perch
Permits: From G J Laity at the above address
Cost: £2 per day; £1.50 for under 14's
Control: Private
Restrictions: Night fishing by arrangement only
BK Rating: Not known
E/A: NRA South West Region
Comments: No close season

Tredidon Barton Lake

Location: Near Launceston
Type and Size: Small farm pond
Carp Stock: Some carp best reported 23lbs
Category: Mixed Fishery
Other Species: Tench and some other coarse fish
Permits: G Jones. Tel: 0156 686288
Cost: About £2 per day
Control: Private
BK Rating: Moderate
E/A: NRA South West Region
Comments: No close season - open all year round

Trenestrall Lake

Location: Trenestrall Farm, Ruan High Lanes, near St Mawes. Tel: 01872 501259
Type and Size: Two acre lake on the King Harry Ferry Road
Carp Stock Well stocked with carp to at least 10lbs
Category: Mixed Fishery
Other Species: Tench and roach
Permits: From Mr Palmer at the above address
Cost: £2 per day
Control: Private
BK Rating: Not known
E/A: South West
Comments: No close season

Trevella Caravan and Camping Park A

Location: Crantock, Newquay. Tel: 01637 830308
Type and Size: Two man-made lakes of about two acres each
How to Find: Take the A30 to Indian Queens, turn right onto the A392, and follow the Newquay signs to Quintrell Downs roundabout, then turn left onto the A3075 Redruth Road. In 200 yards you will see the signpost to Crantock
Carp Stock: Both lakes well stocked with carp including some twenties - best fish a mirror of 27 3/4 lbs, caught in 1990

Category: Mixed Fishery
Other Species: Tench to 6lbs, bream, roach and rudd
Permits: Free at reception to all residents
BK Rating: Moderate
Control: Trevella Caravan Park
Restrictions: None listed
E/A: South West
Comments: A very attractive site with many facilities, such as showers, launderette, childrens play area, heated swimming pool, restaurant, shop, games room etc. Lakes are on a Nature Reserve, with a new third lake nearby. Beautiful sandy beaches within half a mile. Featured in 'Coarse Fishing Today' (Angling Times) in February 1991, with a picture of Gerry Savage with a 23 pounder from the lake. Ideal for a family holiday with good fishing, and only an hour's drive from anywhere in Cornwall - 41 miles to Land's End. 4 to 8 berth caravans to rent. Sites to rent nightly for your own caravans, with no charge for tents, touring caravans, or motorhomes - electrical hook-up £1.75 per night. No close season

Wheal Grey Pool

Location: Ashton on the main Penzance-Helston Road
Type and Size: Old four acre pit, very deep
Carp Stock: Well stocked with carp to nearly 30lbs
Category: Mixed Fishery
Other Species: Bream, roach, rudd and perch
Permits: Marazion Angling Club. B Trevitt, 6 Chyandaunce Close, Gulval, Penzance. Tel: 01736 65638 The Shop, Newtown. Tel: 01736 763721; Ken's Tackle, Penzance. Tel: 01736 61969
Cost: Day £3.50, £2 for juniors
Control: Club
Restrictions: Night fishing by arrangement only
BK Rating: Moderate
E/A: South West
Comments: No close season. Permit includes several other waters

Wheal Rashleigh Pits

Location: Luxulyan, St. Blazey, near St. Austell
Type and Size: Two clay pits; 9 acres and 5 acres, with depths up to 60 ft
Carp Stock: Well stocked with carp to mid-twenties
Category: Mixed Fishery
Other Species: Roach, perch, bream and tench
Permits: Local tackle shops
Cost: About £5 per day; £30 per season
Control: Roche A.C. Tel: 01726 883199
Restrictions: Barbless hooks only
BK Rating: Moderate
Baits/Methods: Margin fishing, with boilies is the best method
E/A: South West

White Acres A

Location: White Acres Holiday Park, White Cross, Newquay TR8 4LW. Tel: 01716 860220
Type and Size: Four lakes, all of which contain carp
Carp Stock: Carp to 25lbs in the specimen lake, and plenty of all sizes in the other lakes
Category: Mixed Fishery
Other Species: Tench, roach and ghost carp

Permits: On site - details from the address above, £1 to £6 per day
Control: Private
BK Rating: Moderate; Easy for small carp in some of the lakes
E/A: South West
Comments: Luxury caravans for rent close to the lakes. Sites for touring caravans and tents. Heated indoor swimming pool, sauna and gym.Club with nightly cabaret. A good place for a holiday combined with some very good fishing. Some carp deaths reported in 1996

Woodlay Farm A

Location: Herodsfoot, Liskeard
How to Find: Near Liskeard
Type and Size: Six small farm lakes
Carp Stock: Well stocked with carp to 24lbs
Category: Mixed Fishery
Other Species: Tench, roach, rudd
Permits: P C Hawke, Woodlay Farm, Herodsfoot, Liskeard. Tel: 01503 220221
Control: Private
BK Rating: Easy
E/A: South West
Comments: Holiday fishery with a self catering country cottage. Picturesque surroundings. No close season. Send stamp for brochure

Woonsmith Fishery

Location: Off the B 3311 St. Ives - Penzance road, near Georgia, St. Ives
Type and Size: One acre lake
Carp Stock: Small carp
Category: Mixed Fishery
Other Species: Rudd, tench, small bream, roach, perch, gudgeon and eels
Permits: In advance only from Newton Angling Centre, St. Ives
Cost: £3.50 per day; £2 for juniors
Control: St. Ives Freshwater A.C. Tel: 01736 763721
BK Rating: Not known
E/A: South West
Comments: Probably open all year

Litter

Pick it up before it damages wildlife or loses you the fishing.
A carrier bag fits in a pocket and a little care goes a long way.

CUMBRIA

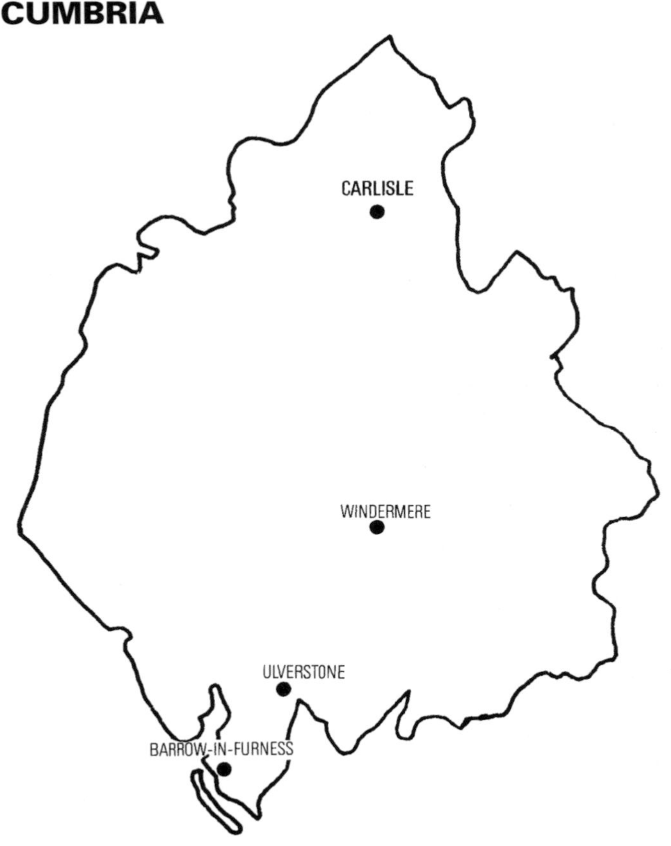

Barn Lake

Location: Longtown, north of Carlisle
Type and Size: 10 acre matured gravel pit
Carp Stock: Carp to doubles
Category: Carp Water
Other Species: Possibly some
Permits: From the lodge
Cost: About £8 per day
Control: Tel: 01228 791108
Restrictions: Night fishing by prior arrangement
BK Rating: Not known
E/A: North West
Comments: Probably open all year. Caravan and camping pitches. Toilets. Facilities for the disabled anglers. Attractive site.

Bigland Hall Lake

Location: Blackbarrow, on the A590, 6 miles from Ulverstone
Type and Size: Small lake
Carp Stock: Some carp to mid-doubles

Category: Few carp
Others Species: Roach and tench
Permits: Day tickets from Estate Office near lake
Control: Bigland Hall Estate
Restrictions: No night fishing
BK Rating: Difficult, due to hordes of other species
E/A: North West
Comments: No close season

Brayton Pond

Location: Brayton Hall Farm, Aspatria
Type and Size: Large shallow lake of the farm type; 8 acres
How to Find: Take the A596 from Carlisle, 15 miles west to Brayton
Carp Stock: Very heavily stocked with genuine wild carp to about 8 lbs. Fish up to 12lbs reported
Other Species: Crucians
Permits: Day tickets from the farm. Must be bought in advance
Control: Private. Mr RH Ward, Home Farm, Brayton, Aspatria. Tel: Aspatria 20262
Restrictions: No night fishing
BK Rating: Easy
E / A: NRA North West Region
Comments: Heavily fished, especially at weekends. Many matches are held. Cafe

Cleabarrow Lake

Location: Near the golf course at Windermere; take B5284 to Bowness
Type and Size: Small lake
Carp Stock: Well stocked with carp to 10lbs
Category: Carp water
Permits: Day tickets from Smyths Record Shop, Ashe Street, Bowness - on-Windermere
Control: Private
Restrictions: No night fishing
BK Rating: Moderate
E/A: NRA North West Region

Crossfield Fishery A

Location: Off the B6413 at Kirkoswald
Type and Size: 3 acre lake
Carp Stock: Well stocked with carp to about 10 lbs
Category: Mixed Fishery
Other Species: Roach, rudd, tench and bream
Permits: On site or from Crossfield Farm
Cost: About £4 per day - £5 in summer
Control: Tel: 01768 896275
BK Rating: Easy
Baits/Methods: Legered luncheon meat
E/A: North West
Comments: Self-catering accommodation on bank. Discounted fishing for those staying. Trout pool on site.

Ellerbeck Pond

Location: Brigham, near Cockermouth
Type and Size: Small farm pool
Carp Stock: Small carp to 5 lbs
Category: Mixed Fishery
Other Species: Roach, bream, crucians, perch, eels and trout

Permits: On bank
Cost: £4 per day; £2 evenings. Under 12s half price
Control: Tel: 01900 825268
Restrictions: No boilies; no carp in keepnets; no night fishing; barbless hooks
BK Rating: Easy
E/A: North West
Comments: Accommodation available - enquire from control

Holehird Tarn

Location: Near Windermere, off the A582
Type and Size: Three acre Lake District tarn
Carp Stock: Quite well stocked with carp to 10lbs, and one or two low doubles
Category: Mixed Fishery
Other Species: Coarse fish including perch; some trout
Permits: Day tickets on site
Control: Private
BK Rating: Moderate
E/A: North West

Mockerkin Tarn

Location: Mockerkin, near Loweswater
Type and Size: Small tarn
How to Find: Just off the A5086 Cockermouth Road, west of Loweswater village
Carp Stock: Well stocked with carp, sizes unknown
Category: Carp Water
Other Species: Not known
Permits: Day and week tickets from The Gun Shop, Lorton Street, Cockermouth
Control: Cockermouth Angling Association
Cost: On application
BK Rating: Insufficient information
E/A: North West
Comments: This water has been stocked with carp by the club and we can find out little about it, but as there are so few carp in Cumbria....

Oakbank Lakes Country Park

Location: One mile north of Longtown
Type and Size: Three lakes of 25 acres
How to Find: Follow A7 north of Longtown, take second turn left after crossing river, fishery 300 yards along road
Carp Stock: Barn Lake - many doubles (max. 21 lbs) Middle Lake - 2,000 carp
Category: Mixed Fishery
Other Species: Trout in all lakes
Permits: Season and day tickets
Cost: £8 per day + £2 per night bivvie charge for day visitors. Juniors, O.A.P's and disabled - concessions
Control: Tel: 01228 791108
Restrictions: No tiger nuts; no spinning
BK Rating: Not known
E/A: North West
Comments: Open all year. Touring caravan and camping site. Toilets. Facilities for disabled anglers. Attractive site. Quality static caravans for hire

Rather Heath Tarn

Location: Rather Heath Lane, Burnside, near Windermere
Type and Size: Attractive 5 acre tarn in the Lake District
Carp Stock: Some carp, numbers and sizes not known
Category: Mixed Fishery
Other Species: Bream, perch, crucians, chub, rudd and gudgeon
Permits: In advance only from local tackle shops
Cost: About £4 per day
Control: Tel: 01539 445083
BK Rating: Difficult
E/A: Cumbrian
Comments: Probably open all year

Roanhead Fisheries

Location: Near Barrow - in - Furness
Type and Size: Six very deep pits of about ten acres
Carp Stock: Quite a few carp to well over 20lbs
Category: Mixed Fishery
Other Species: Roach and rudd; big eels
Permits: Members only water of Furness FA, Hannay, 50 Crellin Street, Barrow
Cost: About £10 per year
Control: Club
BK Rating: Easy for one pit; difficult for the others
E/A: North West

Ulverston Canal

Location: Ulverston, near Barrow-in-Furness, southern Lake District
Type and Size: Short, narrow canal
Carp Stock: Some carp to low doubles
Category: Few Carp
Other Species: Tench, roach and other coarse fish
Permits: Day and season tickets from the Canal Tavern Inn, Ulverston; Angling and Hiking Centre, 62 Forshaw Street, Barrow-in-Furness
Cost: About £2 per day, £5 per season
Control: Ulverston Angling Associaton. H B Whittam, 29 Lyndhurst Road, Ulverston
BK Rating: Difficult
E/A: North West

DERBYSHIRE

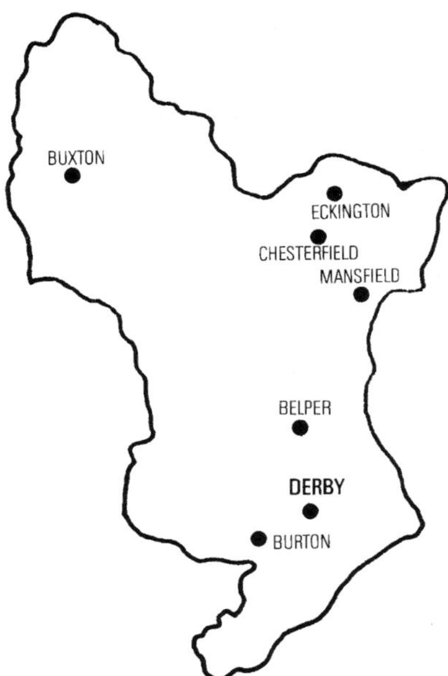

Aldamore Pool

Location: Off the A50 at Sudbury, near Utoxetter
Type and Size: Five acre estate lake
Carp Stock: Very heavily stocked with many small carp
Category: Carp Only
Permits: Dove Valley AC; try local tackle shops
Cost: £35 per season; joining fee £20
Restrictions: One rod only
BK Rating: Very Easy
E/A: Severn Trent

Belper Pond

Location: Wyver Lane, Belper
Type and Size: Three acre lake
Carp Stock: Well stocked with carp to over 20lbs; plenty of doubles
Category: Mixed Fishery
Other Species: Pike and tench
Permits: Season tickets from Belper and District AA; try local tackle shops
Cost: £20 per season, with a £10 joining fee
Restrictions: No night fishing
BK Rating: Moderate
E/A: Severn Trent

Catton Park Lake

Location: Catton Park Fisheries, Round Lodge, Catton, near Walton - on - Trent
Type and Size: 10 acre gravel pit with island
How to Find: Off the A 38 between Lichfield and Burton - on - Trent

Carp Stock: Heavily stocked with carp to 25 lbs; many doubles
Category: Mixed Fishery
Other Species: Roach, tench, bream, perch and a few barbel
Permits: On site
Cost: From £3 to £5 per day, according to the time of year
Control: Graham and Pam Davis. Tel: 01283 716876
Restrictions: No night fishing
BK Rating: Moderate
E/A: Severn Trent
Comments: Good access for the disabled

Chapel Wheel Dam

Location: Just outside Chesterfield
Type and Size: Old reservoir of about ten acres
Carp Stock: Lake stocked long ago, but contains a few good carp
Category: Few Carp
Other Species: Mixed coarse fish
Permits: Enquire locally - no details obtainable
Control: Possibly small local angling club - name not known
Restrictions: No night fishing
BK Rating: Super-Difficult
E/A: Severn-Trent

Codnor Park Reservoir

Location: Ambergate, near Belper
Type and Size: Small reservoir
Carp Stock: Some carp, sizes not known
Category: Mixed Fishery
Other Species: Roach, bream, tench and pike
Permits: From tackle shops and on bank
Cost: About £2 per day; £10 per season
Control: Club - Ripley and District AC. R Turner, 2a Argyll Road, Ripley
BK Rating: Not known
E/A: Severn-Trent

Derwent Valley Fishery

Location: Darley Abbey, near Derby
Type and Size: Small lake
Carp Stock: Well stocked with small carp to 10 lbs
Category: Mixed Fishery
Other Species: Chub and tench
Permits: On bank
Cost: £4 per day; £5 for two rods
Control: Tel: 01332 874116
BK Rating: Easy
E/A: Severn Trent

Foxton Dam

Location: Eckington, just off the A616 between Sheffield and Bolsover
Type and Size: Small lake
Carp Stock: Probably only one or two to 20lbs - stocked many years ago
Category: Few Carp
Other Species: Roach, perch, tench and pike
Permits: Day ticket on bank
Control: Private - enquire locally

BK Rating: Super-Difficult
E/A: Severn-Trent

Harwick Hall Lakes

Location: Between Mansfield and Chesterfield, close to the M1 at junction 29
Type and Size: Two estate lakes of 3 and 7 acres
Carp Stock: Very well stocked with small carp, and a few doubles and 20's to about 27lbs
Category: Mixed Fishery
Other Species: Roach, tench, perch and bream
Permits: Day tickets from bailiff on bank at low cost. Season tickets also available at about £25
Control: Private
Restrictons: No night fishing
BK Rating: Moderate
E/A: Yorkshire
Comments: This is a beautiful venue in the grounds of a National Trust property. Most of the bigger fish have come from the small lake. The water is shallow and weedy, but very attractive

Higham Farm

Location: Higham Farm, near Alfreton
Type and Size: Four farm lakes, about three acres each
How to Find: Take the A61 road from Alfreton to Higham
Carp Stock: Fairly well stocked with carp to 20lbs plus
Category: Mixed Fishery
Other Species: Tench, chub, roach and bream
Permits: Higham Farm Hotel, Old Higham, Alfreton. Tel: 01773 602741. £5 per day
Baits/Methods: Normal carp methods and baits. Boilies are good
BK Rating: Moderate
E/A: Severn-Trent
Comments: Pleasant surroundings. Lakes contain little weed and are quite deep, up to 12ft in places.Barbless hooks.Night fishing by arrangement

K J S Fisheries

Location: Station Road, Killamarch, near Sheffield
Type and Size: Two half acre pools
Carp Stock: Well stocked with small carp to 3 lbs
Category: Mixed Fishery
Other Species: Roach, rudd, perch, crucians, tench, orfe and bream
Permits: On bank
Cost: £3 per day; £25 per season
Control: Tel: 01142 470876
Restrictions: No groundbait
BK Rating: Easy
E/A: Yorkshire

Locho Park

Location: Spondon, near Derby - off Locho Road, Spondon
Type and Size: Fifteen acre estate lake
Carp Size: Some carp, number and sizes not known, as this water has only been fished for a short while, but carp have been reported to over 20lbs
Category: Mixed Fishery
Other Species: Tench and roach
Permits: K Glynn. Tel: 01332 751938

Cost: £50 per season, syndicate only
Restrictions: No night fishing
BK Rating: Very Difficult
E/A: Severn Trent

Mapperley Reservoir

Location: Near Ilkeston
Type an Size: Big reservoir
How to Find: North west of Ilkeston off the A609
Carp Stock: Some large carp
Category: Few Carp
Others Species: General coarse fish
Permits: On site. Ranger post, Tel: 017737 5480
Cost: On application
Control: Derbyshire County Council
Restrictions: Much of the lake cannot be fished
BK Rating: Very Difficult

Pebley Reservoir

Location: Near Clowne
Type and Size: 25 acre canal feeder reservoir
Carp Stock: Some carp to doubles
Category: Few Carp
Other Species: Bream to doubles; pike, roach and tench
Permits: On bank
Cost: About £3 per day. Season tickets available
Control: Tel: 01742 474378
BK Rating: Difficult
E/A: Severn Trent

Ringwood Lake

Location: In the town of Chesterfield
Type and Size: Attractive, four acre town lake, very busy and open to the public
Carp Stock: Heavily stocked with many doubles to over 15lbs
Category: Carp Water
Permits: Day tickets from bailiff on bank
Cost: About £3 per day
Control: Council
BK Rating: Easy
E/A: Severn-Trent

Swarkestone Gravel Pits

Location: Swarkestone
Type and Size: 67 acre gravel pit
How to Find: South west of Derby on the A514
Carp Stock: Few carp to 26lbs
Other Species: Roach, bream, tench, perch, pike
Permits: Day tickets from the Rising Sun Public House, Willington
Cost: £5 per week; £24 per season
Control: Derby Angling Association, PO Box 167, Derby DE3 7UE. Enclose an SAE
BK Rating: East to catch; hard to find
E/A: Severn-Trent

The Coppice Water

Location: Heanor/Ilkeston
Type and Size: Five acre lake
How to FInd: Near the American Adventure Theme Park, off the A6007 between Ilkeston and Heanor
Carp Stock: Stocked with carp to 25lbs
Category: Mixed Fishery
Other Species: Tench, roach, perch, pike
Permits: The Coppice Inn and Restaurant, Shipley Park, Shipley. Tel: 01773 712606
Cost: Day tickets about £5; season about £25
Control: Private
E/A: Severn-Trent

Trent and Mersey Canal

Location: Egginton, on the A38 between Derby and Burton-on-Trent. Park by the road, walk over the bridge, and the canal is to your right towards the trees
Type and Size: Attractive, narrow canal
Carp Stock: Some carp to doubles
Category: Few Carp
Other Species: Roach, perch, gudgeon, and a few chub
Permits: Season tickets from Derby AA - send an SAE to the Membership Secretary, Derby AA, PO Box 167, Derby DE3 7UE. Information from Mrs D Taft. Tel: 01332 766866
BK Rating: Difficult
E/A: Severn-Trent

DEVON

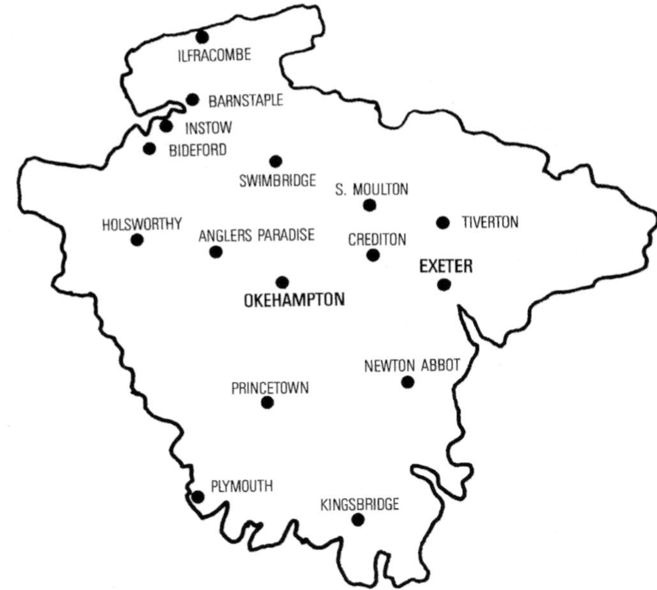

Abbrook Pond

Location: Abbrook, near Kingsteignton, Newton Abbot
Type and Size: Old matured pit of about 3 acres
Carp and Stock: Well stocked with carp to double figures; in the past this lake contained carp to over 30lbs, some probable 20's spotted recently
Category: Mixed Fishery
Other Species: Tench, roach and bream
Permits: Exeter and District AA; Hon Sec, D Cornish, 9 Denmark Road, Exeter. Tel: 01392 56770; also from tackle shops in Exeter, such as Exeter Angling Centre, Smythen Street, Torquay and Newton Abbot
Cost: Day visitors: £2; week - £6. Club membership £14 per season, open to all
Control: Club
BK Rating: Moderate
Comments: There is a normal close season on this water. Could contain some very big carp, though those of the original stocking are almost certainly all dead

Alder Farm Quarry A

Location: On the left hand side of the A30 Okehampton-Launceston Road, just before crossing into Cornwall
Type and Size: Four acre, very old quarry, said by local people to be bottomless
Carp Stock: Some carp to 20lbs
Category: Mixed Fishery
Other Species: Trout, roach, rudd, bream and tench
Permits: Call at Alder Farm for day tickets and accommodation. £3 per day

Control: Private. Tel: 01566 783444
BK Rating: Not known
E/A: South West
Comments: There are self-catering chalets close to the lake, which can be rented from the farm. A very deep quarry

Alleron Ponds

Location: Alleron, Loddiswell, near Kingsbridge. Tel: 01548 550306
Type and Size: Two small man-made ponds on private land - half acre and quarter acre
Carp Stock: Abut 30 carp in each pond, from 7lbs to 15lbs - best reported 24lb mirror
Category: Carp Only
Permits: From house
Cost: £4 per day
Control: Private
Restrictions: Barbless hooks; night fishing by arrangement; no fixed leads. Minimum breaking strain - 6lbs. Two rods only. No dogs or radios
BK Rating: Easy
E/A: South West

Anglers Eldorado

Location: Chilla Road, opposite the entrance to Anglers' Paradise, Halwill Junction, Beaworthy
Type and Size: Four man-made lakes from one to three acres, with many more lakes soon to be opened on the same site
How to Find: Take the old A30 from Okehampton, and at the top of the hill turn right on the B3218 to Halwill Junction (10 miles). At Halwill Junction, turn right by the new houses, pass the pub on your right, and the entrance to Eldorado is 400 yards on the left hand side

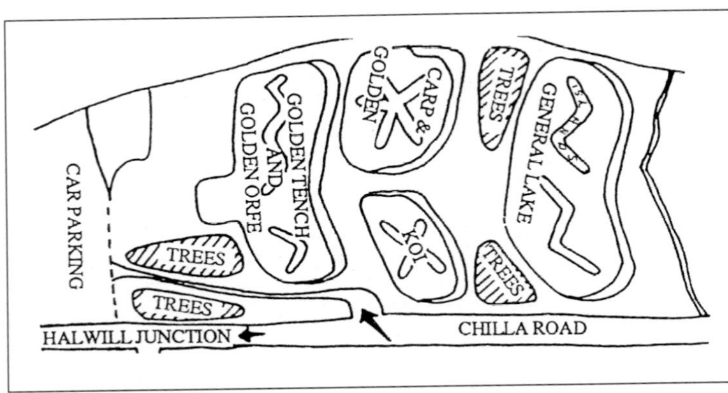

Carp Stock: The two acre lake is very heavily stocked with high singles and some doubles to over 20lbs; the three acre lake has many good doubles, including commons, and more good carp are being stocked regularly in both waters
Category: Mixed Fishery (Carp Only lake now made)
Other Species: Big koi and other coarse fish, including golden carp, golden tench, golden rudd, double figure catfish and grass carp
Permits: Day tickets from Zyg at Anglers Paradise, The Gables, Winsford, Halwill Junction. Tel: 01409 221559 (down track opposite lakes); from the Newsagents in the village, from the bailiff's house in Chilla Road, close to the lakes

Cost: £4 per rod per day
Control: Private; Zyg Gregorek
Restrictions: No night fishing; barbless hooks; fixed leads only if back-stops used; min. line b/s - 3lbs; no keepnets or carp sacks
BK Rating: Easy for all lakes
E/A: South West
Comments: No close season. A unique fishing experience. Pleasant, quiet fishing, which has already become as famous as Zyg's other fishery, Anglers' Paradise.

Anglers' Paradise Holidays A

Location: The Gables, Winsford, Halwill Junction, Beaworthy. Tel: 01409 221559
Type and Size: Main lake, 5 acres, stream fed with five islands and a boathouse; eight other carp lakes close to each other, of about one and a half acres each
How to Find: Call first at Zyg's house, The Gables. To get there take the B3218 Holsworthy Road, turning right off the A30 a mile west of Okehampton. At Halwill Junction, turn right, pass the pub and take the right turn signposted 'Winsford' in 400 yards, opposite the entrance to Zyg's day ticket water Anglers' Eldorado. Continue down the rough track until you reach Anglers' Paradise on your left

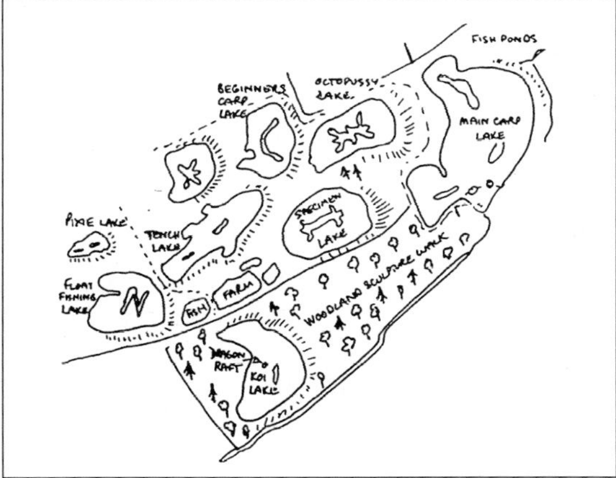

Carp Stock: Main Lake - very heaily stocked with carp to 30lbs, 50 twenties and thirties, and about 165 doubles, average size 16lbs; Spessy Lake - 30 twenties and thirties. Some now approaching 40lbs. The first 30 was caught in January 1991 by the owner Zyg, and there have been many thirties caught since. Octopussy Lake - 40 doubles. Beginners Lake - heavily stocked with high singles and low doubles to 20lbs
Category: All 4 lakes are Carp Only
Permits: Fishing only for those who book accommodation, except for occasional syndicate vacancies for the famous 'Five C's Carp Syndicate'. No day tickets
Control: Zyg and Rose Gregorek. Tel: 01409 221559
Baits/Methods: All normal carp fishing methods and rigs, and float fishing with sweetcorn often succeeds when boilies fail
Restrictions: Night fishing by arrangement only, barbless hooks; no bent hook rigs; minimum 8lb b/s line and size 8 hook
BK Rating: Main Lake - Moderate. Spessy - Difficult. Octopussy - Easy. Beginners - Very Easy

E/A: South West

Comments: Beautiful 128 acre estate, with over 20 lakes full of koi, crucians, golden tench, golden rudd, golden and blue orfe, and even a tench-shaped lake! Catfish to doubles. Plenty of easy float fishing for beginners and youngsters. Fish farm - quality fish for sale including golden tench and rudd, and blue orfe. Woodland sculpture walk. Luxury up-market self catering accommodation, with 32 villas and cottages, some with whirlpool baths, ornate four posters, leather Chesterfields, and decorated with antique fishing rods and other valuable tackle. Luxury heated indoor swimming pool. Anglers Paradise is justly rated as the best place in the country for an angling holiday, either for dedicated carp anglers, or for the family. There is clay pigeon shooting, a games room, a table tennis room, a tackle shop, and many attractions for the children, including donkey rides and other animals, including emus. The large, fabulously decorated African bar is the social centre of the complex, where you can drink Zyg's homemade wine and look at the many pictures of big carp caught in the lakes - some of which are soon expected to reach 40lbs, and all of which were 'grown on' from small fish by Zyg himself - no big imports here to create an instant fishery. Anglers' Paradise appears regularly on most TV programmes, and as the winner of the self-catering holiday of the year was given the gold award by the English Tourist Board - a paradise indeed! PM stays there twice a year - and there is nowhere in the country where you can have a better angling holiday, with a most pleasant and friendly atmosphere. Telephone Zyg for his first class colour brochure, and book well in advance, as those who holiday there once, usually keep going back. Zyg and Rose have three young daughters, Wanda, Anna, and Zenia, all of whom are very beautiful (they made me put that!), so Anglers' Paradise is understandably a family centre - but it's a serious carp fishery too: some of the leading carp anglers in the country have stayed and fished there, and more will do so now the fish are into the thirties - and the central location in Devon makes it ideal for all types of holidays. This is the largest site of its type in Europe, with villas for the disabled and an Easy Access lake for disabled anglers. There are now concrete paths round most lakes, and pagodas for shelter

Arjays Fishing Retreat — A

Location: Oldborough, Morchard Bishop, Crediton Ex16 6SQ - off the A377

Type and Size: Two spring-fed, interconnecting lakes of about two acres, in an old sandstone quarry

Carp Stock: Some carp, sizes and numbers not quoted in brochure

Category: Mixed Fishery

Other Species: Tench, perch, rudd and eels

Permits: Roy and Jenny Fancett, at the address above. Tel: 01363 877437

Cost: Day tickets at £3 per day; children £2

Restrictions: No groundbait or boilies (the owners obviously don't know that boilies are about the best food for fish!); no fish over 1lb to be kept in keepnets

BK Rating: Not known

E/A: South West

Comments: This is a beautiful wildlife reserve with a stream, deer, badgers and foxes; much other wildlife and flowers. Three self-catering chalets: breakfast and evening meals at the house by arrangement. No pets. Prices £100 per week; fishing extra. Bed and breakfast in house from £12 per night. Lake has been stocked for 30 years, but was only recently opened for fishing. Car park and toilet facilities. Excellent location for holidays, between Dartmoor and Exmoor. Send for brochure

Ashcombe Valley

Location: Ashcombe, between Exeter and Teignmouth
Type and Size: Two pools of about an acre each, both with islands
Carp Stock: Carp averaging about 5 lbs
Category: Mixed Fishery
Other Species: Tench, roach and small bream
Permits: On site
Cost: £4 per day; £20 per season; reductions for juniors, O.A.P's and disabled
Control: Newton Abbot F.A. Tel: 01626 866048
Restrictions: No night fishing; barbless hooks
BK Rating: Moderate
Baits/Methods: Boilies and luncheon meat are best baits
E/A: South West
Comments: Open all year; toilet

Berrynarbor Mill Pond A

Location: Mill Park Caravan and Camping Site, Berrynarbor, Combe Martin
Type and Size: Three acre lake
How to Find: The camping and caravan site is near the village of Berrynarbor in North Devon. Take the A399 from Combe Martin towards Ilfracombe, and turn south to the village
Carp Stock: A reasonable number of mirrors to about 15lbs. One fish of 24lbs reported, but this could be the only 20
Category: Mixed Fishery
Other Species: Roach, perch and bream
Permits: Mr Brain, Mill Park Caravan Site, Berrynarbor, Combe Martin. Tel: 01271 882647
Cost: About £1 per day, day tickets
Control: Private
BK Rating: Moderate
E/A: South West
Comments: No close season

Bickerton Farm Fishery

Location: Bickerton Farm, Kellaton, Hallsands, off the A 379 Kingsbridge to Dartmouth road
Type and Size: Two small farm ponds
Carp Stock: Well stocked with small carp to 8 lbs
Category: Mixed Fishery
Other Species: Roach, rudd, tench, perch, eels and small bream
Permits: From the farm
Cost: £3.50 per day; £2.50 juniors
Control: Tel: 01548 511220
Restrictions: No boilies; no night fishing; no keepnets; barbless hooks
BK Rating: Easy
E/A: South West
Comments: Close to the spectacular cliffs and coves of Start Point. Disabled access. Probably open all year

Billingsmoor Farm

Location: Butterleigh, near Cullompton
Type and Size: Three ponds of 1½ acres, 1 acre and ½ acre
Carp Stock: Well stocked with carp to doubles
Category: Mixed Fishery
Other Species: Tench, roach and rudd

Permits: From the farm
Cost: £5 per day
Control: Tel: 01884 855248
Restrictions: No boilies
BK Rating: Not known
E/A: South West

Bulworthy Farm Cottage A

Location: The Barton, Instow, Bideford, North Devon
Type and Size: Five small lakes
Carp Stock: Some carp to 20lbs
Category: Mixed Fishery
Other Species: Some coarse fishing (species not listed), rainbow trout to 4lbs
Permits: From the address above (Mrs R May)
Control: Private
BK Rating: Not known
E/A: South West
Coments: Cottage to rent at the lakes, with fishing for guests. Another lake with a rowing boat. Two other cottages about 7 miles away, but still with the same fishing rights.

Cadover Bridge Pits

Location: Cadover Bridge
Type and Size: Several china clay pits
How to Find: Cadover Bridge, between Yelverton and Ivybridge
Carp Stock: Some carp to doubles
Category: Mixed Fishery
Other Species: Coarse fish
Permits: Plymouth and District A.A.
Cost: About £3 per day
Control: Plymouth and District A.A.
BK Rating: Moderate
E/A: South West
Comments: Open all year. High up on a South Dartmoor beauty spot

Clawford Vineyard A

Location: Clawford Vineyard, Clawton, Holsworthy, EX22 6PN
Type and Size: 2 acre lake
How to Find: Off the A 388 Holsworthy to Bideford road

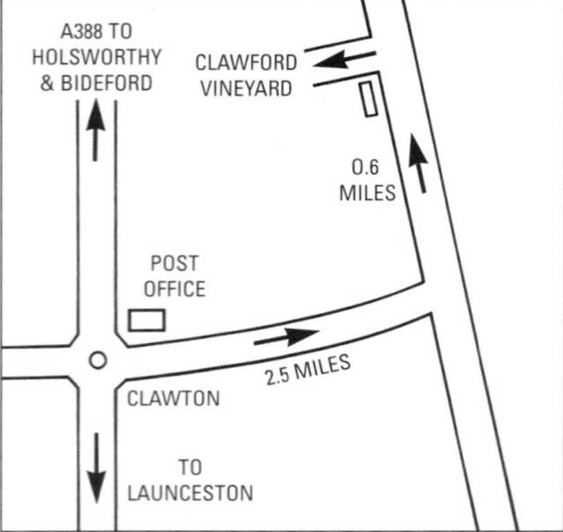

Carp Stock: Well stocked with carp to 20 lbs
Category: Mixed Fishery
Other Species: Koi, crucians, tench, roach, rudd and orfe
Permits: From the farmhouse in front of the lake
Cost: About £4 from dawn to dusk. Extra rods £1 per rod
Control: Private. Tel: 01409 254177
Restrictions: No night fishing; no nuts, peas, seeds or beans; no keepnets
BK Rating: Moderate
E/A: South West
Comments: Open all year. Toilet. Bed and breakfast with free fishing. Working vineyard - home made wines and apple juice. Guided tours. We have inspected this one - it is a very pleasant place with high class accommodation

Clifford Farm Holidays A

Location: Woolsery, near Clovelly
Type and Size: Small farm pool
How to Find: Woolsery is a village near Clovelly on the North Devon coast
Carp Stock: Well stocked with carp of good size
Category: Carp Water
Other Species: Trout
Permits: On site
Cost: On application
BK Rating: Moderate
E/A: South West
Comments: No close season. Luxury self catering cottages in beautiful countryside near coast. Brochure and information from Tel: 01237 3319. Also game and clay pigeon shooting

Clovelly Golf and Country Club A

Location: Off the A39 south of Clovelly
Type and Size: Two lakes of 4 acres and 2 acres
Carp Stock: Well stocked with carp to over 20 lbs
Category: Mixed Fishery
Other Species: Tench and rudd
Permits: From reception
Cost: About £6 per day; concessions
Control: Tel: 01237 431442
BK Rating: Not known
E/A: South West
Comments: Probably open all year. Attractive country club with bars, accommodation, etc.

Cofton Park Farm A

Location: Cofton Park Farm, Starcross, Dawlish
Type and Size: Small lake
How to Find: Between Starcross and Dawlish in South Devon
Carp Stock: Well stocked
Category: Mixed Fishery
Other Species: Tench, roach, skimmer bream
Permits: On site
Cost: On application
BK Rating: Moderate
Control: Private
E/A: South West
Comments: Holiday caravans, tourers, camping. Heated swiming pool, shopping

and all amenities. Free brochure and details from Mrs T Jeffery. Tel: 01626 8900358. No close season

Coombe Farm Lakes

Location: Little Silver, Cadeleigh, near Tiverton
Type and Size: Two tiny farm pools
Carp Stock: Carp to over 20 lbs
Category: Mixed Fishery
Other Species: Roach, tench and bream
Permits: On bank
Cost: About £3 per day
Control: Tel: 01884 855337
Restrictions: Night fishing by arrangement only
BK Rating: Moderate
E/A: South West
Comments: Probably open all year

Coombe Water Fishery A

Location: Near Kingsbridge, South Devon
Type and Size: Three small lakes
How to Find: Enquire from owner
Carp Stock: Well stocked with carp to 20lbs
Category: Mixed Fishery
Other Species: Bream, tench and roach
Permits: Jonathan Robinson. Tel: 01548 852038
Cost: £4 per day; £3 after 5.30 pm
BK Rating: Moderate
Control: Private
E/A: South West
Comments: This lake is in the beautiful South Hams area of Devon where there is little carp fishing. All details from the owner. Barbless hooks. Bed and breakfast in 16th century farmhouse

Creedy Lakes

Location: Off the A3072 Tiverton Road; turn left one mle from Crediton, and then first right, and right again; the lake is opposite a farm, Long Barn, Crediton, EX17 4AB
Type and Size: Heavily stocked with carp to 25lbs, most of which are commons, though small mirrors have been stocked, and some have now reached 20lbs
Category: Mixed Fishery
Other Species: Tench and eels
Permits: Day tickets from machine on bank
Cost: £5 for 5.30am to 11pm, and an evening ticket from 5pm to 11pm costs £3
Control: Private. Tel: 01363 772684
Restrictions: No season tickets; no night fishing; no keepnets; 3 rods allowed. Barbless hooks
Baits/Methods: Floaters, boilies, luncheon meat and sweetcorn
BK Rating: Moderate, though an angler has taken more than 100lbs of carp in a day
E/A: South West

Darracott

Location: Off the Bideford to Barnstaple Road, near Torrington
Type and Size: Reservoir of 2.6 acres
How to Find: Turn off the A386 Okehampton to Bideford Road opposite Torrington Church, and then turn right towards Huntshaw. The entrance to Darracott is past the factory on the right

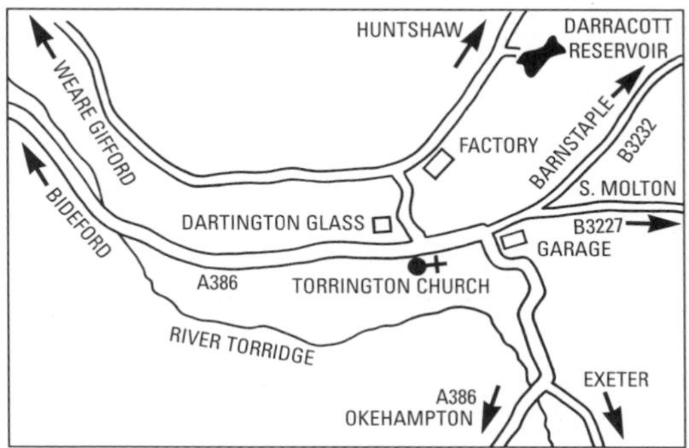

Carp Stock: Well stocked with carp to 14lbs
Category: Mixed Fishery
Other Species: Bream, perch, roach and rudd
Permits: Sports, 9 High Street, The Square, Torrington: The Kingfisher, 22 Castle Street, Barnstaple. Tel: 01271 44919: The Tackle Box, Kings Shopping Centre, Cooper Street, Bideford. Tel: (01271) 470043 Summerlands Tackle, 3 Golflinks Road, Westward Ho. Tel: (01237) 471291
Cost: Day £2.50, Concesion rate for OAP's, SDP/MOB, students and children under 16 £1.50: 24 hours £5 : 7 day castabout, (valid at all Peninsula Coarse Fisheries, except Jennets and Crafthole), day £15, concession day £10: Day and night £30. No season permits
Control: Mr Dell Mills, Manager, Peninsula Coarse Fisheries, St Cleer Depot, Liskeard, Cornwall PL14 6EQ. Tel: (01579) 43929
BK Rating: Moderate
E/A: South West
Restrictions: No keepnets for carp. Barbless hooks requested. Permits must be obtained before fishing
Comments: NO CLOSED SEASON. Night fishing is now allowed

Dunsley Farm A

Location: West Anstey, South Molton. Tel: 01398 4246
Type and Size: Small farm pond
Category: Mixed Fishery
Carp Stock: Well stocked with small carp
Other Species: Tench, roach and rudd
Permits: From the farmhouse before fishing - £3 per day
Control: Mrs M Robins, at the above address
BK Rating: Moderate
E/A: South West
Comments: Self-catering cottage, overlooking a valley, and the woodland pond. Cost from £120 per week, to include fishing

East Devon Pond

A

Location: Near Honiton
Type and Size: Small farm pond - about half an acre
Carp Stock: Well stocked with carp to about 15lbs
Category: Carp Water
Other Species: Some coarse fish
Permits: Tel: 01404 891244 for information and details
Control: Private
BK Rating: Not known, as the water was not fished until 1991
E/A: South West
Comments: Country bungalow to let for self catering holidays with fishing on own pond. Six acres of land - cottage sleeps six. Open during the winter for the week or weekend booking. No close season. Cost from £200 per week, to include fishing

Edison Pond

Location: Kingsteignton, near Newton Abbot
Type and Size: One acre clay pit with many snags and sunken trees
How to Find: Take the B3191 north from Kingsteignton. About half a mile from the roundabout, and straight on, you will see the pond on the right, in some trees
Carp Stock: Some carp, mainly commons, to about mid-doubles
Category: Mixed Fishery
Other Species: Roach, rudd and tench
Permits: 24 hour tickets from tackle shops in Newton Abbot, which must be obtained in advance
Control: Newton Abbot FA
BK Rating: Difficult
E/A: South West
Comments: Heavy tackle needed - at least 15lb line - as most of the carp are taken in the heavy snags and lilies, often on floaters

Exeter Canal

Location: Exeter
Type and Size: 6 mile canal from Basin to Turf
Carp Stock: Some carp to over 40lbs
Category: Few Carp
Other Species: Dace, roach, perch, tench, bream, pike and eels
Permits: Exeter and District AA Hon Sec D Cornish, 9 Denmark Road Exeter. Tel: 01392 56770. Tickets from tackle shops in Exeter, such as Exeter Angling Centre, Smythen Street; Benett's, Crediton; Drum Sports, Newton Abbot; Plainmoor Angling Centre, Torquay.
Cost: Visitor's day ticket at £3. Season £20 Reductions for juniors and OAP's
Control: Club
Restrictions: Limited access points - details from Agents and Secretary
BK Rating: Very Difficult
E/A: South West
Comments: No close season

Fishponds House

Location: Fishponds House, Dunkeswell, Honiton. Tel: 01823 680460
Type and Size: Three acre lake
Carp Stock: Carp to double figures
Category: Mixed Fishery
Other Species: Tench and rudd
Permits: Mr and Mrs K Farmer at the address above

Cost: Day tickets at £2
Control: Private
Restrictions: No night fishing - open 8am till sunset only
BK Rating: Not known
E/A: South West
Comments: No close season

Grand Western Canal

Location: Tiverton Basin to Burlescombe
Type and Size: Narrow, weedy disused canal
Carp Stock: Said to be some carp to over 20 lbs
Category: Few Carp
Other Species: Big pike and tench; perch, roach, rudd, bream and eels
Permits: Local tackle shops, in Tiverton
Cost: £17 per season (£12 associate member); £6 per week; £2.50 per day. Reduced prices for juniors and OAP's
Control: Malcolm Trump, Canal Liaison Officer, 5 Middle Lane, Cullompton. Tel: 01844 34448 (home), or 01844 32059 (work)
Restrictions: Dawn to dusk fishing only. Open from June 1st to last day in February
BK Rating: Difficult
E/A: South West
Comments: Excessively weedy

Hartsmoor Fisheries

Location: Bolham Water, Clayhidon, Nr Hemyock
Type and Size: Three small ponds, one of which is heavily stocked with carp to mid-twenties
Category: Mixed Fishery
Restrictions: Not known
Other Species: Tench, crucians and roach in a carp pond
Permits: Tel: 0183 680460
BK Rating: Difficult
E/A: South West
Comments: No close season The two other ponds are mainly match fisheries

Hogsbrook Lake

Location: Greensdale Barton, Woodbury Salterton, Exeter
Type and Size: Two lakes of 2½ acres and 1½ acres
Carp Stock: Well stocked with carp to doubles
Category: Mixed Fishery
Other Species: Tench, roach, bream
Permits: Miss M McDowell, FWS Carter and Sons Ltd, Greendale Barton, Woodbury Salterton. Tel: 01395 32855 (day); 01395 68183 (evening)
Cost: £2.50 per day; £1.25 evening after 6pm. Reduced prices for children under 8. Season ticket at £50 annually (no close season)
Control: Private
BK Rating: Not known
E/A: South West
Comments: No close season; night fishing allowed. No fish under 1lb in keepnets(!); children under 14 must be accompanied by adults. Touring caravan and camping site

Hollies Trout Farm

Location: Sheldon, near Honiton. Tel: 1404 84428
Type and Size: Half acre lake
Carp Stock: Well stocked with carp to upper doubles
Category: Mixed Fishery
Other Species: Roach, bream, tench, dace and rudd
Permits: From J Roles at the address above
Cost: Day tickets at £3
Control: Private
Restrictions: No night fishing; open sunrise to sunset. No keepnets
BK Rating: Not known
E/A: South West
Comments: No close season

Home Farm Fishery

Location: Off the A 380 at Mamhead, south of Exeter
Type and Size: Small pool of about an acre
Carp Stock: Well stocked with carp to 25 lbs
Category: Mixed Fishery
Other Species: Roach, tench and some koi
Permits: On bank
Cost: About £4 per day; £5 for two rods
Control: Tel: 01626 866259
Restrictions: Night fishing by arrangement
BK Rating: Easy
E/A: South West
Comments: Probably open all year. Toilets and hut. Disabled parking

Indio Pond A

Location: Greywalls Lodge, Newton Road, Bovey Tracey, near Newton Abbot
Type and Size: Estate lake of 2 acres
How to Find: Take the M5 to Exeter, then the A38 towards Plymouth. After 8 miles at the big roundabout turn right onto the road to Bovey Tracey; this is the Newton Road. After 1½ miles the entrance to Greywalls Lodge will be seen on the right, 200 yards after crossing the old railway bridge
Carp Stock: Well stocked with carp to 27lbs
Category: Mixed Fishery
Other Species: Tench, troun, rudd, eels, perch
Permits: Day tickets are limited, and are sold in advance only by the resident owner, Mr M Charlier, at the house on the property. Fishing is from 6am till dusk; night fishing is by arrangement with the owners. Fishing is available at a reduced price for those staying at the Lodge. There are plans for a unique free exclusive membership scheme - details from Mr Charlier
Cost: On application
Restrictions: No bolt rigs. Barbless hooks only. No keepnets
BK Rating: Carp up to 10lbs - Easy; 10-15lbs - Moderate; 20lbs plus - Difficult (April till June). Carp to 20lbs - Moderate; over 20lbs - Difficult (June till October). Winter - Easy if you find the fish. (Categories provided by the proprietor in this instance)
Control: Private
E/A: South West
Baits/Methods: Normal carp fishing baits and methods. Hard boilies needed to defeat the numerous tench
Comments: First class accommodation is available at the Lodge which is only a few yards from the lake. Bed and breakfast and evening meal. Rooms

have wash basins and tea-making facilities, and there is a guest lounge with colour TV. The house is a beautiful 100 year old stone built property in 10 acres of private grounds situated between Torquay and Dartmoor - ideal for a family fishing holiday. No close season. Brochure from Mr Charlier, Greywalls, Newton Road, Bovey Tracey, Devon TQ13 9DY. Tel: 01626 832508. Record fish a mirror of 27lbs 3ozs

Jennetts A

Location: Near Bideford, North Devon
Type and Size: Reservoir of eight acres
How to Find: Signposted from the Torrington to Bideford road
Carp Stock: Well stocked with carp to 23lbs
Category: Carp Water
Other Species: Tench, roach and bream
Permits: The Tackle Box, Kings Shopping Centre, Cooper Street, Bideford. Tel: 01237 470043
Cost: Day (6.30am to 10.00pm) £4, Concessions. Children under 16 £1.50. No season permits. Tel: 01837 871565
E/A: South West
BK Rating: Moderate
Restrictions: No night fishing. No cereal based groundbaits, except swimfeeders. No keepnets for carp. Barbless hooks requested. Permits must be obtained before fishing
Comments: NO CLOSED SEASON. Attractive enclosed water. Accommodation at the Beaufort Hotel, Tors Park, Ilfracombe. Tel: 01271 865483

Legge Farm Coarse Fishery A

Location: Church Road, Highhampton, EX21 5LF
Type and Size: Two farm ponds
Carp Stock: Well stocked with carp to doubles
Category: Mixed Fishery
Other Species: Tench
Permits: From farm
Cost: Not known
Control: Tel: 01409 23464
BK Rating: Not known
E/A: South West
Comments: Open all year. Self-catering accommodation and bed and breakfast. Camping and caravans

Leworthy Farm A

Location: Between Holsworthy and Bude
Type and Size: Small lake
Carp Stock: Stocked with carp, sizes and numbers not known
Category: Mixed Fishery
Other Species: Coarse fish
Permits: Enquire from owners
Cost: Not known
Control: Leworthy Farm, Holsworthy, EX22 6SJ. Tel: 01409 253485
BK Rating: Not known
E/A: South West
Comments: Probably open all year. Two self-catering farm cottages with fishing. River fishing also - A.A. and R.A.C. listed. Licensed

Little Comfort Farm A

Location: Little Comfort Farm, West Down, Braunton, North Devon. Tel: 01271 812414
Type and Size: One acre farm pond
Carp Stock: Well stocked with carp to double figures
Category: Mixed Fishery
Other Species: Rudd, bream and trout
Permits: From Rolf Alvsaker at the address above
Cost: £5 per day; £4 half day; £3 evening
Control: Private
Restrictions: No night fishing - daylight till dark only
BK Rating: Moderate
E/A: South West
Comments: No close season. Self-catering cottages available. Toilets

Longlands Farm A

Location: Near Coombe Martin, Ilfracombe, North Devon EX34 OPD. Tel: 01271 883522
Type and Size: Small farm pond
How to Find: Off the A399 Ilfracombe - Lynmouth Road; turn left by RAC box going south
Carp Stock: Some carp, numbers and sizes not known
Category: Mixed Fishery
Other Species: General coarse fish
Permits: Fishing free to residents, details from Mary Peacock at the address above
BK Rating: Not known
E/A: South West
Comments: Little is known, as the brochure only mentions a private fishing lake, but gives no details. Bed and breakfast, evening meal if required, on working farm near Exmoor and the sea. B and B £12.50 per person per night, £87 a week

Luccombes Ponds

Location: Dayspottles Lane, Exminster
Type and Size: Five small ponds
Carp Stock: Well stocked with carp to 20 lbs
Category: Mixed Fishery
Other Species: Tench, roach and rudd
Permits: On bank
Cost: About £4 per day
Control: Tel: 01647 61088
BK Rating: Not known
E/A: South West
Comments: Probably open all year

Melbury

Location: Parkham, near Bideford, North Devon
Type and Size: Reservoir of 12 acres
How to Find: From the Bradworthy to Bideford Road, the fishery is 1 mile from Powlers Piece Garage
Carp Stock: Moderately stocked with carp to 22lbs. Restocked early 1991 with commons to over 20lbs - a 27 pounder was caught in 1990, hooked on a boilie
Category: Mixed Fishery

Other Species: Rudd, tench, bream and perch
Permits: The Tackle Box, Kings Shopping Centre, Cooper Street, Bideford. Tel: 01237 470043: Powlers Piece Garage, Powlers Piece, East Putford. Tel: 0123 75282: Summerlands Tackle, Golfinks Road, Westward Ho. Tel: 01237 471291
Cost: Day £2.50. Concession rate for OAP's, SDP/MOB, students and children under 16 £1.50: 24 hours £5: 7 day castabout, (valid at all Peninsula Coarse Fisheries, except Jennetts and Crafthole), day £15, concession day £10: Day and night £30. No season permits
Control: Tel: 01837 871565
E/A: South West
BK Rating: Moderate
Restrictions: Fishing is allowed from 6.30am to 10.00pm only. No cereal based groundbaits, except swimfeeders. No keepnets for carp. Barbless hooks requested. Permits must be obtained before fishing
Comments: No closed season

Milemead Fisheries

Location: Mill Hill, near Tavistock, PL 198MP
How to Find: Take the A385 from Tavistock towards Launceston, and turn left towards Mill Hill just outside the town. After about a mile you will see a turn on the right which leads to the fishery
Type and Size: Two acre lake
Carp Stock: Well stocked with carp to doubles, including some ghost carp
Category: Mixed Fishery
Other Species: Tench, roach, rudd and bream
Permits: At the fishery
Cost: £4.50 per day; Concessions £3.50
Control: Andrew or Paul Evenden. Tel: 01822 610888
Restrictions: No keepnets; barbless hooks; no night fishing
BK Rating: Moderate
E/A: South West
Comments: No close season

Millhayes Pond

Location: Kentisbeare, off the A373 between Honiton and Tiverton
Type and Size: Two acre lake
Carp Stock: Well stocked with carp to about 20lbs
Category: Mixed Fishery
Other Species: Tench, rudd and roach
Permits: Tel: 01884 266412
Restrictions: No boilies. No night fishing. Barbless hooks
BK Rating: Easy
E/A: South West
Comments: No close season

Milton Farm

Location: Payhembury, near Honiton
Type and Size: Five small pools
Carp Stock: Well stocked with small carp to 5 lbs
Category: Mixed Fishery
Other Species: Tench and roach
Permits: On bank
Cost: About £4 per day
Control: Tel: 01404 850236
Restrictions: Night fishing by arrangement only

BK Rating: Easy
E/A: South West
Comments: Probably open all year

Newcourt Ponds

Location: Langford, near Cullompton
Type and Size: Four small pools
Carp Stock: Well stocked with carp to doubles
Category: Mixed Fishery
Other Species: Tench, bream, rudd and golden orfe
Permits: On bank
Cost: About £4 per day
Control: Tel: 01884 277326
Restrictions: No boilies; no night fishing; barbless hooks
BK Rating: Not known
E/A: South West
Comments: Probably open all year

Oldborough Fishing Retreat

Location: Off the Crediton to Morchard Bishop road, one mile from Morchard Bishop
Type and Size: Two small connected pools - a former quarry
Carp Stock: Well stocked with doubles to about 15 lbs
Category: Mixed Fishery
Other Species: Tench, rudd, roach, perch and eels
Permits: On bank
Cost: £4 per day; £3 juniors
Control: Private. Tel: 01363 877437
Restrictions: No boilies or cereal groundbait. Barbless hooks only. No keepnets
BK Rating: Not known
E/A: South West

Old Mill

Location: Near Dartmouth in South Devon
Type and Size: Reservoir of 4.7 acres
How to Find: The reservoir is off the B3207 Halwell to Dittisham Road, near Old Mill Creek on the River Dart

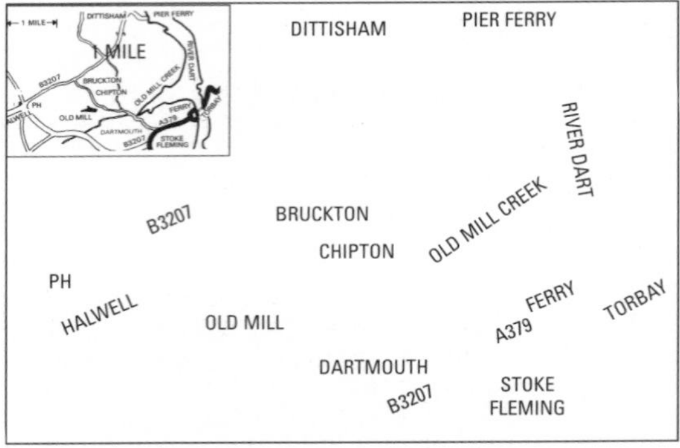

Carp Stock: Well stocked with carp to 21lbs. Restocked early in 1991 with commons to 20 1/2 lbs
Category: Mixed Fishery
Other Species: Roach, bream and tench
Permits: Season only
Cost: Price on application
Control: Peninsula Coarse Fisheries. Tel: 01837 871565
E/A: South West
BK Rating: Moderate
Restrictions: No cereal based groundbaits except swimfeeders.No keepnets for carp. Barbless hooks requested. Permits must be obtained before fishing
Comments: NO CLOSED SEASON. Open 24 hours. Very mature and attractive water

Pound Farm A

Location: Butterley, near Tiverton
Type and Size: Tiny farm pond just big enough for four anglers
Carp Stock: Some carp to about 8lbs
Category: Mixed Fishery
Other Species: Tench and perch
Permits: Tel: 01884 (Tiverton) 855208 for information
BK Rating: Not known
E/A: South West
Commens: Six berth caravan for hire at £100 to £130 weekly, fishing included

Pyewell Farm A

Location: Pyewell Farm, Holmacott, near Instow, North Devon. Tel: 0127 830357
Type and Size: Two small farm ponds
Carp Stock: Well stocked with carp to doubles
Category: Mixed Fishery
Other Species: Tench
Permits: From Mrs Steer at the above address
Control: Private
BK Rating: Not known
E/A: South West
Comments: Dinner, bed and breakfast in 16th century farmhouse with fishing from £20 per day, which includes food and overnight accommodation. Three miles from sandy beach and only 4 miles from the North Devon link road. No close season

Rackerhayes

Location: Newton Abbot
Type and Size: Island Pool is about five acres - old pit
How to Find: Take the Exeter road from Newton Abbot, and the lakes are down a track opposite the Racecourse
Carp Stock: Quite well stocked with small carp to 10lbs, small number of doubles including some twenties and one fish of about 30lbs
Category: Mixed Fishery
Other Species: General coarse fish
Permits: For Rackerhayes you must live within 10 mile radius of Newton Abbot. The Newton Abbot FA has other waters with carp in the area, for which day and season tickets are issued. Details and tickets from Percy Hodge (Sports) 104 Queen Street, Newton Abbot; Drum Sports, 48a Courtenay Street, Newton Abbot
Control: Newton Abbot Fishing Association. Secretary: D Hooder, 22 Mount Pleasant Road Newton Abbot

BK Rating: Rackerhayes - Difficult. Other water - Moderate to Easy
E/A: South West

Riverton Fishery A

Location: Off the A361 at Swimbridge, near Barnstable, EX32 OQX
Type and Size: Two lakes of three acres and 2 acres
Carp Stock: Well stocked with carp to 20lbs
Category: Mixed Fishery
Other Species: Tench, bream, roach, rudd and perch
Permits: Hugh and Rosemary Smith
Cost: £4 per day; £3 for the evening; reduced price for juniors.
Control: Private. Tel: 01271 830009
Restrictions: Night fishing by arrangement. Barbless hooks
BK Rating: Not known
E/A: South West
Comments: No close season. Self catering accommodation. Bed and breakfast; dinner and tea. Caravan site

Rub - a - Dub Pond

Location: Exeter road, Kingsteignton, near Newton Abbot
Type and Size: One acre pool
Carp Stock: Well stocked with carp to 20 lbs
Category: Mixed Fishery
Other Species: Tench, perch and roach
Permits: In advance only from local tackle shops
Cost: £3 per day. Season tickets also available
Control: Newton Abbot F.A. Tel: 01626 64173
Restrictions: Barbless hooks
BK Rating: Moderate
E/A: South West

Salmonhutch Fishery A

Location: Uton Farm, near Crediton, EX17 3QL
Type and Size: Three small spring fed lakes
Carp Stock: Well stocked with commons and mirrors to 20lbs
Category: Carp Water
Other Species: Tench
Permits: From the fishery. About £4 per day. Concessions. Season £75
Control: Private. Tel: 01363 772749; 01647 24035
BK Rating: Moderate
E/A: South West
Comments: Camping and caravan site; facilities for disabled anglers. Toilets. Open all year. Send for brochure

Sampford Peverell Ponds

Location: Just off the M5, where the A373 Tiverton road crosses the railway near the village of Sampford Peverell
Type and Size: Two little pits of about half an acre and 1/4 acre
Carp Stock: Some good carp to upper doubles
Category: Mixed Fishery
Other Species: Tench, bream, pike and roach
Permits: Members only water of Exeter and District AA (no day tickets). Permits from tackle shops in Exeter. Secretary: D Cornish, 9 Denmark Road, Exeter. Tel: 01392 567700. Includes a number of other good waters. £20 per season

Restrictions: Normal close season. No carp in keepnets. No groundbait
BK Rating: Difficult
E/A: South West
Comments: We have personal experience of this one. The pond on the Tiverton side of the railway line is known as The Clear Pond. This used to contain only a dozen or so carp, most of which were doubles to about 20lbs, which could be seen but were very hard to catch, (a friend had an 18 on a floating Osborne biscuit many years ago, believe it or not); we are not sure if these big fish still survive. The other pond, part of which was taken for road construction, was always so heavily weeded that it was almost impossible to get the fish out, even on very heavy line, though this may have changed now. PM once tried to go in for a hooked double, and sank in mud almost to chest level, managed to scramble out....and never did get the fish out!

Shobrooke Park

Location: Off the A3072 between Crediton and Tiverton, on the Shobrooke Estate
Type and Size: Attractive nine acre estate lake
Carp Stock: Quite well stocked with carp to over 20lbs
Category: Mixed Fishery
Other Species: Roach and tench
Permits: Day tickets £10 from Ladds Sports, High Street, Crediton. Tel: 01363 772666
Cost: £6 per day; - half price for juniors, OAP's and the disabled
Control: Shobrooke Park Estate, 27 South Street, Molton, North Devon EX36 4AA
Restrictions: No night fishing; no fishing allowed on about half on the bank - the other side is private
BK Rating: Moderate
E/A: South West

Simpson Valley Fishery

Location: One and a half miles from Holsworthy on the A3072 Holsworthy to Hatherleigh Road. Tel: 01409 253593
Type and Size; Five small farm pools in valley
Carp Stock: Carp Pool - heavily stocked with carp to upper doubles; other pools - some carp
Category: Carp Pool - Carp Only; other pools - Mixed Fisheries
Other Species: Tench, roach and rudd
Permits: Day tickets from the farm - there is a sign on the main road
Cost: Carp Pool - £3 per day; other pools - £2 per day; half price for children and pensioners on all pools
Control: Private. Simpson Farm, Holsworthy EX22 6JW
BK Rating: Easy
Restrictions: Barbless hooks only; no boilies; no cereal groundbait; no keepnets
E/A: South West
Comments: Pleasant farm fishery with good fishing in the carp pool. Farming and wildlife award. Nature trail. Bed and breakfast at the Bickford Arms, Brandis Corner. Restaurant Tel: 10409 22318

Slade

Location: Near Ilfracombe, North Devon
Type and Size: Two reservoirs. Upper Slade 4 acres. Lower Slade 6 acres
How to Find: From Ilfracombe, pick up the B3231, and the entrance to the reservoirs is on the left
Carp Stock: Well stocked with carp to 20lbs
Category: Mixed Fisheries

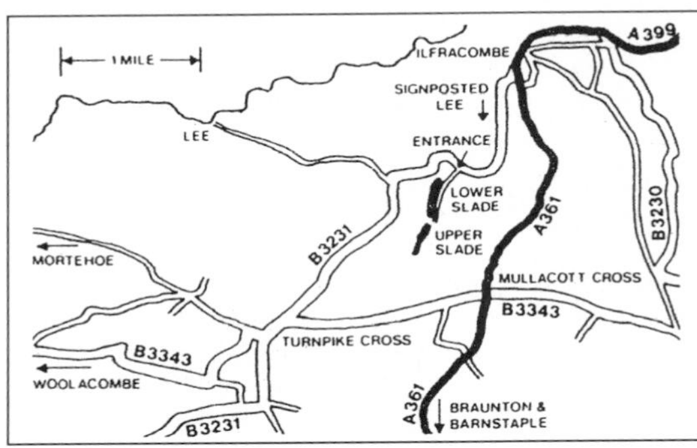

Other Species: Tench to 7lbs, roach to 3lbs 7ozs, bream and perch
Permits: The Tackle Box, 2b Portland Street, Ilfracombe. Tel: 01271 862570: The Kingfisher, 22 Castle Street, Barnstaple. Tel: 01271 44919: Summerlands Tackle, 3 Golflinks Road, Westward Ho. Tel: 01237 47129. Season and day permits from The Post Office, Slade. Tel: 01271 862257
Cost: Day £4. Concessions. Season permits £65. Concessions
Control: Peninsula Coarse Fisheries. Tel: 01837 871565
E/A: South West
BK Rating: Moderate
Restrictions: No cereal based groundbait except swimfeeders. No keepnets for carp. Barbless hooks requested. Permits must be obtained before fishing
Comments: Attractive water with NO CLOSED SEASON. Night fishing is now allowed

Southcombe Waters

Location: South Farm, Ashill, Cullompton, near Exeter
Type and Size: Three small pools
Carp Stock: Well stocked with carp averaging about 4 lbs, but with a few big fish to over 20 lbs
Category: Carp Water
Other Species: Roach and a few chub
Permits: On bank
Cost: About £5 a day
Control: Private. Tel: 01823 640447
BK Rating: Easy
Baits/Methods: Boilies are the best bait
E/A: South West
Comments: Toilets. Probably open all year

South Farm Ponds — A

Location: Blackborough, Cullompton
Type and Size: Two small farm ponds
How to Find: South Farm, Blackborough, Cullompton, near Exeter EX15 2SE
Carp Stock: Well stocked with carp to 15lbs
Category: Mixed Fishery
Other Species: Tench and roach
Permits: From Colin and Sylvia Shortis, South Farm. Tel: 01823 681078
Cost: On application
BK Rating: Moderate
Control: Private

Restrictions: Not known
E/A: South West
Comments: No close season. Holidays in four holiday homes. Health spa, games rooms, swimming pool. Colour brochure on application

South Hay Farm A

Location: South Hay Farm, Shebbear, Beaworthy. Tel: 01409 28614
Type and Size: Two acre lake
Carp Stock: Some carp to 10lbs
Category: Mixed Fishery
Other Species: Tench, rudd, orfe, chub and trout
Permits: Mr Nigel Brown or Miss Penelope Douglas, at the above address
Cost: £5 per day; £3 from 2pm
Control: Private
Restrictions: Open 7.30am till sunset, night fishing by arrangement. Barbless hooks
BK Rating: Not known
E/A: South West
Comments: No close season. Accommodation on site. Children's fishing pond. One mile salmon, sea trout and brown trout on fishing on River Torridge

South Reed Fisheries Carp Lake

Location: Boasley Cross, Bratton Clovelly, near Okehampton EX20 4JJ. Tel: 01837 87295
Type and Size: Three acre man-made lake
How to Find: The fishery is signposted from the B3218 road between Okehampton and Halwill, about 4 miles from Okehampton, on the left hand side of the road
Carp Stock: 30 doubles to 30lbs
Category: Carp Only
Permits: In advance only - phone or call for bookings. Only 3 anglers per day from June till October
Cost: £15 for 24 hours
Control: Private
Restrictions: Barbless hooks, not smaller than size 6; nets to be knotless and not smaller than 30 inches: 8lb minimum line strength; no dogs, no nuts
BK Rating: Easy to Moderate
E/A: South West
Comments: This lake has been specially stocked for specialist carp anglers - each fish is marked for identification purposes. Pleasant nature conservation area - other lakes on site (see separate entry). Quiet, peaceful site well away from main roads

South Reed Fisheries Coarse Lake

Location: Boasley Cross, Bratton Clovelly, near Okehampton EX20 4JJ. Tel: 01837 87295
Type and Size: Three and a half acre man - made lake
How to Find: Take the old A30 from Okehampton towards Launceston, and turn right onto the B3218 Holsworthy road at the top of Okehampton Hill. You will see a sign to the fishery on the left about 4 miles from Okehampton
Carp Stock: Well stocked with carp to 23lbs
Category: Mixed Fishery
Permits: On bank
Cost: £4 per day
Control: Private
Baits/Methods: All normal methods, including float fishing, with maggots, sweetcorn, luncheon meat and boilies

Restrictions: Barbless hooks; no keepnets for carp; all fish to be returned; no dogs
BK Rating: Easy
E/A: South West
Coments: Tackle hire is available for £1 per day; angling tuition if required, by appointment only. Coarse fish, koi and ornamental fish for sale from fish farm on site, also water lilies and other aquatic plants. Some non-fishing ponds available for bird watching by special arrangement on this nature conservation area. Very quiet and peaceful site well away from main roads. Trout fishing

South View Farm

Location: Shilingford St George, south west of Exeter near Alphington
Type and Size: Three small farm ponds with a total area of three acres
Carp Stock: Top Pond well stocked with carp to over 20lbs; Middle Pond has carp to 17lbs
Category: Mixed Fishery
Other Species: Tench, golden tench, roach, rudd, gudgeon, bream and ghost carp
Permits: Day tickets on bank
Cost: £4 for adults; £3 for juniors, who must be accompanied by an adult. Evening tickets from 5pm at £2.50, Weekly permits at £19
Control: Tel: 01392 832278
Restrictions: No night fishing; no boilies or keepnets
BK Rating: Moderate
E/A: South West
Comments: Open all year

Spires Lake

Location: North Tawton
Type and Size: Two lakes
Carp Stock: Carp to doubles
Category: Carp Water
Other Species: Some
Permits: Telephone control
Cost: Not known
Control: Tel: 01837 82499
BK Rating: Not known
E/A: South West
Comments: Open all year

Spring Ponds

Location: Lower Rocombe Farm, Rocombe, between Maidencombe and Combinteignhead
Type and Size: Five small ponds
Carp Stock: Well stocked with small carp; some doubles
Category: Mixed Fishery
Other Species: Tench, rudd and bream
Permits: In advance only from local tackle shops
Cost: £3 per day; £20 per season. Reduced prices for concessions
Control: Newton Abbot F.C. Tel: 01803 328652
Restrictions: No boilies; nuts or bivvies
BK Rating: Moderate
E/A: South West
Comments: Probably open all year

Squabmoor

Location: Near Budleigh Salterton
Type and Size: Reservoir of 4.3 acres
How to Find: Turn off the A377 Exeter to Exmouth road at Clyst St. George into the B3179, and the reservoir is on the left, just before Knowle and Budleigh Salterton
Carp Stock: Well stocked with carp to over 20lbs
Category: Mixed Fishery
Other Species: Roach to over 3lbs, tench to 5½ lbs, bream and rudd
Permits: The Tackle Shop, 20 The Strand, Exmouth; Exeter Angling Centre, Smythen Street, Exeter. Day and season pemits from Knowle Post Office
Cost: Day £3.50. Concessions. SDP/MOB and students £20, children under 16 £12.50: Day and night £56
Control: Peninsula Coarse Fisheries. Tel: 01837 871565
E/A: South West
BK Rating: Moderate
Restrictions: No cereal based groundbaits except swimfeeders. No keepnets for carp. Barbless hooks requested. Permits must be obtained before fishing
Comments: Attractive water with NO CLOSED SEASON. Night fishing is now allowed

Star Barton Ponds

Location: Cowley, near Exeter
Type and Size: Two small farm ponds
Carp Stock: Well stocked with carp to doubles
Category: Carp Water
Other Species: Tench
Permits: Exeter and District AA. Secretary: D Cornish, 9 Denmark Road, Exeter. Tel: 01392 56770. Tickets from tackle shops such as Angling Centre, Smythen Street, Exeter; Bennets, Crediton; Drum Sport, Newton Abbot; Plainmoor Angling Centre, Torquay
Cost: Day visitors - £2; weekly - £6; season - £14
Control: Club
BK Rating: Easy
E/A: South West
Comments: No close season. Exeter and District AA is an excellent club with many other waters on the same ticket

Stevenstone Lakes

Location: St Giles in the Wood, near Great Torrington
Type and Size: Three old estate lakes of three and a half acres, three-quarters, and one and a quarter acres, very attractive, in a steep valley
How to Find: With difficulty! Take the B3227 Umberleigh road from Torrington and afer two miles take a private road on the right, where you will see the entrance to the bungalow. The lakes can be seen from the house
Carp Stock: All three lakes are well stocked with long commons, which are almost certainly genuine wildies, of which there are now very few in the country. These fish have been caught to just over 12lbs
Category: Mixed Fishery
Other Species: Tench, rudd and perch
Permits: In advance only from the owner at the bungalow above the lakes
Cost: £1.50 per rod
Control: Private. Tel: 01805 22102
Restrictions: No night fishing; dawn to dusk only; no dogs
BK Rating: Moderate
E/A: South West

Comments: One of the few places left where king carp have not been stocked, and where you can catch genuine wild carp (most reported wildies are just long, thin commons); owner only requires genuine anglers; no families or picnickers

Stone Farm Quarry

Location: Stone Farm, near Bridestow, just to the right hand size of the old A30, about 7 miles from Okehampton
Type and Size: Large and remarkably deep quarry, with very steep sides at one end, but easy access and fishing from the farm end
Carp Stock: Some carp, thought to go to about 10lbs
Category: Mixed Fishery
Other Species: Rudd, roach, tench and bream; possibly a few trout
Permits: From Stone Farm
Control: Private
BK Rating: Difficult
E/A: South West
Comments: PM has known this one for 50 years, although it probably only had a few trout in it from the nearby river then. Dangerous, almost vertical sides at the end away from the farm. Last time he put out an Arlesey Bomb from the 'easy' bank, it just kept going straight down, perhaps to 60 feet or more!

Stour Farm Fishery

Location: Bilingsmoor Farm, Butterleigh, Cullompton
Type and Size: Small farm pond
How to Find: Come off the motorway at junction 28, and take various lanes to the west. Butterleigh is south of Tiverton and west of Cullompton
Carp Stock: The pond mentioned has been well stocked with carp to double figure size
Category: Carp Water
Permits: Day tickets from E Berry, Billingsmoor Farm, Butterleigh. Tel: 01884 5248
Cost: About £2 per day
Control: Private
BK Rating: Thought to be Fairly Easy
E/A: South West
Comments: No close season. Two other ponds contain mixed coarse fish, on same ticket

Sunridge Nurseries A

Location: Worston, Yealmpton, off the A379 about eight miles west of Plymouth
Type and Size: Very small pond of about half an acre
Carp Stock: Well stocked with carp to 22lbs
Category: Mixed Fishery
Other Species: Roach and tench
Permits: On site. Tel: 01752 880438
BK Rating: Moderate
E/A: South West
Comments: Fishing lodge to rent - an attractive converted barn with two bedrooms

Swimbridge Pool

Location: Swimbridge, near Barnstaple
Type and Size: Small quarry
Carp Stock: Quite well stocked with carp to doubles
Other Species: Tench, bream, rudd and perch
Permits: Barnstaple and District AA. Visitors tickets from local tackle shops, who give details of membership
Control: Club
Restrictions: Members only weekends and Bank Holidays; visitors' tickets week days only
BK Rating: Moderate
E/A: South West

The Blue Lake A

Location: South Tawton, Okehampton
Type and Size: Deep old limestone quarry, dug in 1903
How to Find: Enquire from owners
Carp Stock: Many carp of 1 lb to 5 lbs. Some bigger fish to 23 lbs
Category: Carp Water
Other Species: Rudd
Permits: From owners Andy Spencer (Tel: 01203 422248) or Brad Green (01203 465403
Cost: £12 per 24 hours or £8 per day
Control: Private
Restrictions: No particle baits. Barbless hooks only
BK Rating: Easy
Baits/Methods: Boilies, bread and luncheon meat
E/A: South West
Comments: P.M. controlled this beautiful clear lake for many years - it was his first syndicate water, and he stocked it in 1972. At that time it only contained very large brown trout. He spent many happy hours fishing it, and had huge catches of carp, including two of over 20 lbs. The new owners are looking after it very well, and it is strongly recommended. Bivvies, long stay and night fishing welcome. Toilet and fishing hut. Open April to September. Caravan accommodation.

Tinney Waters A

Location: Pyworthy, Holsworthy EX22 6LF
Type and Size: Thee small lakes
How to Find: From Holsworthy take Bodmin Street, and after about 3 miles, and past a white house, take the second turning marked 'Whitstone 4 miles'. After a mile, turn right, and then left in three-quarters of a mile
Carp Stock: Well stocked with carp between 5lbs and 10lbs, with some much bigger mirrors and commons to over 20lbs
Category: Mixed Fishery
Other Species: Rudd, tench and trout
Permits: Jeff and Jane Mason at the address above. Tel: 01409 27362 (North Tamerton)
Restirctions: Fishing probably only for those staying on site. No tiger nuts or peanuts
BK Rating: Easy
E/A: South West
Comments: Two 6-berth static caravants to rent, or B and B in house - evening meals if required; full English breakfast at £2.95. Send for brochure. Caravan costs; from £95 per week to £195 a week; B and B from £14.50 per person per night; fishing included in all prices. Weekend breaks. Open all year

Trago Mills

Location: On the Newton Abbot - Bovey Tracey Road
Type and Size: Small lake
Carp Stock: Well stocked with carp to double figures
Category: Mixed Fishery
Other Species: Rudd, roach, bream, and tench
Permis: The Warden on site; Geoff Mole. Tel 01626 821111
Cost: £3 per day; children and OAP's £2
Control: Trago Mills
Restrictions: Open March 1st to November 30th only, from 8.30am to 5pm
BK Rating: Not known
E/A: South West
Comments: Trago Mills is a large supermarket (see local papers for publicity)

Upham Farm

Location: Upham Farm, Farringdon, Exeter
Type and Size: 6 small farm ponds
How to Find: Farringdon is 6 miles of Exeter on the A3052 Exeter-Sidmouth road
Carp Stock: Plenty of carp - many doubles to 24lbs
Category: Carp Water
Other Species: Tench
Permits: J Willcocks, Upham Farm, Farringdon, Exeter. Tel: 01395 232247
Cost: Day tickets about £4. Concessions
Control: Private. J Willcocks 01395 232247
BK Rating: Moderate
E/A: South West
Restrictions: Night fishing must be booked in advance, no keepnets
Comments: No close season. Parties of 20 or more must book in advance

Upper Tamar

Location: Between Holsworthy and Bideford, North Devon
Type and Size: Reservoir of 40 acres
How to Find: Turn off the A39 Bideford to Bude road at Kirkhampton and proceed towards Bradworthy Cross. The water will bee seen on the right. The car park is the south of the lake

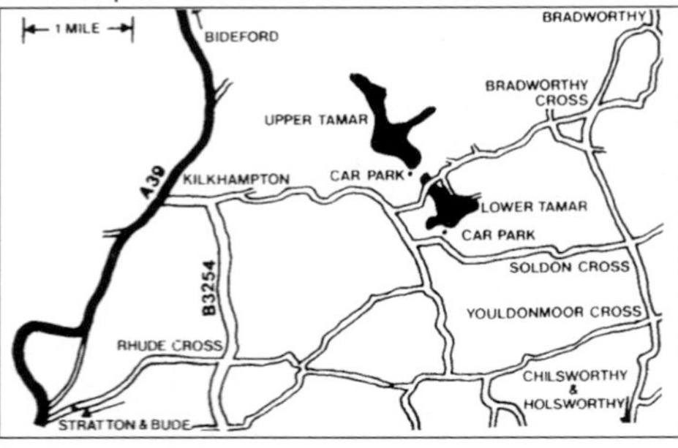

Carp Stock: Well stocked with carp to 28lbs. Restocked in 1991 with commons to 26 1/2 lbs
Category: Mixed Fishery
Other Species: Tench, bream, roach and rudd
Permits: Day or day and night permits from the self service unit on the car park: The Tackle Box, Kings Shopping Centre, Cooper Street, Bideford. Tel: 01237 470043: Summerlands Tackle, Golflinks Road, Westward Ho. Tel: 01237 471291. Clive's Tackle and Bait, 182 Exeter Street, Plymouth. Tel: 01752 228940. Season permits from the ranger at Upper Tamar Lake.

Tel: 01288 82262

Cost: £4 per day; £65 per season. Concessions
Control: Peninsula Coarse Fisheries. Tel: 01837 871565
E/A: South West
BK Rating: Moderate
Restrictions: No cereal based groundbaits except swimfeeders. No keepnets for carp. Barbless hooks requested. Permits must be obtained before fishing
Comments: NO CLOSE SEASON. Night fishing is now allowed. Long stay carp anglers generally do well

Upton Lake

Location: Cullompton
Type and Size: 2 acre farm pond with island
Carp Stock: Well stocked with carp averaging about 5 lbs
Category: Mixed Fishery
Other Species: Tench, crucians, roach, bream, perch and rudd
Permis: On bank
Cost: £3.50 per day; £2.50 juniors
Control: Tel: 01884 33097
Restrictions: No night fishing; barbless hooks
BK Rating: Not known
E/A: South West
Comments: Toilet

Valley View Fishery

Location: Near the Pathfinder Holiday Village, Tedburn St. Mary, near Crediton
Type and Size: Four pools of about an acre each
Carp Stock: Heavily stocked with carp only, mostly small, but some doubles
Category: Carp only
Permits: In advance only from local tackle shops
Cost: £18 per season, to include other club waters
Control: Tiverton D.A.A. Tel: 01884 242275
Restrictions: No night fishing; no keepnets; barbless hooks; no boilies
BK Rating: Easy
E/A: South West
Comments: Locked gate; club key required

Venn Pool

Location: Near Barnstaple, North Devon
Type and Size: Small and very deep quarry
Carp Stock: Well stocked with carp to upper doubles
Category: Mixed Fishery
Other Species: Tench, bream, rudd, perch
Permits: Barnstaple and District AA. Martin Turner, 67 Taw View, Freminton, Barnstaple. Visitors' tickets from local tackle shops
Control: Club
Restrictions: Visitors' tickets weekdays only; members only on weekends and Bank Holidays
BK Rating: Moderate
E/A: South West

West Pitt Farm Fishery A

Location: Uplowman, Tiverton, North Devon EX16 7DU
Type and Size: Three farm ponds, the biggest one and a quarter acres
How to Find: Village near Tiverton, 2½ miles from the M5
Carp Stock: Well stocked with carp to 21½ lbs

Category: Mixed Fishery
Other Species: Tench, rudd, roach, bream, chub, perch and crucians
Permis: Self-service ticket machine
Cost: £3.50 dawn till dusk
BK Rating: Fairly Hard
Control: Private. Tel: 01884 820296
Baits/Methods: Normal carp methods
E/A: South West
Comments: Self catering accommodation in cottages and lodge. Indoor heated swimming pool and sauna; tennis and games room. Groundbaiting limited. No close season. Brochure available. Open all year. Barbless hooks. No boilies

West View Pond

Location: Ottery St.Mary, near Exeter
Type and Size: Five acre lake
Carp Stock: Plenty of small carp
Category: Mixed Fishery
Other Species: Rudd and roach
Permits: Members only water of Exeter and District AA. Secretary: D Cornish, 9 Denmark Road, Exeter. Tel: 01392 56770; also from tackle shops in Exeter, Newton Abbot and Torquay
Cost: £20 a year, open to all
Control: Club
BK Rating: Easy
E/A: South West
Comments: Membership includes a number of other carp waters. Normal close season

Willowfield Lake Cottages A

Location: Saunton, N.Devon - 2 miles from Saunton beach
Type and Size: $1\frac{1}{2}$ acre attractive lake in 12 acres of grounds
Carp Stock: Stocked with carp to 15 lbs
Category: Mixed Fishery
Other Species: Roach and tench
Permits: Fishing for cottage residents only
Cost: Free to guests
Control: Tel: 01271 814346 / 7
BK Rating: Not known
E/A: South West
Comments: Self-catering cottages. Heated indoor swimming pool, games room and solarium

Wiscombe Park A

Location: Southleigh, Colyton, Devon, EX13 6JE, between Seaton and Honiton
Type and Size: $\frac{1}{2}$ acre pond
Carp Stock: Some carp, sizes and numbers not known
Category: Mixed Fishery
Other Species: Tench and bream
Permits: From the above address. Tel: 01404 871474
Cost: Free with accommodation
Control: Sara Chichester, Wiscombe Park
BK Rating: Not known
E/A: South West
Comments: 600 acre estate in beautiful valley - self-catering flats. Two small trout lakes. Probably open all year

DORSET

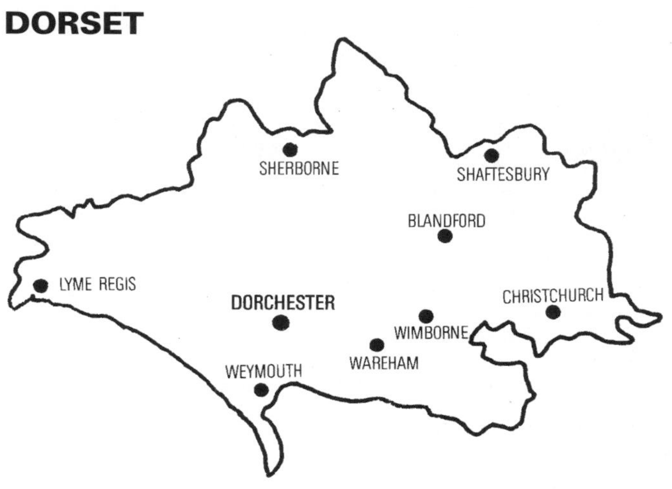

Blashford Lakes

Location: Off the A338 near Christchurch
Type and Size: Two lakes, one large, and one small, which contain carp
Carp Stock: Spinnaker Lake (large) - well stocked with carp, average low doubles. Roach Pit - few carp to 29lbs
Category: Spinnaker - Carp Water; Roach Pit - Few Carp
Other Species: Roach Pit - Roach, pike, tench, chub and bream
Permits: Members only water of Christchurch AC; R Andrews, 4 Marley Close, New Milton, Hants
Cost: £54 per season, to include many other waters
Control: Club
Restrictions: No night fishing; some parts of the bank are out of bounds; locked gate open with club key for members only; no day tickets; fishing allowed to 11pm on Roach Pit
BK Rating: Moderate
E/A: Wessex

Butterwick Farm — A

Location: Butterwick Farm, Holnest, near Sherborne
Type and Size: Half acre farm pond
How to Find: Near Sherborne
Carp Stock: Up to 6lbs, well stocked
Category: Mixed Fishery
Other Species: Tench, rudd, eels
Permits: From Mrs Vickery. No day tickets
Cost: Price on application
BK Rating: Easy/Moderate
Control: Private
Baits/Methods: General angling baits and methods
E/A: Wessex
Comments: This lake can only be fished by those who book mobile homes - no other permits available. Some accommodation in the farmhouse

Crooked Willows

Location: Holt Road, Mannington, near Ringwood
Type and Size: One acre attractive pool with island
Carp Stock: Carp to lower doubles
Category: Mixed Fishery
Other Species: Crucians, roach, rudd, perch, bream, tench and chub
Permits: In advance only from Minster Sports, Wimborne Minster
Cost: £4 per day; £2 juniors
Control: Tel: 01202 882240
Restrictions: No carp over 3 lbs in nets; no night fishing; barbless hooks
BK Rating: Not known
E/A: Wessex

Crow Pool

Location: Ibsley Pools, near Christchurch, just off the A38
Type and Size: Small, irregularly shaped pool alongside the Ibsley Trout Stream off the Avon
Carp Stock: Well stocked with carp from 10-18lbs - about 20-30 doubles
Category: Mixed Fishery
Other Species: Chub, dace, perch, pike, roach, rudd and tench
Permits: Members only water of Christchurch AC; C Bungay, 8 Purewell, Christchurch or P Reading, 17 Mayford Road, Poole, Dorset; details and some tickets from Ringwood Tackle, Ringwood.
Cost: No day tickets £54 per season, to include many other waters
Control: Club
Restrictions: No night fishing; no cars before 9am; lakeside car park for disabled anglers only
BK Rating: Moderate
E/A: Wessex

Dorset Springs Fishery

Location: Sturminster Marshall, off the A350 west of Wimborne
Type and Size: Three acre lake
Carp Stock: Well stocked with carp from 7lbs to 25lbs
Category: Mixed Fishery
Other Species: Big pike, crucians, grass carp, tench, bream, roach and rudd
Permits: Day tickets on site at £5 for one rod; £6 for two
Control: Tel: 01258 857653
Restrictions: No barbed or bent hooks. No hooks larger than size 4. No keepnets or carp sacks. No nuts. Night fishing by arrangement only
BK Rating: Moderate
E/A: Wessex

Gold Oak Farm

Location: Cranbourne - off the B 3078
Type and Size: Seven small pools
Carp Stock: Well stocked with carp to 15 lbs
Category: Mixed Fishery
Other Species: Tench, perch, roach, chub, small bream, crucians and barbel
Permits: On bank
Cost: £5 per day; juniors £3. £10 per night
Control: Tel: 01725 517275
Restrictions: No groundbaiting with boilies. No carp over 3 lbs in keepnets; barbless hooks only
BK Rating: Easy

E/A: Southern
Comments: Toilet on site

Harrow Pond

Location: Harrow Lodge, Holmesley, near Christchurch
Type and Size: Small forest pool
Carp Stock: A few carp to 22lbs
Category: Few Carp
Other Species: Pike, roach and tench
How to Find: Take the Lyndhurst road from Christchurch (A35), and turn left just after the Cat and Fiddle pub, then turn first right up Harrow Hill. A white house - Beech House Lodge - is on the right, and the entrance to the pond is 100yds further on left
Permits: Members only water of Christchurch AC; R Andrews, 4 Marley Close, New Milton, Hants
Cost: £80 per season, to include many other waters
Restrictions: No night fishing; members only; locked gate with key; no litter; carp must not be retained in keepnets or sacks; no access in close season
BK Rating: Difficult
E/A: Wessex

Hermitage Coarse Lake

Location: Off the B 3146 at Hermitage, near Sherborne
Type and Size: Tiny pool in the garden of a house
Carp Stock: Heavily stocked with small carp to 10 lbs
Category: Carp Only
Other Species: None
Permits: From the fishing hut, but advance booking is advised
Cost: About £5 per day; £3 half day
Control: Tel: 01963 210856
Restrictions: No night fishing; no high protein baits; no keepnets
BK Rating: Easy
Baits/Methods: Sweetcorn and luncheon meat are good baits
E/A: Wessex

Hillview Farm Lake

Location: Hillview Farm, Corfe Mullen
Type and Size: Sheltered farm lake of two acres
Carp Stock: Heavily stocked with carp from 4lbs to 20lbs
Category: Carp Water
Other Species: Crucians, tench and perch
Permits: Day tickets from farmhouse. Tel: 01258 857238
Cost: £4 per day; £2 half day
Control: Private
Restrictions: 8am till dusk fishing only
BK Rating: Easy
E/A: Wessex

Holtwood Ponds

Location: Holtwood, Horton, near Wimborne
Type and Size: Three small forest-type ponds
How to Find: Take the B3078 from Wimborne towards Cranborne
Carp Stock: All three ponds are well stocked with small carp, mostly 5-9lbs and possibly commons

Category:	Upper Pond - Carp Only; Middle Pond - Carp Water; Lower Pond - Mixed Fishery
Other Species:	Middle Pond - tench; Lower Pond - crucians, rudd and tench
Permits:	Members only water of Christchurch AC; R Andrews, 4 Marley Close, New Milton, Hants
Cost:	£54 per season, to include many other waters
Restrictions:	Members only; barbless hooks only; no night fishing - open 6am to 11pm only; carp must not be put in sacks or keepnets; no picnics; no groundbait; entrance gate must be kept locked at all times; arrive and depart quietly
BK Rating:	Easy
E/A:	Wessex

Hyde Lake

Location:	Hyde, near Wareham
Type and Size:	One and a half acre lake
How to Find:	5 miles from Wareham, just off the Bovington to Wareham road
Carp Stock:	Stocked with mirrors and commons to 20lbs. Good head of carp
Category:	Mixed Fishery
Other Species:	Tench, roach, rudd and crucians
Permits:	Hyde AC. Secretary: Jim Bagley, Heather Lodge, Hyde, near Wareham. Tel: Bere Regis 471402 or Bindon Abbey 463127
Cost:	About £20 per season
BK Rating:	Moderate
Control:	Club/syndicate
Restrictions:	None
E/A:	Wessex
Comments:	Night fishing allowed. 3 rods also allowed. Quiet countryside lake, very peaceful surroundings

Kingsbridge Lakes

Location:	Near Wareham, on a complex of trout waters
Type and Size:	Old pit of about six acres
Carp Stock:	Well stocked with carp to over 15lbs with quite a few doubles
Category:	Mixed Fishery
Other Species:	Roach and bream
Permits:	Members only water of Dumbourne and District AC. Season tickets only from local tackle shops
Control:	Club
BK Rating:	Easy
E/A:	Wessex

Lakeside **A**

Location:	Dorset
Type and Size:	Small lake
Carp Stock:	Well stocked with carp
Category:	Not known
Other Species:	Possibly some
Permits:	From owner
Cost:	Not known
Control:	Tel: 01425 663383
BK Rating:	Not known
E/A:	Wessex
Comments:	2 berth caravan by lake, with fishing

Luckfield Lake

Location: Watergates Lane, Broadmayne, near Dorchester
Type and Size: Clay pit of about 1 1/4 acres
How to Find: On the B352 Dorchester to Wareham Road, about 3 miles from Dorchester

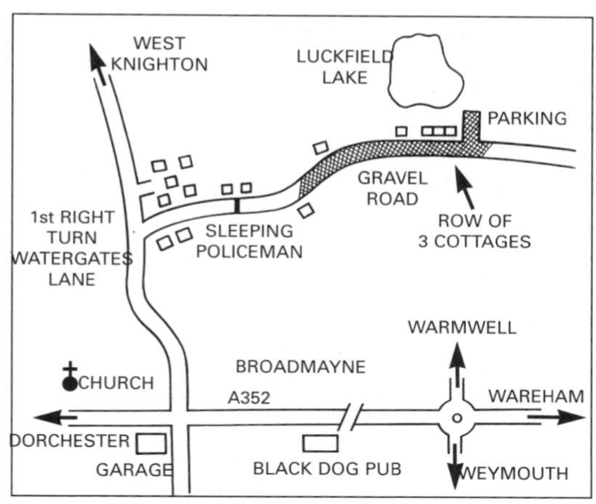

Carp Stock: Good head of mirrors to about 18lbs. Three fish of 20lbs+
Category: Carp Water
Other Species: Tench and roach to over 2lbs
Permits: Only from John Aplin Specialist Angling Supplies, 1 Athelstan Road, Dorchester. Tel: 01305 266500 in advance only
Cost: £4.50 per day; £6.50 per night. £55 per season
BK Rating: Easy
Control: Private
Baits/Methods: Bottom baits at night; floaters during the day
E/A: South West
Comments: A peaceful, attractive water in natural surroundings with overhanging trees. Barbless hooks. Open June 16th to March 14th

Martin's Farm

Location: New Road, Verwood, near Ringwood
Type and Size: 2 1/2 acre lake
How to Find: Take the A 31 west from Ringwood, then the B 3081 to Verwood, then left into Woodlands Road and New Road
Carp Stock: Well stocked with small carp to about 4 lbs
Category: Mixed Fishery
Other Species: Tench, perch, roach, crucians and eels
Permits: On site
Cost: £5 per day; £2.50 evenings and juniors
Control: Private. Tel: 01202 822335
Restrictions: No hemp
BK Rating: Moderate
Baits/Methods: Luncheon meat and sweetcorn best
E/A: Southern

Moor Valley Country Park

Location: Horton Road, Ashley Heath, near Ringwood
Type and Size: Long narrow river fed lake
Carp Stock: Carp to 20 lbs
Category: Mixed Fishery
Other Species: Tench, trout, pike, dace, perch, roach and eels
Permits: On site
Cost: About £3 per day; concessions
Control: Warden's Office. Tel: 01425 470721
Restrictions: No cereal groundbait; no keepnets; no floating baits; barbless hooks only
BK Rating: Not known
E/A: Wessex

New Meadows Lake

Location: Off the Christchurch to Lymington road (A337), turning right up New Road and Smugglers Copse Way, close to the bowling green
Carp Stock: Well stocked with carp to 15lbs
Category: Mixed Fishery
Other Species: Roach, perch and bream
Permits: Members only water of Christchurch AC. R Andrews, 4 Marley Close, New Milton, Hants
Cost: £54 per season, to include many other waters
Restrictions: Members only; no night fishing
BK Rating: Not known
E/A: Wessex

Osmington Mills Lake A

Location: Osmington Mills is by the sea, just off the A353 between Weymouth and Wareham. Turn off the main road at Osmington about 4 miles from Weymouth
Type and Size: Two acre gravel pit
Carp Stock: Many carp, average 10-13lbs, quite a few doubles to 19lbs and said to be two thirties
Category: Mixed Fishery
Other Species: Tench, roach, rudd, perch and crucians
Control: Private: Tel: 01305 832311
Permits: Tackle dealer L Rathbone, The Tackle Shop, West Bay, Bridport, Tel: 01308 23475. Also on bank and The Ranch House, Caravan Park, Osmington Mills
Cost: £4 per day
Restrictions: No night fishing; barbless hooks
BK Rating: Easy
E/A: Wessex
Comments: Busy in summer, fishes well in winter. Accommodation. Fishing for residents only. Toilet

Pallington Lakes

Location: Tincleton, near Dorchester
Type and Size: Lake of about 7 acres
How to Find: Off the B3390 at Waddock Cross, 7 miles east of Dorchester
Carp Stock: Many small mirrors and commons. A few low doubles. Lake record is a common of 19lbs 4ozs
Category: Mixed Fishery
Other Species: Tench to over 7lbs; roach, chub, perch and bream
Permits: On site to be purchased before fishing. Tel: 01305 848141

Cost: £4.50 per day
BK Rating: Moderate
Control: Private
E/A: Wessex
Comments: Fishing 8am to dusk only - open all year

Radipole Lake

Location: In the town of Weymouth
Type and Size: Very large lake close to the sea (70 acres plus)
How to Find: Weymouth
Carp Stock: Some commons to about 10lbs. Bigger fish rumoured but hard to find possibly up to 26lbs, but we are told this was 60 years ago! A 33lb mirror was caught in 1990 and an upper 40 in 1992
Category: Few Carp
Other Species: Eels, roach, dace and mullet
Permits: Day tickets from tackle shops in Weymouth
Control: Local council
BK Rating: Difficult
E/A: Wessex
Comments: Not seriously fished for carp, but might contain a few good fish. Boats, amusements, people, refreshments, etc especially at south end nearest town. No fishing in bird sanctuary. 1996 reports suggest there are now many carp in the lake

Revells Farm **A**

Location: Cosmore, Dorchester, DT2 7TW
Type and Size: Six small lakes - about an acre each
How to Find: On the old Sherborne road about 8 miles from Dorchester
Carp Stock: All varieties to 26lb in top pond. Small carp in other ponds; one lake doubles only
Category: Mixed Fishery
Other Species: Bream, tench, chub, perch, rudd and roach
Permits: Obtainable from shop on site, or on bank. Tel: 01300 345301 or 01935 78526
Cost: £4 per day;
BK Rating: Easy
Control: Private
E/A: Wessex
Comments: Pleasant surroundings. Accommodation available. Tackle for sale. Chalet type mobile homes. Open all year. Colour brochure. Toilet

River Stour

Location: Different sections of the lower Stour
Type and Size: Famous river where most fish grow very big
Carp Stock: Not known, but big carp reported from time to time - a 16 lb was caught on luncheon meat in 1990, and the same angler had caught other Stour carp to 15lbs
Other Species: Most of them, including big barbel and chub
Permits: Local angling clubs - enquire in tackle shops for information and permits, especially in Christchurch
BK Rating: Difficult, though once the carp are located, they can be quite easy to catch, as few have been taken before
E/A: Wessex

Throop Fisheries

Location: 2 1/2 miles from Christchurch Station
Type and Size: Dorset Stour and a mill pool
Carp Stock: Well stocked with carp to 25lbs
Category: Mixed Fishery
Other Species: Pike to nearly 30lb, barbel to 13 1/2 lbs, chub to over 7lbs, and roach to 3 3/4 lbs; some bream in mill pool
Permits: Glen Sutcliffe, Manager, South Lodge, Holdenhurst Village, Bournemouth. Tel: 01202 35532
Cost: Day tickets £5; weekly tickets £20; season £60
Control: Private
BK Rating: Moderate
E/A: Southern
Comments: Throop is a famous fishery, with 5 1/2 miles of the River Stour and the mill pool. All species run to a very big size. Reduced rate for juniors and OAP's and special rates for clubs - booking essential

Warmwell Leisure Centre **A**

Location: Between Bournemouth and Weymouth
Type and Size: Two lakes
Carp Stock: Well stocked with carp to over 40 lbs
Category: Mixed Fishery
Other Species: General coarse fish
Permits: Tel: 01305 852911
Cost: On application
Control: Leisure Centre
BK Rating: Moderate
W / A: Wessex
Comments: Self-catering cabins. Indoor fun pool. Ski slope. Roller skating. Gym.Restaurant and club house. Family entertainment programme. Send for free colour brochure.

Linear Fisheries Oxford

31lb 6oz Manor Farm Lake

Wedgehill Ponds

Location: Verwood, near Ringwood

Type and Size: Three small forest ponds close to disused railway line - possibly old ballast pits

How to Find: From Christchurch take the B3081 to Verwood, and turn left down Manor Road, then right into Church Hill and Margards Lane. Then turn left into Horton Way, and after going under the railway bridge turn right at the T-junction, and the ponds are at the end of the lane - 10mph speed limit

Carp Stock: Well stocked with carp from 4-6lbs

Category: Mixed Fishery

Other Species: Goldfish, golden rudd, crucians and tench
Permits: Members only water of Christchurch AC; R Andrews, 4 Marley Close, New Milton, Hants
Cost: £54 per season, to include many other waters
Restrictions: Members only; barbless hooks; no carp to be put in sacks or keep nets; no night fishing - fishing is 6am to 11pm only; one rod only; gate must be locked at all times; quiet arrival and leaving essential
BK Rating: Easy
E/A: Wessex

Whitemoor Lake

Location: Off the B 3072 road near Three - Legged Cross
Type and Size: Two acre newly dug lake with islands
Carp Stock: Stocked with small carp
Category: Mixed Fishery
Other Species: Carp, tench, bream, roach, rudd, crucians, koi and goldfish
Permits: Day tickets from Paul Miller
Cost: £5 per day; £3 half day, juniors and O.A.P's
Control: Tel: 01202 581562
Restrictions: No keepnets or barbed hooks
BK Rating: Not known
E/A: Southern

DURHAM

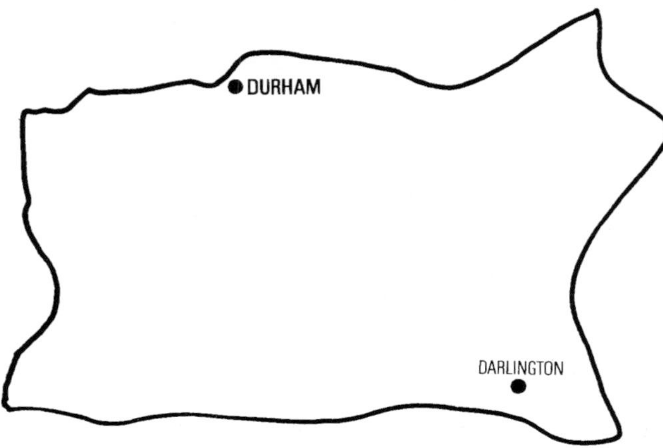

Beaumont Fisheries

Location: Trimdon Station, Wingate
Type and Size: 2 acre lake with islands
Carp Stock: Well stocked with carp to doubles
Category: Mixed Fishery
Other Species: Crucians, tench, roach and rudd
Permits: From bailiff on site
Cost: About £5 per day; £3 for the evening
Control: Tel: 01429 838274
Restrictions: No night fishing
BK Rating: Not known
E/A: Northumbrian
Comments: Probably open all year

Brasside Pool

Location: Newton Hall, Brasside, near Durham
Type and Size: Eight acre, weedy lake, with depths up to 10 feet, and gravel bars in one area
Carp Stock: Well stocked with smallish carp, mostly 4 to 9lbs, a few low doubles, including some commons
Category: Mixed Fishery
Other Species: Roach, bream, tench and pike
Permits: Members only water of Durham City AC - try local tackle shops
Cost: About £35 per year. Concessions
Control: Durham City AC. Open to all - Secretary: G Hedley, 3 Hawthorn Crescent, Durham. Tel: 01207 232401
Restrictions: Members only
BK Rating: Moderate
Comments: There is no close season on this water, and it fishes well all the year

Edmondsley Pond

Location: Chester - le - Street
Type and Size: Small pool
How to Find: Follow signs from Chester-le-Street to Waldridge; the fishery is 400 yards after the village on the left

Carp Stock: Small carp averaging about 5 lbs
Category: Mixed Fishery
Other Species: Roach, crucians, perch, tench and small bream
Permits: In advance only
Cost: £24 per season; £6 for juniors
Control: Tel: 0191 373 6325 - Langley Park A.C.
BK Rating: Not known
E/A: Yorkshire
Comments: Probably open all year

Fieldson Pond

Location: Shildon, near Aycliffe
Type and Size: 1½ acre pond with islands
How to Find: Take the A 68 towards Shildon, then the A 6072. Turn left after Redworth Hall
Carp Stock: Fairly well stocked with carp to upper doubles
Category: Mixed Fishery
Other Species: Rudd, perch, roach, tench, dace, chub and eels
Permits: Day tickets from Bert Sowerby. Tel: 01388 775044
Cost: £3 per day, weekdays only. Season tickets £20 per season Ladies and juniors £8; O.A.P's and disabled £14
Control: Ferryhill D.A.C. Tel: 0191 388 3557
Restrictions: Night fishing by arrangement. Limited bivvies
BK Rating: Not known
E/A: Yorkshire
Comments: Some grass carp

Fighting Cocks Reservoir

Location: Middleton St George, Darlington
Type and Size: Two lakes, about 10 acres in all
Carp Stock: Carp to about 15lbs; well stocked with fish from 5-8lbs
Category: Mixed Fishery
Other Species: Perch, roach, bream
Permits: On bank at £2 per day, or from W P Adams Fishing Tackle, 42 Duke Street, Darlington Tel: 01325 468069
Cost: Day tickets £2. Annual permits £20 + 50p each visit
BK Rating: Moderate
E/A: Northumbrian

Greencroft Pond

Location: Greencroft Industrial Estate, Annfield Plain, off the A 693 near Stanley
Type and Size: One acre lake
Carp Stock: Small carp
Category: Mixed Fishery
Other Species: Perch, roach, rudd and gudgeon
Permits: In advance only
Cost: £7 per season; £3 juniors - includes other waters
Control: Schmitz Cargoball A.C. Tel: 01207 282786
Restrictions: No barbed hooks
BK Rating: Not known
E/A: Northumbrian
Comments: Former Fire Brigade emergency water source

Halneby Lake

Location: Middleton Tyas, south west of Darlington
Type and Size: Five and a half acre lake
Carp Stock: Very well stocked with carp to 10lbs
Category: Mixed Fishery
Other Species: Bream, roach and tench
Permits: W P Adams Fishing Tackle, 42 Duke Street, Darlington. Tel: 01325 468069
Cost: About £35 per season
Control: Yarm AA - members only
BK Rating: Easy
E/A: Yorkshire
Comments: Carp growing well. Attractive water with good potential

Kellow Law Pond

Location: Deaf Hill, which we think is near Ferryhill, on the A167 between Darlington and Durham
Type and Size: Small pond
Carp Stock: Some commons
Category: Mixed Fishery
Other Species: Crucians, perch and rudd
Permits: Mr Barry Hignett. Tel: 01913 883557
Control: Senior members of the Ferryhill and District AC
BK Rating: Not known
E/A: Northumbrian

Middleton Water Park

Location: Middleton St George, Darlington
Type and Size: Three unused Victorian reservoirs
Carp Stock: Some carp to about 10lbs
Category: Mixed Fishery
Permits: From the bailiff on site, or from the Parish Clerk, 8 Grendon Gardens, Middleton St. George, Darlington. Tel: 01325 332894
Cost: £2.50 per rod per day (£1.50 for children). Annual permits also available
Control: Council
BK Rating: Not known
E/A: Northumbrian
Comments: Contains roach, tench and perch

Shotton Pond

Location: Shotton Colliery, just off the A19 south of Peterlee, between Hartlepool and Sunderland
Type and Size: Four and a half acre lake
Carp Stock: Carp to nearly 20lbs
Category: Mixed Fishery
Other Species: Crucians, rudd, roach, tench, perch and bream
Permits: Limited day tickets from A and M Insurance, Friar Street, Shotton Colliery Tel: 0191 5861642
Cost: About £2 per day; £20 per season. Concessions
Control: Shotton Colliery AC; Mr Ian Proudfoot, 19 Lincoln Walk, Great Lumley, Chester-le-Street. Tel: 0191 3982325 (after 6pm)
BK Rating: Not known
E/A: Northumbrian
Comments: No night fishing. Disabled access

Tilery Lake

Location: Wingate
Type and Size: 5 acre pool with island
How to Find: Turn off the B 1280 near Station Town
Carp Stock: Carp to mid - doubles
Category: Mixed Fishery
Other Species: Roach, perch, tench, bream, rudd and gudgeon
Permits: In advance only from local tackle shops
Cost: £2.50 per day; £20 per season plus £10 joining fee
Control: Hartlepool D.A.C. Tel: 01642 562275
BK Rating: Not known
E/A: Northumbrian

Turnside Pool

Location: Ferryhill, near Durham
Type and Size: Attractive one acre pool, very weedy and heavily fished
Carp Stock: There are only a small number of carp, but they go to over 20lbs
Category: Few Carp
Other Species: Roach, tench and perch
Permits: Try local tackle shops for club membership - no day tickets
Control: Ferryhill and District AC. Secretary: A Roxley, 60 Linden Road, West Cornforth, County Durham. Tel: 0191 3883557
Restrictions: Members only; one rod only; no multiple baits; no night fishing
BK Rating: Very Difficult
E/A: Northumbrian

Wellfield Pond

Location: Wingate on the B1280 between Hartlepool and Shotton Colliery
Type and Size: Small pond
Carp Stock: Some carp
Category: Mixed Fishery
Other Species: Bream, tench, rudd, roach and perch
Permits: Alan Blackmore, 17 Station Road South, Murton, Seaham SR7 9RS. Tel: 0191 5267327
Control: Easington and District AC; some guest permits
BK Rating: Not known
E/A: Northumbrian

West Farm Lake

Location: Off the A177 between Stockton and Sedgefield
Type and Size: Two acre lake, formerly a trout fishery
Carp Stock: Recently stocked with carp to 10lbs
Category: Mixed Fishery
Other Species: Tench, rudd and trout
Permits: On bank or at farmhouse
Cost: £3 per rod and £2 for OAP's and under twelves
Control: Tel: 01740 31045
Restrictions: Barbless hooks and no carp in nets. Night fishing by prior arrangement only
BK Rating: Not known
E/A: North West

DYFED (Wales)

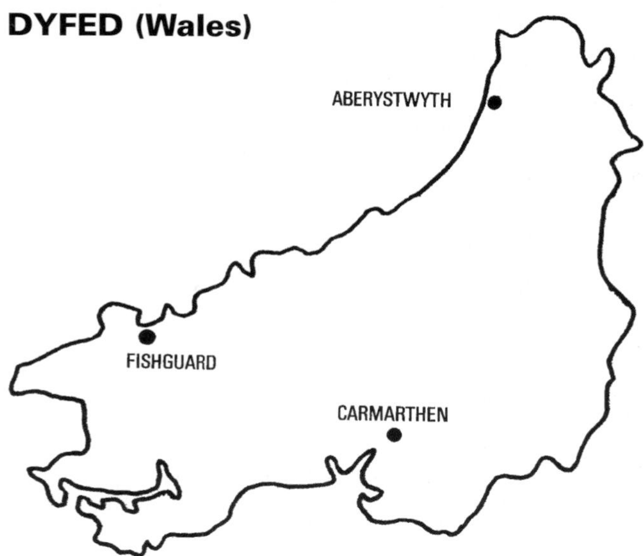

Glas-Llyn Fishery

Location: Fynnon-Las-Isaf, Blaenwaun, Whitland, SA34 OJH
Type and Size: Two acre lake
How to Find: Glas-Llyn is one mile from the village of Blaenwaun, 8 miles north of Whitland, and 5 miles east of Crymch
Carp Stock: Heavily stocked with carp to 20lbs
Category: Carp Water
Other Species: Tench to 8lbs; roach, rudd, trout
Permits: On bank
Cost: £5 per day - £3.50 juniors. £7 for 24 hours; £3.50 from 3pm
Control: Private; Terry and Gwen Forbes. Tel: 01994 (Hebron) 419466
Restrictions: Three rods only; no carp in keepnets; juniors must be accompanied by an adult. Barbless hooks. No night fishing
BK Rating: Not known
E/A: Welsh
Comments: Toilet, fisherman's hut, and ample parking space. A former trout fishery, Glas-Llyn is set in a picturesque valley with much wild life. The lake is spring fed and is 30 feet deep in places. This is one of the very few carp fisheries in West Wales, and as it has been little fished it could produce some surprises

Ludchurch Farm

Location: Ludchurch, Narbeth, near Tenby
Type and Size: 3 acre disused lime pit
Carp Stock: Some carp to lower doubles
Category: Mixed Fishery
Other Species: Rudd, perch and tench
Permits: From farm by lake
Cost: About £5 per day; £3 for evenings. Some concessions
Control: Tel: 01834 83255
Restrictions: No night fishing

BK Rating: Not known
Baits/Methods: Sweetcorn and luncheon meat are the best baits
E/A: Welsh
Comments: Toilets. Probably open all year

Nine Oaks A

Location: On the A 487 between Aberaeron and Newquay
Type and Size: One acre pool
How to Find: Two miles from Aberaeron towards Cardigan; turn left at crossroads by petrol station
Carp Stock: Well stocked with carp to 20 lbs
Category: Mixed Fishery
Other Species: Bream, roach and tench
Permits: On site
Cost: £5 per rod per day
Control: Nine Oaks Trout and Coarse Fishery, Oakford, near Aberaeron, SA47 0RW. Tel: 01545 580482
Restrictions: No night fishing; keepnets or groundbait. Barbless hooks
BK Rating: Not known
E/A: Welsh
Comments: Self-catering accommodation. Probably open all year. Fly fishing for trout also available

Roadside Farm

Location: Templeton, near Narbeth
Type and Size: Small irrigation reservoir
How to Find: Off the A 4115 road near Templeton
Carp Stock: Heavily stocked with small carp to about 6 lbs
Category: Mixed Fishery
Other Species: Small crucians and skimmers
Permits: On bank
Cost: About £4; £3 juniors and O.A.P's
Control: Tel: 01834 891283
Restrictions: No boilies; night fishing by arrangement only
BK Rating: Easy
E/A: Welsh
Comments: Probably open all year. Attractive countryside; organic farm

THE BEEKAY GUIDE TO 2000 BRITISH & EUROPEAN CARP WATERS

Is YOUR Water listed? If so, are the details correct?
If you spot omissions, inaccuracies, or know of any changes, please let us know by filling in the Waters Questionnaire at the back of this guide and return it to us at:

Beekay International
Withy Pool
Henlow Camp
Bedfordshire
SG16 6EA

Two Acre Lake

Location: Near Aberystwyth
Type and Size: Two small lakes
Carp Stock: Well stocked with carp to doubles
Category: Mixed Fishery
Other Species: Tench and roach
Permits: Tel: 0197 084239 for information and permits
BK Rating: Moderate
E/A: Welsh

White Springs

Location: Garrnwllt Road, Pontarddulais
Type and Size: 3 acre lake with islands
Carp Stock: Stocked with carp to mid - doubles
Category: Mixed Fishery
Other Species: Tench, bream, rudd, roach and crucians
Permits: On bank
Cost: £4 per day
Control: Tel: 01792 885699
Restrictions: No keepnets; barbless hooks
BK Rating: Not known
E/A: Welsh
Comments: Probably open all year. Toilets

EAST SUSSEX

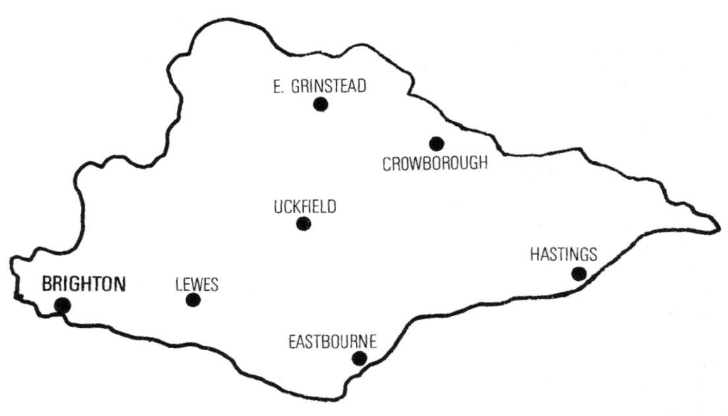

Bartley Mill Fishery

Location: Off the B2109 near Frant
Type and Size: Small pool with island
Carp Stock: Well stocked with small carp to about 8 lbs
Category: Mixed Fishery
Other Species: Tench and rudd
Permits: On bank
Costs: £5 for two rods; £25 per season
Control: Tel: 01892 891403
Restrictions: No night fishing
BK Rating: Easy
E/A: Southern
Comments: Any method and fly only trout lakes on site. Toilets. Disabled access

Belfrey Coarse Fishery

Location: Near Hailsham
Type and Size: Small, attractive lake
Carp Stock: Well stocked with carp to 26lbs
Category: Mixed Fishery
Other Species: Usual coarse fish
Permits: Day, night and evening tickets. Tel: 01323 841247/844238
BK Rating: Moderate
E/A: Southern
Comments: Camping allowed

Broomham Fishery

Location: White Hart pub, Catsfield, near Battle
Type and Size: Estate lakes of 4 acres and 2 acres
Carp Stock: Well stocked with carp to doubles
Category: Mixed Fishery
Other Species: Crucians, roach, rudd, tench and perch
Permits: In advance only
Cost: £32 per season

Control:	Hastings and Bexhill D.F.A.A. Tel: 01424 715218
Restrictions:	No night fishing
BK Rating:	Moderate
Baits/Methods:	Boilies are the best bait
E/A:	Southern

Buckshole Reservoir

Location:	Hastings, off the A2102 north
Type and Size:	Ten acre town reservoir
Carp Stock:	Well stocked with carp to over 30lbs
Category:	Mixed Fishery
Other Species:	Roach, bream, tench and pike
Permits:	Hastings and Bexhill DFAA
Control:	Club. Tel: 01424 715218. About £5 per day; £40 per season. Concessions
Restrictions:	No keepnets
BK Rating:	Moderate
E/A:	Southern

Buxted Oast Fishery

Location:	Off the A272 at Buxted, near Uckfield
Type and Size:	Quarter acre pond
Carp Stock:	Well stocked with carp to 20lbs, but mostly under 2lbs
Category:	Carp Water
Other Species:	Roach
Permits:	From farm shop
Control:	About £5 per day
Control:	Tel: 01825 734446
Restrictions:	No night fishing; barbless hooks
BK Rating:	Easy
E/A:	Southern
Comments:	Farm shop and toilet

Linear Fisheries Oxford

32lb 10 oz
Guy's Lakes

Buxted Park Fishery

Location: Buxted, near Uckfield
Type and Size: Attractive three and a half acre lake
Carp Stock: Well stocked with carp to 10lbs
Category: Mixed Fishery
Other Species: Tench, roach, rudd, perch and chub
Permits: Day tickets from Buxted Park Fishery, Buxted, near Uckfield, East Sussex. Tel: 01860 372625 (9am to 6pm) or 01825 812711 any time. Club bookings also available
BK Rating: Not known
E/A: Southern

Clive Vale and Ecclesbourne Reservoirs

Location: Hastings:
Type and Size: Small reservoirs
How to Find: In Hastings
Carp Stock: Well stocked with carp to 30lbs
Category: Mixed Fishery
Other Species: General coarse fish, including large pike
Permits: Hastings Clive Vale Angling Club. J Greenhalf, 33 Hollington Park Road, St Leonards-on-Sea, TN OSE. Try local tackle shops
Cost: About £4 per day. £23 per season
BK Rating: Moderate
Control: Club
Restrictions: No juveniles. Barbless hooks. Night fishing for members only
E/A: Southern
Comments: Enquire locally for more information

Decoy Lake

Location: Halland, near Lewes
Type and Size: Small lake
Carp Stock: Well stocked with carp to doubles
Category: Mixed Fishery
Other Species: Rudd and some others
Permits: In advance only from Percy's Tackle, Lewes
Cost: About £4 per day
Control: Tel: 01273 473207
BK Rating: Easy
E/A: Southern

Falkenvil Fishery

Location: Saltmarsh Lane, near Hailsham
Type and Size: 4 acre farm pool
How to Find: Take the B 2104 from Hailsham and turn right at the garage into Saltmarsh Lane
Carp Stock: Well stocked with carp to upper doubles
Category: Mixed Fishery
Other Species: Tench, roach and chub
Permits: On bank
Cost: £6 per day
Control: Tel: 01323 847445
Restrictions: No boilies; no night fishing; no keepnets; barbless hooks only
BK Rating: Moderate
E/A: Southern
Comments: On site toilet. Some of the carp are said to be wildies, but other carp have been stocked

Farthings Lake

Location: Near Battle, Hastings
Type and Size; Estate lake of three acres
How to Find: Take the B2095 west from Battle towards Catsfield and Bexhill. After about 1 1/2 miles you will see a track on the right marked 'Millers Farm'. The footpath to the lake is opposite this. The car park is a further 100 yards on the right
Carp Stock: Some carp, sizes not known
Category: Mixed Fishery
Other Species: Tench, bream, roach and rudd
Permits: Tickets must be obtained before fishing. Season tickets from 6 Warwick Road, Bexhill-on-Sea, East Sussex. Tel: 0142 224908
Restrictions: No night fishing. Lake is open 8am till sunset. Season ticket holders may start at sunrise. No day tickets - syndicate only
BK Rating: Moderate
Control: Redland Angling Scheme
E/A: Southern
Comments: Attractive lake in beautiful wooded valley. If you want to start before 9am you will need to hold a season ticket. Information on 01424 420358. New unique match lake opened in June 1992, built in channels

Framfield Park Fishery

Location: Framfield, off the B 2192 near Uckfield
Type and Size: Three lakes of about 3 acres each
Carp Stock: Two lakes heavily stocked with carp to 8 lbs. The third has carp to 20 lbs
Category: Mixed Fishery
Other Species: Tench, golden orfe, roach, bream and perch
Permits: On site
Cost: About £6 per day; £4 evenings. Some concessions
Control: Tel: 01825 890948; 01323 430888 Fax: 01323 423412
Restrictions: Booking essential for Bury Wood Lake
BK Rating: Moderate
E/A: Southern
Comments: Toilets and refreshments

Furnace Brook Fishery

Location: Cowbeach, near Hailsham
Type and Size: 7 acre lake with island
Carp Stock: Well stocked with carp to 20 lbs
Category: Mixed Fishery
Other Species: Grass carp, perch, tench, roach, rudd and bream
Permits: On bank
Cost: £5 per day; £4 O.A.P's; £3 juniors
Control: Tel: 01435 830882
Restrictions: No peanuts or tiger nuts
BK Rating: Moderate
E/A: Southern

Furnace Pond

Location: Near East Grinstead
Type and Size: Seven acre estate lake
How to Find: Ordnance Survey Sheet No.187; Ref/348391
Carp Stock: Carp to 18lbs, with some low 20's
Category: Carp Water
Other Species: Some coarse fish
Permits: Wallington Specimen Group. No day tickets but season tickets at about £130, contact: Mrs A Yexley, 25 Oakley Road, South Norwood, London SE25
Control: Private
BK Rating: Easy
E/A: Southern

Hastings Lake

Location: In the town of Hastings
Type and Size: Ten acre lake
Carp Stock: Heavily stocked with carp to 10lbs
Category: Mixed Fishery
Other Species: Tench and pike
Permits: Local tackle shops, or the Secretary, Hastings, Bexhill and District FA, P K Jury, 5 Old Church Road, St Leonards, East Sussex
Cost: Day tickets at £1.25
Control: Club; season tickets £12-£13 only for those living within 25 miles of Hastings
BK Rating: Easy
E/A: Southern

Hurst Haven

Location: Rickney Bridge, north west of Pevensey off the Hailsham road
Type and Size: Narrow drain with sluice
Carp Stock: Not many carp, but some doubles
Category: Few Carp
Other Species: Bream, roach, tench and pike to 25lbs
Permits: Polegate Angling Centre, 101 Station Road, Polegate
Cost: £2 per day
Control: Hailsham AA. Tel: 01323 486379
Restrictions: No livebaiting (!)
BK Rating: Very Difficult
E/A: Southern

Iden Wood Fishery

Location: Coldharbour Lane off the A268 near Rye
Type and Size: Three small ponds, the largest of which is about two acres
Carp Stock: Well stocked with carp to about 20lbs; many doubles
Category: Mixed Fishery
Other Species: Perch, roach, bream and tench
Permits: On bank for day tickets; 24 hour tickets must be booked in advance
Cost: £4 per day; £6 for 24 hours. About £60 per season
Control: Tel: 0179 230241
BK Rating: Easy
E/A: Southern
Comments: No night fishing unless booked in advance; no close season

Lynd Farm Pond

Location: Near Haywards Heath
Type and Size: Small pond
Carp Stock: Well stocked with small carp to about 4lbs but growing
Category: Mixed Fishery
Other Species: Tench, roach and rudd
Permits: Tel: 01815 585718
Control: Private
BK Rating: Easy
E/A: Southern

Michelham Priory Moat

Location: Michelham Priory, Upper Dicker, Hailsham, near Eastbourne (off the A22 Eastbourne-East Grinstead road)
Type and Size: Possibly the largest moat in England, with several acres of water
Carp Stock: Carp to 10lbs, probably commons and possibly wildies
Category: Mixed Fishery
Other Species: Tench, roach, bream, rudd, pke and eels
Cost: £3.80 per day
Permits: Day tickets from the 14th century gatehouse
Control: Private
Restrictons: Thought to be no night fishing; no dogs. Fishing from 11am to 5.30pm
BK Rating: Not known
E/A: Southern
Comments: One of the most beautiful buildings and grounds in the country - an Augustinian Priory which dates from the 13th century, but which became a farmhouse at the Dissoluton of the Monasteries. There is an Elizabethan wing, and lovely gardens. There is a restaurant and halls for conferences and dinners, the specialities being home-made bread and cakes from their own baker, using flour ground in the Priory Water Mill, fed from the moat, and local ale, apple juice and Sussex wines. Art exhibitions etc are held in the house, which is open from 25th March until 31st October from 11am to 5.30pm, and on Sundays in February, March and November. Information at the address above. Tel: 01323 440161 or 01323 844224

Piltdown Pond

Location: Piltdown Common, near Newick, between Haywards Heath and Uckfield
Type and Size: Small common land pond
How to Find: Take the A272 from Maresfield towards Newick. Turn left at Piltdown Common. The pond is 100 yards further on the left
Carp Stock: Some carp to 10lbs

Category: Mixed Fishery
Other Species: General coarse fish
Permits: Free fishing
Cost: None
BK Rating: Difficult
E/A: Southern
Comments: Very heavily weeded pond - but worth a try, as there's not much free fishing these days!

Pippingford Park Estate Lakes

Location: Pippingford Corner, Nutley, near East Grinstead
Type and Size: Five man-made lakes of three quarter acre to five acres
How to Find: Take the A22 from East Grinstead towards Eastbourne. Estate is one mile before Nutley and Pippingford Corner. Entrance on left. Pathfinder OS Map Ref TQ43/53
Carp Stock: Army Lake (three quarters of an acre) - carp to 15lbs; Lake 1 (four acres) - 40 carp to 18lbs (average 8lbs); Lake 2 (as for Lake 1; Lake 3 (five acres) - many small commons to 15lbs; Lake 4 (three quarters of an acre) - very few small fish
Category: Carp Waters
Other Species: Many good chub to 5lbs; bream, tench, orfe
Permits: Richard Morris, Home Farm, Pippingford Park, Nutley TN22 3NW. Tel: 01825 712966
Cost: Senior - £120 per season
BK Rating: Army - Easy to Moderate. Others - Easy for small fish
Control: Pippingford Estate Co. Ltd
Restrictions: No carp sacks or keepnets
E/A: Southern
Comments: No day tickets. Half season tickets available. Camouflage clothing not advised as this is an army training area. A truly beautiful lake to fish, situated in Ashdown Forest in a peaceful wooded valley full of wild animals and rare plants. Weedy waters, excellent for stalking, 3 fish per day common, 7 to 8 a day possible. Army often on night manoeuvres - beware!

Searles Lake

Location: Near Nutley, off the A22 just south of Ashdown Forest (home of Winnie the Pooh)
Type and Size: Six acre estate lake, much used for match fishing
Carp Stock: Carp to 20lbs
Category: Mixed Fishery
Other Species: Roach, rudd, tench, bream and pike to 35lbs
Permits: Tanyard Fisheries, Tanyard Lane, Furners Green, Danehill, Uckfield. Tel: 01825 791010 (9am to 7pm only)
Cost: £6 - one rod; £10 for 2 rods, in advance only
Control: Private, although a club fishes one bank
Restrictions: Barbless hooks; no keepnets; no night fishing - open 8am till 9pm; no pike fishing until October 1st; 40 anglers only per day
BK Rating: Not known
E/A: Southern

Southbourne Lake

Location: Lottbridge Drove, Eastbourne
Type and Size: 3 acre lake
Carp Stock: Well stocked with carp to over 20 lbs, although most are small
Category: Mixed Fishery

Other Species: Roach, perch and bream
Permits: From the ticket kiosk
Cost: About £4; concessions
Control: Tel: 01323 520229
Restrictions: No keepnets; barbless hooks
BK Rating: Easy
E/A: Southern
Comments: The Eastbourne Miniature Steam Railway runs right round the lake! Toilets and cafe

Sparks Farm Fishery

Location: Cuckfield, near Haywards Heath
Type and Size: Farm pond with two islands
How to Find: Take the B2115 road from Cuckfield, and turn at the farm shop about one and a half miles from the village
Carp Stock: Well stocked with carp to doubles
Category: Carp Water
Other Species: Tench
Permits: Day tickets from the farm shop, or on the bank
Cost: £6 per day; £4.50 from 1pm; £3 from 5pm
Control: Tel: 01444 441511
Restrictions: No night fishing
BK Rating: Easy
E/A: Southern

Sparks Farm Pond

Location: Sparks Farm Shop, near Cuckfield
Type and Size: Two small lakes of two acres
Carp Stock: Heavily stocked with small carp to 2½ lbs
Category: Mixed Fishery
Other Species: Roach, rudd, perch, bream and crucians
Permits: Day tickets at Farm Shop. Tel: 01444 441511
Cost: £5 per day
BK Rating: Easy
E/A: Southern
Comments: Easy day ticket water, used for small matches

Tanyard Fisheries

Location: Tanyard Lane, off the A275 near Uckfield
Type and Size: Two lakes of one and a half and one acre
Carp Stock: Larger lake is a specialist carp water stocked with carp from 8lb to 20lb; smaller lake has carp to 15lbs
Category: Larger lake - Carp Water; small lake - Mixed Fishery
Other Species: Tench, roach, rudd, bream and perch
Permits: Day tickets on site
Cost: Carp Lake - £8 per day for two rods
Control: Tanyard Fisheries, Tanyard Lane, Furners Green, Danehill. Tel: 01825 791010 (between 9am to 7pm only)
BK Rating: Not known
E/A: Southern
Comments: No close season; trout fishing. Toilets and refreshment hut

Wilderness Lake

Location: Dormans Park, East Grinstead
Type and Size: Park lake, at the start of River Eden; main lake is five acres and a smaller lake of an acre
Carp Stock: Heavily stocked with carp of 2-3lbs, with some bigger to 10lbs
Category: Mixed Fishery
Other Species: Roach, rudd, and gudgeon
Permits: Isfield and District AS
Cost: £37.50 per year, plus an entrance fee
BK Rating: Easy
E/A: Southern

Wishing Tree Reservoir

Location: Near Hastings, off the B2092 towards Battle
Type and Size: Four acre reservoir
Carp Stock: Heavily stocked with carp to nearly 20lbs
Category: Mixed Fishery
Other Species: Tench and a few roach and perch
Permits: Day tickets on the bank at about £4. About £35 per season
Control: Hastings and Bexhill DAA. Peter Maclean. Tel: 01424 715218
Restrictions: Night fishing for season ticket holders only. No keepnets
BK Rating: Very Easy
E/A: Southern
Comments: Easy access for all, including the disabled. 10-15 carp possible in a day

Wyland Lakes A

Location: Powdermill Lane, Catsfield, Battle, TN33 OSU
Type and Size: Seven farm lakes
How to Find: Take the A2100 Hastings-Battle road and turn left on the B2095 just before Battle. Wyland Farm is on the left
Carp Stock: All the lakes contain some carp. One is designated as a specimen carp lake and the record fish for the water is said to be 28lbs. Three of the lakes produced 20's
Category: Carp Waters
Other Species: Rudd, tench, perch, bream and roach - all large
Permits: From Wyland Farm, Powdermill Lane, Battle. Tel: 01424 893394. Day tickets. Chalet tariffs include 24 hours a day fishing

Cost: Specimen Carp Lake £7 per day (24 hours), other lakes about £6 per day
Control: Private - Colin Bourner, Wyland Lakes Angling Centre
Restrictions: No nuts or peas, barbless or semi-barbed hooks requested
BK Rating: Moderate
E/A: Southern, available from farmhouse
Comments: This is a working farm, mainly sheep, where you can go for a holiday. There are chalets with various tariffs, for example £220 a week for two adults including fishing. One day costs £46, with £36 for each subsequent day. Touring caravans pay £4 per day (fishing extra). Tents are £3 per day; £15 per week, fishing extra. Bivvies allowed at lakeside at no extra charge - fishing rates only. Near Hastings, Eastbourne and Rye. Please note prices are approximate. Toilets. Snack bar. Open all year. Send for brochure. Much wildlfe. Excellent reputation

ESSEX

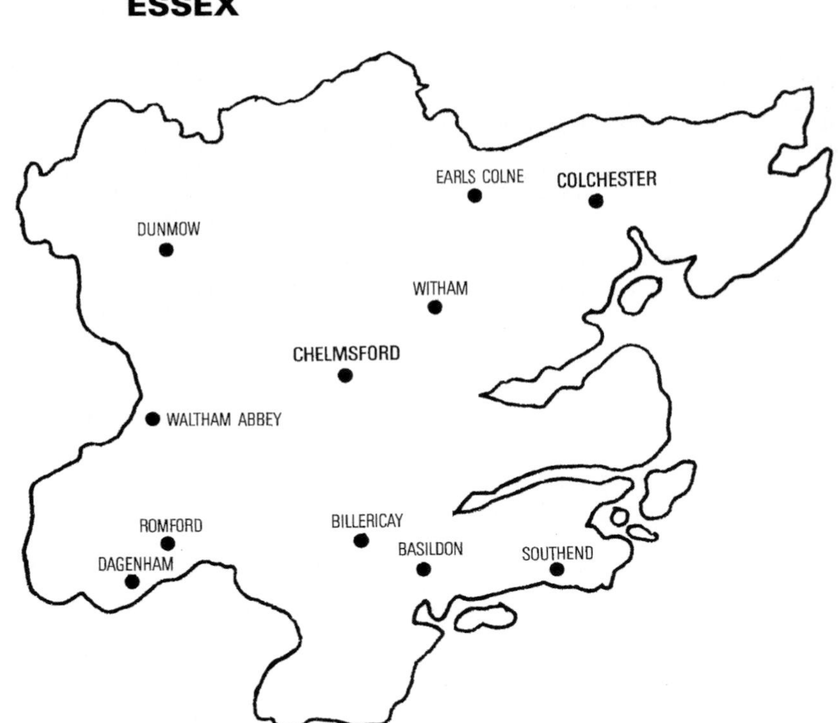

Ardleigh Reservoir

Location: Near Colchester
How to Find: On the road to Manningtree, about four miles out of Colchester
Type and Size: 440 acre reservoir
Carp Stock: Few carp, but very large
Category: Mixed Fishery
Other Species: Most species to specimen sizes. Pike to 44¾ lbs
Permits: From the lodge at fishery entrance
BK Rating: Super-Difficult
E/A: Anglian
Comments: Location of carp very difficult. Depths to 60 feet. Upper 30's caught every year by the specialist - larger fish present

Arena Lake

Location: Near Thurrock - off the old A13 and not far from the M25/Dartford Tunnel
Type and Size: Open pit of about ten acres; very weedy
Carp Stock: Well stocked with carp to mid-doubles, and a few 20's
Category: Carp Water
Permits: Day tickets on bank
BK Rating: Moderate
E/A: Thames

Aveley Lakes

Location: Romford Road, Aveley, near Romford
Carp Stock: Well stocked with carp to over 20lbs
Category: Mixed Fishery
Other Species: Tench and rudd
Permits: Aveley Lakes, Romford Road, Aveley, near Romford...waiting list, season tickets only
Control: Private
BK Rating: Moderate
E/A: Thames

Blasford Hill Fishery

Location: Broomfield, Little Waltham, near Chelmsford off the B 1008
Type and Size: 3 acre lake
Carp Stock: Well stocked with carp to mid - doubles
Category: Mixed fishery
Other Species: Tench, roach, rudd, chub and crucians
Permits: On bank
Cost: £5 per day; £3 juniors and O.A.P's
Control: Edwards Tackle, Chelsford. Tel: 01245 357689
Restrictions: No nuts; no night fishing; no keepnets; barbless hooks
BK Rating: Moderate
E/A: Anglian

Blunts Mere

Location: Alongside Cants, Hoe Mill, Hatfield Peverel, south of Witham
Type and Size: Gravel pit of three acres
Carp Stock: Not very many carp, to low 20's
Category: Few Carp
Other Species: Usual coarse fish
Permits: Chelmsford AA, 60 Delamere Road, Chelmsford
Restrictions: No night fishing
BK Rating: Easy
E/A: Anglian
Comments: Could produce some good fish for anyone prepared to fish it hard

Bog Grove

Location: Near Totham, Maldon area
Type and Size: Lake of about two acres
Carp Stock: Well stocked, mainly with fully-scaled mirrors to mid-twenties
Category: Mixed Fishery
Other Species: Usual coarse fish
Permits: Maldon AC. Tel: 01621 854765
Control: Club
Restrictions: Night fishing on Mondays, Wednesday and Fridays and only by special application
BK Rating: Easy
E/A: Anglian
Comments: An excellent winter water

Boreham

Location: Wallace's Farm, Russell Green, Little Waltham, near Chelmsford
Type and Size: Gravel pit of one and a quarter acres
How to Find: Take the A12 towards Chelmsford, then the B1137 towards Boreham. Keep to the right of the slip road and turn right at the traffic lights along

300 yards of dual carriageway under the main A12 to the roundabout. Take the Boreham exit and go through the village to the Cock Inn. Turn left over the A12 bridge and follow the road for about one and a half miles to the Anglia Building Supplies Yard on the left. Wallace's Farm is opposite this. Car park is opposite the RMC Plant area

Carp Stock: About 40, mainly doubles, to over 20lbs
Category: Mixed Fishery
Other Species: Pike, bream, tench and roach
Permits: This is a Leisure Sport Angling Special Venue. Limited tickets for the season from LSA, Thorpe Park, Staines Road, Chertsey, Surrey.
Cost: £25 for the season. Concessions
Restrictions: No night fishing, dawn to dusk only
BK Rating: Easy
Control: Leisure Sport Angling. Tel: 01932 564872
E/A: Thames

Boreham Mere

Location: Wallace's Farm, Russell Green, Little Waltham, near Chelmsford
Type and Size: Eight acre gravel pit alongside Boreham, the Leisure Sport water
Carp Stock: Plenty of doubles, with 10-15 twenties
Category: Mixed Fishery
Other Species: Usual coarse fish
Permits: Chelmsford AA, 60 Delamere Road, Chelmsford, Essex
Control: Club
Restrictions: Separate permit for night fishing
BK Rating: Moderate
E/A: Anglian

Bournebridge Lakes

Location: Bournebridge Lane, Stapleford Abbotts, Romford. Tel: 01708 688279
Type and Size: Three small lakes
Carp Stock: All well stocked with carp to about 12lbs
Category: Mixed Fishery
Other Species: Tench and rudd
Permits: Day tickets in advance, from the above address - phone for details
Control: Private
BK Rating: Easy
E/A: Anglian
Comment: Refreshments and toilets on site; good family water

Braxted Park Lake

Location: Braxted Park, Braxted, near Witham
Type and Size: Eleven acre estate lake
Carp Stock: About 200 carp, of which most are over 10lbs, a number of 20's including two commons, and at least one 30 pounder
Category: Carp Water
Other Species: Some coarse fish
Permits: We think this water is now controlled by a syndicate; you might be able to get information from Mr M Clark, Braxted Park Estate Office, Braxted, near Witham. Cost is said to be £500 a season!
Control: Private syndicate Tel: 01376 570401
Restrictions: Syndicate membership only - no other permits
BK Rating: Moderate
E/A: Anglian

Braxted Park Reservoir

Location: Braxted Park, Braxted, near Witham
Type and Size: Seven acre estate reservoir
Carp Stock: Stocked in 1987 with about 50 carp from 8-14lbs. As this has been a trout fishery several carp have been caught on the fly, the best weighing 24lbs
Category: Mixed Fishery
Other Species: Trout and possibly some other coarse fish apart from the carp
Permits: Probably now controlled by a syndicate. For information try Mr M Clark, Braxted Park Estate Office, Braxted, near Witham
Control: Private syndicate
Restrictions: No permits - syndicate members only
BK Rating: Moderate
E/A: Anglian

Brickhouse Farm Fisheries

Location: Doddinghurst Road, Brentwood
Type and Size: Three small lakes
How to Find: From junction 28 of the M 25 take the A 1023 into Brentwood. Turn left onto the A 125, then right into Doddinghurst Road
Carp Stock: Well stocked with small carp
Category: Mixed Fishery
Other Species: Bream, tench, perch, chub, eels and rudd
Permits: On bank
Cost: £5 per day
Control: Private. Tel: 01277 261405
Restrictions: No boilies, nuts or cereal groundbait
BK Rating: Moderate
E/A: Anglian
Comments: No night fishing. Toilets on site

Bulphan Park

Location: Off the A128 near Brentwood
Type and Size: Three acre lake
Carp Stock: Well stocked with carp over 20lbs
Category: Mixed Fishery
Other Species: Roach, bream, golden tench, koi, and perch
Permits: Day tickets on bank - about £5. Concessions
BK Rating: Fairly Easy
E/A: Thames
Comments: Tel: 01375 89150

Burrows Farm

Location: Bulpham, near Basildon - off the A127
Type and Size: 5 acre lake
Carp Stock: Quite well stocked with carp to 8lbs
Category: Mixed Fishery
Other Species: Perch, bream and roach
Permits: On bank
Cost: £8 per day; £12 for a night
BK Rating: Not known
Baits/Methods: Legered boilies and floaters
E/A: Anglian

Cants Mere

Location: Hoe Mill, near Hatfield Peverel, just south of Witham
Type and Size: Gravel pit of about two and a half acres
Carp Stock: Heavily stocked, mainly with commons, from 8 to 10lbs
Category: Mixed Fishery
Other Species: Usual coarse fish
Permits: Chelmsford AA, 60 Delamere Road, Chelmsford, Essex
Control: Club
Restrictions: No night fishing
BK Rating: Easy
E/A: Anglian

Central Park Lake

Location: Chelmsford
Type and Size: Good sized town park lake
Carp Stock: Well stocked with carp - a 19 pounder was reported in 1990
Category: Mixed Fishery
Other Species: Tench, roach, and rudd
Permits: From tackle dealers in Essex
Cost: Season £15 per rod; day tickets £2
Control: RHP Angling Club - try tackle shops, or Chelmsford Borough Council for details
Restrictions: No barbless hooks, boilies, particle baits or floating baits (sounds as if they don't want the carp caught, doesn't it?)
BK Rating: Moderate
E/A: Anglian
Comments: The draconian restrictions are apparently because the Council was under pressure by the Royal Society for the Prevention of Cruelty to Birds to close the lake to anglers (I hope no angler supports the RSPB in any way, as we have come across many 'anti-angling' instances by this organisation, which we understand often catches birds in fine nets in which they become trapped so that they can examine and 'ring' them!)

Chigborough Fisheries

Location: Maldon, not far from Southend - Chigborough Farm, Chigborough Road, Heybridge,Maldon, CM9 7RE
Type and Size: Several large, matured gravel pits with island and bars
Carp Stock: Heavily stocked with carp to upper doubles and some twenties
Category: Mixed Fishery
Other Species: Roach, bream, tench, perch and catfish to 20lbs
Permits: Day tickets from bailiffs on bank - season tickets also available from £60
Control: Private. Tel: 01402 244440. Fax 01621 855563
BK Rating: Easy
E/A: Anglian
Comments: Day tickets about £9 for 24 hours

Churchwood Fisheries

Location: Doddington Place, Blackmore Road, Brentwood CM15 OHX
Type and Size: Two estate lakes of three acres and one acre
Carp Stock: Jenkinsons - carp between 12lbs and 24lbs. Bottom Lake (3 acres) - some small carp
Category: Mixed Fisheries
Other Species: Tench (Jenkinsons); tench, bream, roach, rudd and perch (Bottom)
Permits: At the time of going to press control of this water was changing
Restrictions: No animals; no carp sacks; no keepnets; barbless hooks recommended

BK Rating: Moderate
E/A: Anglian
Comments: Private nature reserve - over 400 species of wild flowers. 20 anglers per day only. Club bookings allowed. Tackle and bait to order when booking ticket - all booking on 01277 200985

Claverhambury Lake

Location: Claverhabury, Waltham Abbey
Type and Size: Dammed estate lakes, a bit less than 2 acres each
How to Find: Find Galley Hill Road, Waltham Abbey and follow this to Claverhambury Road
Carp Stock: Well stocked with carp to double figure size
Category: Carp Only
Permits: P and B Hall, 44 Highbridge Street, Waltham Abbey. Tel: 01992 711932
Baits/Methods: Normal carp methods with boilies and multiples as baits
Control: Private, day ticket
BK Rating: Moderate
E/A: Thames
Comments: A pleasant little fishery, stream-fed with trees on one side. Depths from 2ft to just over 8ft

Cobblers Mead Lake

Location: Herd Lane, Corringham
Type and Size: Five acre gravel pit
How to Find: In Corringham
Carp Stock: Some big carp to 24lbs
Category: Mixed Fishery
Other Species: Bream, tench, roach, catfish and crucians
Permits: M.G.H Properties, Box 18, Canvey Island, Essex. Tel: 01268 683946
Restrictions: Members only
BK Rating: Moderate
Control: Private
Comments: Information and permits also from Basildon Angling Centre, Whitemore Way

Danbury Country Park

Location: Off the A 414 between Danbury and Sandon
Type and Size: Two lakes
Carp Stock: Well stocked with carp to 20 lbs
Category: Mixed Fishery
Other Species: Bream, perch, roach, tench, crucians and eels
Permits: On bank
Cost: About £3 per day
Control: Essex County Council. Tel: 01245 222350
Restrictions: No night fishing; barbless hooks
BK Rating: Not known
E/A: Anglian
Comments: Toilets

Dedham Mill

Location: Clovers Mill Ltd, Gunhill, Dedham, Colchester
Type and Size: Mill Pool and River Stour
Carp Stock: Well stocked with carp to at least double figure size
Category: Mixed Fishery
Other Species: Bream, pike and dace
Permits: Day and season tickets from the mill, or from K D Radclife Fishing Tackle, High Street, Colchester
Cost: £1 per day - £10 per season
Control: Private
BK Rating: Moderate
E/A: Anglian

Dunmow Lake

Location: Near Dunmow in north Essex, just off the M11
Type and Size: Nine acre lake
Carp Stock: Well stocked with carp to 20lbs plus
Category: Carp Only
Permits: Season (syndicate) only; for details tel: 01376 20662
Control: Private
Restrictions: No day tickets
BK Rating: Moderate
E/A: Anglian

Epping Forest Ponds

Location: Epping Forest
Type and Size: Small ponds
How to Find: Chingford, Loughton area off the A11
Carp Stock: Most have small carp, but fish to over 30lbs have been taken
Category: Mixed Fisheries
Other Species: General coarse fish
Permits: Many are free; Warren Pond; Perch Pond; Hollow Pond; Eagle Pond; Highams Park Lake; Connaught Water; Ornamental Water
Cost: Day tickets about £2 per day on bank
BK Rating: Moderate, some are Easy
Control: Superintendent of Epping Forest, The Warren, Loughton
Restrictions: On application
E/A: Thames
Comments: Busy forest ponds, some of which contain more and bigger fish than might be expected - never despise 'public' waters

Fairlop Waters, Ilford

Location: Forest Road, Fulwell Cross, Ilford
Type and Size: Two lakes of 7 and 4 acres
How to Find: From Ilford, take the A 123 to Fulwell Cross. The lakes are on the right near the Tube Station
Carp Stock: Well stocked with carp to over 20 lbs, many doubles
Category: Mixed Fishery
Other Species: Tench, perch, roach, bream, rudd, crucians, eels and gudgeon
Permits: On bank
Cost: £5 per day; £3.50 juniors, O.A.P's and disabled. £50 per season
Control: Redbridge Council. Tel: 0181 500 9911 or 0181 504 1929
Restrictions: No boilies, bent hooks or bolt rigs. Compulsory unhooking mats and 36" minimum landing nets
BK Rating: Moderate
E A: Thames

Fennes Fishing

Location: Fennes Road, Bocking, near Braintree
Type and Size: Three lakes, two of which are 6 acres and 3 1/2 acres
Carp Stock: Stocked with carp to doubles
Category: Mixed Fishery
Other Species: Roach, bream, perch, tench and hybrids
Permits: On site
Cost: £6 per day for one rod; £8 for two rods. Concessions and evening reductions
Control: Private
Restrictions: No barbed hooks
BK Rating: Not known
E/A: Anglian
Comments: Tackle and bait for sale on site

Gosfield Lake

Location: Halstead
Type and Size: Big 45 acre gravel pit
How to Find: Gosfield, near Halstead, off the A1017 north of Braintree
Carp Stock: Well stocked with carp over 20lbs, biggest common about 30
Category: Mixed Fishery
Other Species: Perch, roach, tench, pike
Permits: C W Turp, Gosfield Lake, Church Road, Gosfield
Cost: Season ticket - about £66. 12 hour - about £2.75 (1 rod); 24 hours - about £5.50
BK Rating: Difficult
Control: Private
Restrictions: 75% of the bank, fishing not allowed
E/A: Thames
Comments: Details and permts from shop on site. Boats for hire

Grange

Location: South Ockendon
Type and Size: Gravel pit of about 6 acres
Carp Stock: Quite well stocked with carp to about 35lbs
Category: Mixed Fishery
Other Species: Usual coarse fish
Permits: Thurrock Angling Club - no day tickets. Fishing only by seasonal club membership
BK Rating: Difficult

E/A: NRA Anglian Region
Comments: A famous water once fished by Fred Wilton

Grange Water

Location: South Ockendon
Type and Size: Gravel pit of about 20 acres
Carp Stock: There are said to be only 20-40 carp, to well over 30lbs, including commons of this size
Category: Few Carp
Other Species: Usual coarse fish
Permits: Day tickets from Thurrock Council - try the Council Offices
Control: Thurrock Council
BK Rating: Very Difficult
E/A: Anglian
Comments: Lots of potential for the dedicated big fish angler, but there is much public use of the lake and surrounds

Hainault Park

Location: Hainault, off the Romford-Chigwell Road
Type and Size: Five acre lake
Carp Stock: Heavily stocked with small carp, doubles, several twenties and two 30's, the best about 35lbs
Category: Mixed Fishery
Other Species: Roach, perch and pike
Permits: Day tickets on site. £3 per day. Season tickets
Restrictions: No night fishing except for syndicate members
BK Rating: Moderate
E/A: Thames
Comments: A well known water, heavily fished - danger of cars being broken into. Tel: 0181 5218534

Handley Barns Fisheries

Location: Ingatestone
Type and Size: 18 acre attractive lake
Carp Stock: Heavily stocked with upper doubles to over 20 lbs
Category: Carp Water
Other Species: Not known
Permits: Syndicate, possibly some day tickets
Cost: On application
Control: Tel: 01277 352245 / 821554
Restrictions: Not known
BK Rating: Moderate
E/A: Anglian
Comments: Open all year

Hatfield Forest Lake

Location: Near Bishops Stortford
Type and Size: Large lake, plus a small lake
How to Find: Information from the Lake Warden
Carp Stock: Some carp in the main lake; small lake contains carp to 30+
Category: Mixed Fishery
Other Species: Pike, tench, roach, rudd small lake
Permits: The Warden, The Shell House, Takeley, Bishops Stortford. Tel: 01279 870678
Cost: Season tickets about £7; day tickets on bank £3.50. Concessions

BK Rating: Easy
Control: National Trust
Restrictions: No groundbait
E/A: Thames

Highams Park Lake

Location: Charter Road, Woodford Green
Type and Size: 4 acre lake
Carp Stock: Some carp to 20 lbs
Category: Few Carp
Other Species: Pike, roach, perch, bream and gudgeon
Permits: On bank
Cost: About £4 per day; half price for juniors, O.A.P's and disabled. £30 per season
Control: Hollow A.C. Tel: 0181 521 8534
Restrictions: No keepnets
E/A: Anglian

Holy Field Carp Fishery

Location: Fishers Green Lane, Crooked Mile, Waltham Abbey. Tel: 01992 768012
Type and Size: Large lake near London
Carp Stock: Heavily stocked with carp, many doubles and several twenties to 23lb 10oz (a common)
Category: Carp Water
Permits: Don Spinks on the phone number above
Cost: Season tickets at £115
Control: Private
Restrictions: Season tickets only
BK Rating: Moderate
E/A: Thames
Comments: Clubhouse, cafeteria, full licensed bar, toilets, showers and colour TV

Home Farm Fishery

Location: Petts Lane, Little Walden - off the B 1052 near Saffron Walden
Type and Size: 1 1/2 acre lake
Carp Stock: Heavily stocked with small carp to about 6 lbs
Category: Mixed Fishery
Other Species: Tench, roach and perch
Permits: On bank
Cost: £6 per day
Control: Private. Tel: 01787 277468
Restrictions: No heavy groundbaiting
BK Rating: Easy
E/A: Anglian

Knights Pit

Location: Nazeing, near Waltham Abbey
Type and Size: Six acre lake
Carp Stock: Very well stocked with carp to over 20lbs
Category: Mixed Fishery
Other Species: Tench and bream
Permits: Lee Valley Regional Park Authority, Myddelton House, Bulls Cross, Enfield. Tel: 01992 717711
Cost: Weekly permits, cost on application
Control: Moderate
E/A: Thames

Comments: Known in the past as an excellent winter water, with some big commons present

Lake Meadows

Location: Billericay
Carp Stock: Well stocked with many carp up to low 20's
Category: Carp Water
Permits: Day tickets available on the bank
BK Rating: Easy
E/A: Anglian

Layer Pits

Location: Colchester
Carp Stock: Very heaily stocked with many small carp, but plenty of doubles and 20's
Category: Mixed Fishery
Control: Colchester Angling Preservation Society. PO Box 1286, Colchester,CO2 8PG
Restrictions: No night fishing
BK Rating: Easy
E/A: Anglian
Comments: A very easy water where you can catch many carp in a day. An ideal place for one to practice methods and tactics

Lyatts Lake

Location: Just off main A120 between Dunmow and Braintree at Rayne in Essex
Type and Size: Approx 10 acres - gravel pit, spring fed, very clear water
Carp Stock: Recently stocked with 350 mirror, leather and common carp up to 20lbs. Most fish between 7lbs - 14lbs
Category: Carp Water
Restrictions: No night fishing, no sacking. See season ticket for all club rules
Control: Privately owned. For season tickets, contact the owner, John Harvey, on 01376 20662, numbers restricted
E/A: Anglian
Comments: Attractive lake with excellent water quality, car parking available

Manningtree River Pools

Location: Off the A137 near Manningtree
Type and Size: Two large pools on the Suffolk Stour
Carp Stock: Well stocked with carp to doubles
Category: Mixed Fishery
Other Species: Bream, tench, roach, rudd and a few pike
Permits: Free
Control: Council
Restrictions: No night fishing; dawn to dusk only
BK Rating: Moderate
E/A: Anglian

Marconi's Pit

Location: Close to Boreham
Type and Size: Three pits, of which Pit Two, of four acres is the main carp lake
Carp Stock: Well stocked with carp which include about 10 twenties and a common of about 30lbs
Category: Mixed Fishery
Other Species: Usual coarse fish
Permits: Edwards Tackle Shop, 16 Broomfield Road, Chelmsford
Cost: £20 per season

Control: Marconi AS
Restrictions: No day tickets; night fishing by special permit only, available from club
BK Rating: Moderate
E/A: Anglian

Maybrand Fish Farm

Location: Bournebridge Lane, Stapleford Abbots, north of Romford
Type and Size: Four small lakes, quite deep in parts, two of which have islands
How to Find: Take the B175 from Romford. After Stapleford Abbots, turn left into Bournebridge Lane, and the lakes are on the left, past the houses
Carp Stock: All three lakes are well stocked with carp to doubles
Category: Mixed Fishery
Other Species: Roach, tench, chub, perch and eels
Permits: Day tickets on site
Cost: £6 for adults; £4 for juniors under 14, OAP's and the disabled
Control: Private. Tel: 01708 688279
Restrictions: Barbless hooks; no boilies, bloodworm or groundbait. Night fishing by arrangement
BK Rating: Moderate
E/A: Thames
Comments: Toilets; refreshments; pay phone; camping; special swims for the disabled

Mayesbrook Lakes

Location: Lodge Avenue (A1153) Barking
Type and Size: Two small park lakes
Carp Stock: Well stocked with carp to 20 lbs
Category: Mixed Fishery
Other Species: Roach, perch, bream and tench
Permits: On bank
Cost: About £2 per day - half price for juniors
Control: S.E.G.A.C. Tel: 01815 920348
Restrictions: No night fishing
E/A: Thames
Comments: Beware bathers in summer!

Nazeing Meads

Location: Meadgate Lane, Nazeing
Type and Size: Four gravel pits of 60 acres, 30 acres, 30 acres and 2 1/2 acres
Carp Stock: Some carp to 30 lbs
Category: Mixed Fishery
Other Species: Bream to 10 lbs+, tench, pike, perch, roach and eels
Permits: In advance
Cost: £62 per season
Control: Lea Valley Park. Tel: 01992 717711
Restrictions: No tigernuts or peanuts
BK Rating: Difficult
E/A: Thames
Comments: Sailing, and residential properties on edge of lakes

Newland Hall Carp Fishery

Location: Near Colchester
Type and Size: Lake of two acres
How to Find: The lake is on the A1060, 4 miles from Chelmsford
Carp Stock: Well stocked with carp to 25lbs
Category: Carp Water
Permits: Control changing at time of press
Cost: Day tickets at £12
BK Rating: Fairly Easy
Control: Private
E/A: Anglian
Comments: Small spring-fed lake in pleasant surroundings

Old Heath Lake (Snake Pit)

Location: Colchester
How to Find: In the town of Old Heath, 5 miles from Colchester
Type and Size: Some carp to over 20lbs
Category: Mixed Fishery
Other Species: Roach, rudd, bream, tench and pike
Permits: Maldon AC. Available from local tackle shops. Tel: 01621 854765
Cost: Approx £20 a season
BK Rating: Super-Difficult
E/A: Anglian

Oliver's Lake

Location: Witham, near Colchester
Type and Size: 4 1/2 acre lake
How to Find: Turn off the A 12 towards Witham, then on the B 1018 towards Maldon
Carp Stock: Well stocked with small carp with a few doubles
Category: Mixed Fishery
Other Species: Bream, tench, roach, rudd, perch, crucians and eels
Permits: Seasonal from local tackle shops
Cost: £36 per season. Reduced prices for juniors, O.A.P's and disabled
Control: Colchester A.P.S. Tel: 01206 272918
BK Rating: Easy for carp averaging 2 1/2 lbs
E/A: Anglian
Comments: Open June 16th to March 14th

Picks Cottage Carp Lakes

Location: Sewardstone, near Waltham Abbey
Type and Size: Two lakes of 2 acres and 1 acre
How to Find: Turn left 3 miles after Waltham Abbey on the A112 road towar Chingford
Carp Stock: Top lake; carp to doubles. Bottom lake; small carp
Category: Mixed Fishery
Other Species: Tench, roach, rudd, bream, perch, and gudgeon
Permits: On bank
Cost: £6 per day; £4 after 1pm; £2.50 after 4 pm
Control: Private. Tel: 0181 529 3922
Restrictions: No nuts
BK Rating: Moderate
Baits/Methods: Legered boilies best
E/A: Thames
Comments: Fish the margins for carp. Open all year

Pipps Hill Fisheries

A

Location: Basildon
Type and Size: 25 acre lake, with big hotel by the lake
How to Find: Cranes Farm Road, Basildon
Carp Stock: Some large carp, doubles and twenties
Category: Mixed Fishery
Other Species: General coarse fish
Permits: Day tickets on bank
Cost: £2 per rod for 12 hours; £3.50 per rod for 24 hours; weekend - £7.50 (two rods)
BK Rating: Very Difficult
Restrictions: No sacking
Control: Pipps Hill Country Club, Cranes Farm Road, Basildon Tel: 01268 23456
E/A: Thames
Comments: Formerley known as Aquatels. Carp caught to 25¾ lbs in 1990

Preston's Lake

Location: Off the A604 at Pebmarsh, White Colne, near Colchester
Type and Size: 20 acre lake, with islands
Carp Stock: Well stocked with doubles to mid - twenties
Category: Mixed Fishery
Other Species: Tench, bream, roach, rudd, perch, eels, hybrids, chub and gudgeon
Permits: In advance only from local tackle shops
Cost: £40 per season
Control: Colchester A.P.S. Tel: 01206 272981
Restrictions: No nuts
BK Rating: Moderate
E/A: Anglian
Comments: No fishing in Nature Reserve at top end

Priory Park Lakes

Location: Priory Park, Southend
Type and Size: Park Lake
How to Find: In Southend
Carp Stock: Well stocked with carp to over 20lbs
Category: Carp Water
Other Species: Mixed coarse fish
Permits: Day tickets on site
Cost: On application
BK Rating: Moderate
Control: Council
E/A: Thames
Comments: Busy park lake, heavily fished by carp anglers. Plenty of doubles

Rayne Lodge Farm

Location: Rayne, near Braintree
Type and Size: Three lakes
Carp Stock: Well stocked with carp to 20lbs
Category: Mixed Fishery
Other Species: Usual coarse fish
Permits: From the farm. Tel: 01376 345719
Cost: £5 per day; £7 for two rods
Restrictions: Barbless hooks and no keepnets; no peanuts
BK Rating: Moderate
E/A: Anglian

River Roding

Location: Passingford Bridge, near Abridge
Type and Size: Thirty miles long river, tributary of the Thames
Carp Stock: Some carp in the Passingford Bridge area, sizes not known
Category: Few Carp
Other Species: Roach, chub, pike, bream, and tench
Control: Woodford AS, north of bridge, members only, details from Secretary, 22 Evanrigg Terrace, Woodford Green, Essex (no day tickets). Barkingside and District AS has one and a half miles downstream of bridge. Secretary: D J French, 64 Khartoum Road, Ilford. Other information from Edko Sports, 136 North Street, Romford
BK Rating: Difficult
E/A: Thames

Rochford Reservoir

Location: Near Southend Airport; take the A127 then turn onto the B1013 towards Rochford. The reservoir is near the railway station
Type and Size: Small reservoir
Carp Stock: Some carp to 20lbs
Category: Few Carp
Other Species: Usual coarse fish
Permits: Day tickets on bank at £2 for adults and £1 for juniors and OAP's
Restrictions: Two rods only
BK Rating: Moderate
E/A: Thames

Rockells Farm

Location: Duddenhoe End, Saffron Walden
Type and Size: 34 acre lake, with fishing platforms
Carp Stock: Heavily stocked with many small carp, and plenty of doubles to 18lbs
Category: Mixed Fishery
Other Species: Tench, roach and rudd
Permits: Day tickets on bank during the week; booking in advance only at weekends from the owner E. Westerhuis, at the above address Tel: 01763 838053
Cost: £7 per day
Control: Private
Restrictions: Weekend fishing must be booked in advance - no tickets on bank barbless hooks only. No groundbait or boilies
BK Rating: Easy
E/A: Anglian
Comments: Some good doubles but 50-100lb 'bags' of fish using match tactics are common. Dawn to dusk fishing only

Shoebury Park

Location: Elm Road, Shoeburyness
Type and Size: Small park lake of about two acres
Carp Stock: Well stocked with small carp and several 20lb commons
Category: Mixed Fishery
Other Species: Tench and roach
Permits: Day tickets on bank
BK Rating: Moderate for small fish. Difficult for the big ones
E/A: Anglian

Silver End Pit

Location: Silver End, near Witham
Type and Size: Gravel pit of about two acres, with another of five acres nearby, called Silver End Back Lake
Carp Stock: Well stocked with carp to low thirties; the 40 pounder is now dead. Back Lake has carp to over 20lbs
Category: Mixed Fishery
Other Species: Big eels, bream to over 10lbs, and pike to over 20lbs
Permits: Permits from local tackle shops - no day tickets
Control: Kelvedon Angling Club - fishing by seasonal membership only
BK Rating: Moderate
E/A: Anglian

Slough House Lake

Location: Bulphan, off the A21 between Basildon and Grays
Type and Size: Four acre lake
Carp Stock: Heavily stocked with carp to upper doubles
Category: Mixed Fishery
Other Species: Most coarse fish
Permits: Basildon Angling Centre, 402 Whitmore Way, Basildon and County Angling
Cost: Day tickets - £5 for one rod; £8 for two rods in advance, £2 extra on bank
Restrictions: No night fishing - start at 7.30am; barbless hooks and no keepnets
BK Rating: Easy
E/A: Anglian

Southminster Pits

Location: Southmister, near Maldon
Type and Size: Several very small pits
Carp Stock: Well stocked with carp to doubles
Category: Mixed Fishery
Other Species: Pike, roach and bream
Permits: Members only water of Billericay AC - membership from local tackle shops, open to all
BK Rating: Easy
E/A: Anglian
Comments: Billericay AC have other carp waters on the same ticket, including Straight Mill

South Weald

Location: South Weald Park, near Brentwood
Type and Size: Two estate lakes of six acres and three acres
Carp Stock: Well stocked with carp, including a number of 20's
Category: Carp Water
Permits: Day tickets from Parks Office in car park. Tel: 01277 216297
Baits/Methods: Advanced carp fishing baits and methods
Cost: £35 per season
Control: Essex County Council
BK Rating: Difficult
E/A: Thames
Comments: No night fishing. Top Lake day tickets at £2 per day, Bottom Lake season only - carp to 27lbs

Stanford-le-Hope

Location: Wharfe Road, Stanford-le-Hope
Type and Size: Two open gravel pits of six and seven acres. Few carp, but fish to 18 1/2 lbs reported
How to Find: Take the A13 from the Dartford Tunnel towards Southend. After 6 1/2 miles take the A1014 Standford-le-Hope/Crayton turn off. Follow the Stanford signs to Southend Road, fork left at the Burmah Garage, and take Wharfe Road under the railway bridge onto the unmade road and the entrance is on the left. Park cars in either car park but not on the causeway between the lakes
Carp Stock: Well stocked with carp to 30lbs
Category: Mixed Fishery
Other Species: Pike, perch, roach, bream, tench, rudd, eels, crucian carp, all of which grow to large sizes
Permits: Season tickets only from Leisure Sport, Thorpe Park, Staines Road, Chertsey, Surrey. Tel: 01932 564872
Cost: £24 per season. Juniors/OAP/disabled £12
Restrictions: No restrictions - night fishing allowed
BK Rating: Moderate
Control: Leisure Sport Angling
E/A: Anglian

Starlane

Location: Wakering, near Southend
Type and Size: Two small lakes, and a larger water
Carp Stock: Small lakes - well stocked with carp to just under 20lbs; large lake - plenty of carp to 35lbs
Category: Mixed Fishery
Other Species: Pike, tench and roach
Permits: Small lakes - day ticket on bank; larger lake - syndicate (enquire at small lakes)
BK Rating: Moderate
E/A: Anglian

Swanscombe Farm Fishery

Location: Lamberts Lane, off Tey Road, Earls Colne. Tel: 01787 223562
Type and Size: Lake of about three acres
Carp Stock: Well stocked with carp, best reported was 22lbs
Category: Carp Water
Other Species: Tench
Permits: Day tickets on site
Cost: £5 per day
Control: Private
BK Rating: Moderate
E/A: Anglian
Comments: Reduced rates for OAP's and children. Lodge, toilets and tackle hire. Facilities for the disabled. There is also a 4 1/2 acre trout lake stocked with rainbow and brown trout to 10lbs. The fishery is open all the year

The Chase

Location: Dagenham
Type and Size: Large gravel pit
How to Find: Near Dagenham East Underground Station
Carp Stock: Good carp
Category: Mixed Fishery

Other Species: Roach, bream, tench, pike, perch, crucians
Permits: Day tickets from bailiff on bank
Cost: On application
BK Rating: Moderate
Control: White Hart Anglers' Club
Restrictions: No night fishing
E/A: Thames
Comments: Information from Edko Sports, 136 North Street, Romford

Thorndon Park

Location: Halway Lane, off the A127 Brentwood
Type and Size: Park lake of 2 - 3 acres
Carp Stock: Only about twenty, from 20-25lbs
Category: Mixed Fishery
Other Species: Pike, tench, bream, roach
Permits: Day tickets on bank
Restrictions: No night fishing
BK Rating: Difficult
E/A: Anglian

Totham Pit

Location: Just outside the village of Great Totham, near Maldon
Type and Size: Gravel pit of about six acres
Carp Stock: Quite well stocked with carp to low 20's
Category: Mixed Fishery
Other Species: Usual coarse fish
Permits: Maldon AC. Tel: 01621 854765
Cost: About £27 per season
Control: Club
BK Rating: Easy
E/A: Anglian

Tufnell's Mere

Location: Near Little Waltham
Type and Size: Gravel pit of about 12 acres
Carp Stock: Little known, but carp to 27lbs have been caught
Category: Mixed Fishery
Other Species: Usual coarse fish
Permits: Chelmsford AA, 60 Delamere Road, Chelmsford
Control: Club
Restrictions: No night fishing
BK Rating: Moderate
E/A: Anglian
Comments: Lots of potential. Water table has been low for some time

Litter

Pick it up before it damages wildlife or loses you the fishing.
A carrier bag fits in a pocket and a little care goes a long way.

Wanstead and Woodford Ponds

Location: Woodford and Snaresbrook areas
Type and Size: Small ponds
How to Find: Near Wanstead
Carp Stock: Some carp, sizes not known
Category: Eagle Pond, Hollow Pond, Whipps Cross Pond, Knighton Wood Pond - Mixed Fisheries
Other Species: General coarse fish
Permits: None required
Cost: Free
BK Rating: Insufficient information
Control: Public
E/A: Thames
Comments: Some free fishing near London! Make sure that you have Water Authority Licences

Warren Pond

Location: Near Chingford
Type and Size: Forest pond of 1¼ acres. Some carp to double figures
Category: Mixed Fishery
Other Species: Perch and rudd
Permits: Free fishing
Control: Epping Forest Conservators. Tel: 0181 5082266
BK Rating: Difficult
E/A: Thames

Weeley Bridge Holiday Park

A

Location: Weeley, near Clacton
Type and Size: Small lake on caravan park
Carp Stock: Well stocked with carp to upper doubles
Category: Mixed Fishery
Other Species: Roach, tench and other coarse fish
Permits: On site. Tel: 01255 830403 for details and brochure
Control: Club
BK Rating: Moderate
E/A: Anglian
Comments: Caravans to rent on site for holidays with fishing

Wick Mere

Location: Old School House, Ulting, near Maldon
Type and Size: 6 acre lake
Carp Stock: Well stocked with doubles to 20 lbs
Category: Mixed Fishery
Other Species: Bream, tench, roach and rudd
Permits: In advance only, from club secretary and local tackle shops
Cost: £35 per season; £23 O.A.P's, disabled and ladies
Control: Chelmsford A.A. Tel: 01245 474246
BK Rating: Moderate
E/A: Anglian

Willowside Carp Lake

Location: Off the A112 between Waltham Abbey and Chingford
Type and Size: One acre man-made lake
Carp Stock: Well stocked with carp to about 20lbs
Category: Mixed Fishery
Other Species: Chub and golden tench
Permits: Day tickets on bank
Cost: £5 per day; £3 for the evening;
Control: Tel: 0181 5291371
Restrictions: No boilies or keepnets. Barbless hooks
BK Rating: Easy
E/A: Thames
Comments: Toilet. Disabled access

GLOUCESTERSHIRE

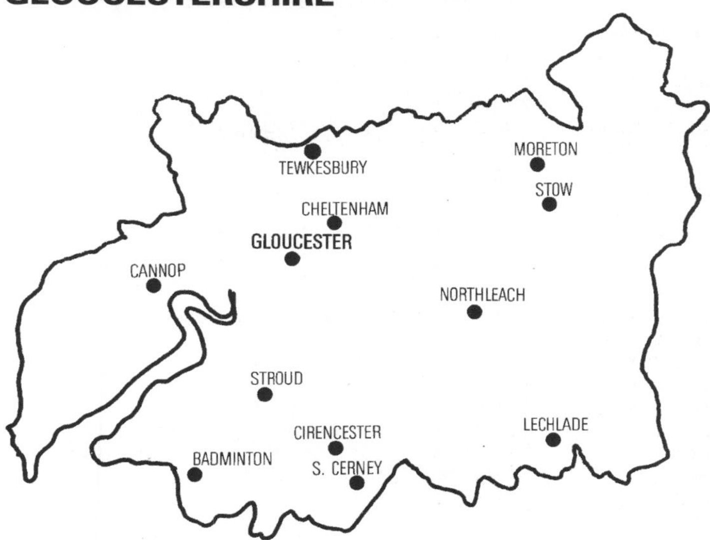

Adlestrop Lake

Location: Near Adlestrop Station, Stow-on-the-Wold

How to Find: Take the A436 road from Stow-on-the-Wold towards Chipping Norton. After about 2 miles and immediately after a railway bridge, turn left towards Evenlode. The lake is on the right

Type and Size: Stream-fed dammed estate lake, long and narrow, two and a half acres

Carp Stock: Probably only 20-30 mirrors, mostly doubles to about 18lbs. Now restocked with smaller carp

Category: Few Carp

Other Species: Tench, roach

Permits: Moreton-in-Marsh Angling Club. Enquire locally

Control: Moreton-in-Marsh Angling Club

BK Rating: Difficult

E/A: Severn-Trent

Comments: Weedy water, quite shallow, with big bed of broad-leaved pondweed at the dam end. Most carp caught after dark but can be stalked in weed at shallow end in daytime in warm weather. This is the only water we know of on which a sheep has been hooked and played! Whilst Roger Emmet was fishing there several sheep jumped into the water and swam across the lake. One of these swam through Roger's line before he could remove it and was hooked. He was unable to control the sheep, which swam across the lake, climbed the further bank and went through a barbed wire fence, breaking the line!

Apperley Pools

Location: Apperley, near Tewkesbury

Type and Size: Two pools, about 4 acres in all

How to Find: Take the A38 Gloucester road from Tewkesbury, turn right at the sign for Apperley. Continue from village on Gabbs Lane to where road bears left. Pools are on your left

Carp Stock: Carp to 20lbs

Category: Few Carp
Other Species: Bream, roach, chub, perch
Permits: Birmingham Anglers Association (members only), 100 Icknield Port Road, Rotton Park, Birmingham B16 OAP. Tel: 0121 4549111 (9.30am to 1.30pm, and 7pm to 9pm)
Cost: About £20 per year (includes all BAA waters)
BK Rating: Difficult, as there are few carp
Control: Birmingham AA
Restrictions: No groundbait of any kind
E/A: Severn-Trent
Comments: Not worth considering for serious carp fishing, unless you just want a day's fishing, with the chance of an occasional carp

Ashton Keynes Pool

Location: Ashton Keynes, near Cirencester
Type and Size: 100 acre gravel pit
Carp Stock: Well stocked with carp to doubles
Category: Mixed Fishery
Other Species: Bream, roach, rudd, perch and crucians
Permits: £2 per day in advance, from the clubhouse on site or £4 on bank
Control: South Cerney AC. 01285 658117
Restrictions: No carp in keepnets
BK Rating: Moderate
E/A: Thames

Badminton Lake

Location: On Duke of Beaufort's Badminton Estate, Badminton Village
Type and Size: Estate lake, one and a half acres
How to FInd: Turn off the A46 Bath to Stroud road at traffic lights by Cross Hands Hotel. Right turn is signposted Badminton. In village, turn right and take left turn at end into the Badminton estate. Lake on right in front of house
Carp Stock: Numerous small commons; a few mirrors to 19lbs recently introduced
Category: Carp Water
Other Species: Roach
Permits: Badminton Estate Office, Badminton, Glos. Season only, limited
Cost: About £30 per season
Baits/Methods: Normal carp methods, some surface fishing. Usual baits
Control: Season ticket, Badminton Estate
Restrictions: No night fishing
E/A: Wessex
BK Rating: Easy
Comments: Muddy type water, very open with no cover and little weed

Bradley's Pit

Location: On the edge of the village of South Cerney, near Cirencester
Type and Size: Huge gravel pit of 115 acres
How to Find: Take the Cerney Wick road from South Cerney and Bradley's will be seen on the right just outside the village
Carp Stock: Few carp, but said to be some very big fish. Commons to about 15lbs and every year there are rumours of 30's and 40's being caught, none of which are authenticated. Authenticated 26 1/4 lbs common caught in July 1985. The lake almost certainly contains some thirties
Category: Few Carp
Other Species: Tench, pike, roach, bream, chub
Permits: South Cerney Angling Club. Tackle shops in Swindon and Cirencester. Tel: 01452 883202

Cost: About £15 a season
Control: Club
BK Rating: Very Difficult
E/A: Thames
Comments: South Cerney AC have a club house here and the club has most of the best fishng in this area, which contains thousands of acres of flooded gravel pits. Ignore the stories of huge carp caught from this lake and only believe what you see

Bredons Hardwick

Location: Tewkesbury to Bredon road, about two miles from Tewkesbury
Type and Size: Ten acre gravel pit
Carp Stock: Heavily stocked with small carp and doubles, and said to be fish to 30lbs
Category: Mixed Fishery
Other Species: Roach, bream, tench, perch and rudd
Permits: Tredworth Tackle, High Street, Gloucester. Tel: 01452 23009
Cost: Season tickets only at £30 - syndicate
Restrictions: No fishing allowed in the shallows(!)
BK Rating: Fairly Hard
E/A: Severn-Trent
Comments: Very clear, weedy water; fish location very important

Bulley Lane Fishery

Location: Bulley Lane, Churcham, off the A 40 between Gloucester and Ross-on-Wye
Type and Size: 2 acre lake with island
Carp Stock: Well stocked with carp to doubles, average about 6 lbs
Category: Carp Water
Other Species: Some roach and bream
Permits: On bank
Cost: £4 per day; £6 for two rods; £2.50 juniors
Control: Tel: 01452 750320
Restrictions: No boilies or cereal groundbait. No night fishing. Barbless hooks
BK Rating: Easy
E/ A: Severn Trent

Burley Fields Lake

Location: Crippetts Lane, Leckhampton, Cheltenham. Tel: 01242 862905
Type and Size: Two connected pools
Carp Stock: Heavily stocked with carp to 20lbs
Category: Mixed Fishery
Other Species: Perch, roach, bream, rudd, tench and barbel
Permits: On bank
Cost: £5 per season, then £3 per day, or £5 per day for non-members
Restrictions: No keepnets
BK Rating: Easy
E/A: Severn-Trent
Comments: Weed-free fishery with easily accessible pitches for disabled anglers

Cannop Ponds

Location: Cannop Valley, Parkend, between Coleford and Lydney
Type and Size: Two very beautiful forest lakes, in the Forest of Dean - four and a half acres and five and a half acres. Most of the carp are in the lower lake
Carp Stock: Not a large number, and hard to locate, but they do go to over 20lbs, with some good commons
Category: Few Carp

Other Species: Bream, roach, tench and pike
Permits: Bailiff on bank
Control: Yorkley and District AC. Permits and details from Sport and Leisure, Market Place, Coleford; Robert Sports, 31 Market Street, Cinderford; Peter James Sports, 17 Newerne Street, Lydney. Tel: 01594 842515
BK Rating: Very Difficult
E/A: Severn-Trent
Comments: Ranges from 2 feet deep at the top end, where a stream comes in from the upper lake, to 18 feet at the big dam. There are said to be a few big carp in the upper lake

Chad Lakes

Location: Near Stow-on-the-Wold, off the B4450 near Bledington
Type and Size: Two and a half acre lake
Carp Stock: Well stocked with carp to over 20lbs
Category: Mixed Fishery
Other Species: Roach, bream, tench, perch, and chub
Permits: Day tickets, information on 01608 74252
Cost: £3 for one rod; £5 for two rods
BK Rating: Moderate
Control: Private - Dave Wren
Restrictions: Barbless hooks; no keepnets or groundbait; night fishing by arrangement
E/A: Thames
Comments: There is another lake on the site, a syndicate carp water; attractive Cotswold location, with toilet

Claydon Park Fishery

Location: Off the A417 road between Lechlade and Fairford
Type and Size: Five acre matured gravel pit
Carp Stock: Well stocked with carp, sizes not known
Category: Mixed Fishery
Other Species: Tench, bream, pike, perch, and roach
Permit: From the self-service hut on site
Cost: £3 per day; £1.50 for under 16;s OAP's and the disabled (two rods)
Control: Bernard Sparkes. Tel: 01367 52397 (day) or 01367 5268 (evenings)
Restrictions: No night fishing; sunrise to sunset only; no dyed baits; no dogs
BK Rating: Not known
E/A: Thames

Cokes Pit

Location: On the road from South Cerney to Ashton Keynes
Type and Size: Gravel pit of about 12 acres
Carp Stock: Some carp to 18lbs, bigger fish have been seen and a fish of well over 30lbs was caught several years ago, although this fish is now dead
Category: Mixed Fishery
Other Species: Tench, roach, rudd, bream, and pike
Permits: Ashton Keynes AC - tickets from local tackle shops in Cirencester and Swindon at £10 per season, to include other waters
Control: Club
BK Rating: Difficult
E/A: Thames
Comments: This lake is little fished by carp anglers, though it is a good tench water. Since it is a Nature Reserve quite a large part of the bank cannot be fished. Very weedy with lots of shallow bars and islands

Cotswold Hoburne **A**

Location: Cotswold Water Park, near Cirencester
Type and Size: Two quite large gravel pits
Carp Stock: Said to be some carp - numbers and sizes not known
Category: Few Carp?
Other Species: Roach, bream, tench, rudd and perch
Permits: Residents only - at reception
Control: Private
BK Rating: Difficult
E/A: Thames
Comments: Seventy acre site with timber built lodges to let. Swimming pool, licenced lakeside club, boating, shop etc - holiday camp type atmosphere. Open Easter to end of October. Bookings from Hoseasons Holidays, Sunway House, Lowestoft NR32 3LT. Tel: 01502 500500. Dozens of other lakes in the area, a number of which hold carp to over 20lbs

Court Farm

Location: Court Farm, Lemington, Todenham Road, Moreton-in-Marsh, GL56 9NP
Type and Size: Two and a half acre man-made lake
Carp Stock: About 150 fish to 16lbs, best to date is 20lbs, but the average is about 4lb
Category: Carp Water
Other Species: Rudd, perch, chub, grass carp
Permits: Bill Gadsby, Court Farm. Tel: 01608 50872
Cost: Day tickets at £5 per day
Control: Private
BK Rating: Moderate
E/A: Severn-Trent
Comments: Night fishing is allowed, and another pond for carp is being constructed. There is also a one acre trout lake on the farm. Barbless hooks only. No boilies. No night fishing. Cafe. Toilets.Open all year

Crooked Withies Lake

Location: Near Tewkesbury
Type and Size: Two and a half acre lake
Carp Stock: Heavily stocked with carp only to about 14lbs
Category: Carp Only
Permits: Syndicate season tickets only from: The FIshery Controller, 15 Stafford Court, Riverside Close, Bedford MK42 9DE. Tel: 01234 212066 / 365085. Some vacancies in April each year, and occasionally throughout the season
Cost: About £120 per season
Control: Private
BK Rating: Moderate
Restrictions: No long stay fishing or camping (maximum 24 hours). Alternate Saturday and Sunday rota. No bivvies
E/A: Severn-Trent
Comments: A very attractive lake with an island, and surrounded by mature flowering bushes and trees. Very quiet and peaceful. Plenty of mirrors and commons from 4 to 10lbs, and a good number of lower doubles. Small exclusive syndicate, with vacancies every year. Guest tickets for friends of members. Night fishing allowed though the water fishes best in the daytime. Good winter water. Warning - private property; do not visit without permission. Season and day tickets available on other carp only waters, on application to the above address

Gardners Pool

Location: Village of Saul, 8 miles south of Gloucester
Type and Size: Mature gravel pit - 5 acres
How to Find: On the Gloucester-Bristol road (A38), turn right for Frampton-on-Severn just after roundabout. Cross Gloucester-Sharpness canal, water is on the right just before the village of Saul. Ordnance Survey Sheet 163
Carp Stock: Number not known, but not very heavily stocked. A number of doubles and perhaps two or three 20's to about 21lbs. Bigger fish are mirrors - some commons to about 13lbs
Category: Mixed Fishery
Other Species: Roach, tench, many eels
Permits: Gloucester United Angler's Association, from tackle shops in Gloucester. Secretary: J Gibby, 70 Robert Raikes Avenue, Tuffley, Gloucester. Tel: 01452 413972
Cost: £10.50 per season, limited in number
Baits/Methods: Normal, fairly advanced carp rigs and methods with boilies or some multiple baits
Control: Club
E/A: Severn-Trent
BK Rating: Difficult
Comments: Shallow, weedy water. Very patchy - long spells with no takes

Hailes Fruit Farm

Location: Hailes Abbey, Winchcombe, near Cheltenham
Type and Size: 2 acre irrigation reservoir
Carp Stock: Quite well stocked with carp to 10 lbs
Category: Mixed Fishery
Other Species: Rudd, roach and crucians
Permits: From farm shop
Cost: About £4 - weekends £5 per day
Control: Tel: 01242 602123
Restrictions: No night fishing; no keepnets; barbless hooks
BK Rating: Easy
E/A: Severn Trent
Comments: Toilets. Disabled access. Cafe at farm shop

Ham Pool

Location: Near South Cerney, Cirencester
Type and Size: Gravel pit of 24 acres
How to Find: Ham Pool is the smaller water next to Bradley's on the edge of South Cerney Village
Carp Stock: Carp to over 20lbs
Category: Mixed Fishery
Other Species: Roach, tench, rudd, bream and pike
Permits: South Cerney Angling Club. Membership Secretary: D Savage, 35 Alexandra Drive, Cirencester, Glos, and also from tackle shops in Swindon and Cirencester
Cost: About £25 per season
Control: Club. Tel: 01285 658117
BK Rating: Very Difficult
E/A: Thames
Comments: Toilet. Disabled access

Highnam Court Lake

Location: Just off the A40, 3 miles west of Gloucester on the Ross-on-Wye road
Type and Size: Three acre attractive estate lake covered with lilies
Carp Stock: Some carp to 20lbs
Category: Few Carp
Other Species: Tench, roach, bream and rudd
Permits: Day tickets in advance from Tredworth Fishing Tackle, 78 High Street, Tredworth, Gloucester
Cost: £4 per day; £5 on bank
Control: Brian Ingram. Tel: 01452 23009
Restrictions: No groundbaiting
BK Rating: Very Difficult
E/A: Seven-Trent

Hillview Fishery

Location: Off the A 38 near the M 50 junction
Type and Size: Two small man - made pools
How to Find: Turn off the M 50 at junction 1, and take the A 38 Tewkesbury road. Turn left at Puckrup
Carp Stock: Well stocked with small carp to 8 lbs
Category: Mixed Fishery
Other Species: Tench, crucians, grass carp, roach, rudd and orfe
Permits: Day tickets on site
Cost: £4 for two rods. £3 O.A.P's and juniors on some days
Control: Keith Hill Tel: 01684 296719
Restrictions: No groundbait, hemp or keepnets
BK Rating: Easy
E/A: Severn Trent
Comments: Bank suitable for the disabled. Cafe and toilets

Huntley Carp Pools

Location: Huntley, 10 miles north west of Glourcester, off the A40
Type and Size: Two attractive stream-fed forest lakes of about four acres each, weedy and about 10 feet deep
Carp Stock: Well stocked with carp to over 20lbs
Category: Mixed Fishery
Other Species: Roach, rudd, tench, eels and trout
Permits: Seasonal membership only from J R Tipper, South View, Green Lane, Hardwicke, Gloucester LG4 7TH. Tel: 01452 883202
Cost: On application
Control: Private
BK Rating: Moderate
E/A: Severn Trent
Comments: Beautiful location in huge forest; former trout pools. Membership limited. No glass bottles because of possible fires. Well behaved anglers only. A fairly new water for carp requires genuine anglers; no families or picnickers

Lake 19

Location: South Cerney, near Cirencester
Type and Size: Eight acre gravel pit
Carp Stock: Well stocked with carp to 15½ lbs, mostly commons from 8-10lbs, but growing well
Category: Carp Water
Other Species: Some other coarse fish

Permits: Club membership of Isis Angling Club from local tackle shops in Cirencester and Swindon
Cost: £15.50 per season
Control: Isis Angling Club - P Gilbert, Havelock Street, Swindon, Wilts
BK Rating: Easy
E/A: Thames

Lydney Boating Lake

Location: On the edge of the town of Lydney, between Gloucester and Chepstow
Type and Size: Town boating lake, five acres
How to Find: Take the A40 from Gloucester towards Ross, then the A48 towards Chepstow. At Lydney, turn left opposite Woolworths, and then right again past the houses
Carp Stock: Heavily stocked with commons to about 8lbs. Some mirrors to 19lbs
Category: Mixed Fishery
Other Species: Roach, tench, bream, rudd, eels, barbel
Permits: Sports shop in Lydney High Street on left going towards Chepstow
Cost: About £15 per season. Day tickets £3 on bank
Baits/Methods: Fairly unsophisticated carp methods and baits. Float fishing
Control: Lydney Angling Club. Secretary. K Jones, 45 Hughes Crescent, Garden City, Chepstow. Tel: 01291 621402
BK Rating: Easy
E/A: Severn Trent
Comments: Busy town water, walkers, children and boats which are restricted to one end only. Very large island. No night fishing for those living out of the Forest of Dean. Unhooking mats compulsory. No floating baits. No nut baits

Meadow Pond

Location: Norton, near Gloucester
Type and Size: Tiny farm pool
Carp Stock: Mostly small - best about 10lbs
Category: Mixed Fishery
Other Species: Rudd, roach and bream
Permits: In advance only from Red Lion Inn by fishery entrance
Cost: About £5 per day
Control: Tel: 01452 730251
Restrictions: No night fishing. No keepnets; barbless hooks
BK Rating: Easy
E/A: Severn Trent
Comments: Toilet

Manor Brook Lake

Location: Lake 59, Friday Ham Lane, Ashton Keynes, Cirencester; off the A419, Swindon road
Type and Size: 40 acre gravel pit of irregular shape, with an island
Carp Stock: Carp to 10lbs
Category: Mixed Fishery
Other Species: Roach, perch, tench, pike and some big trout
Permits: From the self service kiosk in the car park at £5 per day
Control: Tel: 01452 306050
Restrictions: No night fishing. No carp in keepnets
BK Rating: Moderate
E/A: Thames
Comments: Boats can be hired for pike fishing; net divides the coarse fishery from a trout fishery, and from the carp fishery

Milestone Fisheries

Location: One mile east of Fairford on the A 417 Lechlade to Cirencester road
Type and Size: Two lakes of 6 and 5 acres, both very deep
Carp Stock: Smaller lake is well stocked with carp to over 20 lbs
Category: Mixed Fishery
Other Species: Tench, bream, rudd and perch
Permits: On bank
Cost: £5 per day; juniors and O.A.P's £3
Control: Tel: 01285 713908
Restrictions: Night fishing by prior arrangement only
BK Rating: Moderate
E/A: Thames

Mill Avon

Location: Lower Lodge Lane, off the Gloucester road in Tewkesbury
Type and Size: Three-quarter of a mile stretch of river between the Severn and the Avon
Carp Stock: Not many carp, but they have been caught to nearly 20lbs
Category: Few Carp
Other Species: Most coarse fish
Permits: Tewkesbury Fishing Tackle. Tel: 01684 293234
Cost: £10 per season; £5.50 for two weeks
Control: Tewkesbury Popular AC
Restrictions: No night fishing
BK Rating: Very Difficult
E/A: Severn Trent

Moreton Pits

Location: Bourton - on -the - Water
Type and Size: Two gravel pits of 14 acres
How to Find: Take the A 429 from Stow-on-the-Wold towards Cirencester. Turn towards Bourton and after the village the fishery is on the left
Carp Stock: Heavily stocked with carp to 30 lbs
Category: Mixed Fishery
Other Species: Roach, perch, tench, pike and small bream
Permits: In advance only from tackle shops
Cost: About £12 per season; reduced prices for O.A.P's and juniors
Control: Moreton A.C. Tel: 01451 821719
BK Rating: Moderate
E/A: Thames

Norton Fruit Farm

Location: Tewkesbury Road, Norton, Gloucester GL2 9LH. Tel: 01452 731203
Type and Size: One acre irrigation reservoir
How to Find: Norton Fruit Farm is on the A38 between Coombe Hill and Twigworth
Carp Stock: Heavily stocked with 40 doubles to over 20lbs
Category: Mixed Fishery
Other Species: Roach, rudd, tench, bream, perch and golden orfe
Permits: Mr Feakins, Norton Fruit Farm - day tickets at about £5 per day
BK Rating: Very Easy
E/A: Severn-Trent
Comments: Open banks with room for about 20 anglers; no night fishing. Barbless hooks. Toilet

Old Manor House Carp Ponds

Location: Gloucestershire
Type and Size: 3 small interconnected ponds with islands
Carp Stock: Well stocked with small carp, mostly 4 -8lbs.One or two doubles to 12lbs
Category: Carp Water
Other Species: Eels
Permits: In advance only - day permits reserved in writing at least a week in advance
Cost: £10 per day
Control: Fishery Controller, 15 Stafford Court, Riverside Close, Bedford, MK42 9DE. Tel: 01234 212066 / 365085
Restrictions: No night fishing, floating baits or bread
BK Rating: Moderate
Baits/Methods: Float fished luncheon meat and sweetcorn best; boilies also successful
E/A: Severn Trent
Comments: A unique fishery - no other tickets issued for your day; for £10 /day each you have the ponds to yourself, or you can 'hire' the ponds for yourself and one or two friends at £10 per day each. Little fished; beautiful scenery. Open all year

River Severn

Location: Four hundred yards of the River Severn at Wainlode, near Gloucester
Type and Size: Wide lower Severn and about quarter of a mile of the River Chelt
How to Find: Take the A38 from Gloucester towards Tewkesbury. Turn left at Norton, and follow signs to Wainlode and the river by the Red Lion pub
Carp Stock: Only a few carp, but some to 20lbs
Category: Few Carp
Other Species: Roach, chub, bream, barbel and big pike
Permits: Day tickets from Red Lion Inn
Cost: £2 per day; £1 for juniors. Evening tickets £1
Control: Red Lion Inn
Restrictions: No night fishing
BK Rating: Very Difficult
E/A: Severn Trent
Comments: Ideal for family fishing. The Inn has a campsite for tents and caravans

Roughgrounds Farm Lake

Location: Just north of Lechlade
Type and Size: Gravel pit of about three acres
How to Find: Take the A361 Lechlade to Burford road, and the entrance to the lake will be seen on the left hand side after about a mile, and just beyond the entrance to Horseshoe
Carp Stock: Well stocked with carp including a number of doubles
Category: Carp Water
Other Species: Some small mixed coarse fish
Permits: Day tickets from the Paper Shop, Burford Road, Lechlade. Tel: 52323. Limited to 15 anglers per day
Cost: About £3 per day
Control: Private
BK Rating: Easy to Moderate
Restrictions: No keepnets
E/A: Thames

Russell's End Reservoir

Location: Playley Green, off the A 417 Ledbury to Gloucester road
Type and Size: 4 acre farm reservoir
Carp Stock: Stocked with small carp to about 5 lbs

Category:	Mixed Fishery
Other Species:	Roach, rudd, tench and big eels
Permits:	On bank
Cost:	£4 per day; £3 juniors
Control:	Private. Tel: 01531 890455
Restrictions:	No cereal groundbait; no night fishing; no keepnets; barbless hooks
BK Rating:	Easy
E/A:	Severn Trent

Staunton Court

Location:	A417 from Gloucester 8 miles. From M50 (junction 2) 3 miles A417 by church at Staunton
Type and Size:	Three pools in manor house grounds
Carp Stock:	Stocked well with mirrors, commons and crucians up to 25lbs
Category:	Mixed Fishery
Other Species:	Tench, rudd, roach and bream
Permits:	On bank - £4 per rod
Control:	Private. Tel: 01452 840230
Restrictions:	Night arrival before 10.30pm. Barbless hooks. No keepnets or weigh sacks
BK Rating:	Easy - Moderate
E/A:	Severn-Trent
Comments:	Must dip nets on arrival in tanks provided

Stroudwater Canal

Location:	Ryford to Bridgend, just to the west of Stroud off the A419
Type and Size:	Narrow, shallow disused stretch of canal
Carp Stock:	Some carp to doubles
Category:	Few Carp
Other Species:	Tench, roach, bream, perch and pike
Permits:	Permits from local tackle shops at about £10 per season
Control:	Lobby's Tackle. Tel: 01453 791417
BK Rating:	Difficult
E/A:	Severn Trent

Walham Lake

Location:	Off the A 40 Gloucester by - pass at Walham electricity sub station, Gloucester
Type and Size:	4 acre lake
Carp Stock:	Quite well stocked with doubles to over 20 lbs
Category:	Mixed Fishery
Other Species:	Pike, tench, roach, perch, rudd and small bream
Permits:	In advance from local tackle shops
Cost:	£15 per season; £ 5 O.A.P's and juniors
Control:	Walham A.C. Tel; 01452 411543
Restrictions:	No boilies over 13 mm diameter
BK Rating:	Moderate
Baits/Methods:	Trout pellets are a good bait
E/A:	Severn Trent

Waterloo Screens

Location:	Brierly, Forest of Dean, near Gloucester
Type and Size:	Half acre pool
Carp Stock:	Some carp to about 8 lbs
Category:	Mixed Fishery
Other Species:	Tench, roach, rudd and perch

Permits: On bank
Cost: About £3 per day; £15 a season
Control: Royal Forest of Dean A / C. Tel: 01594 824413
Restrictions: No boilies, nuts or cereal groundbait
BK Rating: Not known
E/A: Severn Trent

Watersmeet A

Location: Hartpury, near Gloucester. Tel: 01452 700358
Type and Size: Three mature pits of about two acres, half and a quarter of an acre
How to Find: Take the A40 Gloucester to Ross-on-Wye road and after about a mile turn right on the A417 towards Ledbury. The ponds will be seen on the left hand side just after the village of Hartpury and next to a white-painted guest house called 'Watersmeet'
Carp Stock: Numbers not known, although there are enough to be worth fishing for. Some commons to about 9lbs, and mirrors to around 15lbs. A few larger fish have been reported
Category: Mixed Fishery
Other Species: Tench, roach, rudd, bream
Permits: From Mr and Mrs Ring at the guest house. Some day tickets are issued and you can fish if you stay at the guest house, which is right on the edge of the lake. There is a bar and you can have meals etc - quite a pleasant spot for a fishing holiday, though quite busy in the summer. Night fishing for residents only
Cost: On application to Watersmeet, Hartpury, Gloucester
BK Rating: Difficult
Control: Private
Baits/Methods: This is not an easy water and there are not great numbers of carp, so fairly advanced baits and methods would be needed
E/A: Severn-Trent
Comments: Quite a pleasant place to stay and the fishing is very close to the accommodation. Most carp caught after dark. Front Pool - small carp only to 5lbs. Rear Pool - few carp, but two upper doubles. Main Pool - most fish up to 5lbs only; about 15 doubles to 18lbs. Very snaggy, line minimum 10lbs. Barbless hooks advised

Whelford Pools Specimen Lake

Location: Whelford Road, Fairford
Type and Size: Three acre lake
How to Find: Take the A417 from Lechlade to Fairford; the Whelford road is a left turn after a few miles, with the lakes on the right
Carp Stock: Very heavily stocked with more than 100 doubles to over 20lbs
Category: Mixed Fishery
Other Species: Pike over 20lbs, tench, roach and pike
Permits: Day tickets on bank. Tel: 01285 713649
Cost: £5 for two rods; 5pm to 9pm - £3; 24 hours - £8
Control: Gerry and Ros Godden
Baits/Methods: Usual carp baits; floaters do well
Restrictions: No night fishing except by special arrangement; no keepnets; barbless hooks; unhooking mats must be used
BK Rating: Easy
E/A: Thames
Comments: Attractive lakes. Snacks, bait and tackle

GREATER LONDON

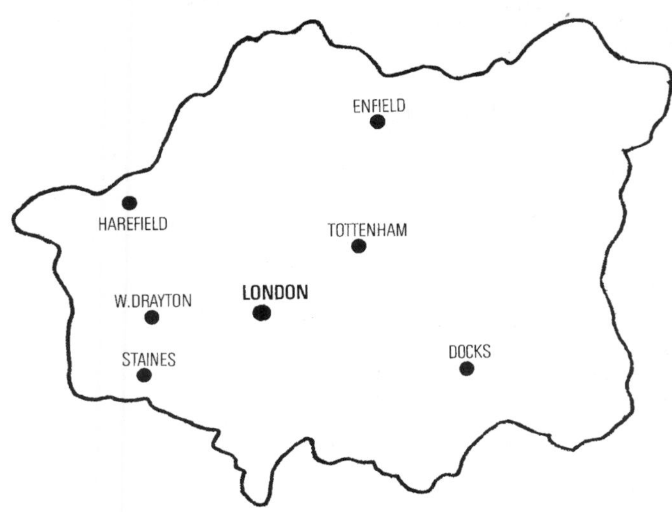

Alexandra Park Lake

Location: Alexandra Palace, Haringey, North London
Type and Size: Large park lake with boats etc.
Carp Stock: Some carp to over 20 lbs
Category: Few Carp
Other Species: Crucians, roach, rudd, tench and small bream
Permits: FREE Fishing
Cost: None
Control: Tel: 0181 881 8809
Restrictions: No night fishing
BK Rating: Difficult
E/A: Thames
Comments: Toilet. Disabled access

Angling Products T.P. A

Location: Wraysbury - near Heathrow Airport
Type and Size: Lake
Carp Stock: Some carp, sizes and numbers not known
Category: Mixed Fishery
Other Species: Pike and some others
Permits: Contact Les Webber
Cost: Probably free
Control: Les Webber Tel: 01734 431701 between 6.30pm and 8.30pm weekdays
BK Rating: Not known
E/A: Thames
Comments: Advertises 'angling and conservation' courses. Lakeside fully equipped accommodation. Pre - booking for groups led by teachers etc. Facilities for the disabled

Bedfont Lake

Location: Off the B137 between Ashford and Feltham
Type and Size: Nine acre lake
Carp Stock: Well stocked with carp to 20lbs
Category: Mixed Fishery

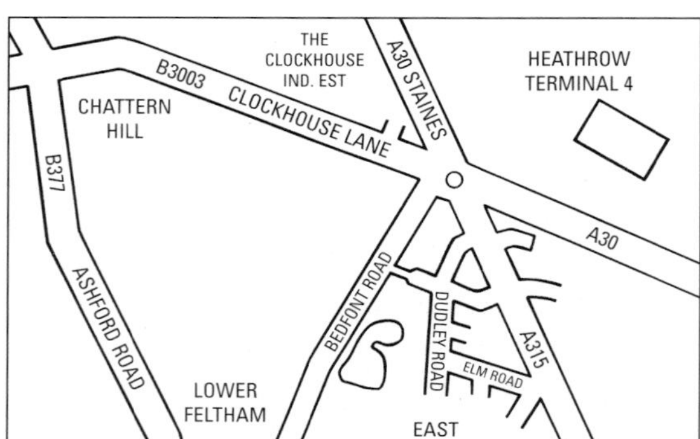

Other Species: Crucians, tench, perch, roach and pike
Permits: Boyer Leisure, Trout Road, West Drayton, Middx UB7 7SN. Adults £40 per season; juniors, OAP's, disabled £25. Reductions for juniors, OAP's. Day tickets obtainable from Lakeside Garden Centre at entrance to lake before fishing £3.50; £5.50 for two rods
Control: Boyer Leisure. Tel: 01895 444707
Restrictions: Unhooking mats compulsory. Night fishing for season ticket holders only.
BK Rating: Moderate
E/A: Thames
Comments: After Farlows, this is the best known of the Boyer lakes, and is a first class carp fishery. Toilets at Garden Centre. Tel: 0181 8442261

Boxer's Lake

Location: Lowther Drive, Enfield, London
Type and Size: Old estate lake of four acres
How to Find: From Enfield turn right onto the A 110 and then left into Lowther Drive in 2 miles
Carp Stock: Quite well stocked with carp to mid - doubles
Category: Mixed Fishery
Other Species: Roach, tench, crucians, rudd, gudgeon and eels
Permits: On bank
Cost: £2 per day; juniors and O.A.P's £1. Season tickets for local residents
Control: Boxer's Lake A.A. Tel: 0181 367 8944
Restrictions: No boilies, no bombs over 1/2 oz. Unhooking mats compulsory
BK Rating: Not known
Baits/Methods: Luncheon meat and sweetcorn best
E/A: Thames
Comments: Open June 16th to March 14th

Clapham Common Pond

Location: Clapham Common, SE London
Type and Size: Two acre park lake
How to Find: Clapham
Carp Stock: Well stocked with carp to over 20lbs. Mirrors and commons
Category: Mixed Fishery
Other Species: General coarse fish
Permits: Free fishing
Cost: No cost
BK Rating: Moderate
Control: Council
E/A: Thames
Comments: Crowded park lake. Anglers have reported up to 12 carp in a night's fishing, mostly of 8-10lbs, with the best at 20lbs

Colnbrook West

Location: Between Langley and West Drayton
Type and Size; Five acre lake
How to Find: On the A4 off Lakeside Road
Carp Stock: Well stocked with carp to over 20lbs
Category: Mixed Fishery
Other Species: Tench, perch, roach and pike
Permits: Boyer Leisure, Trout Road, West Drayton, Middx UB7 7SN. Tel: 01895 444707
Cost: £60 per season. Group permits available at discounted rates
Control: Boyer Leisure
Restrictions: Season tickets only
BK Rating; Easy
E/A: Thames
Comments: Regular catches of carp to 28lbs

Coppermill Stream

Location: Ferry Lane, Tottenham
Type and Size: One mile of river
How to Find: Near Tottenham Hale Underground Station, Ferry Lane
Carp Stock: Some carp to about 20lbs
Category: Mixed Fishery
Other Species: Barbel, bream, roach, chub, dace, pike and grayling
Permits: From machine. £1.00, 50p and 20p coins required. Day or season
Cost: About £5 per day; £60 per season
Control: Thames Water. Tel: 0181 8081527
Restrictions: No night fishing. Fishing is from 7.30am to half an hour after sunset. No groundbaiting
BK Rating: Moderate
E/A: Thames
Comments: The only 'stream' in our Guide! Tickets also from the lodge

East Warwick

Location: Ferry Lane, Tottenham N17 (opposite Ferry Boat Inn)
Type and Size: Reservoir of 43 acres
How to Find: Find the Ferry Boat Inn in Ferry Lane, Tottenham; Underground Station - Tottenham Hale
Carp Stock: Some carp present, sizes not known
Category: Few Carp
Other Species: Tench, roach, bream, perch

Permits: From machines at reservoir. £1.00, 50p and 20p coins needed
Cost: £2.50 per day, £35 per season
Control: Thames Water. Tel: 0181 8081527
Restrictions: No night fishng; fishing 7.30am to half an house after sunset. Closed Christmas Day
BK Rating: Very Difficult
E/A: Thames
Comments: Not a carp water, but it does contain a few. Suitable for ambulatory and some wheelchair anglers, although they may need help to net fish. Additional swims for anglers have been provided on steep banks

Farlows Lake

Location: Ford Lane, off Iver Lane, Bucks SLO 9LL - can be seen from M25
Type and Size: Large old gravel pit of 37 acres
Carp Stock: Heavily stocked with carp to 35lb, four other 30's, about 200 twenties and many doubles
Carp Stock: Carp Water
Other Species: Bream, perch, roach, tench, pike and trout
Permits: Boyer Leisure, Trout Road, West Drayton, Middx UB7 7SN
Cost: Season tickets £75 adults; £35 OAP's, disabled, juniors
Control: Boyer Leisure
Restrictions: Unhooking mats compulsory
BK Rating: Moderate, although Difficult for the big fish
E/A: Thames
Comments: Farlows is the 'flagship' for Boyer Leisure, who have a number of well run waters with big fish and excellent facilities The water is open all year. Carp are caught on all methods and baits, from maggots to boilies. Good facilities for the disabled. On site at Farlows Lake is a cafeteria, open all day, 7 days a week. Hot meals, sandwiches and drinks supplied all the year round. There is also a bar. Toilets and a shower available for all users of the lake. The Heron Point Bar is on the same site, and is open for normal pub hours, and is pleasantly situated on the water's edge. Drinks till midnight for sit-down meals at the cafeteria on Friday and Saturday nights. Low price drinks, pool table, juke box, fruit machine and darts - Farlows is one of the best big carp waters in the country. Tackle shop on site - Tel: 01895 444707 For full details of a the Boyers Fisheries apply to the office for their excellent and well illustrated brochure and application form, which gives details and maps of all their waters. Boyers also have carp fishing at Rodney Meadows

Hampstead Heath Pond

Location: Hampstead Heath
Type and Size: Small commons pond, very weedy and shallow
Carp Stock: A few carp to about 15lbs
Category: Few Carp
Other Species: Roach, rudd, bream and perch
Permits: None necessary - free fishing
BK Rating: Difficult
E/A: Thames

Harefield Carp Lake

Location: Moorhall Road, Harefield, opposite the Horse and Barge pub and one mile from Denham station
Type and Size: 47acre working gravel pit
Carp Stock: One of the best big fish carp waters in the country, with many thirties, and over 200 twenties. Several forties caught

Category: Carp Water
Other Species: Large bream and large roach
Permits: Boyer Leisure, Trout Road, West Drayton, Middx UB7 7SN. Tel: 01895 444707
Cost: On application - waiting list. Apply to Boyer Leisure to be put on waiting list
Control: Boyer Leisure
Restrictions: 100 places only on 2 - weekly rotas. Unhooking mats compulsory. Carp sacks banned
BK Rating: Difficult
E/A: Thames
Comments: Harefield is one of the best known and most famous carp waters in the country, and is fished by many of the leading carp anglers. Advanced methods and baits needed. Membership is available only if sponsored by existing member. Members are alowed to take guests by arrangement in advance only from 1st October. Toilet and showers available

Heath Vale Pond

Location: Hampstead Heath, London
Type and Size: Small, weedy lake, one of several ponds containing carp on the Heath
Carp Stock: Quite well stocked wtih carp to over 20lbs
Category: Mixed Fishery
Other Species: Roach, rudd, bream and pike
Permits: None necessary - free fishing. Rod licences essential
Restrictions: No fishing on one bank
BK Rating: Moderate
E/A: Thames
Comments: Like most of the free London waters, this pond is heavily fished, and the carp are caught quite often

High Maynard

Location: Blackhorse Lane, Walthamstow. Car park Ferry Lane, Tottenham, N17 (opposite Ferry Boat Inn)
Type and Size: Reservoir of 38 acres
How to Find: Blackhorse Lane, near Blackhorse Lane Underground Station or Tottenham Hale Underground Station (nearest)
Carp Stock: Some carp to over 20lbs
Category: Mixed Fishery
Other Species: Mixed coarse fish, including tench and perch
Permits: Day and season tickets available on site from ticket machine
Cost: £5 per day; £60 season. Tel: 0181 8081527
Control: Thames Water, Send for leaflet to Amenity and Recreation Officer, Thames Water, Nugent House, Vastern Road, Reading, Berks, Tel: 01734 593391. Thames Area Angling Guide also published at £1.95 from tackle dealers and bookshops
Restrictions: No night fishing; fishing is from 7.30am to half an hour after sunset. No groundbait
Baits/Methods: Boilies best at present
BK Rating: Difficult
E/A: Thames
Comments: It is said that this reservoir could produce a surprise in the form of a big carp; its potential is not really known. Toilet

Hollow Pond

Location: Whipps Cross Road (A114), north west of Wanstead, NE London
Type and Size: Large, shallow and weedy forest/commons-type lake
Carp Stock: Small number of carp to about 20lbs
Category: Few Carp
Other Species: Roach, bream, rudd, perch, pike and tench
Permits: About £4 per day. £40 per season. Concessions. Tel: 0181 5218534
BK Rating: Very Difficult
E/A: Thames

Kingfisher Lake (Pit 4)

Location: Pass the entrance to Savay on your right, coming from Denham. Cross the canal bridge and the entrance is on the right, just before the houses. Very long rough track
Type and Size: Mature gravel pit of 19 acres
How to Find: With difficulty. The lake is down a very long track of about a mile between Savay Lake and Harefield. There is a locked gate at the beginning of the track so it is better not to visit until you have a permit
Carp Stock: Most of the carp are doubles with a good number of twenties and one or two thirties. Probably not heavily stocked for its size. Carp occasionally escape upstream to next lake!
Category: Carp Water
Other Species: Tench, pike, roach, bream
Permits: Formerly controlled by the Greater London Council, now Hillingdon Borough Council: M Francis, Civic Centre, Uxbridge UB8 1UW. Tel: 01895 50111 Ext 2352
Cost: £50 season ticket
Control: Council
Restrictions: No night fishing. Rules against long stay fishing
BK Rating: Difficult
Baits/Methods: You will need the most advanced baits and methods at this water. Peanuts did well in the past but most now seem to use boilies
Comments: A well-known carp water hard fished by leading carp specialists. Chance of some very good twenties, but you can go very long periods without a take. An attractive lake, L-shaped and surrounded by trees and bushes. Very tranquil and pleasant to fish

Korda Lake

Location: Colne Valley, Harefield, near Savay Lake
Type and Size: Fifteen acre gravel pit
Carp Stock: Well stocked with plenty of doubles and some twenties to over 30lbs
Category: Mixed Fishery
Other Species: Usual coarse fish
Permits: Day tickets on bank
Cost: £2.50 one rod; £5 for two rods (12 hours); £4 and £8 for 24 hour session; season ticket (two rods) costs £50
Control: Tel: 01895 824455
Restrictions: Safe rigs and unhooking mats essential
BK Rating: Difficult
E/A: Thames

Please support the ACA see ad on page 167.

Lea Valley Leisure Park

Location: Enfield area
Type and Size: A number of lakes and gravel pits
How to Find: In the Lea valley between Enfield and Ware
Carp Stock: Some carp lakes - details from Fisheries Manager
Category: Mixed Fisheries
Other Species: General coarse fish
Permits: Fisheries Manager, Lea Valley Park, PO Box 88, Enfield EN2 9HG. Tel: 01992 717711
Cost: On application
BK Rating: Insufficient information
Control: Lea Valley Leisure Park
E/A: Thames
Comments: Details of fishing holidays can also be obtained from the Fisheries Manager. Includes Northmet Pit, Cheshunt, with pike to 35lb

Little Britain Lake

Location: Packet Boat Lane, Uxbridge
Type and Size: Attractive 7 acre lake
Carp Stock: Well stocked with carp to 30 lbs
Category: Mixed Fishery
Other Species: Roach, perch, tench, pike, catfish and crucians
Permits: On bank
Cost: About £3 per day
Control: Tel: 0181 573 3196
Restrictions: No keepnets
BK Rating: Moderate
Baits/Methods: Boilies good for the big carp
E/A: Thames
Comments: Toilets. Access for the disabled

Lockwood Reservoir

Location: Forest Road, Walthamstow
Type and Size: Reservoir of eighty acres
How to Find: Lea Bridge Road, in Walthamstow. Underground Staton - Blackhorse Road, 1 mile
Carp Stock: 300-500 carp to over 30lbs; average size about 18lbs
Category: Carp Water
Other Species: Bream, pike, chub, roach
Permits: Not easy to obtain membership - mainly for employees
Cost: £5 a season
Control: Private - EMWA Employees Sports Club
Restrictions: No night fishing - 7am till dusk only. No groundbaiting, no wading
BK Rating: Difficult
Comments: A huge London reservoir, sometimes with waves on it almost like the sea. Concrete bank. Very hard to find the fish. Carp angler Kevin Maddocks says that if this lake was drained he wouldn't be surprised to find a carp of over 40lbs

London Docks

Location: East End of London
Type and Size: Very large freshwater Docks: big areas of very deep water
Carp Stock: Said to be some very big carp, but they are hard to find because of the huge areas of these disused docks. One or two twenties have been reported caught

Category: Few Carp
Other Species: Most coarse fish
Permits: Try the Isle of Dogs AC, which is open to all; Jim's Tackle, Bethnal Green, Tel: 0171-7912961
Control: Club
BK Rating: Super-Difficult
E/A: Thames

Low Maynard: Walthamstow Nos 2 and 3

Location: Forest Road, Tottenham N17
Type and Size: Reservoirs: Low Maynard - 25 acres; No.2 - 13 acres; No3 - 12 acres
How to Find: Take the A10 from London and at Tottenham turn right along High Cross Road to Ferry Lane. Tottenham Hale tube station on left
Carp Stock: All well stocked with carp, with plenty of doubles and carp to over 30lbs
Category: Mixed Fishery
Other Species: Tench, bream and roach
Permits: Day and season permits from machines at the reservoir
Cost: £5 per day; £60 per season £1.00, 50p and 20p coins needed for machines
Control: Thames Water. Tel: 0181 8081527
Restrictions: No night fishing. Fishing is from 7.30am until half an hour after sunset. Closed Christmas Day. No peanuts, bent hooks or fixed leads
BK Rating: Moderate
E/A: Thames
Comments: Car park and toilets. Fishes quite well in winter

New Cut

Location: Ferry Lane, Tottenham
Type and Size: River Cut about three quarters of a mile long
How to Find: Near Tottenham Hale Underground Station, Ferry Lane, Tottenham
Carp Stock: Occasional carp only, but we hear some large carp have been sighted
Category: Few Carp
Other Species: Roach, chub, bream
Permits: Day and season from machines. £1.00, 50p and 20p coins required
Cost: £5 per day; £50 season
Control: Thames Water. Tel: 0181 8081527
Restrictions: No night fishing. Open from 7.30am to half an hour after sunset
BK Rating: We cannot assess this, as we do not know of anyone who has taken carp from the water, so we should have to enter an estimated rating of Very Difficult
E/A: Thames
Comments: Not suitable for disabled anglers

Norwood Lake

Location: Norwood Hill, London SE25
Type and Size: Town park lake of about three acres, with toilets on bank
How to Find: Off the A215, near Selhurst Park. The entrance is just off Woodvale Avenue
Carp Stock: Surprisingly well stocked with carp to doubles
Category: Mixed Fishery
Other Species: Roach, perch and bream
Permits: On bank
Cost: About £2 per day and £1.50 for juniors and OAP's. Season tickets - £27, £18 for juniors and £9 for OAP's

Control: Parks and Recreation Dept, Borough of Croydon
Restrictions: No night fishing. No fishing on either side of kiosk
BK Rating: Difficult
E/A: Thames

One Island Pond

Location: Mitcham Common, Greater London, off the A235 Croydon road; opposite Seven Island Pond
Type and Size: Pond of three-quarters of an acre
Carp Stock: Plenty of carp of 5-6lbs, some bigger fish to 16lbs
Category: Mixed Fishery
Other Species: Pike, roach, rudd, tench and perch
Permits: None - free fishing
Control: Local Council. Tel: 0181 6401171 (Parks Dept)
BK Rating: Very Difficult for the big carp
Baits/Methods: Boilies best for big fish; bread for the smaller carp
E/A: Thames

Orlitts Lakes

Location: Alongside the River Colnbrook, Lakeside Road, off the M4 between Langley and West Drayton
Type and Size: A pair of lakes, one fifteen acres, one four acres
Carp Stock: Some carp to 20lbs
Category: Few Carp in large lake,number in Little Orlitts
Other Species: Perch, bream, pike and large head of tench
Permits: Boyer Leisure, Trout Road, West Drayton, Middx UX7 7SN. Tel: 01895 444707
Cost: Season tickets at £30. Also available on group permit
Control: Boyer Leisure
BK Rating: Difficult in large; Moderate in small
E/A: Thames
Comments: River fishing included in the R Colnbrook

Ornamental Lake

Location: Wanstead Park, London
Type and Size: 15 acre park lake
How to Find: Off the A 12, Eastern Avenue
Carp Stock: Well stocked to doubles
Category: Mixed Fishery
Other Species: Pike, bream, tench, crucians, roach, eels and gudgeon
Permits: On bank
Cost: £2.50 per day, half price juniors and O.A.P's £25 per season
Control: Epping Forest Conservators. Tel: 0181 508 2266
Restrictions: No legering
BK Rating: Not known
E/A: Thames

Osterley Park

Location: Osterley Park, near Twickenham
Type and Size: Park lake of about seven acres
Permits: Season tickets - see notice on bank
Cost: About £12
BK Rating: Easy
E/A: Thames
Comments: We could not find out much about this water, but it certainly contains carp

Potomac Pond

Location: Gunnersbury Park, Brentford, West London
Type and Size: Small pond
Carp Stock: Well stocked with small commons to about 5lbs
Category: Mixed Fishery
Other Species: Roach, rudd and perch
Permits: Day tickets from bailiff on bank
Control: Council
Restrictions: No night fishing
BK Rating: Easy
E/A: Thames
Comments: A good town water for beginners and float anglers

Regents Canal (Camley Street)

Location: Off St Pancras Way, North London, near the Post Office building
Type and Size: Narrow city canal
Carp Stock: Some carp to doubles
Category: Few Carp
Other Species: Roach, perch, bream and a few rudd, tench and eels
Permits: Day tickets on the bank at about £2
Control: Mac McEndoo. Tel: 0181 9044988; Raven AC
BK Rating: Difficult
E/A: Thames

River Thames

Location: Best areas for big carp are said to be at Twickenham, Canbury Gardens, Walton-on-Thames and Shepperton
Type and Size: Wide river
Carp Stock: Few fish, and hard to find, but carp to well over 20lbs have been caught
Other Species: Nearly all of them!
Permits: Most of the Thames in these areas is free fishing
E/A: Thames
Comments: Carp to about 30lbs have been caught from the Thames, but there are not many of them, they are notoriously hard to find and to catch intentionally, although every now and then they are caught whilst fishing for other species

Savay Lake

Location: Moorhall Road, Harefield, Denham. Ordnance Survey Map Sheet No.160.Ref.048 885

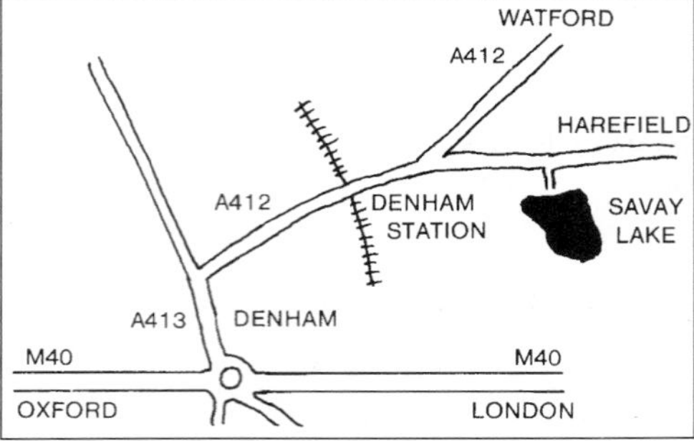

Type and Size: Mature gravel pit of 60 acres
How to Find: Take the A40 from London and at Denham turn right onto the A412 towards Watford. After half a mile go under the railway bridge and leaving Denham station on your right turn right into Moorfield Road towards Harefield. The Savay lake entrance is about half a mile on the right
Carp Stock: Whilst this lake does not contain a huge number of carp there are plenty of very big fish, enough for it to be regarded as a specialist carp water although it is really a mixed fishery. There are many twenties and thirties. Carp to 45lbs have been caught and this is one of the top carp fisheries in the country as far as very big carp are concerned
Category: Carp Water / Mixed Fishery
Other Species: Bream, tench, pike, roach and perch. The bream, tench and pike all grow very large
Permits: Fishery Manager; Peter Broxup, 309 Shirland Road, London W9
Cost: Not known
Restrictions: Not known
BK Rating: Very Difficult
Baits/Methods: You will need all of the latest rigs, methods and baits to stand much chance of catching any of the big carp from this famous water. Many are caught at ranges of 100 yards plus, although in some swims they are taken close in
Control: Private, Fishery Manager: Peter Broxup
E/A: Thames
Comments: Savay was sold in 1996, and current information is hard to obtain - Contact: Peter Broxup for details

Seven Islands Pond

Location: Mitcham Common, off the A236 Croydon road
Type and Size; One acre pond
Carp Stock: Quite well stocked with carp to 5-6lbs; a few bigger fish to 21lbs
Category: Mixed Fishery
Other Species: Roach, tench, perch, pike and rudd
Permits: None - free fishing
Control: Local Council. Tel: 0181 640 1171 (Parks Dept)
BK Rating: Very Difficult for the bigger carp
Baits/Methods: Boilies best for the bigger fish
E/A: Thames

South Norwood Lake

Location: Woodvale, South Norwood
Type and Size: Two acre park lake, very shallow
Carp Stock: The occasional carp is reported
Category: Few Carp
Other Species: Pike, roach, rudd, tench and perch
Permits: Day tickets on bank at low cost
Restrictions: No sacks; no night fishing
BK Rating: Very Difficult
E/A: Thames

Stockley Road Lakes

Location: Stockley Road, Hillingdon, Hayes
Type and Size: Two old pits, of three acres and half an acre
How to Find: Turn off the M4 at junction 4, go north through lights - 250 yards on right
Carp Stock: Lightly stocked with carp to 20lbs; small pond - about 55 carp to upper doubles

Category: Mixed Fishery
Other Species: Tench, rudd, roach, perch and pike
Permits: Boyer Leisure, Trout Road, West Drayton, Middx UB7 7SN. Tel: 01895 444707
Cost: £45 per season. Permit for this water on application. Reductions for juniors, OAP's and the disabled
Control: Boyer Leisure
Restrictions: Entry gate must be locked at all times. Unhooking mats compulsory
BK Rating: Moderate
E/A: Thames
Comments: A former carp syndicate, and a very pleasant water

Stonebridge Lock

Location: River Lea, Ferry Lane, Tottenham, near the Walthamstow Reservoirs
Type and Size: Canal-like section of the River Lea
Carp Stock: Some carp to nearly 20lbs
Category: Few Carp
Other Species: Chub, roach, bream, perch, gudgeon, dace, bleak and tench
Permits: Day tickets £1 on bank
Control: Club
BK Rating: Difficult
E/A: Thames
Comments: Near the Pipe Bridge is said to be a good area for carp

Swimming Lake

Location: Parliament Hill, Hampstead Heath
Type and Size: Small commons pond with concrete banks, much used by year round swimmers
Carp Stock: A few carp to over 20lbs
Category: Few Carp
Other Species: Roach, rudd, perch and pike
Permits: None necessary - free fishing
BK Rating: Very Difficult
E/A: Thames

Thorney Pool

Location: Thorney Road, West Drayton, just off junction 15 of the M25
Type and Size: 2 acre gravel pit

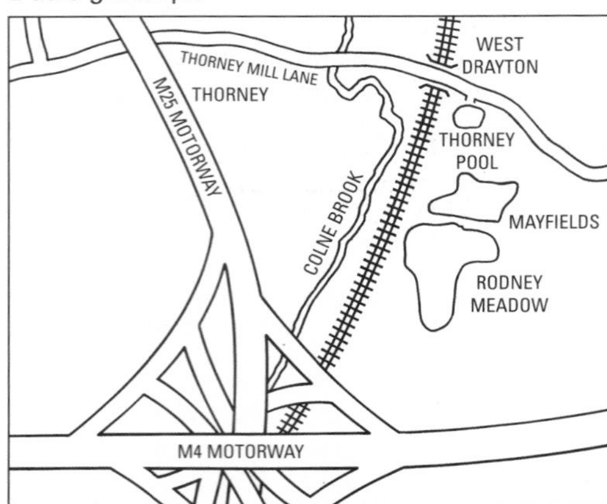

Carp Stock: Match water, stocked with carp to doubles
Category: Mixed Fishery
Other Species: Pike, tench, roach, crucian carp and bream
Permits: Boyer Leisure, Trout Road, West Drayton, Middx UB7 7SN. Tel: 01895 444707
Cost: £35 per season. Apply to Boyer's office if you want a permit to fish Thorney Pool only. Reduced prices for juniors, OAP's and the disabled
Control: Boyer Leisure
Restrictions: Unhooking mats compulsory. No cereal groundbait
E/A: Thames

Vale of Heath Pond

Location: East Heath Road, Hampstead Common, off the A502
Type and Size: Attractive two acre common pond
Carp Stock: Well stocked with carp to over 20lbs
Category: Mixed Fishery
Other Species: Roach, perch, pike, eels, tench and bream
Permits: Free fishing, althogh you must have an E.A.licence
Restrictions: None, for a change, although you cannot fish the area close to the houses and gardens - which is where the carp spend a lot of their time, of course!
BK Rating: Difficult - heavily fished free water
E/A: Thames
Comments: Tel: 0171 4854491 for information

Walthamstow No.1

Location: Ferry Lane, Tottenham N17
Type and Size: Reservoir of 19 acres
How to Find: Near Tottenham Hale Underground Station, Ferry Lane, Tottenham
Carp Stock: Quite well stocked with carp, most of which are 6-12lbs. Some to about 30lbs
Category: Carp Water
Other Species: Tench, roach, and bream
Permits: From the gatehouse
Cost: About £5 per day
Control: Thames Water. Tel: 0181 8081527
Restrictions: No night fishing. Fishing from 7.30am till half an hour after sunset
BK Rating: Moderate
E/A: Thames
Comments: A platform has been built out into the lake suitable for wheelchair-bound anglers. Reservoir rim suitable for some ambulatory disabled. Toilet

Wandsworth Common Pond

Location: Wandsworth Common, London SW18
Type and Size: Small, public 'commons' pond
Carp Stock: Some fish to about 15lbs, numbers unknown
Category: Few Carp
Other Species: Roach, rudd, bream and pike
Permits: Wandsworth Borough Council, Town Hall, Wandsworth
Control: Council
BK Rating: Difficult
E/A: Thames

West Warwick

Location: Ferry Lane, Tottenham
Type and Size: Reservoir of 34 acres
How to Find: Car park near Tottenham Hale Underground Station, Ferry Lane, Tottenham
Carp Stock: Well stocked with carp to mid-twenties. Average size 10½lbs. Growth rates of 4lbs a year recorded by Thames Water. More carp stocking in 1985
Category: Carp Only
Permits: From machines at reservoir. £1, 50p and 20p coins needed
Cost: Season £50
Control: Thames Water
Restrictions: No night fishing. Fishing is from 7.30am to half an hour after sunset. No groundbait
BK Rating: Moderate
E/A: Thames. Tel: 0181 8081527
Comments: Suitable for ambulatory handicapped able to cover long distance. Toilets. On all Walthamstow reservoirs wardens will give help and advice on request

Wraysbury

Location: Lake 1 - Douglas Lane, Wraysbury; Lake 2 - High Street, Wraysbury, near Staines
Type and Size: Gravel pits; Lake 1 - 61½ acres, Lake 2 - 76½ acres
How to Find: Take the A30 from Staines to the Staines by-pass. Take the B376 towards Wraysbury at the roundabout. Go through the village on Station Road, turn left onto Douglas Lane where there is a car park (Lake 1). For Lake 2: where the B276 turns left at Wraysbury village centre the entrance is on the right by the school
Carp Stock: Not known, but probably few. However, some of these are thought by carp specialists to be very large and a 45 is reported from Lake 1. Carp are not listed in the Guide Book for Lake 2 but there are a few big ones to over 30lbs. Wraysbury has now produced a 50 pounder
Category: Few Carp
Permits: Season tickets only from Leisure Sport. Day tickets in advance from: Wraysbury Newsagents in Wraysbury High Street; Davies Angling, 47 Church Street, Staines, or from Leisure Sport
Cost: £100 per season
Restrictions: Night fishing allowed. No fishing within casting distance of trout pens
Baits/Methods: Sophisticated baits and methods possibly needed and probably long casting techniques
Control: Leisure Sport Angling. Tel: 01932 564872. Fax 01932 566367
BK Rating: Super-Difficult
E/A: Thames
Comments: Some of the top anglers in the country fish these huge waters for the very big carp they contain. Some of these anglers have reported losing big fish at extreme range. Leisure Sport syndicate water - send for brochure. Wraysbury 1 is £100 per season. Wraysbury 2 costs £24. Concessions half price

GREATER MANCHESTER

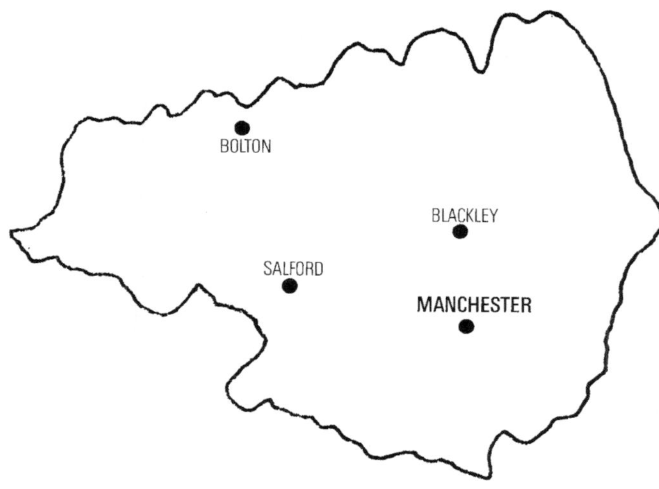

Ashton Canal

Location: East side of Manchester
Type and Size: Narrow city canal only about four feet deep
How to Find: From Junction 26 of the M6, take the A5777 towards Orrell. Turn left at a pub called the Abbey Lake and park by the canal
Carp Stock: Plenty of carp to about 5lbs
Category: Mixed Fishery
Other Species: Roach, bream, tench, perch and pike. Recently stocked with about 20,000 small fish for match fishing
Permits: £1 per day from Gresty's tackle shops, or £1.50 on the bank
Control: Gresty's AC
BK Rating: Easy
E/A: North West

Boggart Hole Clough

Location: Blackley Park, near Manchester
Type and Size: Two small park lakes
Carp Stock: Well stocked with carp to 20 lbs
Category: Mixed Fishery
Other Species: Roach, crucians, perch, tench and bream
Permits: On bank
Cost: About £3 per day. Concessions. Season tickets
Control: Manchester City Council Tel: 0161 740 9970
Restrictions: No carp to be retained
BK Rating: Not known
E/A: North West

Bowker Lakes

Location: Crumpsall, North Manchester, just off the A665
Type and Size: Two small attractive lakes
Carp Stock: Well stocked with carp to upper doubles, and one possible 20
Category: Mixed Fishery
Other Species: Roach, tench and perch
Permits: Season tickets - try local tackle shops, or enquire on bank
Control: Bowker Vale Angling Club
Restrictions: Members only; night fishing by syndicate
E/A: North West

Bradford's Reservoir

Location: Melville Street, Bradford, near the Bolton Wanderers football stadium
Type and Size: 3 acre reservoir
Carp Stock: Some carp to 20 lbs
Category: Few Carp
Other Species: Roach, perch, tench and gudgeon
Permits: In advance from local tackle shops
Cost: About £15 per season; juniors and O.A.P's £5
Control: Bradford A.A. Tel: 01204 393726
Restrictions: No night fishing
BK Rating: Difficult
Baits/Methods: Legered boilies best
E/A: North West

Carcus Lakes

Location: Kirklees Street, Tottington, near Bury
Type and Size: Two small mill lodges
Carp Stock: Carp to 10 lbs in larger pool
Category: Mixed Fishery
Other Species: Roach, bream, perch and tench
Permits: Local tackle shops or club secretary
Cost: £22 per season plus £5 joining fee. Reduced prices for juniors, O.A.P's, ladies and disabled. Includes other club waters.
Control: Bury A/S. Tel: 01204 886001
BK Rating: Not known
E/A: North West

Chorlton Water Park

Location: Maitland Avenue, Chorlton, Manchester 21
Type and Size: Water park lake of 19 acres
How to Find: Come off the M63 motorway at junction 9 and find Maitland Avenue. Water is five miles from Manchester centre and five miles from Stockport
Carp Stock: Quite well stocked from 1977 onwards with carp to upper doubles, the majority of which are commons
Category: Mixed Fishery
Other Species: Usual coarse fish
Permits: About £1 per day from office on site or £1.80 from bailiffs on the bank, 20p extra on Bank Holidays and weekends. Juniors about 40p and 80p. Season tickets: adults £10; juniors £4
Control: Mersey Valley Joint Committee. Water Parks Manager Tel: 0161 8815639
BK Rating: Moderate
Restrictions: Fishing 8am till sunset only, unless special night permit obtained
Baits/Methods: Normal carp fishing tactics and baits

E/A: North West
Comments: Lake is up to 18 feet deep in parts

Clegg Hall Lakes

Location: Clegg Hall Road, Littleborough, near Manchester
Type and Size: 4 acre lake
How to Find: Take the A 58 towards Rochdale, turn left into Dye House Lane and Clegg Hall Road
Carp Stock: Carp average about 8 lbs
Category: Mixed Fishery
Other Species: Small bream, perch, roach, rudd, crucians and gudgeon
Permits: On bank
Cost: £5 per day
Control: Tel: 01706 42177
Restrictions: No nuts, boilies or cereal groundbait
BK Rating: Not known
E/A: North West

Clifton Marina

Location: Clifton House Road, Salford, off the A666 Bolton road
Type and Size: 80 acre gravel pit
Carp Stock: Quite well stocked with carp to about 25lbs
Category: Mixed Fishery
Other Species: Tench, bream, roach and pike
Permits: On the bank at £1.50 per day for adults; concessions
Control: Tel: 0161 7942784
Restrictions: No night fishing
BK Rating: Moderate
E/A: North West

Crompton's Water

Location: Railway Terrace, Bury
Type and Size: 3 acre former mill lodge
Carp Stock: Some carp to upper doubles
Category: Few Carp
Other Species: Pike, roach, bream and perch
Permits: In advance only from local tackle shops
Cost: £25 per season; £7 juniors, O.A.P's and disabled. Includes other club waters
Control: Bury D.A.S. Tel: 01204 886001
Restrictions: No fishing from dam end
BK Rating: Difficult
Baits/Methods: Luncheon meat good for carp
E/A: North West

Debdale Reservoirs

Location: Hyde Road, Gorton, near Manchester
Type and Size: Two lakes of 30 and 20 acres
Carp Stock: Some carp to over 30lbs
Category: Few Carp
Other Species: General coarse fish, including some pike
Permits: Day tickets on bank. Season tickets from Manchester City Council. Tel: 0161 223 0816
Control: Council
Restrictions: No night fishing

BK Rating: Very Difficult
E/A: North West
Comments: Uninteresting, like most reservoirs, but could produce a very big fish. Police divers report big catfish in lower reservoir

Dingle Lodge

Location: Radcliffe
Type and Size: One acre lake opening off the Bolton and Bury canal
Carp Stock: Some carp to 20 lbs
Category: Mixed Fishery
Other Species: Bream, roach, tench and perch
Permits: In advance only from local tackle shops
Cost: About £15 a year
Control: Bolton A.A. Tel: 01204 393726
BK Rating: Difficult
E/A: North West

Dixon Green Reservoir

Location: St. Germain Street, Farnworth
Type and Size: Very small reservoir
Carp Stock: Some carp to 20 lbs, mostly large
Category: Mixed Fishery
Other Species: Roach, gudgeon, chub and crucians
Permits: In advance only from local tackle shops
Cost: £7 per season; juniors, O.A.P's and disabled £3
Control: Tel: 0161 799 4242
Restrictions: No boilies; no night fishing
BK Rating: Difficult
E/A: North West
Comments: Disabled access

Farm Lodge

Location: Calf Hey Close, Radcliffe, near Bolton
Type and Size: Small lake
Carp Stock: Well stocked with small carp; a few doubles
Category: Mixed Fishery
Other Species: Roach, small bream and tench
Permits: In advance from local shops
Cost: £12 per season; £4 juniors and O.A.P's
Control: Bolton A.A. Tel: 01204 393726
Restrictions: No night fishing
BK Rating: Not known
E/A: North West

Gleaves Reservoir

Location: Dunscar, near Bolton
Type and Size: 2 acre farm reservoir
Carp Stock: Some big carp
Category: Few Carp
Other Species: Roach, perch and small bream
Permits: In advance only from local tackle shops
Cost: About £15 per season; £5 for juniors, O.A.P's and the disabled
Control: Bolton D.A.A. Tel: 01204 393726
Restrictions: No night fishing
BK Rating: Difficult
E/A: North West

Comments: Probably open all year. Disabled access

Heaton Park Lake

Location: Bury Old Road, Manchester
Type and Size: Eight acre park lake with islands, and used by boats
Carp Stock: Well stocked with small carp, but some doubles
Category: Mixed Fishery
Other Species: General coarse fish
Permits: On bank at £1.60 per day
Control: Council - Ron Telford. Tel: 0161 7731085
BK Rating: Easy
E/A: North West
Comments: Typical park lake, but quite pleasant and easy fishing

Huddersfield Canal

Location: Uppermill, east of Oldham on the A669
Type and Size: Narrow canal with little boat traffic
Carp Stock: Well stocked with carp from 8lb to 12lbs
Category: Mixed Fishery
Other Species: Roach, perch and a few chub
Permits: On the bank, or from Brownhill Visitors Centre, Uppermill
Cost: £2.50 per day
Control: Tel: 0161 7971886
Restrictions: No night fishing
BK Rating: Moderate
E/A: North West

Hulton Park Lake

Location: Garthmere Road, Over Hutton, near Bolton
Type and Size: One acre attractive pool
Carp Stock: Well stocked with carp to 10 lbs
Category: Mixed Fishery
Other Species: Tench, roach and perch
Permits: In advance only from local tackle shops
Cost: About £15 per season
Control: Bolton D.A.A. Tel: 01204 393726
Restrictions: No night fishing; barbless hooks
BK Rating: Moderate
E/A: North West

King William IV Reservoir

Location: Blackley New Road, Manchester, - in the shadow of the tower blocks
Type and Size: 4 acre lake
Carp Stock: Some carp to 20 lbs
Category: Mixed Fishery
Other Species: Tench, roach, perch, bream and rudd
Permits: On bank
Cost: About £3 per day
Control: Tel: 0161 655 3402
BK Rating: Difficult
E/A: North West

Lankys Mill Pond

Location: Blackley, north Manchester
Type and Size: Very clear, weedy pond of about one and a half acres
Carp Stock: Just half a dozen or so, but possibly a couple of 20's
Category: Few Carp
Other Species: Roach and bream
Permits: None necessary - free fishing
BK Rating: Very Difficult
E/A: North West
Comments: No close season; little more than a rubbish dump, but a few good fish. Usual town water problems

Melches

Location: Farnworth, near Bolton
Type and Size: Tiny, half acre pond
Carp Stock: Over 100 carp, with plenty of doubles to 22 1/2 lbs
Category: Carp Water
Permits: Season tickets from Greater Manchester Transport Angling Club and Farnworth Cricket and Angling Club
Control: Club
BK Rating: Easy
E/A: North West

Myrtle Road Lodges

Location: Myrtle Road, Middleton, off the A669 Oldham road
Type and Size: Two small reservoirs
Carp Stock: Quite well stocked with carp to over 20lbs
Category: Mixed Fishery
Other Species: Tench, bream, roach and perch
Permits: Day tickets on bank £2
Control: Tel: 0161 6553402
Restrictions: One rod only; no night fishing
BK Rating: Moderate
E/A: North West

Painswick Park Lake

Location: Portway, Wythenshawe
Type and Size: 2 acre park lake
Carp Stock: Some carp to doubles
Category: Mixed Fishery
Other Species: Crucians, tench, roach, perch and bream
Permits: On bank
Cost: About £2 per day; half price for juniors, O.A.P's and disabled. Season tickets about £15
Control: Woodhouse Park Anglers. Tel: 0161 945 5711
Restrictions: No night fishing
BK Rating: Difficult
E/A: North West

Platt Fields

Location: Fallowfield, on the edge of Manchester
Type and Size: Small, shallow lake of about three acres
Carp Stock: Quite well stocked with plenty of doubles up to about 15lbs
Category: Mixed Fishery
Other Species: Roach, tench and perch

Permits: Day tickets on bank. Day and season tickets from Manchester City Council
Control: Council
Restriction: No night fishing
BK Rating: Moderate
E/A: North West
Comments: Used for boating, and often very busy; good fishing throughout the season

Polly's Flash

Location: Kingsdown Road, Abram - A 573
Type and Size: 5 acre shallow lake
Carp Stock: Well stocked with carp to over 20 lbs, average size 6 lbs
Category: Mixed Fishery
Other Species: Roach, bream, perch, tench, chub and gudgeon
Permits: On bank
Cost: £1.50 per day; £1 juniors, O.A.P's and the disabled. £8 per season
Control: Abram A/C. Tel: 01942 742603
Restrictions: No boilies or trout pellets
BK Rating: Not known
E/A: North West

River Irwell

Location: Salford area of Manchester
Type and Size: Small river
Carp Stock: Stocked with small carp in 1990 by the Mayor of Salford
Category: Mixed Fishery
Other Species: Roach, bream and perch
Permits: Jubilee Disabled Angling Club
Control: Salford City Council
Restrictions: No night fishing
BK Rating: Not known
E/A: North West
Comments: 30 wooden platforms installed with ideal facilities for the disabled

Stamford Park Lakes

Location: Mellor Road, Ashton - under - Lyne
Type and Size: Two park lakes
Carp Stock: Well stocked with carp to doubles
Category: Mixed Fishery
Other Species: Pike, roach, tench, perch, bream and crucians
Permits: On bank
Cost: About £2 per day
Control: Council. Tel: 01613 423394
Restrictions: No night fishing
BK Rating: Moderate
E/A: North West

Stoney Pit Reservoir

Location: Black Bower Lane, Hyde, near Stockport
Type and Size: One acre lake
Carp Stock: Carp to 20 lbs
Category: Mixed Fishery
Other Species: Roach, perch, tench, bream and gudgeon
Permits: Local tackle shops
Cost: About £10 per year, O.A.P's and disabled free

Control: Tel: 0161 494 2671 - Tameside F.A.
BK Rating: Not known
E/A: North West

Swan Lodge

Location: Between Bury and Radcliffe, off the A56 north west of Manchester
Type and Size: Small shallow lake
Carp Stock: Some carp mostly very small
Category: Few Carp
Other Species: Roach, tench and bream
Permits: Day tickets on the bank or from Elton Tackle, Radcliffe. Tel: 016172 45425
Cost: £2.50; £1.50 for juniors, OAP's and the disabled
Restrictions: No night fishing
BK Rating: Moderate
E/A: North West

Tanner's Dam

Location: Greenfield, off the A 635 Ashton - under - Lyne road
Type and Size: 2 acre mill dam with an island
Carp Stock: Carp to over 20 lbs
Category: Mixed Fishery
Other Species: Bream, roach, perch and tench
Permits: In advance only
Cost: £26 per season, plus £13 joining fee
Control: Diggle A.C. Tel: 01457 875818
Restrictions: No night fishing
BK Rating: Not known
E/A: North West

Temple Springs

Location: Smithills Dean Road, Bolton (access through the school)
Type and Size: Small pool
Carp Stock: Small carp
Category: Mixed Fishery
Other Species: Rudd, roach and tench
Permits: In advance only from local tackle shops
Cost: About £15 per season
Control: Bolton A.A. Tel: 01204 393726
Restrictions: No night fishing
BK Rating: Not known
E/A: North West

Wrightington Pond

Location: Wrightington, near Standish, on the A 5209
Type and Size: 4 acre lake
Carp Stock: Some carp to doubles
Category: Few Carp
Other Species: Bream, tench and roach
Permits: In advance only from local tackle shops
Cost: About £15 per season
Control: Wigan A.A. Tel: 01257 265905
Restrictions: No night fishing
BK Rating: Difficult
E/A: Severn Trent

GWENT (Wales)

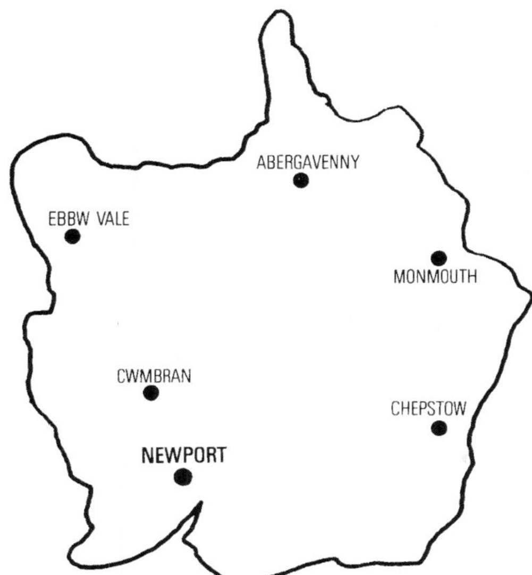

Blue Lake

Location: Waun -y-Pound Industrial Estate, Ebbw Vale
Type and Size: Four acre reservoir
How to Find: Find the Waun -y-Pound Industrial Estate in Ebbw Vale, which is on the road from Newport
Carp Stock: Quite well stocked with smallish carp, average 4-5lbs. There are some bigger fish, with some 20's reported
Category: Mixed Fishery
Other Species: Perch, roach, chub, tench and gudgeon
Permits: Season tickets only by club membership. Ebbw Vale Welfare Angling Club Membership (no day tickets): 52 Bethcar Street, Ebbw Vale. Tel: 01495 301392; or E Bynon Tackle Shop, King Street, Brynmawr; R Satterley, 8 Pen -y-Lan, Ebbw Vale. Tel: 01495 308457
Cost: About £10 per season
Control: Club
BK Rating: Moderate
Baits/Methods Modern carp fishing baits and methods needed
E/A: Welsh
Comments: This lake goes down to a depth of 35 feet in places and has concrete and shale banks and no features

Boat Pond, Beaufort

Location: Highlands Road, Beaufort Hill, Ebbw Vale
Type and Size: Reservoir of three and a half acres
How to Find: Address as above. Beaufort is north of Ebbw Vale just off the A465, 8 miles east of Abergavenny
Carp Stock: Well stocked with mirrors and commons to a good size

Category:	Mixed Fishery
Other Species:	Dace, roach, perch, crucians
Permits:	Season tickets only by membership of Ebbw Vale Welfare Angling Club. Membership from 52 Bethcar Street, Ebbw Vale. Tel: 01495 301392 or Pen-y-Lan, Ebbw Vale. Tel: 01495 308547
Cost:	About £10 per season
Control:	Club
BK Rating:	Difficult
Baits/Methods:	Standard carp fishing baits and methods
E/A:	Welsh
Comments:	Fish location is easy in this very clear and very heavily weeded water, but the fish are not easy to tempt

Cwmbran Boating Lake

Location:	Cwmbran, between Malpas and Pontypool
Type and Size:	Man-made boating lake of one and a half acres
How to Find:	The lake is near the Police HQ, just off the A4042, at Cwmbran between Malpas and Pontypool
Carp Stock:	Quite well stocked with commons and mirrors to 18lbs
Category:	Mixed Fishery
Other Species:	Tench, bream, roach, perch
Permits:	Day tickets available at the boathouse
Cost:	About £3 per day. Boathouse Tel: 01633 867642
BK Rating:	Easy
Baits/Methods	Standard carp fishing methods with boilies and floaters
E/A:	Welsh
Comments:	'Public' water, boats etc. No night fishing

Cwmcelyn Club Water

Location:	Blaina, near Ebbw Vale
Type and Size:	Man-made lake of one and a half acres
How to Find:	Take the A467 from Abertillery north, through Blaina and at the second roundabut take the third exit. Turn left at the next junction
Carp Stock:	Well stocked with commons and mirrors to 17lbs
Category:	Mixed Fishery
Other Species:	Crucian carp, tench, trout, chub, roach, dace, perch, gudgeon and goldfish
Permits:	Day tickets from Granville Derrick. Tel: 01495 291110; or Des Hillman, 99 Roundhouse Close, Nantyglo
Cost:	On application
Control:	Club
BK Rating:	Easy
E/A:	Welsh

THE BEEKAY GUIDE TO 2000 BRITISH & EUROPEAN CARP WATERS

Is YOUR Water listed? If so, are the details correct?
If you spot omissions, inaccuracies, or know of any changes, please let us know by filling in the Waters Questionnaire at the back of this guide and return it to us at:

Beekay International
Withy Pool
Henlow Camp
Bedfordshire
SG16 6EA

Lliswerry Pond

Location: Three miles north of Newport
Type and Size: Narrow, canal-like lake, very weedy and on housing estate - about two acres
Carp Stock: Well stocked with doubles to about 20lbs
Category: Mixed Fishery
Other Species: Tench, roach, bream and rudd
Permits: Day tickets on bank
Cost: £3 per day
Control: Newport AA, L Clarke, Tel: 01633 267047 - night fishing for members only, not on day ticket
BK Rating: Moderate
E/A: Welsh

Machine Pond

Location: Warwick Road, Brynmawr, between Abergavenny and Merthyr Tydfil
Carp Stock: Well stocked wtih commons and mirrors to about 12lbs, average size about 7lbs
Category: Mixed Fishery
Other Species: Pike, perch, roach, chub, tench and gudgeon
Permits: Season ticket only by club membership. No day tickets. Ebbw Vale Welfare Club Angling Club. Club membership from Petsville, 52 Bethcar Street, Ebbw Vale. Tel: 01495 301292; E Bynon Tackle Shop, King Street, Brynmawr ; Ray Satterley, 8 Pen - Y - Lan, Ebbw Vale. Tel: 01495 308547
Cost: About £10 per season
Control: Club
BK Rating: Easy
Baits/Methods: Traditional baits and methods, and also boilies and multiple baits
E/A: Welsh

Monmouthshire and Brecon Canal

Location: The canal runs between Newport and Brecon, about 40 miles
Type and Size: Narrow, shallow canal
Carp Stock: Some carp to 20lbs, mostly in concentrated areas, and hard to locate
Category: Few Carp, except in some areas which would qualify as Mixed Fishery
Other Species: Most coarse fish
Permits: Newport AA, L Clarke. Tel: 01633 267047
Control: Club
BK Rating: Very Difficult
E/A: Welsh
Comments: A 16 pounder was caught on floating crust in 1990

Morgans Pool

Location: Close to the M5, junction 26 to Cymbran
Type and Size: Lake of about four acres
Carp Stock: Well stocked with small carp to lower doubles
Category: Carp Water
Permits: Day tickets on bank
Cost: £2.50 per day
Control: Newport AA, Secretary: P Climo, 2 Darwin Drive, Newport. Club membership open to all at about £20; night fishing for members only
BK Rating: Easy
E/A: Welsh

Woodstock Pool

Location: Cymbran, near Newport
Type and Size: Two and a half acre lake with island
Carp Stock: Quite well stocked with carp, mostly doubles, to about 20lbs
Category: Mixed Fishery
Other Species: Roach and tench
Permits: Day tickets from bailiff's cabin
Cost: £3 per day
Control: Newport AA. Tel: 01633 212953. Membership open to all at about £20 per season; night fishing for members only
BK Rating: Moderate
E/A: Welsh

GWYNEDD (Wales)

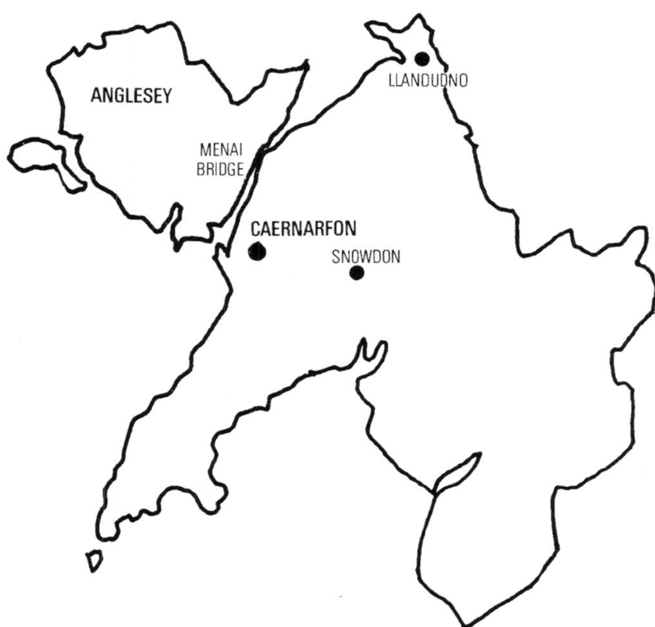

Conwy Valley Fisheries A

Location: Rowen, near Conwy
Type and Size: One acre man - made lake
How to Find: Leave Conwy Castle on the A 55, then take the B 5106, then take the turn to Rowen; the fishery is signposted from here
Carp Stock: Well stocked with carp, thought to be small
Category: Mixed Fishery
Other Species: Tench, rudd, roach and bream
Permits: On site
Cost: About £5 per day
Control: Tel: 01492 650063
Restrictions: No night fishing; boilies; nuts or beans
BK Rating: Not known
E/A: Welsh
Comments: Probably open all year. Tackle shop, cafe and toilets. Self-catering cottages available

Llyn -y-Gors Lakes A

Location: Llyn -y-Gors, Llandegfan, Menai Bridge, Anglesey, Gwynedd, Wales LL59 5PN
Type and Size: Two man-made lakes; carp lake - 5 acres; other lake -2 3/4 acres
How to Find: Follow the A5 towards Holyhead. Cross the Britannia Bridge to Anglesey and take the left hand spur (A5025) to Amlwych. Follow signs to Llandegfan. Turn left at church. Llyn-y-Gors is on the right in one and a half miles

Carp Stock: 300 fish to 25lbs, average 10-15lbs in carp lake
Other Species: Catfish
Category: Carp Water
Permits: On site. Tel: 01248 713410 (Roger Thompson). Fax 01248 716324. Winter syndicate with a 'no secrets' rule
Cost: £8 per day; £12 for 24 hours bookable in advance. Prices approximate
BK Rating: Easy to Moderate
Restrictions: No particle baits. Unhooking mats must be used, 10lbs minimum B/S line
Control: Private - the owner is an experienced carp angler
Tel: 01378 8708250 (mobile)
E/A: Welsh
Comments: No close season. Attractive lakes. Regularly stocked. Other lake - mixed coarse fish - 50lb bags of ghost carp common. Four holiday cottages to let; send for brochure. Many twenties caught. This is a place we can both strongly recommend, as we have stayed there. There couldn't be anywhere pleasanter for a relaxed holiday of any kind, with the bonus of big carp only 75 yards from your cottage door, and a fabulous view of the Snowdon mountain range from your window. Tents and caravans allowed. Carp lake extended in 1995. 'One not to be missed'

Ty-Hen

Location: Rhosneigr, Ty Hen, Station Road
Type and Size: One and a half acre spring-fed farm pond
Carp Stock: Heavily stocked with carp over 20lbs
Category: Mixed Fishery
Other Species: Tench, rudd, roach, and crucians
Permits: Tel: 01407 810331/535583
Cost: £5 per day on bank
BK Rating: Not known
E/A: Welsh
Comments: Dawn to dusk only. Barbless hooks. No keepnets. Open April to October. Toilet and showers

HAMPSHIRE

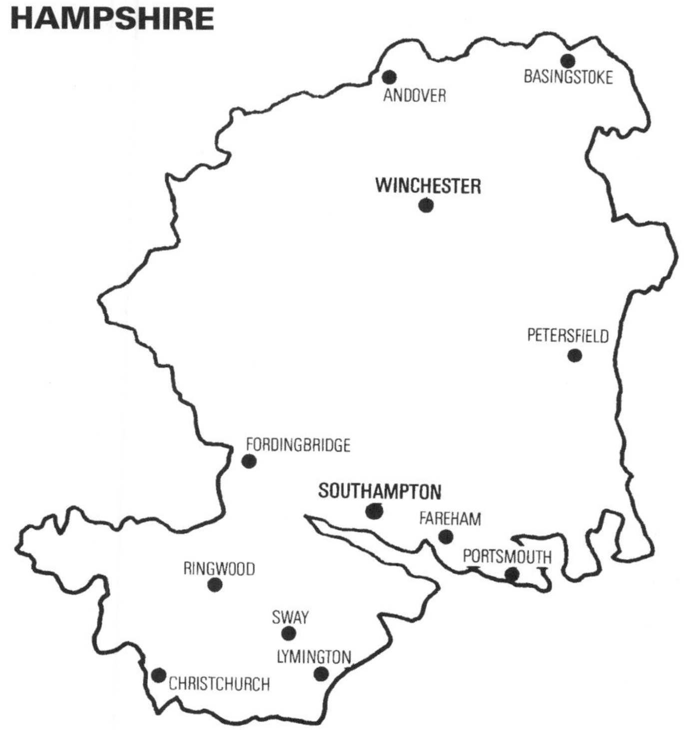

Baron's Ponds

Location: St. Patrick's Lane, Petersfield
Type and Size: Two large pits
Carp Stock: Well stocked with carp to 25 lbs
Category: Mixed Fishery
Other Species: Tench, roach, rudd, chub and crucians
Permits: In advance from Tackle-Up
Cost: £5 - £10 per day
Control: Tackle - Up. Tel: 01252 614066
BK Rating: Not known
E/A: Southern

Basingstoke Canal

Location: Aldershot - Basingstoke
Type and Size: Narrow restored canal, about 15 miles long
How to Find: Try Claycart Bridge, off the A323 between Aldershot and Fleet
Carp Stock: Plenty of carp especially at Claycart, with fish to 20lbs
Category: Mixed Fishery
Other Species: General coarse fish
Permits: Day and monthly tickets from local tackle shops and on the bank
Cost: Day tickets in advance about £2; on bank £2.50
Control: Basingstoke Canal Anglers Association
BK Rating: Moderate
E/A: Thames

Comments: Claycart area produced 14 doubles to two carp anglers on the first day of the 1988 season. This canal could produce some very big fish in the future

Ben's Lake

Location: Bishops Green, near Newbury
Type and Size: Two small lakes with islands
How to Find: Take the A 34 south from Newbury, and in 2 miles turn left onto the A 339 Basingstoke road. Then turn right towards Bishop's Green - the fishery is half a mile on the right
Carp Stock: Carp averaging 5 lbs
Category: Mixed Fishery
Other Species: Goldfish, roach, rudd, bream, tench and gudgeon
Permits: On bank
Cost: £5 per day; £2.50 O.A.P's and juniors
Control: Private. Tel: 01635 268447
Restrictions: None
BK Rating: Not known
E/A: Southern

Broadlands Lake

Location: Ower, between Romsey and Totton, Southampton
Type and Size: Large lake fomed in 1977 by the construction of the M27 motorway
Carp Stock: Well stocked with carp to about 30lbs
Category: Mixed Fishery
Other Species: The lake is noted for its pike to over 30lbs, best 39 1/4 , and perch, roach, tench, bream and rudd
Permits: Day and season tickets from Fishery Manager Tel: 01703 733167/869881
Cost: About £5 per day. £50 per season
BK Rating: Moderate
Baits/Methods: Carp can be caught on luncheon meat and sweetcorn, but better methods are the use of boilies on bolt or hair rigs
Control: Private
E/A: Wessex
Comments: A new lake which has produced huge pike and may well contain some big carp in the future. All information from the Fishery Manager. 35 pounder stocked in 1988 and caught

Cadnam's Pool

Location: In the New Forest at Stoney Cross, just off the end of the M27
Type and Size: Small forest pool
How to Find: Leave the M27 at Junction 1, and take the B3078 north. Turn left towards Stoney Cross. Lake is on the right, with car park
Carp Stock: Well stocked with carp to nearly 20lbs
Category: Mixed Fishery
Other Species: Roach, rudd and small bream
Permits: Day tickets from local tackle shops, campsites and the Forestry Commission at Queen House, Lyndhurst (hope you have better luck at the Forestry Commission H/Q than we did; we wrote to ask them for details of all their waters, but they didn't reply!) Tel: 01425 478072 or 01202 485169 (I expect they do answer the phone)
Cost: About £4 per day (two rods), half price for juniors; £10 per week;
Restrictions: No night fishing; barbless hooks
BK Rating: Easy; good for youngsters
E/A: Wessex

Carrow Row Farm Lakes

Location: Segensworth Road, near Titchfield
How to Find: Take the A27 from the M27 at Junction 9, then turn left to Segensworth Road. The ponds are on the left
Type and Size: Three small shallow ponds
Carp Stock: Well stocked with carp to upper doubles
Category: Mixed Fishery
Other Species: Rudd and tench
Permits: Day tickets on bank
Cost: £4.50 per day; £3.50 half day: £2.50 evenings
Control: Ian Hammond. Tel: 01329 45102
Restrictions: No night fishing
BK Rating: Easy
E/A: Southern

Charlton Pits

Location: Charlton, near Andover
Type and Size: Matured gravel pit of about ten acres
Carp Stock: Well stocked with carp to 20lbs, including some good commons
Category: Mixed Fishery
Other Species: Perch, roach, rudd, tench and dace
Permits: Andover AC, day tickets from local tackle shops or from the Secretary, R L Adcock, Flat 2, Bridge House, 154 Junction Road, Andover
Cost: Day tickets - £3; season £20
Control: Club
BK Rating: Difficult
E/A: Southern
Comments: Back in the seventies, this was a well known (and rather secret) big carp water, but later the lake was partialy drained, and most of the big fish netted and sold. The pits are flooded by the River Anton, and are said now to contain grayling as well as other species

Fordingbridge Farm A

Location: Fordingbridge
Type and Size: Three acre lake
Carp Stock: Well stocked with carp to doubles
Category: Carp Water
Other Species: Possibly some
Permits: P.S.Birch, 18 Elmwood Ave, Fordingbridge SP6 1DN
Cost: See comments
Control: Tel: 01425 653383
Restrictions: No children
BK Rating: Not known
E/A: Southern
Comments: Two berth caravan on site at about £200 per week - fishing included

Frimley

Location: Frimley High Street, Frimley, Farnborough
Type and Size: 10 gravel pits, most of which are small, but one is eleven acres and one about six acres
How to Find: Find the A325 and go through Farnborough to Farnborough Green roundabout. Continue on the A325, and cross the railway bridge, to park in Frimley High Street car park. No car parking elsewhere - access to lakes by foot only
Carp Stock: Well stocked with carp to 20lbs

Category: Mixed Fishery
Other Species: Bream, tench, roach, perch, pike, crucian carp
Permits: Season tickets only from Leisure Sport, Thorpe Park, Staines Road, Chertsey, Surrey KT1 68PN. Tel: 01932 564872
Cost: £24 per season. Juniors/OAP/disabled £12
Restrictions: No night fishing. Access not available to some parts of area which are a Nature Reserve - details from Leisure Sport Guide Book
BK Rating: Difficult
E/A: Thames
Comments: Send to Leisure Sport Angling for brochure

Golden Springs Lakes

Location: Near Christchurch
Type and Size: 12 small pools
Carp Stock: Most of the pools contain carp to about 10lbs
Category: Mixed Fishery
Other Species: Tench, roach and trout
Permits: Christchurch AC - tickets from local tackle shops or R Andrews, 4 Marley Close, New Milton, Hants
Control: Club
Restrictions: No night fishing - 6am to 30 minutes after sunset only - do not go onto the banks of the River Frome
BK Rating: Moderate
E/A: Wessex

Hatchet Pond and Cadmans Pool

Location: Near Cadnam, New Forest
Type and Size: Medium sized forest pools
How to Find: Enquire from Forestry Comission
Carp Stock: Some carp to doubles
Other Species: Bream, tench, pike and berch
Cost: Season about £60, about £4 per day
BK Rating: Difficult
Control: Forestry Commission. Tel: 01703 283771
Comments: Licences not required for New Forest ponds

Hightown Lake

Location: Near Ringwood
Type and Size: Twenty acre gravel pit
Carp Stock: Quite well stocked with carp to 20lbs
Category: Mixed Fishery
Other Species: Tench, roach and eels
Permits: Members only water of Ringwood and District AA. Secretary: R Smith, 1 Avon Castle Drive, Matchams Lane, Ringwood
Restrictions: No day tickets; no night fishing except for members
BK Rating: Moderate
E/A: Wessex

H.M.S.Dryad Lake

Location: Portsmouth
Type and Size: Four acre lake
Carp Stock: Well stocked, mostly small carp
Category: Mixed Fishery
Other Species: Mixed coarse fish
Permits: Controlled by the Royal Navy

Carp Stock: On application
BK Rating: Easy
Control: Royal Navy
E/A: Southern
Comments: You could try the Admiralty, but more seriously, local tackle shops would be able to tell you how to go about getting permission - a Naval uniform might help!

Hollybush Lane Lakes

Location: Farnborough
Type and Size: Three lakes totalling 20 acres. Mature gravel pits
How to Find: From London take the M3 motorway and leave at junction 4. Take the A325 towards Farnborough for 3 miles and at the Queens Hotel roundabout turn left onto the A3011. The fishery entrance is one mile along this road opposite the Fir Tree public house. Car park is 300 yards down the lane on the left
Carp Stock: Middle lake mainly carp with several 20's. Others contain some carp. Main lake suffered a fish kill in 1991
Category: Mixed Fishery
Other Species: Bream, tench, roach, perch, pike
Permits: Day tickets £4 (juniors/OAP £2) from Raison Bros Tackle Shop, Farnborough. Tel: 01252 543470. Tickets must be obtained before fishing. Season tickets
Restrictions: No night fishing. No sacking
Baits/Methods: Normal carp rigs and baits
Control: Redland Angling Scheme
BK Rating: Moderate
E/A: Thames
Comments: Commercial fishery, Redland. Carp to 20lbs reported. Number 44 bus from Aldershot to Woking passes fishery entrance. Ash Vale railway station 10 minutes from fishery. We are reliably informed that the lake itself is just in Surrey!

Home Farm

Location: Home Farm, Rotherwick, near Hook, Basingstoke
Type and Size: One acre farm pond
Carp Stock: Well stocked with carp to about 15lbs
Category: Mixed Fishery
Other Species: Rudd, roach and tench
Permits: Day tickets booked in advance at £6 per day
Control: Tel: 01256 760281
BK Rating: Difficult
E/A: Southern

Huckelsbrook Lake

Location: Off the A338, Christchurch to Fordingbridge road, near Huckelsbrook Garage. Lake entrance on the left hand side going north, past Ibsley and over Huckelsbrook Stream
Type and Size: Unfished twelve acre matured gravel pit, with large island
Carp Stock: Sizes not known, as the water has not been fished until recently, but thought to be only about 30 fish
Category: Mixed Fishery
Other Species: Roach, rudd, perch and tench
Permits: Members only water of Christchurch AC. R Andrews, 4 Marley Close, New Milton, Hants. Tel: 01425 477827
Cost: £54 per season, to include many other waters

Restrictions: Barbless hooks; members only; no guest tickets; carp must not be put into sacks; some areas out of bounds, as this is an S.S.S.I. Car parking inside and outside gate only; no carp in nets; open for night fishing
BK Rating: Not known
E/A: Wessex

Hurst Pond

Location: Headland Business Park, Blashford, off the A 38 Fordingbridge to Ringwood road
Type and Size: Two acre pool with islands and lilies
Carp Stock: Some carp to upper doubles
Category: Mixed Fishery
Other Species: Roach, rudd, perch, tench, crucians and eels
Permits: In advance only from Ringwood Tackle, Ringwood
Cost: £5 per day; £3.50 juniors. £8.50 for 24 hours
Control: Tel: 01425 475155
Restrictions: No carp over 3 lbs in keepnets
BK Rating: Moderate
Baits/Methods: Boilies and luncheon meat best
E/A: Southern

Kingfisher Lake (a)

Location: Teswood Lane, near Southampton
Type and Size: Gravel pit of three acres
How to Find: From Southampton take the Bournemouth road (A35) and at the roundabout take the Totton road (A36). At the Salmon Leap pub, take a track on the right to Kingfisher Lake. Ordnance Survey Sheet No.196. Grid Reference 358146
Carp Stock: Well stocked with carp doubles; a 31 has been reported which was probably genuine, but spawn bound. Many commons of 6-12lbs. We are reliably informed that the best 'normal' fish is a common of 14lbs 6ozs
Category: Mixed Fishery
Other Species: Tench, roach, perch, pike and chub
Permits: Day tickets from Mr Hoskins, 40 Aldermoor Aven, Aldermoor, Southampton. Tel: 01703 780105, who will also give information on costs etc
BK Rating: Moderate
Control: Private
E/A: Southern

Kingfisher lake (b)

Location: Near Ringwood
Type and Size: Matured gravel pit of 40 acres
Carp Stock: Very well stocked with good carp, many of which are 20's up to just over 30lbs. Some big commons to 28lbs
Category: Carp Water
Permits: Privately owned by limited company, now a syndicate water
BK Rating: Moderate
Control: Private Tel: 01703 293376
E/A: Wessex
Comments: Water is hard fished by good carp anglers, although numbers are limited. Caravans, cafe and other facilities

Lake Farm

Location: Near Fordingbridge - to the west, off the road which joins the A354 - at Alderholt
Type and Size: Four acre lake
Carp Stock: Hundreds of small carp, with some to 18lbs
Category: Carp Water
Other Species: Some good tench
Permits: On site
Cost: £6 per day
Control: Tel: 01425 653383
Restrictions: Barbless hooks; no keepnets; no night fishing
BK Rating: Very Easy for the little fish
E/A: Wessex

Lakeside

Location: Off the A 335 at Eastleigh, near Southampton
Type and Size: Two lakes of 5 and 2 acres
Carp Stock: Quite well stocked with carp to over 20 lbs
Category: Mixed Fishery
Other Species: Pike, tench, roach, eels and small bream
Permits: In advance from Stoneham Service Station, Eastleigh Angling Centre and Poingdestre Angling Centre
Cost: £4 per day; about £50 per season. Concessions for juniors, O.A.P's and the disabled
Control: Club. Eastleigh and District A.C. Tel: 01703 635540
Restrictions: No surface baits. No carp in sacks or keepnets
BK Rating: Moderate
Baits/Methods: Legered boilies and luncheon meat best
E/A: Southern
Comments: Toilets on site

Leominstead Mill Pond

Location: Minstead, near Lyndhurst
Type and Size: Ancient 5 acre mill pond
How to Find: From Cadnam, take the A 337 towards Lyndhurst. There are two turns to Minstead, take the third right turn, then the second track on the right
Carp Stock: Carp averaging about 5 lbs
Category: Mixed Fishery
Other Species: Carp, tench, roach, bream and rudd
Permits: On bank
Cost: About £5 per day; £50 per season. Half price for juniors
Control: Tel: 01703 282510
Restrictions: No night fishing
BK Rating: Not known
E/A: Southern
Comments: Disabled access

Longbridge Lake

Location: Broadlands Estate, Romsey
Type and Size: Two estate lakes, one narrow and canal-like, the other larger with an island
Carp Stock: Well stocked with commons and mirrors to doubles
Category: Mixed Fishery
Other Species: Crucians, ghost carp, perch, roach, rudd, tench, bream, chub, grass carp and eels

Permits: Day tickets from Poingdestre's Angling Centre, Shirley; Home Stores Tackle, Swaythling: Sports Centre in Chandlers Ford; and at the lake
Cost: £6 for two rods from 7am to 9pm until October; from October fishing finishes at 6pm. 24 hour tickets at £10
Control: Tel: 01703 739438
Restrictions: No boilies; no keepnets
BK Rating: Moderate
E/A: Southern
Comments: No close season

Mill Pond Lake

Location: Lyndhurst
Type and Size: 4 acre stream-fed lake
Carp Stock: Well stocked with carp to over 20 lbs
Category: Mixed Fishery
Other Species: Tench, roach, rudd and bream
Permits: On bank
Cost: About £5 per day; juniors half price
Control: Alf Branscombe, Emery Down, Lyndhurst. Tel: 01703 282610
BK Rating: Difficult
E/A: Southern

Mopley Farm Fishery A

Location: Mopley Farm, Mopley Road, Blackfield, Southampton.Tel: 01703 891617
Type and Size: Two lakes; three acres of water
How to Find: At Blackfield, 15 miles from Southampton on the edge of the New Forest
Carp Stock: Well stocked with carp to double figures; some twenties
Category: Mixed Fishery
Other Species: Trout, grayling, bream, tench, roach, rudd and dace
Permits: Self service ticket machine
Cost: From about £5 per day
Control: Private. Tel: 01703 891616
BK Rating: Moderate
E/A: Southern
Comments: No boilies or beans. Accommodation nearby. Any - method trout fishery with some good carp. Barbless hooks. Toilet. Disabled access

Northfield Lakes

Location: Just north of Ringwood, off the A31 - take the Fordingbridge road, and the lakes are on the left
Type and Size: Three small pits
Carp Stock: Well stocked with carp to 27lbs
Category: Mixed Fishery
Other Species: Big tench, ream and roach; pike and big eels
Control: Ringwood and District AC
Permits: A members only fishery of Ringwood AC; Mr K Grozier, 15 Greenfinch Walk, Hightown, Ringwood BH24 3RJ
Cost: £50 per season, to include many other waters
Control: Club
Restrictions: Members only
BK Rating: Moderate
E/A: Wessex

Orchard Lakes

Location: New Lane, Bashley, near Christchurch
Type and Size: Four small lakes
Carp Stock: Carp to 10 lbs
Category: Mixed Fishery
Other Species: Tench, crucians, bream and rudd
Permits: On bank
Cost: About £4 per day
Control: Tel: 01425 612404
Restrictions: No boilies, groundbait, nuts, beans or keepnets
BK Rating: Not known
E/A: Southern
Comments: Food available. Caravans and tents allowed

Petersfield Heath Lake

Location: On the edge of town of Petersfield, off the B2146
Type and Size: Twenty acre park lake
How to Find: Just off the A3 at Petersfield
Carp Stock: Good carp to 27lbs
Category: Mixed Fishery
Other Species: Bream, roach, rudd and pike
Permits: On bank. Tel: 01428 607768
Cost: About £5 per day. Season £44
BK Rating; Moderate
Control: Hants and Sussex Angling Alliance
Restrictions: No night fishing. No keepnets
E/A: Southern
Comments: Petersfield AC has a number of other lakes, some of which contain carp. Toilet. Disabled access

Queens Road Pond

Location: The Inn on the Sea,Queen's Road, Lee - on - Solent
Type and Size: Small pond in the grounds of the pub - 10 swims only
Carp Stock: Quite well stocked with carp to doubles
Category: Mixed Fishery
Other Species: Tench, rudd and roach
Permits: Day tickets from South Coast Tackle, 7 Marine Parade West, Lee-on-Solent
Cost: £3 and £1.50 for juniors (who must be accompanied by an adult) OAP's and the disabled
Control: Mike Sweeney. Tel: 1705 550209
Restrictions: Fishing from the Queen's Road bank only
BK Rating: Moderate
E/A: Southern
Comments: This pond is very close to the sea - as well as to the pub!

Rotherwick Lakes

Location: Hook, near Basingstoke; off the A30 towards Fleet
Type and Size: Tiny farm ponds
Carp Stock: Carp to doubles
Category: Mixed Fishery
Other Species: General coarse fish and trout
Permits: Tel: 01256 763700
Cost: About £4 per day, on bank
BK Rating: Fairly Easy

Control: Private
E/A: Thames
Comments: Open all year

Somerly Lakes

Location: Near Ringwood
Type and Size: Gravel pit of about seventeen acres
Carp Stock: Well stocked with carp to over 30lbs, best 33lbs
Category: Carp Water
Permits: Christchurch AC
Cost: £5 per day. £10 per night
Control: Christchurch AC, R Andrews, 4 Marley Close, New Milton, Hants. Tel: 01425 477827
BK Rating: Moderate
E/A: Southern
Comments: A well-known water, very popular and hard fished. Night fishing by prior arrangements only. Toilet

Stoneham Lakes

Location: Stoneham Lane, Eastleigh
Type and Size: Two small attractive pools with islands
Carp Stock: Well stocked with carp to mid-doubles
Category: Mixed Fishery
Other Species: Tench, bream, roach, rudd, perch, crucians, pike and eels
Permits: Season tickets in advance only. No day tickets
Cost: £45 per season; concessions. £6 joining fee
Control: Eastleigh D.A.C. Tel: 01489 788569
Restrictions: No weekend or night fishing in winter
BK Rating: Not known
E/A: Southern
Comments: Key required for car parks:

St Patrick's Lane Carp Lakes

Location: Near Frensham, which is just in Surrey
Type and Size: Small lakes
Carp Stock: Heavily stocked with carp to 8lbs
Category: Mixed Fishery
Other Species: Usual coarse fish
Permits: Try local tackle shops
Restrictions: Much used for match fishing
BK Rating: Very Easy
E/A: Southern

Sway Lakes

Location: Barrow Lane, Sway, near Brockenhurst
Type and Size: Three acre lake
How to Find: From Brockenhurst take the Sway road and turn left into Barrow Lane
Carp Stock: Many doubles to over 20lbs
Category: Carp Water
Other Species: Rudd, tench and perch
Permits: From owner on bank
Cost: £5 per day; £5 per night
Restrictions: Barbless hooks; no nuts or pulses; no sacks; no night fishing. Open Ist March to 31st October
Control: Private. Tel: 01590 682177

BK Rating: Moderate
E/A: Wessex
Comments: For information - Mr T Clarke. Tel: 01590 682010

Topacre Lake

Location: Alresford, near Winchester
Type and Size: Very small estate pond
Carp Stock: Small number of carp to about 30lbs
Category: Carp Water
Permits: Syndicate only; details from K Cayzer, Keepers Cottage, New England Estate, Alresford. Tel: 01962 732837
Control: Private
BK Rating: Difficult

Turf Croft Farm

Location: Four miles east of Ringwood - turn off the A31 at Picket Post and take the Burley road, then first left into Forest Road
Type and Size: Small farm lake
Carp Stock: Well stocked with mirrors, commons and ghost carp, to almost 20lbs
Category: Mixed Fishery
Other Species: Roach, rudd, tench and crucians; also stocked rainbow and brown trout
Permits: Day tickets from Turf Croft Farm Tel: 01425 403743
Cost: £5.50 for one rod for trout fishing. £5 from June 16th. £1 for an extra rod
Restrictions: Barbless hooks only. No night fishing. No boilies, keepnets, or nuts
BK Rating: Moderate
E/A: Southern
Comments: No close season. Attractive lake with islands and picnic tables

Waggoner's Wells

Location: Near Hindhead (which is Surrey, but lakes are in Hampshire)
Type and Size: Three lakes, one of which is a trout lake
How to Find: Hindhead area
Carp Stock: Some carp in the two coarse fishing lakes
Category: Mixed Fisheries
Other Species: Perch, tench, roach
Permits: On site - The Ranger, Summerden North, Waggoner's Wells, Grayshott, Hindhead, Surrey. Tel: 01428 723722
Cost: About £10 - season; £1.50 - day; 50p extra for a second rod
BK Rating: Insufficient information
Control: National Trust
Restrictions: Not known
E/A: Southern
Comments: National Trust property, so likely to be busy

Wainsford Reservoir

Location: Near Lymington
Type and Size: 3 acre estate lake
Carp Stock: Carp to 22 lbs
Category: Mixed Fishery
Other Species: Rudd and perch
Permits: From local tackle shops
Cost: £80 per year
Control: Christchurch A.C. R.Andrews, 4 Marley Close, New Milton
Restrictions: No night fishing
BK Rating: Moderate

Baits/Methods: Good floater / stalking water
E/A: Southern
Comments: Open June 16th to March 14th

White House Farm Lake

Location: Tadley, near Reading
Type and Size: Small man - made lake with an island
How to Find: Take the A 340 Tadley to Newbury road and turn into Silchester Road
Carp Stock: Heavily stocked with carp to over 20 lbs
Category: Carp Only
Permits: On bank
Cost: £4 for two rods, dawn to dusk. Juniors £2
Control: Keith Brown. Tel: 01734 813531
Restrictions: Night fishing by arrangement
BK Rating: Easy
Baits/Methods: Boilies best, especially pop - ups. Flavoured sweetcorn and luncheon meat
E/A: Southern
Comments: Open all year

Willow Park Lakes

Location: Willow Park, near Aldershot
Type and Size: Large but attractive gravel pit; shallow with gravel bars
Carp Stock: Heavily stocked with over 500 carp, about 150 doubles and at least 10 twenties to about 28lbs
Category: Mixed Fishery
Other Species: Roach, tench, rudd, bream, perch and pike
Permits: In advance only; day tickets from John Raison on 01252 543470
Control: Private
Restrictions: No boilies until after November; unhooking mats must be used
BK Rating: Moderate
E/A: Thames
Comments: A wel known and pleasant water often featured in the angling press. Fishes well all the year, and is run by a fishing tackle shop owner. Also used for windsurfing, unfortunately. For further information see Clean River's Carp Teach-In video which was made on this water

Woodington Coarse Fishery

Location: Headlands Farm, Romsey Road, Wellow, Romsey
Type and Size: Lake and canal - 2 acres of water
Carp Stock: Well stocked with carp to mid-doubles
Category: Mixed Fishery
Other Species: Pike, tench, roach and rudd
Permits: On site
Cost: About £6 per day; concessions
Control: John Harris. Tel: 01794 23801 or 01860 770070
BK Rating: Not known
E/A: Southern
Comments: Probably open all year

HEREFORD & WORCESTER

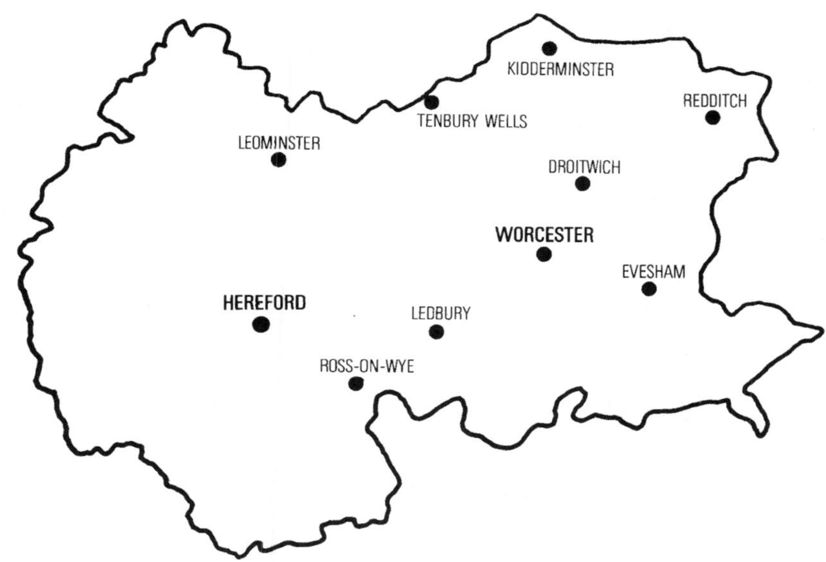

Abbots Salford Park

Location: Abbots Salford, Evesham
Type and Size: Small pool
How to Find: Off the A439 near Evesham
Carp Stock: Not known
Category: Unknown
Other Species: Tench
Permits: On site
Cost: On application. Tel: 01386 870244
BK Rating: Insufficient information
Control: Private
E/A: Severn-Trent
Comments: A country park on the banks of the River Avon, which advertises 'a carp and tench pool'. Self-service shop, licensed club, bowling green and 'all pursuits enjoyed by country lovers'

A.C.R. Fisheries, Evesbatch

Location: Evesbatch, near Worcester
Type and Size: Two small pools
How to Find: Take the A4103 from Worcester to Evesbatch - 11 miles
Carp Stock: Heavily stocked with carp to 20lbs, especially the big lake
Category: Big lake - Carp Water, small lake - Mixed Fishery
Other Species: General coarse fish
Permits: Day tickets in advance only, from Alans Fishing Tackle, St Johns, Worcester
Cost: On application
Control: Private
BK Rating: Easy

E/A:	Severn-Trent
Comments:	Popular, heavily stocked lakes

Alvechurch Fisheries

Location:	Bittle Road (B 4120), Alvechurch, Birmingham
Type and Size:	Five small pools
Carp Stock:	Well stocked with carp to over 25 lbs
Category:	Mixed Fishery
Other Species:	Bream, perch, tench, roach and rudd
Permits:	From tackle shop on site
Cost:	£5 per day; £3.50 juniors and O.A.P's. Season tickets available
Control:	Tel: 0121 445 4274
Restrictions:	No boilies or cereal groundbait. No night fishing Barbless hooks only No keepnets
BK Rating:	Easy
E/A:	Severn Trent
Comments:	Toilets, tackle shop, refreshments and games room (!)

Arrow Fisheries

Location:	Leominster
Type and Size:	Extraordinary man-made 'lakes' in the form of narrow, parallel, canal-like stretches of water constructed for match fishing purposes
Carp Stock:	Heavily stocked with small carp; the owner says he will take out any which reach 3lbs!
Category:	Unique, I should think; a Mixed Fishery
Other Species:	Roach, bream, chub, perch, gudgeon and hybrids
Permits:	Geoff Daw. Tel: 0156 884540
BK Rating:	No idea - should be Easy
E/A:	Welsh (we think)
Comments:	There is a licensed bar and club-house; every angler is said to have a level platform, with a gap between islands opposite. The fishery is still being developed - perhaps the bar might at present be the most interesting part!

Arrow Valley Lake

Location:	Batten Drive, off Holloway Drive, Redditch
Type and Size:	Large excavated lake of 30 acres
Carp Stock:	Well stocked with carp to 25lbs
Category:	Mixed Fishery
Other Species:	Roach, rudd perch, bream and tench, many very large
Permits:	Day tickets from the Warden's hut by the side of the lake. Tel: 01527 68337
Cost:	About £3 per day; reductions for juniors and OAP's and for a half day
Control:	Redditch Borough Council, Amenities Dept,Town Hall, Redditch B98 8HA
BK Rating:	Moderate
E/A:	Severn-Trent
Comments:	Said to be one of the best waters in the area, with bream to 11lbs, and roach to 3lbs. Next to the lake is Redditch Angling Centre, with all the tackle, baits and information you need

Ashperton Moat

Location:	Ashperton Village, on A417 between Leominster and Gloucester
Type and Size:	Small pool, the remains of a castle moat
How to Find:	Go to Ashperton Village Church, the pool is at the bottom of the path

leading through the graveyard!.

Carp Stock: Some small carp to 5-6lbs
Category: Mixed Fishery
Other Species: Bream, tench and roach
Permits: Day tickets in advance only, from the Ledbury Tackle Centre
Cost: On application
Control: Ledbury Angling Association
BK Rating: Easy
E/A: Severn-Trent
Comments: A small, long and narrow lake in pleasant surroundings

Bankes Pool

Location: Great Witley, near Stourport
Type and Size: Small pool
How to Find: On the A451, 5 miles south-west of Stourport
Carp Stock: Well stocked with carp to doubles
Category: Mixed Fishery
Other Species: General coarse fish
Permits: Day tickets from the farm near the pool
Cost: On application
BK Rating: Easy
Control: Private
E/A: Severn-Trent
Comments: Very small, overstocked water. Enquire from the farm or local tackle shops

Betula Waters

Location: South Herefordshire
Type and Size: Two small estate pools
Carp Stock: Well stocked with commons and mirrors to double figure size, with a couple of 20s caught
Category: Carp Only
Other Species: None except for a few golden orfe
Permits: Occasional vacancies for the season only (no day tickets)
Cost: On application
Control: James Sansoni. Tel: 0121 4367510
BK Rating: Fairly Easy to Moderate
E/A: Severn-Trent
Comments: Private property - do not visit without permission for any reason. Barbless hooks. Weekend rotas. Open all year

Bewdley Pool A

Location: Bewdley, near Kidderminster
Type and Size: Small pools
How to Find: In Severn Valley near Bewdley
Carp Stock: Well stocked with carp
Category: Mixed Fishery
Other Species: General coarse fish
Permits: Severn Valley Guest House, Westbourne Street. Tel: 01299 402192
Cost: On application
BK Rating: Moderate
Control: Private
Restrictons: Not known
E/A: Severn-Trent
Comments: Accommodation available in guest house. Licences, tackle and bait. Licensed bar. Also famous for its barbel fishing in the River Severn

Birmingham-Worcester Canal

Location: Best area is said to be Hanbury Wharf, Shernal Green, near Droitwich
Type and Size: Narrow canal
How to Find: Hanbury and the canal are a few miles west of Droitwich
Carp Stock: Said to be plenty of carp to 20lbs
Category: Mixed Fishery
Other Species: Usual coarse fish
Permits: Birmingham Anglers Association (members only), 100 Icknield Port Road, Rotton Park, Birmingham B16 OAP. Tel: 0121 4549111, 9.30am to 1.30pm and 7pm to 9pm, weekdays
Cost: About £20 a season, which includes all other BAA waters
BK Rating: Insufficient information, but good carp are notoriously hard to find on canals
Control: BAA
Restrictions: No groundbait of any kind
E/A: Severn-Trent

Bransford Golf Course Pool

Location: Bransford, near Worcester
Type and Size: Small open pool
How to Find: In the village of Bransford, outside Worcester on the A4103
Carp Stock: Well stocked with small carp
Category: Mixed Fishery
Other Species: General coarse fish
Permits: From the main building on the golf course
Cost: On application
Control: Bransford Golf Club
BK Rating: Easy
E/A: Severn-Trent
Comments: A new, recently constructed fishery on the edge of the golf course Both the pool and golf course are very well signposted

Broad Acres

Location: Hanbury, near Bromsgrove
Type and Size: Two lakes of 2½ and ½ an acre
How to Find: From the A38 south of Bromsgrove take the B 4091 towards Hanbury then turn left into Forest Lane. In 1½ miles turn 1st right
Carp Stock: Small lake heavily stocked with carp to doubles
Larger lake some small carp
Category: Mixed Fishery
Other Species: Roach, perch, tench and bream
Permits: On bank
Cost: £3.50 per day; £2.50 juniors and O.A.P's
Control: Private. Tel: 01527 821880
Restrictions: No boilies, hemp, bloodworm or joker
BK Rating: Not known
E/A: Severn Trent

Church Pool

Location: Opposite the church in the village of Clehonger, near Hereford
Type and Size: Farm pool of approxmately one acre
How to Find: Take the A465 from Hereford to Abergavenney. After two miles turn right past Belmont Abbey and then right again after one mile (signed Clehonger). Park on verge, without obstructing access to the church. The pool is opposite the church

Carp Stock: Well stocked with small carp, Possibly a few doubles present
Category: Carp Water
Other Species: Two or three terrapins, very fond of maggots!!
Permits: Perkins of Hereford, Commercial Road, Hereford. Permits must be obtained before commencing fishing
Cost: £3 per day
Baits/Methods: Any bait and method will score here
Control: Private, day ticket
Restrictions: No keepnets, barbed hooks, groundbait, unsupervised children or litter
E/A: Welsh
BK Rating: Very Easy
Comments: A small water, set in a field by a quiet vilage. Picturesque suroundings. Source of the terrapins - unknown

Court Farm

Location: Bottom of farm track, Court Farm, Tillington, near Hereford
Type and Size: Irrigation reservoir, approx one and a half acres
How to Find: Head north from Hereford on A4110. Turn left at the Three Elms public house and follow signs for Tillington. In Tillington, turn right and follow signs for Court Farm
Carp Stock: Stocked with small mirrors and commons to 8lb
Category: Carp Only
Permits: On site from farmhouse
Cost: £2 per day
Baits/Methods: Standard baits and methods work well here
Control: Day ticket water. Tel: 01432 760271
E/A: Welsh
BK Rating: Easy

Docklow Pools A

Location: West End Farm, Docklow, Leominster
Type and Size: Seven estate lakes, 2 - 3 acres each
How to Find: From Leominster take the A44 Worcester road. Docklow is about 3 miles from Leominster
Carp Stock: All the lakes are well stocked with carp although one is mainly a trout pool. Two of the lakes contain carp to 34 1/2 lbs, although most of the fish are mirrors of under 10lbs
Category: Carp Water
Permits: Day tickets from Mrs J Bozward, West End Farm
Cost: £4 per day
BK Rating: Easy for the smaller carp; Difficult for the bigger fish
Restrictions: No goundbait; no peanuts; no hemp; barbless hooks
Baits/Methods: Normal carp methods; maggots, luncheon meat and boilies
Control: Private
E/A: Welsh
Comments: 305lbs of carp was once caught in a day on one of these pools. Most carp are small. Accommodation in the farmhouse (bed and breakfast). Chalets. There are also 6 attractive self-catering cottages of high standard, some very near the lakes. Brochure from Mrs Bozward at West End Farm. Tel: 0156 882256. Ideal for the family or fishing holiday. No close season; excellent fishing in the spring

Eastnor Castle

Location: Eastnor, near Ledbury
Type and Size: Estate lake about five acres
How to Find: Take the A449 towards Malvern and then about half a mile outside

the town fork right on the A438 towards Tewkesbury. You will pass entrance to the water on the right about 3 miles further on

Carp Stock: Quite well stocked with mirrors and commons to about 15lbs
Category: Mixed Fishery
Other Species: Roach, rudd, bream, tench
Permits: From bailiffs on bank, may now be a syndicate
Control: Private
BK Rating: Severn-Trent
Comments: A beautiful lake surrounded by trees. A big area is thickly covered by lilies which make much of this area almost impossible to fish. Most of the carp are caught from the dam end or near the lilies

Elmbridge Lakes

Location: Long Farm Road, near the Chequers Inn, Cutnall Green, Droitwich
Type and Size: Two lakes of 2 acres each
Carp Stock: Well stocked with carp to over 20 lbs
Category: Mixed Fishery
Other Species: Roach, bream and tench
Permits: On bank
Cost: £3.50 per day; £2.50 juniors and O.A.P's
Control: Tel: 01299 851321
Restrictions: No boilies; cereal groundbait; no night fishing; no keepnets; barbless hooks
BK Rating: Not known
E/A: Severn Trent
Comments: Toilets. Hot food available

Eric's Pool

Location: Shatterford, Kidderminster
Type and Size: Small lake
Carp Stock: Sparsely stocked with carp to about 16lbs
Category: Few Carp
Other Species: Roach, bream and pike
Permits: Day tickets at the lake
Control: Private
BK Rating: Difficult
E/A: Severn-Trent

Evesbatch Top Pool

Location: Evesbatch, near Worcester
Type and Size: Small, dammed pool
How to Find: Continue up the track past ACR Fisheries and the pool is at the top of the hill
Carp Stock: Quite well stocked with carp to mid doubles
Category: Mixed Fishery
Other Species: General coarse fish
Permits: Day tickets, in advance only from the Ledbury Tackle Centre
Cost: On application
Control: Ledbury Angling Association
BK Rating: Moderate
E/A: Severn-Trent
Comments: A very picturesque pool, quite well match fished during the summer

Golden Valley

Location: Golden Valley Common, near Castlemorton, Ledbury
Type and Size: Dammed estate-type lake, stream fed, but on very open common land
How to Find: From Tewkesbury take the A438 Ledbury rod and turn right on the B4208 after about 6 miles. After about a mile, a lane leads onto the common on the left, and the lake wil be seen on the right
Carp Stock: Numbers not known but quite well stocked with commons to about 6lbs
Category: Mixed Fishery
Other Species: Crucians, roach, perch and bream
Permits: This used to be a free fishery but recently someone, presumably the local Council, has been charging 50p a day from bailiffs on the bank
BK Rating: Moderate
E/A: Severn-Trent
Comments: A high and open water with some quite good fun fishing for small commons. Tel: 01531 632768. No night fishing. Barbless hooks

Haye Farm Fishery

Location: Bewdley, near Snuff Mill
Type and Size: Small farm pond
Carp Stock: Well stocked with carp to 15lbs
Category: Carp Water
Other Species: Few coarse fish
Permits: Day tickets on bank
Cost: Low
Control: Private
BK Rating: Moderate
E/A: Severn-Trent
Comments: Man-made pond on farm. In same lane as Snuff Mill Pool

Leigh Sinton Lakes

Location: B 4503 near Great Malvern
Type and Size: Three small farm pools
Carp Stock: Well stocked with carp to 20 lbs
Category: Mixed Fishery
Other Species: Tench, roach, perch, chub and bream
Permits: On bank
Cost: About £4 per day
Control: Tel: 01886 832305
Restrictions: No night fishing; no cereal groundbaits; no boilies; barbless hooks
BK Rating: Easy
E/A: Severn Trent
Comments: Toilets and cafe

Lodge Park Lake

Location: Redditch
Type and Size: Small estate lake
How to Find: In the town of Redditch
Carp Stock: Very heavily stocked with small carp
Category: Carp Water
Other Species: Few
Permits: R Myall, 19 Chaddesley Close, Lodge Park, Redditch. Apply in writing only - with an SAE
Cost: On application
Control: Private
BK Rating: Very Easy

E/A: Severn-Trent
Comments: Many thousands of little carp

Lower Broadheath Pools

Location: Processing factory, Lower Broadheath, Worcester
Type and Size: Three small pools
Carp Stock: Well stocked with small carp to 2 lbs, with some bigger fish
Category: Mixed Fishery
Other Species: Rudd and bream
Permits: On bank
Cost: £3.50 per day
Control: John Jordan Tel: 01905 421357
Restrictions: No night fishing; no hemp; no groundbait
BK Rating: Easy
E/A: Severn Trent

Marsh House Farm A

Location: Wellington, off the A 49 north of Hereford
Type and Size: One acre pool with island
Carp Stock: Well stocked with carp averaging 5 lbs
Category: Mixed Fishery
Other Species: Bream, roach and rudd
Permits: From adjacent guest house
Cost: About £4 per day; concessions
Control: Tel: 01432 830787
BK Rating: Easy
E/A: Welsh
Comments: Accommodation in guest house.Probably open all year

Moorlands Farm

Location: Hartlebury, near Kidderminster, off the A449
Type and Size: Eight small pools, two of which are for youngsters
How to Find: From Kidderminster take the A449 Worcester road, turn left where the dual carriageway starts, and turn left again on a farm track signposted to the fishery
Carp Stock: Meadow Pool and Bank Pool contain carp to doubles
Category: Mixed Fishery
Other Species: Crucians, bream, tench, chub, rudd, dace and goldfish
Permits: Day tickets from the snack bar on the site. Tel: 01299 250427
Cost: £4 per day; after 2pm £3
Restrictions: Fishing is from constructed platforms, and cars can be driven to swims; keepnets banned; barbless hooks recommended
BK Rating: Moderate
E/A: Severn-Trent
Comments: Toilets; swims for the disabled

Moors Pool

Location: Hartlebury, Kidderminster
Type and Size: Small pool
Carp Stock: Heavily stocked with small carp, much used for match fishing; said to contain carp to about 10lbs
Category: Mixed Fishery
Other Species: Roach, bream and perch
Permits: Try local tackle shops
Control: Club
Restrictions: No night fishing

BK Rating: Easy
E/A: Severn-Trent

Munderfield Harold A

Location: Munderfield Harold, off the A44, 1½ miles north west of Bromyard
Type and Size: Four small ponds
Carp Stock: Carp to about 17 lbs
Category: Carp Water
Other Species: Roach, rudd, bream and tench
Permits: From the farm
Cost: About £4 per day - £1 for guests
Control: Christine Morgan, Tel: 01885 483231
BK Rating: Easy for small carp; Difficult for the bigger ones
E/A: Severn Trent
Comments: Low priced but good standard bed and breakfast.

Pixley Pool

Location: Just off A4172 Leominster to Gloucester road
Type and Size: Irrigation reservior of approx two acres
How to Find: Go south east on A4172. Cross junction with A438 Hereford to Ledbury road. The pool is 500 yards past on the right at the top of an embankment.
Carp Stock: Heavily stocked with carp to up to mid doubles
Category: Carp Only
Permits: £3.50 per day, available from bailiffs on the bank
Baits/Methods: Boilies tend to work for the better fish. Floaters go very well in summer
Control: Three Counties Fisheries, Field Cottage, Ryton, near Dymock, GL15 2DH. Tel: 01531 890495. Three Counties have other carp fisheries - brochure on request
E/A: Severn-Trent
BK Rating: Moderate
Comments: Some matches take place here. There are other waters run by Brian Powell

Pridewood Lake

Location: Pridewood Hop Farm, Trumpet, near Hereford
Type and Size: Small lake
Carp Stock: Mostly small - some doubles
Category: Mixed Fishery
Other Species: Roach, perch, rudd, crucians and eels
Permits: On bank
Cost: About £5 per day
Control: Enquire at farm
Restrictions: No boilies
BK Rating: Easy
E/A: Severn Trent

Red Bank Pools

Location: Ledbury, near Hereford
Type and Size: Two small pools
How to Find: Take the road from Ledbury to Little Marcle, go past the Preserves factory and the fishery is on the right
Carp Stock: Well stocked with carp to 20lbs
Category: Carp Water
Permits: From bailiffs on the bank, about £4 per day. Concessions
Control: Private. Contact Mr B Powell. Tel: 01531 890455

ANGLERS PARADISE HOLIDAYS

Set in rural countryside with views of Dartmoor and close to the seaside. Twelve miles on the B3218 from Okehampton.
Thirty two luxurious villas and cottages (many with jacuzzis and four-poster beds) in a 128-acre estate with 12 lakes exclusively for residents.
Designer Fishing - different sizes and various species in separate lakes with rare water plants, carp, golden tench, orfe, koi, etc.
Lakes with walk-on islands, koi lake with dragon pull-raft.
Four carp lakes with fish to over 30lbs! African Safari bar, pets corner, ship climbing frame and unusual activities such as goat milking, wine making, mushroom picking and Woodland Sculpture Walk.

LEISURE FACILITIES

Includes on site: heated indoor swimming pool, table tennis, pool and video games. Clay pigeon shooting and donkey rides are available at extra cost, and of course fishing!. With 12 lakes stocked with carp, golden tench, koi, golden rudd, catfish, grass carp and goldfish in lovely surroundings, the Angler will certainly feel on holiday.
Villas for the disabled - easy access to most lakes with pagoda shelters.

Contact: Zyg and Rose Gregorek,
The Gables, Winsford, Halwill, Beaworthy, Devon EX21 5XT
Tel: 01409 221559

PM FISHERIES

OLD MANOR HOUSE CARP PONDS, GLOUCESTERSHIRE.

Have all three carp ponds to yourself for only £10 per day or two friends at £10 each per day.
No one else will fish this easy, heavily-stocked, carp-only fishery on your day.
Peaceful and private - no traffic noises and no main roads nearby. Ideal for 'old fashioned' methods, close range fishing. Beautiful surroundings. Possibly the most exclusive carp waters in the country, little fished. Most carp 3 - 8 lbs; a few lower doubles.
No close season.

RED BECK LAKE, NEAR EVESHAM, WORCS.

Four acre open lake on private, quiet estate. Carp only to 11lb, but mostly 3 - 8 lb. Very easy - ideal for beginners or non carp specialists. A season ticket costs only £60.

CROOKED WITHIES LAKE, NEAR TEWKESBURY, GLOS.

Two and a half acres peaceful and attractive. Carp only to 12lb.
Small exclusive syndicate £120
No long stay fishing or bivvies allowed on these lakes. Anglers only, high standards of behaviour expected.

CONTACT: THE FISHERY CONTROLLER, 15 STAFFORD COURT, RIVERSIDE CLOSE, BEDFORD, MK42 9DE TEL: (01234) 212066/365085

BK Rating: Moderate
E/A: Severn-Trent
Comments: No night fishing. Toilet. No keepnets. Disabled access

Red Beck Lake

Location: Near Evesham
Type and Size: Four acre lake
Carp Stock: 300+ of 2lbs to 10lbs, mostly mirrors. A few doubles to 14lbs
Category: Carp Only
Other Species: None
Permits: Season tickets only, limited membership, from Fishery Controller, 15 Stafford Court, Riverside Close, Bedford MK 42 9DE. Tel: 01234 212066/365085
Cost: About £60 per season
Baits/Methods: All known methods including legering with all baits, surface fishing, float fishing with maggots and sweetcorn
Control: Season ticket only; private
Restrictions: No long-stay fishing or camping. No hair rigs; no pulses (beans and peas) as bait; barbless hooks. No bivvies
BK Rating: Very Easy
E/A: Severn-Trent
Comments: One of the easiest waters we know. Catches of 20 carp a day quite common. Ideal for beginners and non-carp specialists. Private estate water - do not visit for any reason without permission. Frequent vacancies throughout the season. Guest day tickets for members' friends. Other carp waters available. Warning: private property - do not visit without permission

River Severn

Location: Holt Fleet, between Ombersley and Tenbury Wells - turn right off the A443, where there is an island and a lock
Type and Size: Attractive, medium - sized river, deep above the weir and shallow below
Carp Stock: Some carp to 17lbs
Category: Few Carp
Other Species: Barbel, chub, roach, pike, bream and perch
Permits: Day tickets from lock keeper
Cost: £3 per day - £35 per season (no day tickets on Sundays - season ticket holders ony)
Restrictions: No night fishing - 5am to 10pm only; fishing on main river side only
BK Rating: Difficult
E/A: Severn-Trent

River Wye

Location: Upsteam of A49 road bridge in Hereford
Type and Size: Slow reach of large, normally rapid river
How to Find: Go to A49 road bridge and look down
Carp Stock: Few commons, possibly up to 20lbs
Category: Mixed Fishery
Other Species: Chub, roach, perch, bream, tench, barbel, pike, gudgeon, salmon, trout, dace, bleak, eels, grayling, shad during May, and the occasional sturgeon has been seen!
Permits: Hattons of Hereford, St Owens Street, or Perkins of Hereford, Commercial Road
Cost: £3 daily
Baits/Methods: Most baits and methods will work here, but unless cast to specific fish bait could be taken by the hordes of other fish present

Control: Club - day ticket
Restrictions: No night fishing
E/A: Welsh
BK Rating: Difficult
Comments: Location is the key to avoid problems with other fish. The water is heavily matched fished during summer

Rotherwas Long Pool

Location: Industrial Estate, south east of Hereford
Type and Size: Small, rectangular pool of about one and a third acres
How to Find: Take B4299 from Hereford. Turn left signed Rotherwas Chapel. The pool is on the left
Carp Stock: Very heavily stocked with small carp up to 5lbs
Category: Carp Only
Permits: On bank
Cost: £3 daily
Baits/Methods: Anything works on this easy water
Control: Private, day tickets
Restrictions: No keepnets
E/A: Welsh
BK Rating: Very Easy
Comments: This water is unusual in that many fish are fully scaled mirrors

Royal Oak Pool

Location: Village of Portway, five miles north of Hereford on A4110
Type and Size: Farm pond of approx one acre
How to Find: Leave Hereford on A4110. Royal Oak public house is on the left in village of Portway. The pool is behind the public house
Carp Stock: Well stocked with commons and mirrors up to low doubles
Category: Carp Water
Other Species: Roach
Permits: Royal Oak public house
Baits/Methods: Any standard baits and methods
Control: Private, day ticket
E/A: Welsh
BK Rating: Easy
Comments: Some match fishing takes place. Ideally positioned for those days when it gets too hot and dry to fish!

Shatterford Lakes

Location: At Romsley, off the A 442 between Kidderminster and Bridgnorth
Type and Size: Two small lakes
Carp Stock: Well stocked with carp to over 20 lbs
Category: Mixed Fishery
Other Species: Catfish, barbel, golden orfe and koi
Permits: From the lodge
Cost: About £5 per day
Control: Tel: 012997 597
Restrictions: Night fishing by arrangement only. No keepnets
BK Rating: Moderate
E/A: Severn Trent

Sion Farm Pool

Location: Hillpool, near Kidderminster
Type and Size: 2 1/2 acre lake with island
Carp Stock: Well stocked with carp to over 20 lbs
Category: Mixed Fishery
Other Species: Crucians, roach, tench, bream and perch
Permits: On bank
Cost: About £4 per day
Control: Tel: 01562 730386
BK Rating: Not known
E/A: Severn Trent

Snuff Mill

Location: Bewdley
Type and Size: Small old pool
How to Find: Near the River Severn at Bewdley
Carp Stock: Carp to over 20lbs
Category: Mixed Fishery
Other Species: Tench, roach, bream
Permits: S Lewis Tackle, Severnside South, Bewdley
Cost: On application
Control: Private Tel: 01299 403358
BK Rating: Moderate
Comments: Toilet. No night fishing. Barbless hooks

Stanklin Pool

Location: Just to the south of Kidderminster
Type and Size: Six acre lake, shallow and heavily reeded, with very boggy surrounds and smelly, silty mud
Carp Stock: Very heavily stocked with small carp to abut 8lbs, many of which are commons
Category: Carp Water
Other Species: Some tench, roach and eels
Permits: Phoenix AC - small local club with limited membership - enquire locally or in tackle shops
Baits/Methods: Very good floating crust water
BK Rating: Very Easy
E/A: Severn-Trent

Two Five Nine

Location: On the left hand side of the B4077 Stow-on-the Wold to Tewkesbury road, about 2 miles before you reach the A435 at Teddington Hands
Type and Size: Pit of about two acres, with some caravans near it
Carp Stock: Quite well stocked with carp to about 15lbs
Category: Mixed Fishery
Other Species: Usual coarse fish
Permits: Enuire from the owner whose house is alongside the road (Brooklands Farm)
BK Rating: Moderate
E/A: Severn-Trent

Twyford Farm Lake

Location: Twyford County Centre, one mile north of Evesham on the A435
Type and Size: Small specially dug pond of about two acres, with island
Carp Stock: Plenty of small carp and a few bigger fish to 20lbs
Category: Mixed Fishery
Other Species: Roach, chub, perch, crucians, bream, tench and gudgeon
Permits: On bank at £3.50 per day. Concessions
Control: May Vince. Tel: 01386 446108
Restrictions: Fishing is 7am till dusk only; no keepnets
BK Rating: Moderate
E/A: Severn Trent
Comments: Cafe and garden centre

Uckinghall Pool

Location: Ripple, Uckinghall, between Worcester and Tewkesbury
Type and Size: Small pit alongside River Severn
How to Find: South from Worcester on A38 towards Tewkesbury, and then to Uckinghall
Carp Stock: Fairly well stocked with carp to about 10lbs
Category: Mixed Fishery
Other Species: Pike, roach, perch, a few rudd
Permits: Birmingham Anglers Association (members only), 100 Icknield Park Road, Rotton Park, Birmingham B16 OAP. Tel: 0121 4549111, 9.30am to 1.30pm, and 7pm to 9pm, Monday to Friday
Cost: About £20 a season, which includes all other BAA waters
BK Rating: Not known
Control: BAA
Restrictions: No groundbait of any kind
E/A: Severn-Trent

Upton Warren Lake

Location: Between the M5, junction 5 and Droitwich, about a mile from the town
Type and Size: Lake of nearly 20 acres
Carp Stock: Quite well stocked with carp to 20lbs
Category: Mixed Fishery
Other Species: Bream, roach, rudd, perch, dace and eels
Permits: Day tickets from the office on the site
Cost: £2 per day; £1 for the unemployed, under 21's and OAP's
Control: Council
Restrictions: No night fishing - 8am till dusk only; 8am till 5pm on Tuesdays
BK Rating: Moderate
E/A: Severn-Trent
Comments: Stands for disabled anglers; some match pegs often booked; no fishing on one bank, which is a Nature Reserve; sailing takes place on this lake, as well as many matches

Welfield Pools

Location: Highley, Kidderminster
Type and Size: Three lakes
Carp Stock: Carp to 20lbs
Category: Mixed Fishery
Other Species: Tench, bream, roach and chub
Permits: Day tickets from Stan Lewis', tackle shop in Bewdley
Cost: On application
BK Rating: Insufficient information

Control: Private. Tel: 01299 403358
E/A: Severn-Trent
Comments: Try local tackle shops for information. Toilet. No night fishing. Disabled access

Wilden Pool

Location: Wilden, Stourport-on-Severn
Type and Size: Medium-sized pool
How to Find: Near the River Stour at Wilden, just south of Kidderminster
Carp Stock: Heavily stocked with small carp to 3lbs. A few doubles
Category: Carp Water
Other Species: Some coarse fish
Permits: Day tickets on the bank. Night fishing extra
Cost: On application
BK Rating: Easy
Control: Private - Ron Russell
E/A: Severn-Trent
Comments: Standard float fishing methods and baits, as well as legering, will catch these small carp, especially near the island. Try local tackle shops for information

Witley Fishery

Location: Great Witley, near Stourport
Type and Size: Two pools, one quite large
How to Find: Take the A 451 from Stourport, then the B 4196 towards Worcester. Turn right at Shrawley, and the fishery is on the left
Carp Stock: Well stocked with carp. The large lake, Dingle Pool, has mainly doubles to over 20 lbs
Category: Mixed Fishery
Other Species: Tench, chub, bream and roach
Permits: On bank
Cost: £5 per day on weekdays; £4 at weekends. Concessionary tickets £2
Control: Private. Frank or Jackie Colwill. Tel: 01299 896600
Restrictions: No groundbait
BK Rating: Not known
E/A: Severn Trent

Woodland View

Location: At Hadley, off the A 4133 Droitwich to Ombersley road
Type and Size: Five small pools
Carp Stock: Well stocked with small carp to about 5 lbs
Category: Mixed Fishery
Other Species: Roach, bream, hybrids, tench, crucians, orfe, perch and (believe it or not!) - barbel
Permits: From on site tackle shop
Cost: £5 per day; £3.50 after 1 pm. Juniors, O.A.P's and disabled £4 per day
Control: Tel: 01905 620872
Restrictions: No boilies, seed baits, groundbait or barbed hooks
BK Rating: Easy
E/A: Severn Trent
Comments: Tackle shop, toilets and canteen

Woodrow Fish Pond

Location: Forest Lane, Hanbury, near Droitwich
Type and Size: 2 acre farm pool
Carp Stock: Well stocked with carp averaging 3 lbs; some doubles
Category: Mixed FIshery
Other Species: Crucians, chub, tench and rudd
Permits: On bank
Cost: £4 per day
Control: Tel: 01527 821204
Restrictions: No cereal groundbait; no night fishing; barbless hooks
BK Rating: Easy
E/A: Severn Trent

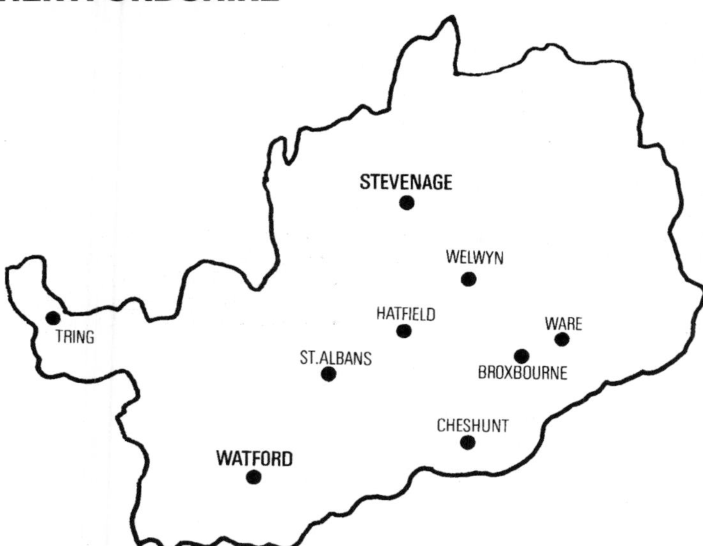

Aldenham Country Park Reservoir

Location: Aldenham, near Elstree
Type and Size: 65 acre reservoir
Carp Stock: Some carp, numbers and sizes not known
Category: Mixed Fishery
Other Species: Tench, roach, pike and bream
Permits: From bailiff on site
Cost: £3 per rod: £1.50 juniors
Control: Herts County Council; tickets and informaton from Park Manager, Park Office, Dagger lane, Elstree. Tel: 0181 9530932
Restrictions: No night fishing; no boilies
BK Rating: Not known
E/A: Thames
Comments: Fishing is also allowed from punts which can be hired at about £5 per day. Evening tickets £1.50

Bowmans Lakes

Location: Coursers Road, London Colney, St Albans
Type and Size: Restored gravel pits. Deep Lake 3 acres; Farm Lake 12 acres; Match Lake 23 acres
How to Find: 1 minute from junction 22 M25. Signposted from Bell Public House roundabout adjacent to motorway. Angler's entrance also via Redlands Gravel Pit on A414 St Albans bypass.
Carp Stock: Very heavilly stocked with carp to 26lb.
Category: Mixed Fishery
Other Species: All including tench to 10lb bream to 6, grass carp to 23lb
Permits: From Pay and Display machines (coins only) at both entrances. Season tickets and details from 10/11 Pleasant Place, West Hyde, Rickmansworth, WD3 2X2
Control: Private. Tel: 01895 824455 contact Ben Tucker

Cost: From £5 adults, £4 juniors. Season ticket 12 months £80
Restrictions: Only 2 rules. No litter and No activities that damage the fish.
BK Rating: Very Easy
E/A: Thames
Comments: Easiest carp water in Hertfordshire. Set on open farm with all facilities available - food, drink, toilets etc. Open 12 months. Full time bailiff lives on site

Bowyers Water

Location: Cheshunt, on the outskirts of North London
Type and Size: 35 acre gravel pit
Carp Stock: Well stocked with carp to over 30lbs
Category: Carp Water
Permits: Season tickets only from Lee Valley Regional Park Authority, Craig Baldwin, Myddelton House, Bulls Cross, Enfield. Tel: 01992 717711
Cost: £62. Concessions
Control: Lee Valley RPA
BK Rating: Difficult
Comments: There was an authenticated carp from this water of 32lbs 3ozs in 1986. Open June 16th to March 14th. Overhead power lines on west bank

Broxbourne

Location: Meadgate Lane, Broxbourne, Hoddesdon
Type and Size: Gravel pits. Lake 1 - 24 acres; Lake 2 - 30 acres, Lake 3 - 68 acres; Lake 4 - 3 1/2 acres
How to Find: Take the A121 to Waltham Abbey, then the B194 1 1/2 miles to Lower Nazeing. Take Pecks Hill Road for 3/4 mile. Turn left into Meadgate Road, keep left at Tile Works and you can then see the lakes. Car parking at Meadgate Lane only
Carp Stock: Not known but carp to 28.14 reported; Brackens (No.4) well stocked
Category: Mixed Fishery
Other Species: Pike, tench, chub, bream, roach, crucian carp, perch, eels.
Permits: Season tickets only from Leisure Sport, Thorpe Park, Chertsey, Surrey. Tel: 01932 564872
Cost: £22 per season. Juniors/OAP/Disabled £11
BK Rating: Very Difficult
Control: Leisure Sports
E/A: Thames
Comments: The large lakes are also used for sailing. Brackens has heavy weed growth and is hard fished

Crown Fishery

Location: Off Station Road, Broxbourne, near Wormley off the A10
Type and Size: Stretch of the River Lea, with much boat traffic in summer
Carp Stock: Not very many, but some go to over 20lbs
Category: Few Carp
Other Species: Chub, roach, perch, tench, bream and pike
Permits: Day tickets on bank at £1.50 and 80p for juniors and OAP's
Control: Private. Tel: 01992 463656
Restrictions: No night fishing
BK Rating: Very Difficult
E/A: Thames

Crown Netherall

Location: Dobbs Weir Road, Hoddesden
Type and Size: 4 acre gravel pit
Carp Stock: Heavilly stocked with fast-growing carp to 37lbs.
Category: Carp Water
Other Species: Catfish to 25lbs, grass carp to 20lb
Permits: Day tickets on bank, season tickets and syndicate tickets from B Hancock Tel: 01992 642401
Cost: From £8 per day
Control: Private Tel: 01992 642401
Restrictions: No tiger nuts or peanuts
BK Rating: Easy
E/A: Thames
Comments: Open 12 months. Toilet on site

Dobbs Weir

Location: Fish and Eels pub, Dobbs Weir Road, Hoddesden
Type and Size: Weir Pool and river - Lee Navigation
Carp Stock: Some carp to 30 lbs
Category: Mixed Fishery
Other Species: Roach, perch, dace, bream, chub, pike and zander
Permits: On bank
Cost: £2.60 per day; concessions
Control: Lee Valley Park. Tel: 01992 717711
Restrictions: No tigernuts or peanuts
BK Rating: Moderate
E/A: Thames
Comments: Once located the fish are easy to catch. Open June 16th to March 14th

Fairlands Park

Location: In Stevenage
Type and Size: Park lake of about ten acres, 25 feet deep in places
How to Find: Enquire at Stevenage
Carp Stock: Fairly heavily stocked with carp to 20lbs+. Plenty of doubles
Category: Carp Water
Other Species: Roach, rudd, bream, tench, pike
Permits: Day tickets from bailiff on the bank
Cost: About £3. Concessions
Control: Council. Tel: 01438 353241
Restrictions: One bank only can be fished; no night fishing
BK Rating: Easy
E/A: NRA Thames Region
Comments: Sailing boats and canoes

Frogmore Lake

Location: Near St Albans
Type and Size: Small lake
Carp Stock: Said to contain some carp to good size, but numbers and sizes not known
Category: Mixed Fishery
Other Species: Usual coarse fish
Permits: Members only water of the London Anglers Association, Forest Road Hall, Hervey Park Road, Walthamstow, London E17 6LJ. Tel: 0181 5207477
Cost: About £20 per season, to include many other waters, including rivers and canal fishing
Control: LAA
BK Rating: Not known
Restrictions: No night fishing
E/A: Thames

Grand Union Canal (a)

Location: Watford to Milton Keynes (Herts/Beds/Bucks)
Type and Size: Canal of several miles in length
Carp Stock: Well stocked in certain areas along this stretch with many carp up to 30lbs - a fish of 30lbs was reported from the Kings Langley area in 1990
Category: Mixed Fishery
Others Species: General coarse fish
Permits: Day tickets from various clubs in the area - you will need to enquire locally
Control: Mainly clubs
BK Rating: Easy to difficult depending on area
E/A: Thames
Comments: Good water for fun fishing and as a change from lakes

Hatfield Broadwater

Location: Essendon, near Hatfield, on River Lea
Type and Size: Seven acre lake
Carp Stock: Carp to over 20lbs
Category: Mixed Fishery
Other Species: Bream, roach and tench
Permits: Members only water of Hatfield and District AS, E F Denchfield, 44 Stockbreach Road, Hatfield, Herts
Control: Club
Restrictions: No day tickets, club members only
BK Rating: Moderate
E/A: Thames

Henlow Grange

Location: Between the vilages of Henlow and Arlesey, both of which are in Bedfordshire!
Type and Size: Gravel pits of nine, five, and three acres
Carp Stock: Large lake fairly well stocked with carp to 44lbs (although this was a spawnbound fish which is thought to be dead). In 1991 a 31½lb common and a mirror of over 30lbs were caught. Other two lakes well stocked with carp to low twenties
Category: Mixed Fishery
Permits: Letchworth Angling Club - season tickets from local tackle shops, in Letchworth and Hitchin
Cost: About £30 per season - no day tickets
BK Rating: Large lake - Difficult; other lakes - Moderate
E/A: Anglian
Comments: Good club waters, with a few very large fish

Holwell Hyde Lake

Location: Cole Green near Welwyn Garden City
Type and Size: Two acre lake
How to Find: Find Hatfield and take the A405 to the left, turn onto the A4134 Hertford Road. After 3 miles turn left onto the B195 and continue for 1½ miles. Turn left into Holwell Hyde Lane. The lake is half a mile on the left
Carp Stock: Well stocked with carp which are thought to be small, but some upper doubles and two 20's
Category: Mixed Fishery
Other Species: Tench, roach and rudd
Permits: Day tickets from bailiffs on the bank or in advance from Fishery Manager, V Bamford Esq., Holwell Hyde Cottage, Holwell Hyde Lane, Welwyn Garden City. Season tickets about £20 (£10 for Juniors/OAP's), evening fishing from Fishery Manager
Cost: Day tickets about £2.50 (£1.25 Juniors/OAP's). Season tickets £25
Restrictions: No night fishing. Sunrise to sunset for season tickets and advance day ticket holders. Those without tickets must not be on the fishery before 8.30am. No unaccompanied juniors unless they hold season tickets. No sacking. One rod only till Octoer
Control: Redland Angling Scheme
BK Rating: Easy
E/A: Thames
Comments: Little is known about this water which has been little fished previously. Do not park anywhere other than in the car park. Bus No.324 from Welwyn Garden City to Hertford passes the end of Holwell Hyde Lane. Car parking close to water

Hook Lake

Location: Northaw, near Potters Bar
Type and Size: 1½ acre pool
How to Find: In the village of Northaw, 200 yards south of the main road
Carp Stock: Well stocked with carp to 30lbs, mostly doubles
Category: Mixed Fishery
Other Species: Tench to 8lb, pike to 24lb, perch to 4lb 8oz, roach and rudd.
Cost: Season £95. June 1 - March 31
Control: Northaw Fisheries Management Ltd., 126 Byng Drive, Potters Bar, Herts, EN6 1VJ. Richard Stangroom. Tel: 01707 268613
E/A: Thames
Comments: Details supplied on receipt of an SAE

Kings Weir Fishery

Location: Lea Navigation, near Wormley
Type and Size: River, weir pool, and one bank of a local lake
How to Find: From the A10 turn towards Turnford (!) and follow the A1170 to Wormley. At Wormley turn right into Wharfe Road, cross the railway, and park in the car park by the river
Carp Stock: Some carp to about mid-doubles
Category: Few Carp
Other Species: Barbel to well over 10lbs, chub, bream, perch, pike, dace and eels
Permits: Day tickets, booked in advance only from B Newton. Tel: 01992 468394
Cost: £5 per day to river and weir pool; £2 per day on lake
Control: Private
BK Rating: Difficult
E/A: Thames
Comments: A very attractive and unusual fishery close to London

Marsworth Reservoir

Location: Marsworth, near Tring
Type and Size: 40 acre reservoir
How to Find: Take the A41 from Tring, and turn right on the B489. You will see the car park on the right
Carp Stock: Some carp to over 20lbs, with a chance of a 30
Category: Mixed Fishery
Other Species: Bit tench, and bream; roach, perch, rudd, pike and catfish
Permits: Day tickets on bank
Cost: £4 per day; OAP's and those under 14, £2 per day
Control: Bernard Double. Tel: 0144282 2379
Restrictions: No keepnets; night fishing for syndicate members only
BK Rating: Very Difficult
E/A: Thames

North Met Pit

Location: Cheshunt, Herts. in the Lea Valley, North London
Type and Size: Gravel pit of 58 acres
Carp Stock: Well stocked with carp to mid-thirties; stocked with 2000lbs of carp between 14 and 18lbs in 1990, with 2,500 more pounds to come
Category: Carp Water
Other Species: Big pike, and tench
Permits: Lee Valley, Regional Park Authority, Craig Baldwin, Myddleton House, Bulls Cross, Enfield. Tel: 01992 717711
Cost: Season £62. Day £2.60
Control: Lee Valley R.P.A
BK Rating: Fairly Hard

Restrictions: No tiger nuts or peanuts
E/A: Thames
Comments: Open June 16th to March 14th

Redlands Crown Fishery

Location: Broxbourne
Type and Size: Three lakes totalling about 40 acres
How to Find: Take the A10 from London and turn off at Hoddesdon. At the round about after 400 yards take the first exit sign marked 'Dobbs Weir Industrial Estate'. Pass the Fish and Eels public house and after another 600 yards enter the fishery through gates on the left near Richard White Sluices
Carp Stock: Not many carp but some are large
Category: Few Carp
Other Species: Tench, bream, roach, perch, pike
Permits: No day tickets. Season tickets only from Fishery Manager. Peter Brill, Carthagena Lock, Broxbourne, Herts Tel: 01992 463656
Cost: About £15 a season. Juniors/OAP £6
BK Rating: Difficult, as there are few carp
Control: Redland Angling Scheme
E/A: Thames

River Gade

Location: Cassiobury Park, off the A412, just after Watford Town Hall
Type and Size: Small river with weirs and sluices
Carp Stock: Some carp to nearly 10lbs
Category: Few Carp
Other Species: Chub, perch, roach, dace, rudd, pike and gudgeon
Permits: Free
Control: Council
BK Rating: Difficult
E/A: Thames

Slipe Lane Pits

Location: Slipe Lane, Turnford
Type and Size: Five pits, 2 of which (Railway and Lee) contain carp
Carp Stock: Railway Pit - carp to mid 20's; Lee - a few to 30 lbs
Category: Mixed Fishery
Other Species: Mixed coarse fish
Permits: Season tickets from Lee Valley Park
Cost: On enquiry
Control: Lee Valley Park. Tel: 01992 717711
Restrictions: No tigernuts or peanuts. No carp sacks
BK Rating: Moderate to Difficult
E/A: Thames
Comments: Open June 16th to March 14th

Springwell Lake

Location: Rickmansworth, near Watford
Type and Size: Medium sized matured gravel pit
Carp Stock: Well stocked with carp to 20lbs
Category: Mixed Fishery
Other Species: Tench, roach and perch
Permits: Members only water of London Anglers Association, Forest Road Hall, Hervey Park Road, Walthamstow, London E17. Tel: 0181 5207477

Cost: About £25 per season, to include a number of other waters - 100 miles of fishing in rivers, canals, lakes and reservoirs
Control: LAA
Restrictions: No night fishing
BK Rating: Not known
E/A: Thames

Stanborough Lake

Location: Welwyn Garden City
Type and Size: Gravel pit of about 20 acres
How to Find: Edge of A1M near Welwyn Garden City
Carp Stock: Very heavily stocked with many doubles to 20lbs. Few twenties to 27lbs.
Category: Carp Water
Other Species: Roach, rudd, tench, bream and catfish
Permits: Day tickets and club membership available on bank. £3.50 at weekends; £2.50 on weekdays
Control: Welwyn Garden City AC
BK Rating: Very Easy
Restrictions: One rod only - you won't need more on this easy water. Two rods after 1st November - no groundbaiting and no boilies; no night fishing
E/A: Thames
Comments: Sailing boats and many people

Stanstead Abbots

Location: High Street, Stanstead Abbot,Ware, Herts
Type and Size: Five lakes
How to Find: From London take the A10 Cambridge road and then the A414 to Stanstead Abbots. Park cars in the public car park in the High Street and walk down the path at the rear of the car park to the lakes
Carp Stock: Stocked with 1,500 carp in 1983, sizes not known, and also a few bigger carp to 31lbs, were stocked in 1984. Mixed fishery although if enough of these carp survived there should be enough to take this into our Carp Water category in the future. Many 20's and 30's caught. Fish up to 42lbs in the bigger lake
Category: Mixed Fishery
Other Species: Tench, bream, roach and chub
Permits: Season tickets from LSA, Thorpe Park, Staines Road, Chertsey, Surrey. Tel: 01932 564872 Fax: 01932 566 367
Cost: £32 per season; Juniors/OAP/Disabled £16. Limited tickets on a first come, first served basis
Restrictions: Usual LSA rules but night fishing is allowed
BK Rating: Difficult to Very Difficult
Control: Leisure Sport Angling
E/A: Thames

Litter

Pick it up before it damages wildlife or loses you the fishing.
A carrier bag fits in a pocket and a little care goes a long way.

Startops, Tring Reservoirs

Location: Near Tring
Type and Size: Reservoir of 65 acres
Carp Stock: Not many carp, but there are some 20's and possibly much bigger fish present
Category: Few Carp
Other Species: Bream, tench, roach, perch, pike, catfish
Permits: Day tickets from bailiff, on the bank - about £4. Season tickets
Restrictions: No night fishing, but there is a night syndicate
Control: Private. Tel: 01442 8222379
BK Rating: Very Difficult
E/A: Thames
Comments: Night syndicate, members only

Weston's Lake

Location: Just outside the village of Weston, near Stevenage
Type and Size: Lake of about three acres
Carp Stock: Lightly stocked with carp to upper doubles
Category: Mixed Fishery
Other Species: Crucians, tench, rudd and bream
Permits: Weston AC; details from local tackle shops
Restrictions: Members only; no night fishing
BK Rating: Difficult
E/A: Anglian
Comments: An attractive lake, used mainly for matches

Wormleybury

Location: Wormley, near Broxbourne, Church Lane
Type and Size: Estate lake of five acres
Carp Stock: Not many carp, mostly very large with about 15 20's including two commons of over 25lbs, some upper 20's. Lake record is 36lbs, but this fish has since died, Possible one other low 30 in the lake
Category: Mixed Fishery
Other Species: Tench, roach, rudd, bream, perch, pike and catfish
Permits: From the owner, Graham Barnes, Wormleybury House, Church Lane, Broxbourne, Herts
Cost: About £80 a season; 1 rod and 2 rod tickets
Control: Private
Baits/Methods: The most up-to-date advanced carp tactics/methods required for this water
BK Rating: Very Difficult
E/A: Thames
Comments: A beautiful crescent shaped estate water in the grounds of a big house. Lots of reeds, lilies etc. Apply in writing to the owners as fishing might never be allowed on this water again

Linear Fisheries Oxford

34 10oz Manor Farm Lake

THE BEEKAY GUIDE TO 2000 BRITISH & EUROPEAN CARP WATERS

Is YOUR Water listed? If so, are the details correct?
If you spot omissions, inaccuracies, or know of any changes, please let us know by filling in the Waters Questionnaire at the back of this guide and return it to us at:

Beekay International
Withy Pool
Henlow Camp
Bedfordshire
SG16 6EA

HUMBERSIDE

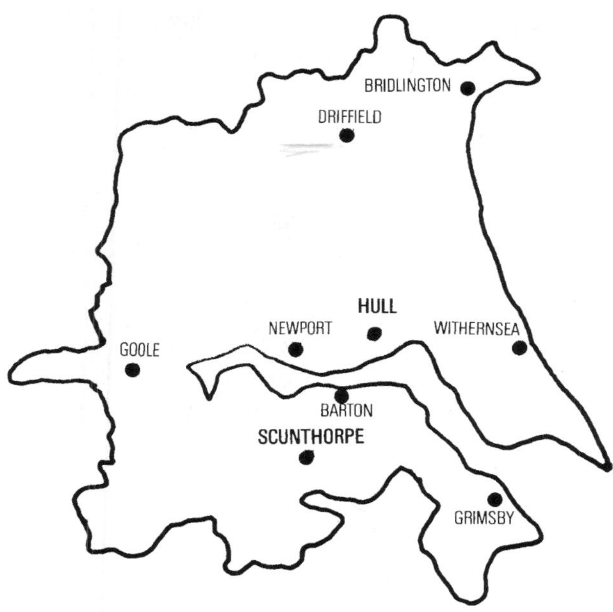

Bakers Pond

Location:	Thimble Hall Lane, Newport, near Hull (white bungalow)
Type and Size:	Two and a half acre lake
How to Find:	Newport Village is at the end of the M62
Carp Stock:	Well stocked with carp to over 30lbs
Category:	Carp Water
Other Species:	Crucians, tench and bream
Permits:	On site - Tel: Bill Baker on 01430 440350 (7am to 10.30pm)
Cost:	On application
BK Rating:	Moderate
Control:	Private
E/A:	Yorkshire
Restrictions:	No tic beans, no keepnets
Comments:	Owner lives on the site. Big catches reported. 10-20 feet deep - snag and weed free except for central island supported by telegraph poles

Barton Broads **A**

Location:	Barton-on-Humber, South Humberside
Type and Size:	11 acre clay pit
How to Find:	Off the A15 just before the Humber Bridge
Carp Stock:	Heavily stocked with 3,000 carp to 21.7lbs. Many doubles
Category:	Mixed Fishery
Other Species:	Catfish, tench, bream, roach, rudd

Permits: On site or telephone 01652 32237
Cost: About £1.50 per day; £2.50 for 24 hours; syndicate £100
BK Rating: Moderate to Difficult
Restrictions: No hemp
Control: Private
E/A: Anglian
Comments: The site includes a cafe, a tackle and bait shop, and caravans for holidays - contact the resident owners for details

Big Hole Pit

Location: Rawcliffe, just west of Goole off the M62
Type and Size: Five acre brick pit, with bars, bays and weed
Carp Stock: Well stocked with small carp to abut 10lbs
Category: Mixed Fishery
Other Species: Roach, rudd, tench and bream
Permits: Members only water of Goole and Dist., AA. Secretary, L Roger, 29 Westfield Square, Goole N.Humberside DN15 6QR
Cost: About £15 per season
Restrictions: No day tickets; no night fishing; no carp sacks or weighing slings!
BK Rating: Easy
E/A: Yorkshire

Brandesburton 3 and 4

Location: Brandesburton near Hull
Type and Size: 8 acre gravel pit
How to Find: Take the A 165 towards Brandesburton, and turn left opposite the gravel works
Carp Stock: Some carp to doubles
Category: Few Carp
Other Species: Pike, eels, bream, perch and roach
Permits: From local tackle shops
Cost: £21 per season; £9 juniors and O.A.P's
Control: Hull and District A.A.; Tel: 01430 440624
BK Rating: Not known
Baits/Methods: Boilies best for carp
E/A: Yorkshire
Comments: Open all year

Burshill 'A' Pond

Location: Off the A 165 at Burshill, near Brandesburton
Type and Size: One acre lake
Carp Stock: Well stocked with small carp to 5 lbs
Category: Mixed Fishery
Other Species: Roach, chub, tench, rudd and small bream
Permits: In advance only from local tackle shops
Cost: £21 per season; £7 juniors, O.A.P's and disabled
Control: Hull D.A.A. Tel: 01430 440624
Restrictions: No night fishing; no keepnets
BK Rating: Easy
E/A: Yorkshire

Burstwick Ski Lake

Location: Burstwick, Hedon, Hull
Type and Size: Eight acre gravel pit
How to Find: From Hull take the A1033 to Hedon, then the B1362 to Burstwick. Go through the village towards Keylingham, and the lake is down an old railway track
Carp Stock: Quite well stocked with carp to 20lbs
Category: Mixed Fishery
Other Species: Bream, tench, roach, rudd, perch and trout
Permits: Day tickets from clubhouse on site - about £3
Cost: Tel: 01964 622777 for costs and information
Control: Private
BK Rating: Thought to be quite hard
E/A: Yorkshire
Comments: There is water skiing on this lake. Night fishing is permitted

Burton Constable Lakes

Location: Burton Constable Hall, Sproatley, near Hull
Type and Size: Several estate lakes, of about 25 acres in all
Carp Stock: Quite well stocked with carp to double figures
Category: Mixed Fishery
Other Species: Roach, bream, perch, tench and pike
Permits: The Warden, Old Lodge, Sproatley, Nr Hull
Cost: Season - £30
Control: Private
Restrictions: Open for fishing from 1st March to 31st October only
BK Rating: Moderate
E/A: Yorkshire
Comments: Very good fishing on an attractive private estate

Emmotland One and Two

Location: Emmotland, North Frodingham, near Driffield
Type and Size: Two lakes
Carp Stock: Well stocked with carp to over 30lbs
Category: Carp Water
Other Species: Some coarse fish
Permits: Syndicate and day tickets
Cost: On application
Control: Information from Mrs M Whitmore, fishery owner. Tel: 0162 488226
BK Rating: Moderate
E/A: Yorkshire

Far Grange Park

Location: Grange Farm, Skipsea, near Bridlington
Type and Size: 3 acre lake
How to Find: Take the B 1242 road from Bridlington towards Hornsea. The fishery is a mile from Skipsea
Carp Stock: Well stocked with carp to doubles
Category: Mixed Fishery
Other Species: Bream, tench, roach and rudd
Permits: From reception
Cost: About £3 per day; £20 per season
Control: Tel: 01262 468248
Restrictions: No keepnets
BK Rating: Moderate

E/A: Yorkshire
Comments: Holiday caravan and camping park. Refreshments and toilets. Probably open all year

Fishponds Farm Fishery

Location: Bridlington
Type and Size: Three small farm ponds
How to Find: From Bridlington town centre, follow Woldgate, which becomes a narrow country lane, and the lakes are on the right
Carp Stock: Well stocked with mirrors and commons, sizes not known
Category: Mixed Fishery
Other Species: Crucians, bream, tench, roach, rudd, perch, brook trout, brown and rainbow trout
Permits: Day tickets at the office. For details, telephone the owner, Mr J Nadin, on 01262 605873
BK Rating: Insufficient information
Control: Private
E/A: Yorkshire
Restrictions: Barbless hooks only. No keepnets. No one under 18 unless accompanied by an adult angler
Comments: This is said to be the most attractive water in Yorkshire, surrounded by woodland and very peaceful

Fish Trades Pond

Location: Newport, between Hull and Goole, on B1239
Type and Size: Small pond of one acre
How to Find: Just off the A64 at Newport Village
Carp Stock: Well stocked with carp to over 30lbs
Category: Carp Water
Other Species: Tench, bream, roach, perch, pike, trout
Permits: Day tickets
Cost: Low
Restrictions: No night fishing
BK Rating: Moderate
Control: Not known - ask on bank
E/A: Yorkshire
Comments: Popular day ticket water. Try Hull and District AA. J Holdenbury, 1 Grebe Road, Thimblehall lane, Newport, N.Humberside HU15 2PJ for information. This club has some excellent carp fisheries in Humberside. No close season

Gowdall Lakes

Location: Gowdall
Type and Size: 2½ acre carp pool and 2 acre mixed pool
How to Find: Turn off the M62 at junction 34 and take the A19 northwards. Then take the Hensall and Gowdall road
Carp Stock: Carp pool well stocked to mid - doubles;
Category: Carp pool: Carp Only. Mixed pool: Mixed Fishery
Other Species: Tench, roach, rudd, perch, bream and crucians
Permits: On bank
Cost: About £5 for carp lake; £4 for the other
Control: Private. Tel: 01405 860756
BK Rating: Not known
Baits/Methods: Boilies and luncheon meat are good baits
E/A: Yorkshire
Comments: Toilet. Disabled access

Halsham Pond

Location: Behind the New Stag public house on the B1362 at Halsham, near Withernsea
Type and Size: Small pond
Carp Stock: Quite well stocked with carp to double figures
Category: Mixed Fishery
Other Species: Bream, tench and rudd and perch
Permits: From Mr Allison, New Stag Inn, Halsham, N.Humberside. Tel:0194 70847
Cost: Low cost day tickets
Control: Private
BK Rating: Moderate
Restrictions: No night fishing - 7.30am till dusk only. Barbless hooks
E/A: Yorkshire
Comments: Park in the pub car park! Some areas suitable for disabled anglers

Hoe Hill Fishery

Location: Pasture Road North, off the A1077 near Barton-on-Humber
Type and Size: Three acre shallow lake
Carp Stock: Quite well stocked with carp to mid-doubles
Category: Mixed Fishery
Other Species: Tench, roach, rudd, perch, chub and bream
Permits: On the bank or from the house on the property
Cost: £3 per day; £4 for night fishing, by special arrangement
Control: John Smith. Tel: 01652 635119
Restrictions: No boilies
BK Rating: Moderate
E/A: Anglian

Holme Lake Fishery

Location: Holme Lane, Messingham, near Scunthorpe. Three miles from junction 4 off the M18
Type and Size: 20 acre sand pit
Carp Stock: Stocked in 1988 with 5,500 carp from 4oz to 8lbs and one 27 pounder
Category: Mixed Fishery
Other Species: Roach, bream, rudd and perch
Permits: Day tickets from Alan Barton. Tel: 01724 850197
Cost: £4 per day
Control: Private
BK Rating: Moderate
E/A: Yorkshire

Leven Canal

Location: Carr Lane, Leven, near Hull
Type and Size: Wide canal
Carp Stock: Well stocked with carp to 10lbs
Category: Mixed Fishery
Other Species: Pike, perch, roach, rudd, tench and eels
Permits: On bank
Cost: £3 per day;£1.50 juniors and OAP's
Control: Tel: 01482 796627
BK Rating: Easy
E/A: Yorkshire

Kingfisher Lodge A

Location: Hibaldstow, off the B1206 south east of Scunthorpe
Type and Size: Man-made lake of about five acres, with a large island
Carp Stock: Heavily stocked with doubles
Category: Mixed Fishery
Other Species: Tench, chub, bream, perch and rudd
Permits: On the bank at £3 per day
Control: Nigel Coulson. Tel: 01652 654652
Restrictions: No night fishing; no groundbaiting
BK Rating: Moderate
E/A: Anglian
Comments: No close season. Six caravans for hire. Toilets and camping areas. Cars can be driven to swims

Langholme Hill Fishery

Location: Emmotland, North Frodingham
Type and Size: Two pools of three acres and one and a half acres
How to Find: Take the B1249 from Driffield to North Frodingham, and after the village turn right to Emmotland. The lakes are on the left at the end of this road
Carp Stock: Well stocked with carp to over 20lbs
Category: Mixed Fishery
Other Species: Big bream and tench, roach, perch, pike, trout
Permits: On bank, at £3 per rod
Control: Private. M Whitfield. Tel:01262 488226
Restrictions: No night fishing. No keepnets
E/A: Yorkshire
Comments: Open for 11 months of the year. Fishing dawn till dusk

Lindholme Lakes

Location: Off the A164 and the M180 south of Thorne at Sandtoft
Type and Size: Three small lakes, one a carp fishery
Carp Stock: Heavily stocked with carp to 5lbs
Category: Carp Water
Other Species: Big tench, roach, perch, bream and a few trout
Permits: Day tickets on site
Cost: £4 or £2.50 for an evening session
Control: Brian Lindley. Tel: 01427 872015; Head Bailiff, Tel: 01427 872906
Restrictions: No night fishing
BK Rating: Easy
E/A: Yorkshire
Comments: Toilet

Motorway Pond

Location: Near Hull
Type and Size: Lake of 18½ acres
How to Find: On the edge of Hull
Carp Stock: About 100 big carp to 37lbs
Category: Mixed Fishery
Other Species: Double figure bream and good tench
Permits: Hull and District AC - local tackle shops. Night fishing syndicate
Cost: On application
BK Rating: Moderate
Control: Club. Kevin Clifford, Sandholme Grange, Newport, North Humberside HU15 2QG. Tel: 01430 440624
E/A: Yorkshire
Comments: Enquire for details from local tackle shops, and Hull AC

Rushyvars Lakes

Location: Near Preston, off the A1033 Hull road to Hedon
Type and Size: Medium-sized lake
Carp Stock: Well stocked with carp, sizes not known
Category: Mixed Fishery
Other Species: Tench, ream, rudd and roach
Permits: On site, low cost
BK Rating: Moderate
Restrictions: No night fishing - dawn to dusk only. Barbless hooks. No groundbait
Control: Private
E/A: Yorkshire
Comments: Toilet facilities, and level banks for disabled angers. There is also a small trout lake on the site. Tel: 01482 898970 for full details of this fishery

Staddlethorpe Lake

Location: Station Road, Giberdyke, near Newport
Type and Size: 4 acre lake
Carp Stock: Mostly small carp, with a few doubles
Category: Mixed Fishery
Other Species: Tench, bream, roach, perch and chub
Permits: On bank
Cost: £4 per day; reduced prices for juniors, OA.P's and disabled
Control: Tel: 01405 762 869
BK Rating: Not known
E/A: Yorkshire

The Billabong Caravan Park A

Location: Hempholme Bridge, Brandesburton, near Driffield YO25 8NB. Tel: 01964 543631
Type and Size: 11 acre pit
How to Find: Off the A165
Carp Stock: Well stocked with carp to 15lbs
Category: Carp Water
Other Species: Pike, perch, roach, bream and trout
Permits: From owner on site - free at present for those staying on site, but day ticket charge being considered
BK Rating: Not known
E/A: Yorkshire
Comments: There is water skiing and other water sports on the lake, with most fishing during the mornings, evening and after dark

The Nest

Location: Wintringham, near Scunthorpe, S.Humberside
Type and Size: One acre man-made pond
How to Find: Just off the A1077 between Scunthorpe and Barton-upon-Humber
Carp Stock: Well stocked, mostly 6 - 8lbs; a few doubles to 11lbs
Category: Mixed Fishery
Other Species: Crucians, grass carp, tench, rudd, roach, perch
Permits: On bank. Tel: Wintringham 732465
Cost: About £3 per day (6am to 8pm)
BK Rating: Easy
Control: Private
Baits/Methods: Sweetcorn, maggots, luncheon meat, cheese paste
E/A: Yorkshire
Restrictions: No night fishing
Comments: Well coloured water with slippery banks when wet. Booking may be necessary in advance as only 20 anglers are allowed to fish the water. Also fished by 'small fish' anglers

Tilery Lake

Location: Broomfleet Tile Factory, near Hull
Type and Size: Clay pit of 20 acres
Carp Stock: Contains about 100 carp, most of which are said to be doubles averaging 20lbs in weight. Plenty of 20's to 34lbs
Category: Carp Water/Mixed Fishery
Other Species: Pike, bream, roach
Permits: Hull and District Angling Association, Hull. Secretary: J Holdenby, 1 Grebe Road, Thimblehall Lane,Newport HU15 2PJ
Cost: Club membership about £22 a year, with an additional £80 for night fishing (waiting list)
BK Rating: Difficult
Control: Club: Kevin Clifford, Sandholme Grange, Newport, North Humberside. Tel: 01430 440624
E/A: Yorkshire
Comments: Night fishing for syndicate members. Open and featureless water, 4-17ft deep

Westfield Lakes A

Location: Westfields Hotel, Barton-on-Humber, off the A15 near the south side of the Humber Bridge
Type and Size: Two small lakes in grounds of hotel
Carp Stock: Well stocked with carp to over 20lbs
Category: Mixed Fishery
Other Species: Tench, roach, rudd, bream, and pike
Permits: From Westfields Hotel
Cost: £3 per rod
Control: Tel: 01652 32313
Restrictions: No night fishing; no live baiting
BK Rating: Moderate
E/A: Anglian
Comments: No close season

The Catfish Conservation Group

Joining the **C.C.G.** offers the following benefits to all members:

- ♦ Three copies of our newsletter *Silurus*
- ♦ Our high quality colour magazine *Whiskers*
- ♦ The opportunity to fish **Adams Pool**, our very own specialist cat water
- ♦ Continental tackle hire for those European monsters
- ♦ The combined knowledge of some of the top catfish anglers in the country
- ♦ Exclusive **C.C.G.** products, including Tee shirts, Sweat shirts, Badges, Stickers, Mugs, Key Fobs and Lighters
- ♦ Specialist catfish hooks and floats available to purchase
- ♦ Our very own Video, *Catfish & How to Catch Them*
- ♦ Free advice on stocking catfish and maintaining specialist cat fisheries

For information about the Catfish Conservation Group write to:

The C.C.G. Secretary,
The Retreat,
Heath Lane,
Ewshot,
Surrey, GU10 5AW

If you wish to join, send £11 subscription for one year's membership to include *Whiskers* colour magazine and at least two copies of *Silurus* newsletter

For a list of waters containing catfish turn to the back of this guide.

Winter's Pool

Location: East Halton, in S.Humberside between Grimsby and Barton-under-Humber
Type and Size: Two acre clay pit with clear banks
How to Find: Take the A180 from Grimsby, then turn onto A1173, then follow signs for East Halton
Carp Stock: Quite well stocked with carp to upper doubles, with possibly a low 20 or two
Category: Mixed Fishery
Other Species: Roach and bream
Permits: Day tickets. Tel: 01469 40238
Control: Private
BK Rating: Moderate
E/A: Yorkshire
Comments: No close season

Woodall's Pond

Location: Canal East Side, Newport, near Hull
Type and Size: 2 acre lake
Carp Stock: Carp to over 30 lbs
Category: Mixed Fishery
Other Species: Pike, tench, chub, roach, bream and perch
Permits: On bank
Cost: About £2, with extra for second rod
Control: Tel: 01430 441127
BK Rating: Not known
Baits/Methods: Boilies are best
E/A: Yorkshire

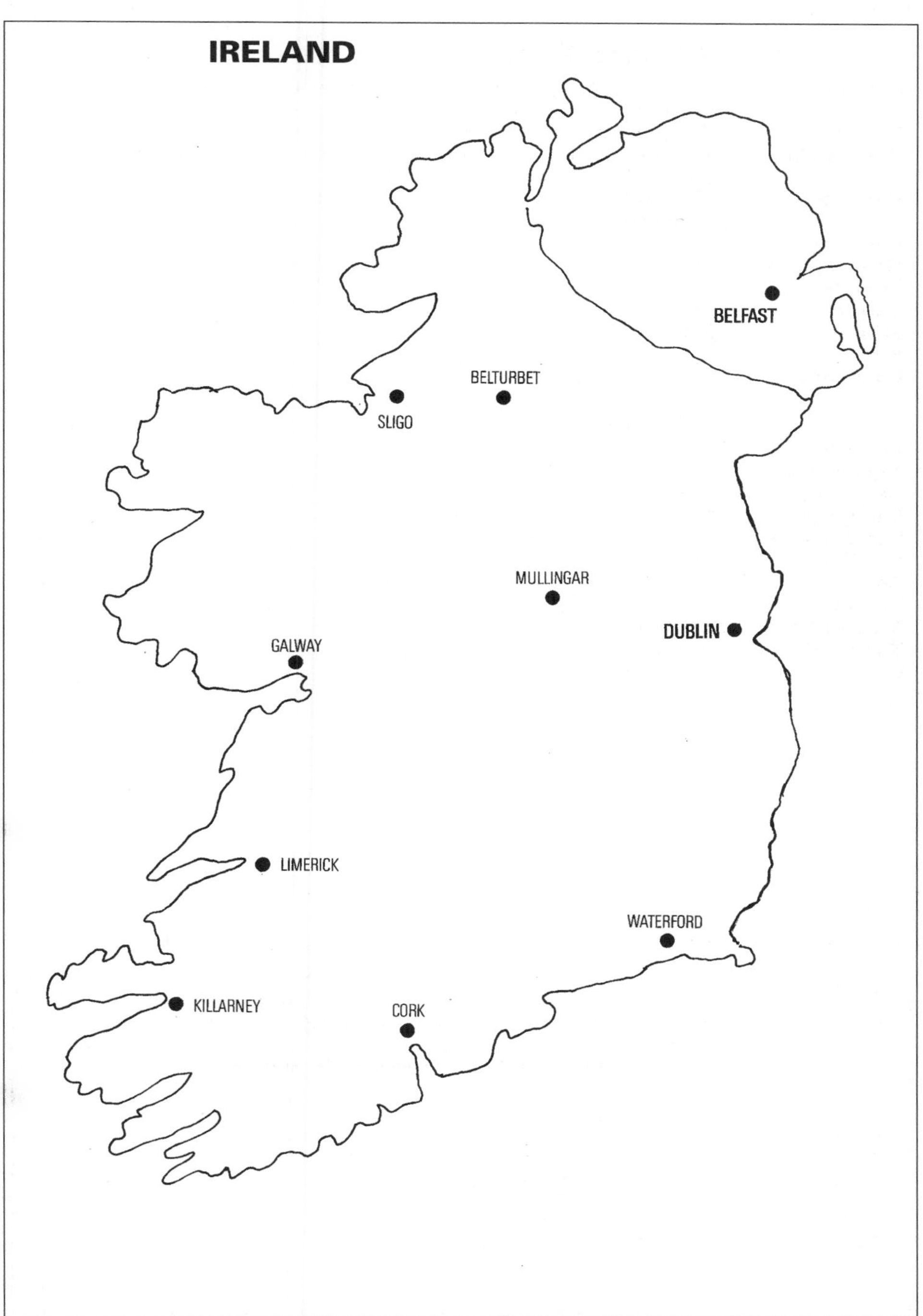
IRELAND
BELFAST
BELTURBET
SLIGO
MULLINGAR
DUBLIN
GALWAY
LIMERICK
WATERFORD
KILLARNEY
CORK

Ballinafid Lake

Location: North of Mullingar, off the N4 Mullingar-Longford road
Type and Size: Small lake
Carp Stock: Quite well stocked with carp to about 15lbs
Category: Mixed Fishery
Other Species: Bream and tench
Permits: Irish State Rod Licence, cost about £10
BK Rating: Moderate
Comments: No close season. Best fishing opposite main road. Soft banks, reeds and a platform

Ballincollig Reservoir

Location: Ballincollig Village, 5 miles west of Cork
Type and Size: 8 acre disused reservoir
Carp Stock: Well stocked with carp to 5 lbs; some upper doubles and twenties
Other Species: Small tench
Permits: FREE FISHING
BK Rating: Easy - Moderate for the bigger fish
Comments: Please respect the countryside on this free Irish water

Bun Lough

Location: Car park on the N3 Belturbet-Cavan road, and across two fields
Type and Size: 21 acre Irish lough, very weedy, with a soft bottom
Carp Stock: Stocked with small carp about 5 years ago, present number and sizes not known
Category: Mixed Fishery
Permits: Difficult - you're likely to catch lots of tench and bream! No close season. If you do catch any carp, please report them to the Irish Fisheries Board, Mobhi Boreen, Glasnevin, Dublin 5 or local Fisheries Board offices, the address of which can be had locally. Make sure you cause no problems crossing the farmer's field to get to the lake

Cork Lough

Location: Off the Western Road in Cork City
Type and Size: Ten acre town lake near houses, very shallow and a wildfowl sanctuary
Category: Mixed Fishery
Other Species: Tench, rudd, perch and big eels
Permits: Irish State Licence, cost about £10
Baits/Methods: Sweetcorn works well, and so do most normal carp baits and methods
BK Rating: Moderate
Comments: No close season; public water, very busy, and heavily fished, as it holds the Irish carp record of 25¾ lbs.caught on sweetcorn and 3lb line. This is Ireland's best carp water. Do not leave line or tackle to damage birds

Litter

Pick it up before it damages wildlife or loses you the fishing.
A carrier bag fits in a pocket and a little care goes a long way.

Doolin Pond

Location: Off the R400 road from Mullingar, near Gaybrook Cross
Type and Size: Small muddy, weedy lake
Carp Stock: This water was set up as an experimental carp fishery, and carp are now caught to about 10lbs
Category: Carp Water
Permits: Irish State Rod Licence, costing about £10
Baits/Methods: Standard specialist carp methods needed
BK Rating: Difficult
Comments: No close season. Easy access

Galmoylestown Lake

Location: North of Mullingar - turn left off the R394 Mullingar-Castlepollard road
Type and Size: Small lake, weedy and only about four feet deep
Carp Stock: Stocked with small carp by the Central Fisheries Board some years ago. These fish are now being caught up to about 10lbs
Category: Carp Water
Other Species: Some trout at this former trout fishery
Permits: State Rod Licence required, the cost which is about £10
Baits/Methods: The water is heavily fished and the carp now need sophisticated baits and methods to be caught
BK Rating: Moderate
Comments: One of Ireland's few carp waters, this pleasant little lake has good access for disabled anglers. You should not require any permits except the Irish State Licence. No close season. An angler had 46 carp to 8lbs in one session in 1992

McEvoys Lake

Location: 3 miles north of Mullingar on the R394
Type and Size: Small lake with fishing platforms
Carp Stock: Some carp to 10lbs
Other species: Roach, tench rudd and pike
Permits: FREE FISHING
BK Rating: Difficult
Comments: Heavy baiting required. Boilies and particles. Please respect the countryside on this free Irish water

Paddy McNamaras Lake

Location: Near O'Briens Bridge, at the junction of the R463 Limerick-Killaloe road, and the R466 O'Brien's Bridge-Broadford road, south west of Killaloe

Type and Size: Ten acre weedy lake, about 10 feet deep

Carp Stock: Stocked with carp to about 8lb by the late Paddy Mac, a well known and distinguished developer of fishing in the area

Category: Mixed Fishery

Other Species: Rudd, perch and tench

Permits: Irish State Rod Licence required, cost about £10

BK Rating: Moderate

Comments: No close season

ISLE OF WIGHT

Gunville Pond

Location: Gunville Pool, Carisbrooke, near Newport
Type and Size: Lake of three acres
Carp Stock: Well stocked with carp to 11lbs
Category: Mixed Fishery
Other Species: Perch, tench, rudd, pike and roach
Permits: Tickets from tackle shops in most towns, such as G C Young, 74 Regent Street, Shanklin. W Bates, 5 Springhill, Ventnor. (Members only)
Cost: About £12 per season
Control: Isle of Wight Freshwater Angling Association. M Steed, 6 Priors Walk, Newport PO30 5RN. Tel: 01983 521267
Restrictions: Members only
BK Rating: Easy
E/A: Southern

River Yar (a)

Location: Alverstone
Type and Size: Small, shallow river, only about 25 feet wide
Carp Stock: Some carp to 6lbs
Category: Few Carp
Other Species: Dace, roach, perch, gudgeon and eels
Permits: Day tickets from Scotties Tackle Shop, Lugley Street, Newport or Doug Stephens, Bait and Tackle, Union Street, Newport
Control: Isle of Wight Freshwater AA. Mr Mick Streed, 6 Priors Walk, Newport PO3 5RN. Tel: 01983 521267
BK Rating: Difficult
E/A: Southern

River Yar (b)

Location: Just south of the main road (A3055) between Sandown and Brading, behind the 'Anglers Inn' public house
Type and Size: Small river, only about 40 feet wide
Carp Stock: Some carp to double figures
Category: Few Carp

Other Species: Dace, roach, perch, gudgeon, tench, rudd, bream and eels
Permits: Day tickets from Scotties Tackle Shop, Lugley Street, Newport or Doug Stephens, Union Street, Newport
Control: Isle of Wight Freshwater AA, Mr Mick Steed, 6 Priors Walk, Newport PO30 5RN. Tel: 01983 521267
BK Rating: Difficult
E/A: Southern

Rookley Country Park A

Location: Rookley, near Godshill
Type and Size: Small lake in twenty acres of parkland
Carp Stock: Some carp
Category: Mixed Fishery
Other Species: Roach and perch
Permits: On site. Tel: 01983 70606
Cost: On application
Control: Private
BK Rating: Unknown
E/A: Southern
Comments: Luxury caravans, licensed bar, restaurant, games room, pitch and putt course, children's adventure playgound, darts, pool and video games, take-away food. Prices from £80 - £200 per caravan including fishing. Rose Award caravan park 1991. Hoseasons for booking

Somerton Reservoir

Location: On the A3020 Newport to West Cowes road, about 3 miles from Newport
Type and Size: Small reservoir
Carp Stock: Well stocked with carp from 2lbs to 5lbs, best about 10lbs
Category: Mixed Fishery
Other Species: Roach, rudd and perch
Permits: Day tickets from bailiff on bank
Cost: £4; Juniors £1.50
Control: Isle of Wight Freshwater AA. Secretary Mr M J Steed, 6 Priors Walk, Newport PO30 5RN. Tel: 01983 521267
Baits/Methods: Luncheon meat very good for the carp
BK Rating: Easy
E/A: Southern

KENT

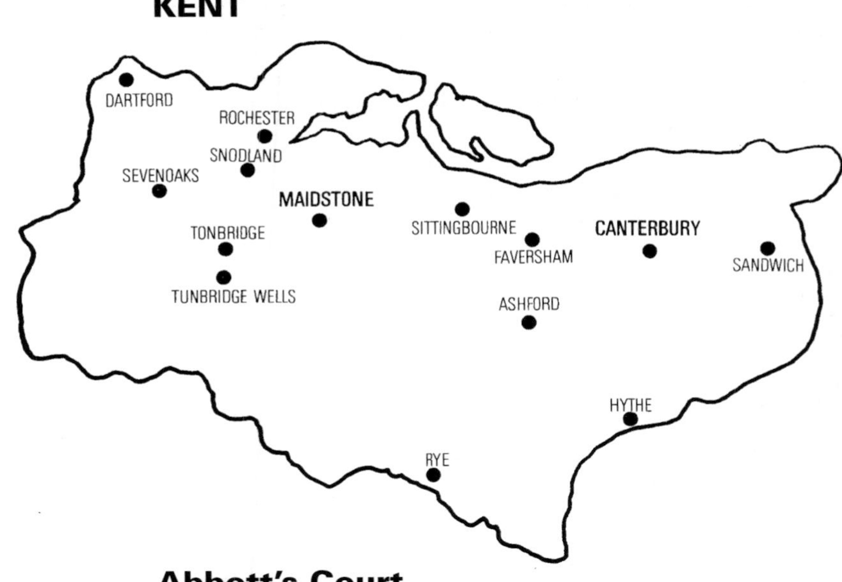

Abbott's Court

Location: Hoo, near Rochester
Type and Size: Three gravel pits. Main lake - 5 acres; Stock Pond and The Cut - 1.5 acres each
How to Find: From Medway towns or the A226 from Gravesend, join A228 to Grain. After passing Chattenden, turn right to Hoo. In village centre, turn right at crossroads by Five Bells. Take first left, then first left again on track towards Kingsnorth Power Station. Park in area in front of stables
Carp Stock: All three lakes contain a fair head of commons and mirrors
Category: Mixed Fishery
Other Species: Crucians, bream, roach, rudd, perch, tench, pike and eels
Permits: Adult Membership and Junior Permit Holders (under 18) Available from: Mrs. A.Thomas, 23 Everest Drive, Hoo, Rochester, Kent. ME3 9AN
Cost: Adults - £36 (plus £36 joining fee) Juniors, O.A.P's and ladies £18 + (£18 joining fee) Family membership available
Control: Kingfisher Angling and Preservation Society
Restrictions: No particle baits except sweetcorn; two rod limit; no prebaiting. Unhooking mats to be used. No live baiting. On The Cut, fishing only allowed on the east bank
BK Rating: Moderate
Baits/Methods: Basic methods and standard baits work well. Floater fishing also good
E/A: Southern
Comments: Open June 16th to March 14th.

Alders Lakes

Location: Near Snodland, close to Reeds Lakes
Type and Size: Three gravel pits with islands etc, the biggest of which is about 6 acres
Carp Stock: All three lakes are well stocked with carp. The biggest lake has a number of 20's to about 29lbs; the Trout Lake contains many low doubles, and the Castle Lake contains small commons

Category: Mixed Fisheries
Other Species: Roach, bream, pike, perch and big eels
Permits: Alders AC, a private club which is hard to get into - try local tackle shops for information - season tickets only
Control: Club
BK Rating: Big Lake - Moderate; others - Easy
E/A: Southern

Allhallows Leisure Park — A

Location: Allhallows-on-Sea, ME3 9BR
Type and Size: Small lake
Carp Stock: Well stocked with carp, sizes not known
Category: Mixed Fishery
Other Species: Usual coarse fish
Permits: All information from the address above, or Tel: 0800 521178
BK Rating: Not known
E/A: Southern
Comments: Caravans for sale; usual entertainment and sports etc

Ashby Farm Lakes — A

Location: Appledore, Ashford
Type and Size: Two reservoirs of two acres each
How to Find: Near Ashford
Carp Stock: Carp to 18lbs
Category: Mixed Fishery
Other Species: General coarse fish
Permits: On site - residents only. Tel: 01233 758378
Cost: Approx £2.75 per day; group week ticket also available
BK Rating: Moderate
Control: Private
Restrictions: Not known
E/A: Southern
Comments: Holiday centre; self catering accommodation in Scandinavian style chalets at water edge. Fishing extra. No fishing unless resident. Beautiful woodland setting

Ashford Pit

Location: Near the town of Ashford
Type and Size: Small pit
Carp Stock: Well stocked with carp to double figures
Category: Mixed Fishery
Other Species: Big tench and rudd
Permits: Ashford Working Mens Club, members only - no day tickets. For details enquire from local tackle shops, such as M and H Angling, 1 Thirlstane Terrace, Hythe
Control: Club:
BK Rating: Not known
E/A: Southern

Barden Park Lake

Location: Barden Park, Brook Street, Tonbridge
Type and Size: Ten acre lake
Carp Stock: Not heavily stocked for the size of water, but one or two big fish to over 30lbs. Many small commons
Category: Mixed Fishery

Other Species: Roach, bream, tench, pike, perch and eels
Permits: Enquire locally, or from local tackle shops
Restrictions: Members only; no night fishing
BK Rating: Fairly Hard
E/A: Southern

Biddenden Lake

Location: Bettenham Manor, Biddenham, Near Tenterden
Type and Size: Two acre estate lake
How to Find: Take the Sissinghurst road from Tenterden, and in one mile, opposite a pub, turn right for another two miles
Carp Stock: Mirrors and commons to 23lbs; numbers not known
Category: Mixed Fishery
Other Species: Roach, bream and perch
Permits: Day tickets at £5 in advance only from the address above
Control: Private - J Hampshire
BK Rating: Moderate
E/A: Southern
Comments: Very old lake with established stock of fish. Limited to only two anglers per day

Blue Lake

Location: Near Northfleet
Type and Size: Old chalk pit of 20 to 30 acres
How to Find: The pit is just off the A2 road at Northfleet
Carp Stock: Quite well stocked with doubles and 20's to 30lbs
Category: Carp Water
Other Species: Tench, bream and eels
Permits: No day tickets, club membership only
Control: Thameside Working Mens Club
BK Rating: Difficult
E/A: Thames
Comments: This pit is 60-70 feet deep in places; surface fishing works well at times. Enquire locally for membership

Brooklands

Location: Dartford
Type and Size: Gravel pit of 16-20 acres
How to Find: Just off the A2 at the traffic lights where you turn towards Dartford
Carp Stock: Huge stock, many doubles and twenties, and two thirties. Said to contain more doubles and 20's for its size than any other water in England
Category: Carp Water
Other Species: Bream, tench, roach, pike, rudd
Permits: Day tickets from bailiffs on bank at £3; juniors £1.50
Control: Club. Dartford and District APS. Hon. Secretary: 2 Walnut Tree Avenue, Dartford, Kent. Membership very hard to obtain; mainly for locals. Tel: 01322 228532
Restrictions: No night fishing; no peanuts; no keepnets
BK Rating: Moderate
E/A: Thames
Comments: A very well-known carp water, where some of the leading carp anglers have fished and where some of the early bait experiments with high protein baits took place. Undoubtedly one of the most heavily fished waters in the country. Here they actually queue for swims and people have been known to wait several days and nights behind someone who is fishing in order to get their place when they leave !

Some of the best pitches are permanently fished, day and night for the whole season.We have heard it said that before the start of the season carp anglers camp on the bank for a week before the season to obtain the best places

Bysingwood

Location: Bysingwood Road, Faversham
Type and Size: Mature gravel pit of about 10 acres
How to Find: Take Bysingwood Road from Faversham and the lake is on the left about 2 miles from the town centre
Carp Stock: Very heavily overstocked with doubles. Occasional 20's to 23lbs
Category: Carp Water
Other Species: Tench, bream and eels
Permits: Faversham Angling Club. Hon Secretary: A O Baldock, 5 Kennedy Close, Faversham. It is very hard to get into the club and you will almost certainly have to live in the Faversham area; worth a try for others
Cost: Approx £15 per season
Control: Club Tel: 01795 533240
BK Rating: Very Easy
E/A: Southern
Comments: This is most certainly one of the best known doubles carp water in the country. 10-12 doubles a day is possible and we have heard that an angler once had 25 doubles in one day. For this reason it is very hard to get into, but we have included it because it is on the same club ticket as the School Pool and you may be able to obtain membership if you live locally. For others it is unlikely, but you can apply and hope for the best. A number of well known carp anglers have fished this water

Chiddingstone Castle Lake

Location: Chiddingstone Castle, near Tonbridge
Type and Size: Estate lake of three acres
How to Find: Take the B2027 road from Tonbridge to Edenbridge
Carp Stock: Well stocked with commons to 10lbs. A few lower doubles
Category: Mixed Fishery
Other Species: Roach, perch, bream, gudgeon, rudd
Permits: From the bailiff on the bank. Details from the Secretary, Chiddingstone Castle, Edenbridge. Tel: 01732 870347
Cost: Approx £5 per day
Baits/Methods: Normal carp fishing methods and baits. Bread will still catch the carp
Control: Private - day ticket book in advance if possble
Restrictions: No night fishing
BK Rating: Easy
E/A: Southern
Comments: Peaceful situation with tree-lined banks, weed and lilies. Grounds of ancient castle

Chilham Castle Carp Syndicate

Location: Chilham Castle grounds, Chilham
Type and Size: Five acre estate lake
How to Find: Seven miles south west of Canterbury on the A252
Carp Stock: Very heavily stocked with thin commons to about 8lbs
Category: Carp Water
Other Species: Some coarse fish
Permits: Albert Brown, Heronsview Fisheries, Drovers End, Pudding Lane, Ash CT3 2EJ. Tel: 01304 812651 or 01843 296031
Cost: On application

Control: Private
BK Rating: Easy
Restrictions: On application; no day tickets
E/A: Southern
Comments: In the beautiful grounds of one of the finest English castles, in one of the prettiest villages in the country. Big catches in fine surroundings

Chilham Mill

Location: Chilham Mill, near Canterbury
Type and Size: Five lakes
Carp Stock: Well stocked with mirrors and commons to over 20lbs, with a possible 40
Category: Mixed Fishery
Other Species: Big pike, double figure bream, roach and catfish
Permits: Mid Kent Fisheries
Cost: About £80 a season. Day tickets on one lake
Control: Chris Logsdon Tel: 01227 730668
BK Rating: Not known, but probably Difficult
E/A: Southern
Comments: Former day ticket lake now taken over by Mid - Kent Fisheries. We understand that Mid - Kent Fisheries has other carp waters, but repeated phone calls only located an answering machine, and a message left received no reply

Chipstead Lakes

Location: Near Sevenoaks
Type and Size: Lake of twenty acres plus
Carp Stock: Well stocked with carp to over 30lbs
Category: Mixed Fishery
Other Species: Tench, bream, roach and rudd
Permits: Mr S Banks, 58 Chevening Road, Chipstead, Sevenoaks
Cost: Seasonal only at £35, with £15 joining fee
Control: Holmesdale AC
BK Rating: Moderate
E/A: Southern

Cotton Farm

Location: Near Dartford, just to the east end of the Dartford Tunnel, and almost within sight of the toll booths and the River Thames
Type and Size: Open pit of near ten acres - once twice this size, but partly filled in
Carp Stock: Well stocked with low doubles, and a number of 20's to about 30lbs
Category: Carp Water
Other Species: Roach, bream and pike
Control: Private; membership and permits from The Tackle Box, Sutton-at-Hone
BK Rating: Fairly Hard
E/A: Southern
Comments: Quite a well known water, and fished by some of the top carp anglers. Fishes well in winter, with a good chance of a winter twenty

Danson Park

Location: Between Welling and Bexleyheath
Type and Size: Large shallow park lake
How to Find: Just off the A2 at Blackfen
Carp Stock: Quite heavily stocked with carp to doubles
Category: Carp Water

Other Species: Roach, tench, perch, crucians and gudgeon
Permits: Day tickets on bank at £4
Control: Council - GLC. Tel: 0181 3043586
Restrictions: No night fishing
BK Rating: Moderate
E/A: Thames

Darenth

Location: Parsonage Lane, Darenth, near Dartford
Type and Size: Four gravel pits; Big Lake - 13 acres; Long Lake 4 acres; Tree Lake - 3 acres; Tip Lake - 9 acres
How to Find: Take the A2 to the traffic lights at Dartford. Turn right onto the A225, after 2 miles turn left at Parsonage Lane (signposted Darenth). Continue for half a mile and the main entrance is on right just after two river bridges
Carp Stock: Big Lake - well stocked with doubles and twenties to over 30 pounds. Long Lake - some doubles and 20's to about 29 pounds. Tree Lake - a few doubles and one or two 20's. Tip Lake - a few twenties and more than a dozen thirties to about 40 pounds
Category: All four lakes are Carp Waters
Other Species: Bream, tench, pike, perch, roach, rudd, chub
Permits: Season tickets only Tel: 01322 290150/01836 222773
Cost: £40 per season
Control: Private
BK Rating: Big Lake - Moderate; Long Lake - Fairly Hard; Tree Lake - Difficult; Tip Lake - Fairly Hard
E/A: Thames
Comments: One of the best known big carp waters in the country. Heavily fished by experienced and successful carp anglers. Modern rigs and sophisticated baits needed

Frant Lakes

Location: Bells Yew Green, Frant, near Tunbridge Wells
Type and Size: Twelve small ponds
Carp Stock: Well stocked with carp to 30 lbs
Category: Mixed Fishery
Other Species: Roach, tench, bream, perch, crucians, rudd and barbel
Permits: On bank
Cost: About £5 per rod per day; £6 for two rods. Night tickets £5. Season ticket £75
Control: Tel: 01892 822388
Restrictions: No keepnets
BK Rating: Not known
E/A: Southern
Comments: Several pools stocked with trout. One lake has double figure koi and catfish

Fordwich Lake

Location: In the Stour valley near Fordwich
Type and Size: Large gravel pit of 33 acres, with a very irregular bottom
How to Find: Take the A28 from Canterbury to Sturry, and turn right. Follow the road past the George and Dragon Hotel, the Fordwich Arms on the left, and go down past the church on the 'The Drove' a private road to the parking area
Carp Stock: Very well stocked with carp to over 20lbs
Category: Mixed Fishery

Other Species: Tench and pike
Permits: Members only water of Canterbury and District AC - Riversdale, 14 Mill Road, Sturry, Canterbury CT2 OAF. Tel: 01227 710830
Cost: £31 per season, with a £15.50 entry fee, which includes many other waters
Control: Club
BK Rating: Moderate
E/A: Southern
Comments: A well known big fish carp water in very attractive surroundings, well looked after by Canterbury club

Horton Kirby

Location: Horton Kirby, near Dartford
Type and Size: Three gravel pits; total area 10 - 14 acres
How to Find: Five minute walk from Farningham Road railway station
Carp Stock: Well stocked with many doubles and twenties to about 28lbs, and lots of small carp also
Category: Carp Water
Other Species: Tench, bream and pike
Permits: Day tickets from bailiff on banks
Control: Club; Dartford and District Angling and Preservation Society. Hon Secretary: D E Reeve, 29 Berkeley Crescent, Dartford, Kent. Membership very hard to obtain
Restrictions: No night fishing
BK Rating: Easy
Comments: A well known water, very heavily fished by day ticket anglers

Johnsons Pit

Location: Larkfield, near Maidstone
Type and Size: Two gravel pits covering about 20 acres in all
How to Find: Just off the M25 at New Hythe junction, Larkfield
Carp Stock: Doubles and 20's to about 30lbs
Category: Mixed Fishery
Other Species: Very big tench, pike, roach, bream
Permits: Day ticket from the bailiff on the bank
Control: Private
BK Rating: Fairly Hard
Comments: This water is said to be not very heavily fished and night fishing is allowed

Kentish Stour

Location: From Fordwich to Plucks Gutter and Grove Ferry, on the River Stour, a tributary of the Medway
Type and Size: Small river
Carp Stock: Some carp to 14lbs
Category: Probably Few Carp
Other Species: Famous for its big roach, and also trout, bream, rudd, tench, pike, gudgeon, dace, chub, eels and even some sea trout
Permits: Members only water of Canterbury and District AC, Riversdale, 14 Mill Road, Canterbury CT2 OAF (C Jardine, Hon Sec). Tel: 01227 710830
Cost: Membership, which includes other waters, costs £31 per year, with an entrance fee of £15.50
Control: Club
Restrictions: Upstream of Fordwich church is fly fishing only
BK Rating: Difficult

E/A: Southern
Comments: 3 1/4 lb roach caught in 1985

Longford Lake

Location: Just north of the A25 near Sevenoaks
Type and Size: Twelve acre lake, 10 - 35 feet deep
Carp Stock: Well stocked with carp; plenty of doubles and six 20's reported in 1990
Category: Mixed Fishery
Other Species: Tench, bream, roach, rudd, perch and pike
Permits: Holmesdale AS, 4 Shoreham Lane, Riverhead, Sevenoaks, Kent
Cost: About £45 per year plus £15 entry fee
Restrictions: No night fishing at weekends; no fishing on competition weekends; members only
BK Rating: Moderate
E/A: Southern

Maidstone Lakes A

Location: Near Maidstone
Type and Size: Local lakes
How to Find: Near Maidstone town centre
Carp Stock: Well stocked with good carp
Category: Mixed Fisheries
Other Species: General coarse fish
Permits: Tel: 01622 676586
Cost: On application
BK Rating: Moderate
Control: Private
E/A: Southern
Comments: Fishing weekends and holidays offered in private hotel. Accommodation and all meals, bar, TV lounge. Fishing in nearby lakes and the River Medway (carp to 20lbs+)

Monk Lake Fishery

Location: Riverfield Farm, Staplefield, near Maidstone
Type and Size: Two lakes of 6 acres and 1 acre
How to Find: On the A 229 Maidstone to Hastings road
Carp Stock: Well stocked with carp to over 20 lbs
Category: Mixed Fishery
Other Species: Tench and roach
Permits: On bank
Cost: £6 one rod; £10 two rods; £4 for 1/2 day. Concessions
Control: Mr. B. Davis. Tel: 01580 890120
BK Rating: Not known
E/A: Southern
Comments: Toilets, bait and tackle shop; hot food

Nicholls Pit

Location: Hythe
Type and Size: Large pit
How to Find: By the Army ranges on the coast road to Hythe
Carp Stock: Quite well stocked with doubles and twenties
Category: Mixed Fishery
Other Species: Tench, bream and roach
Permits: Day tickets from bailiffs on the bank
Control: Private

BK Rating: Fairly Hard
E/A: Southern

Orpington and District

Location: Near Sidcup
Type and Size: Two fair-sized lakes
How to Find: On the A20 at Klingers roundabout
Carp Stock: Quite well stocked with some doubles and some 20's
Category: Mixed Fishery
Other Species: Tench, bream, pike and roach
Permits: Day tickets from local tackle shop at St Mary's Cray
Control: Club - Orpington and District
BK Rating: Fairly Hard
E/A: Thames

Paddlesworth

Location: Paddlesworth Road, Snodland
Type and Size: 4 clay pits. Pollard Lake - 40 acres; 'Pads' - 4 acres; Rugby Lake - 5 acres; Stock Lake - 3 acres
How to Find: From M2/M20 take A228 to Snodland. At crossroads turn right from M2, left on M20, and fork right in 100 m. Narrow lane with dangerous 'S' bend 200 m before entrance (Key needed for gate)
Carp Stock: Well stocked with commons and mirrors to 30 lbs +
Category: Carp Waters
Other Species: Crucians, bream, roach, rudd, perch, tench, pike and eels
Permits: Mrs. A.Thomas 23 Everest Drive, Hoo, Rochester ME3 9AN
Cost: Adults £36 + (£36 joining fee). Juniors; O.A.P's; ladies £18 + (£18 fee)
Control: Kingfisher Angling and Preservation Society
Restrictions: No particle baits except sweetcorn; no prebaiting; no live bait; unhooking mats to be used. Fishing only on south bank on Stock Lake
BK Rating: Pollard and Stock - Moderate; Pads and Rugby - Difficult
Baits/Methods: Large carp in Pads and Rugby difficult to catch; lakes are heavily fished.
E/A: Southern
Comments: Open June 16th to March 14th.

Pett Pools

Location: Between Winchelsea and Hastings
Type and Size: Small pools
How to Find: Winchelsea - 2 miles; Rye - 4 miles; off the Winchelsea-Hastings road
Carp Stock: Some carp
Category: Mixed Fishery
Other Species: General coarse fishing
Permits: M Piddington, Market Stores, Pett
Cost: Approx £3 per day;season tickets
BK Rating: Moderate
Restrictions: None
E/A: Southern
Comments: Local clubs have other waters containing carp on Romney Marsh; try Cinque Ports AS - R MacGregor, 31 Burmarsh Road, Hythe, Kent. Bob MacGregor is a well known local carp angler

Pittlands Lakes

Location: Pittlands Farm, Churn Lane, Horsmonden TN12 8HL
Type and Size: Small lakes
Carp Stock: Well stocked with carp to over 20lbs

Category: Mixed Fishery
Other Species: Roach, rudd, tench and bream
Permits: Send an SAE for details to the address aboveor Tel:01892723838/3142/3143
Cost: On application
Control: Private
BK Rating: Not known
E/A: Southern

Plucks Gutter

Location: River Stour near Sarre, between Canterbury and Ramsgate
Type and Size: Fast flowing river
How to Find: Take the A28 from Canterbury, then the right hand Ramsgate turn, and the next right turn to Preston. This road crosses the river at Plucks Gutter
Carp Stock: Some carp to 20lbs
Category: Few Carp
Other Species: Pike, bream, roach, dace, chub and the occasional sea trout
Permits: On bank at £4 per day
Control: Canterbury DAA, Riverside, 14 Mill Road, Sturry, Canterbury
BK Rating: Super-Difficult
E/A: Southern

Queen's Farm

Location: Queens Farm Road, Shorne, near Gravesend
Type and Size: Small gravel pit of less than 1 acre
How to Find: Shorne exit A2 (1 mile west of A2 / M2), follow signs for Shorne along Brewers Rd, left into Woodlands Rd, left through village. Cross A226 into Green Farm Lane, at end turn left then immediately right into Queen's Farm Rd.After farm buildings, lake across meadow on left.
Carp Stock: Commons and mirrors to 10 lbs
Category: Mixed Fishery
Other Species: Roach, rudd, tench, perch and eels
Permits: Adults and juniors (under 18) Apply - Mrs.A.Thomas 23 Everest Drive, Hoo, Rochester, ME3 9AN
Cost: £36 per year + £36 joining fee. Juniors;O.A.P's and ladies £18 + joining fee
Control: Kingfisher Angling and Preservation Society
Restrictions: No particle baits except sweetcorn; 2 rod limit; no prebaiting; no live bait; unhooking mats to be used
BK Rating: Easy
E/A: Southern
Comments: Open June 16th to March 14th.

Radnor Park Pool

Location: Radnor Park, in Folkestone
Type and Size: Shallow town park lake of about three acres, with island, heavily fished
How to Find: In Cheriton Road; pass the Folkestone football ground, and take the third left turn. The lake is on the right
Category: Mixed Fishery
Other Species: Crucians, tench, roach, perch, rudd and bream
Permits: On bank
Cost: £2
Control: Shepway and District AC. Paul Foot. Tel: 01503 58778
Restrictions: Fishing is 6am to 10pm only; no night fishing; no floaters; no fishing in the reeds
BK Rating: Easy
E/A: Southern

Reeds Lake

Location: Near Snodland, just on the London side of the M20 at junction 4
Type and Size: Three attractive estate-type lakes
Carp Stock: Well stocked with carp to about 20lbs, many of which are lower doubles
Category: Carp Water
Permits: N Martin, 13 Masefield Road, Larkfield, Maidstone - in advance only
Control: Private
BK Rating: Moderate
E/A: Southern

Royal Military Canal A

Location: Hythe and Ashford areas
Type and Size: Short, shallow canal
How to Find: Off the A2070 south of Ashford
Carp Stock: Some very good carp up to 35lbs
Category: Mixed Fishery
Other Species: General coarse fishing
Permits: Day tickets on the bank for some stretches: also from J B Walker Ltd, 84 Slade Street, Hythe. Tel: 01303 66228: and Ashford and District A and PS, C Hyder, 37 Northumberland Avenue, Kennington, Ashford
Cost: Approx £2; season £12
Control: Club
Restrictions: None
E/A: Southern
Comments: A very hard water, with some big fish if you can find them. Tickets also available from some local pubs. Ashford APS also has a lake with some big carp - enquire from Secretary. Accommodation at the Railway Hotel, Appledore. Tel: 01233 758253 for brochure. B'B from £25 per night for a double room

Scarlett's Lake

Location: Near East Grinstead
Type and Size: Three acre lake, stream fed
How to Find: East Grinstead area, access from the A264 near church at Hammerwood
Carp Stock: Many carp, to 23lbs
Category: Mixed Fishery
Other Species: Crucians, grass carp, tench, rudd, roach and perch
Permits: On bank, or J Jackson, Furnace Lane, Cowden, Edenbridge, Kent. Tel: 01342 850414 (6.30 to 9.30pm)
Cost: Day - £3.50, season - £42 (from 8am on bank). Reduced prices for OAP's, the disabled, students and unemployed
BK Rating: Fairly Hard
Control: Private
Restrictions: No preserved boilies. No groundbait till July 16th. Season ticket holders may night fish
E/A: Southern
Comments: Picturesque lake suitable for well controlled families. Easy access for wheelchairs. 20p per ticket donated to conservation or wildlife charities. Bus passes end of road - alight Hammerwood; Tunbridge Wells - East Grinstead

School Pool

Location: In the town of Faversham
Type and Size: Old gravel pit of about eleven acres, many gravel bars
How to Find: Just off the M2 at the Faversham junction; in the town

Carp Stock: Fairly well stocked with quite a number of twenties, and at least two thirties. These include a common of around 33lb
Category: Carp Water
Other Species: Bream, tench, pike
Permits: Day tickets from the Club Secretary in advance only at £4
Control: Faversham and District AC, Mick Kennett, Tel: 01795 534516
Restrictions: No night fishing
BK Rating: Difficult
E/A: Southern
Comments: Another water very well known to carp anglers. Twenties including some upper 20's have been caught here, for as long as we can remember, and the water is famous for a couple of good thirties including 'She', already mentioned which has been caught by a large number of carp anglers including some of the best known names in the country. The lake is surrounded by a school, houses, a road and a factory!

Sittingbourne Lakes

Location: Murston, near Sittingbourne
Type and Size: Three large gravel pits
How to Find: Murston is one and a half miles north of Sittingbourne
Carp Stock: Plenty of good carp to over 20lbs
Category: Mixed Fishery
Other Species: General coarse fishing
Permits: No day tickets; information from Hon Sec, Sittingbourne AC, C Brown, 5 Sunnybanks, Murston, Sittingbourne, Kent
Cost: On application
BK Rating: Difficult
Restrictions: Ask the club secretary
E/A: Southern
Comments: Try also Deans Tackle Shop, East Street, Sittingbourne, Kent

Station Pool(Rookery Lake)

Location: Near Bromley
Type and Size: Small lake of about one and three quarter acres
How to Find: Enquire from owners
Carp Stock: Well stocked with carp to 25lbs
Category: Mixed Fishery
Other Species: Tench, bream, roach and pike
Permits: Fourways Fisheries, Poplars Nursery, Harlington Road, Toddington, Dunstable. Tel: 01525 55584
Control: Fourways Fisheries
E/A: Thames
Comments: Season tickets only, about £65

Stonar Lake

Location: Near Sandwich
Type and Size: Small lake
Carp Stock: Well stocked with carp to 20lbs; plenty of doubles
Category: Mixed Fishery
Other Species: Roach, bream and perch
Permits: Try local tackle shops - possibly an angling club in Sandwich?
Control: Club?
BK Rating: Easy
E/A: Southern

Sundridge Lakes

Location: Sundridge, near Sevenoaks
Type and Size: Gravel pits of about 5 and 15 acres
Carp Stock: Carp to over 20lbs
Category: Carp Water
Permits: Holmesdale AS, 4 Shoreham Lane, Riverhead, Sevenoaks, Kent
Cost: Approx £45 per year, plus £15 entry fee
Control: Members only
BK Rating: Moderate
E/A: Southern
Comments: There are rumours that the water contains some very big carp

Sutton

Location: Sutton-at-Hone, near Dartford
Type and Size: Three gravel pits
How to Find: On the Horley road from Farningham
Carp Stock: Heavily stocked with many doubles and plenty of 20's to over 30lbs
Category: Carp Water
Other Species: Tench, pike, roach and bream
Permits: Leisure Sport Angling. Tel: 01932 564872
Restrictions: No sacks
BK Rating: Easy
Comments: Lakes 1 and 3 cost £40, Lake 2 is £120. Waiting lists

Vauxhall Lakes

Location: Canterbury Nature Reserve, off Broad Oak Road, on the edge of the city
Type and Size: Very large old gravel pits
Carp Stock: Stocked with carp in 1973, which are now being caught to middle twenties; plenty of doubles
Category: Mixed Fishery
Other Species: Roach, perch, bream, rudd, tench, eels and pike
Permits: Members only water of Canterbury and District AC, Riversdale, 14 Mill Road, Sturry, Canterbury.Tel: 01227 710830
Cost: £40 per season with an entry fee of £15.50
Control: Club
BK Rating: Moderate
E/A: Southern
Comments: A pleasant Nature Reserve on the edge of the city, with a Field Centre. No fishing from jetties or bridges. Rich waters with big fish of most species. Some restrictions on fishing hours, indicated on notice boards. Available to local members only. The Canterbury AA is an excellent club with a permanent headquarters with offices open from 9am to 4pm on weekdays

LANCASHIRE

Abbey Lane Lake

Location: Burscough, near Ormskirk
Type and Size: Three acre lake
How to Find: Take the A59 north from Ormskirk. The lake is on the right just after the B5242
Carp Stock: Fairly well stocked with carp to low doubles
Category: Mixed Fishery
Other Species: Tench, roach, bream, perch and thousands of small rudd
Permits: Local tackle shops at £1.50 per day, and £1 for juniors
Control: Maghull and Lydiate AC. J Johnson. Tel: 0151 5264083
Restrictions: No night fishing
BK Rating: Moderate
E/A: North West

Ball Grove

Location: Colne
Type and Size: 2 acre lake
How to Find: Take the A 6068 east from Colne towards Keighley. After 2 miles turn right into the B 6250. Turn left at the fish and chip shop, then left again
Carp Stock: Well stocked with carp to mid-doubles
Category: Mixed Fishery
Other Species: Bream, roach, tench and perch
Permits: On bank
Cost: About £3 per rod; concessions
Control: Tel: 01282 865500 ext. 444
Restrictions: No night fishing
BK Rating: Not known
E/A: North West
Comments: Probably open all year. Toilets

Barrow Lodge

Location: Just off the A59 Preston road at Clitheroe
Type and Size: Ten acre lake
Carp Stock: Well stocked with small carp to about 6lbs
Category: Mixed Fishery
Other Species: Crucians, tench, perch and bream
Permits: In advance from Ken Varey, 4 Newmarket Street, Clitheroe. Tel: 01200 23267
Cost: Day tickets £2; season tickets £10. All permits half price for under 16's and OAP's. Free to the registered disabled
BK Rating: Moderate
E/A: North West
Comments: This lake is often busy with boats during daytime

Baubles Pools

Location: Near Pilling, Fylde - enquire locally
Type and Size: Three small pools, with the best fish in the middle one
Carp Stock: Mainly small carp to doubles
Category: Carp Waters
Permits: Day tickets on bank
Control: Private
BK Rating: Very Easy
E/A: North West
Comments: Many waters in this area now have no close season

Birkacre Lodge

Location: Off the B 5251 at Birkacre, near Chorley
Type and Size: 7 acre lake
Carp Stock: Some carp to over 20 lbs
Category: Few Carp
Other Species: Tench, roach and bream
Permits: On bank
Cost: About £3 per day; half price for juniors and O.A.P's. £15 per season
Control: Wigan A.A. Tel: 01257 265905
Restrictions: No night fishing
BK Rating: Very Difficult
E/A: North West
Comments: Disabled access

Bradshaw Fisheries

Location: Bradshaw, near Bolton
Type and Size: Six small pools
Carp Stock: Well stocked with carp to upper doubles
Category: Mixed Fishery
Other Species: Crucians, chub, roach, perch, bream and gudgeon
Permits: On bank
Cost: About £4 per day; concessions
Control: Tel: 01617 939518
Restrictions: No boilies, no night fishing
BK Rating: Moderate
E/A: North West
Comments: Probably open all year

Bryan Hey Reservoir

Location: Scout Road, Bryan Hey tearooms, off the A58 five miles north west of Bolton
Type and Size: Two and a half acre mill reservoir
Carp Stock: Quite well stocked with carp to doubles, average about 7lbs
Category: Mixed Fishery
Other Species: Bream, roach, tench, crucians and a few perch
Permits: On the bank at £2 for adults and £1 for juniors, OAP's and the disabled. Season £45
Control: Twenty Sixth Lancashire Home Guard AC (sounds like Dad's Army!). Tel: 01257 253650, Password DA 1939)
Restrictions: No night fishing
BK Rating: Moderate
E/A: North West

Brinsall Lodges

Location: Brinsall, Chorley
Type and Size: Small pond of about one and a half acres
Carp Stock: Quite well stocked with carp to about 10lbs
Category: Mixed Fishery
Other Species: Roach, tench and bream
Permits: Day tickets from local tackle shops
Control: Private
BK Rating: Difficult
E/A: North West
Comments: No close season in some places in this area - check first

Cargate Farm Pool

Location: Near Oldham
Type and Size: Small farm pool, much used for match fishing
Carp Stock: Well stocked with small commons and mirrors
Category: Mixed Fishery
Other Species: Roach, tench, crucians and perch
Permits: Day tickets in advance only
Cost: £3
Control: Oldham and District AA. Secretary: B Boff, 369 Shaw Road, Oldham OL1 3JZ. Tel: 0161 6200883 - season tickets available
Restrictions: No night fishing - sunrise to sunset only
BK Rating: Easy
E/A: North West

Chatham Reservoir

Location: Three miles from Todmorden, down a long track off the A 646 Burnley road
Type and Size: 2 acre moorland reservoir
Carp Stock: Some carp to 8 lbs
Category: Mixed Fishery
Other Species: Roach, perch, bream and hybrids
Permits: From Todmorden A/C
Cost: £18 a season plus a £10 joining fee - half price for juniors, ladies and O.A.P's
Control: Tel: 01282 428780
Restrictions: No boilies
BK Rating: Not known
E/A: North West

Clarenden Street Reservoir

Location: Clarenden Street, Accrington, off the A 680 Manchester road
Type and Size: Half acre pool
Carp Stock: Some carp to 10 lbs
Category: Mixed Fishery
Other Species: Roach, chub, perch, bream, pike and gudgeon
Permits: From local tackle shops - no day tickets
Cost: £35 per season; £11 for juniors
Control: Hyndburn and Blackburn A.A. Tel: 01706 224211
BK Rating: Not known
E/A: North West

Clevely Bridge

Location: Garstang - on the A6 between Preston and Lancaster
Type and Size: Small, pleasant fishery
Carp Stock: Well stocked with carp to about 14lbs
Category: Mixed Fishery
Other Species: Usual coarse fish
Permits: In advance only
Control: Private
BK Rating: Moderate
E/A: North West

Clevely Bridge Nature Reserve A

Location: Clevely Bridge, Scorton, near Garstang, PR3 1BY
Type and Size: Thirteen small ponds in 24 acres
How to Find: Take the A6 from Lancaster, and in 7 miles turn left just after the Hollies Inn and continue to Clevely Bank Lane. The fishery is on the left opposite Clevely Mere
Carp Stock: Most ponds contain carp, some of which are over 20 lbs
Category: Mixed Fishery
Other Species: Tench, chub, roach, rudd, bream, barbel and golden orfe
Permits: From the house
Cost: £6 per day for 1 rod: £10 for two rods
Control: Eric Fishwick. Tel: 01524 791637
Restrictions: Barbless hooks only; no boilies or nut - based baits; no keepnets.Some line restrictions
BK Rating: Moderate
E/A: North West
Comments: Attractive site with lots of wildlife, flowers and trees and 100 bird boxes. Deer visit the ponds. Accommodation close to the pond in 3

self-catering apartments from £84 per week - fishing extra but at half price for those staying

Cliviger Fish Ponds

Location: A 646 Burnley to Todmorden road, at Cliviger, near Burnley
Type and Size: Two small ponds, with the tiny River Calder flowing through them
Carp Stock: Stocked with carp to about 10 lbs
Category: Mixed Fishery
Other Species: Tench, roach, rudd, bream, perch, golden orfe, ide, brown trout, chub, dace and gudgeon
Permits: In advance from Cliviger petrol station
Cost: About £3 per day in advance - double this price on the bank
Control: Todmorden A.S.
BK Rating: Not known
E/A: North West
Comments: Get your ticket in advance - or pay double on the bank

Copthorn Fisheries

Location: Nateby, near Garstang
Type and Size: 2 1/2 acre lake and a match canal
How to Find: Take the Pilling Road off the A6 at Garstang. The fishery is on the right
Carp Stock: Heavily stocked with small carp
Category: Carp water
Other Species: Crucian carp
Permits: On site
Cost: £4 per day
Control: Private Tel: 01374 282329
Restrictions: No keepnets. Only groundbait sold at the fishery may be used
BK Rating: Easy
E/A: North West

Coronation Lodge

Location: Near Oldham
Type and Size: Tiny pond, with room for 9 anglers only; very weedy
Carp Stock: Quite well stocked with carp to doubles
Category: Mixed Fishery
Other Species: Tench, roach, rudd, perch and crucians
Permits: Members only water of Oldham and District AA. Secretary: B Boff, 369 Shaw Road, Oldham. Tel: 0161 6200883 - memberships available
Cost: About £15 per season
Restrictions: No night fishing
BK Rating: Moderate
E/A: North West

Croft Fishery

Location: Off the A 6 at Adlington
Type and Size: 1 1/2 acre attractive lake
Carp Stock: Some carp to mid - doubles
Category: Few Carp
Other Species: Roach, bream, rudd, chub and crucians
Permits: On bank
Cost: £3 per day; £2 juniors and O.A.P's
Control: Tel: 01257 483147
Restrictions: No boilies or cereal groundbait
BK Rating: Difficult
E/A: Lancashire

Doffcocker Reservoir

Location: Manchester Road, Bolton
Type and Size: Small mill lodge of about one acre
Carp Stock: About 100, and stocked recently with 6-10lbs fish. Quite a few doubles to 20lbs
Category: Mixed Fishery
Other Species: Roach, bream, tench and pike
Permits: Bolton and District AC - members only. Secretary: T McKee, 1 Lever Edge Lane, Great Lever, Bolton, Greater Manchester. Tel: 01204 393726
Control: Club
BK Rating: Easy
E/A: North West
Comments: About £15 per year

Elton Reservoir

Location: Elton, off the A58 Bury to Bolton road
Type and Size: Big reservoir, 40 feet deep off the dam
How to Find: Turn off the A58 opposite the Washington Hotel towards Eaton Sailing Club. Cross the bridge to Nightingale Hospital, and the reservoir is at the side of the hospital
Carp Stock: Some carp to about 20lbs
Category: Few Carp
Other Species: Pike, bream, roach, perch and tench
Permits: On bank at £2.50
Control: Try T Taylor. Tel: 0161 7642858 for information
BK Rating: Very Difficult
E/A: North West
Comments: There is a sailing club on this lake

Fan Lodge

Location: Off the B 5237 at Platt Bridge, near Bickershaw, Wigan
Type and Size: Two small pools
Carp Stock: Well stocked with carp to upper doubles
Category: Mixed Fishery
Other Species: Tench, perch, roach, crucians and pike
Permits: On bank
Cost: £1.50 per day
Control: Wigan A.A.
Restrictions: No night fishing or keepnets
BK Rating: Moderate
E/A: North West

Farington Lodge Pools

Location: Farington, between Leyland and Preston and between the A59 and the A852, five miles south of Preston
Type and Size: Three small mill lakes
Category: Mixed Fishery
Other Species: Bream, tench, roach, and perch
Permits: Day tickets from Lostock Tackle Box, 16 Watkin Lane, Farington
Control: Private: Tel: 01772 626586
Restrictons: No night fishing except by special arrangement
BK Rating: Easy
E/A: North West
Comments: Some of the waters in this area have no close season

Greenbank Park Lake

Location: Greenbank Drive, off the A5058 road in Liverpool
Type and Size: Small attractive park lake
Carp Stock: Well stocked with carp to about 10lbs
Category: Mixed Fishery
Other Species: Tench, roach, perch and a few bream
Permits: Free, like all Liverpool park lakes
Control: Council
BK Rating: Moderate
E/A: North West
Comments: No close season

Greenhalgh Lodge Fishing

Location: Greenhalgh Lane, Kirkham, near Fleetwood
Type and Size: 2½ acre lake with island
Carp Stock: Very heavily stocked with carp averaging about 3lbs. Big bags
Category: Carp Only
Other Species: None
Permits: On bank
Cost: £4 per day; £3 juniors; O.A.P's and disabled
Control: Tel: 01253 836348
Restrictions: No boilies, nuts or cereal groundbait
BK Rating: Very Easy
E/A: North West
Comments: Very easy, match - type water, thought to be open all year

Heapey Lodges

Location: Chorley, near Manchester
Type and Size: Four reservoirs, totalling about 30 acres, and up to 30 feet deep
How to Find: Off the M61 north west of Manchester
Carp Stock: Fairly well stocked
Category: Mixed Fisheries
Other Species: General coarse fish and trout
Permits: Wigan AA. W Gralton, 66 Balcarres Road, Asphull, Wigan. Day tickets on the bank
Cost: Approx £15 season ticket
BK Rating: Insufficient information
Control: Club
Restrictions: Not known
E/A: North West
Comments: Only Lodge No.1 worth fishing for carp - contains many doubles and a few 20's. Floater fishing best. No close season

Hoddlesdon Reservoir

Location: Darwen, off the A666 north of Bolton
Type and Size: Twenty acre reservoir
Carp Stock: Not many to lower doubles
Category: Few Carp
Other Species: Roach, bream, pike, some trout
Permits: Darwen AA - F W Kendall, 45 Holden Fold, Darwen; and from County Sports, Duckworth Sreet, Darwen
Cost: About £10 per season - no day tickets; in advance only
Restrictions: No night fishing
BK Rating: Very Difficult
E/A: North West

Comments: No close season

Hollingworth Lake

Location: Hollingworth Lake Country Park, two miles from Junction 21 on the M62 near Rochdale
Type and Size: Reservoir of more than 100 acres
Carp Stock: Some carp to doubles
Category: Few Carp
Other Species: Big pike, roach, bream, rudd and a few tench and trout
Permits: On bank £2 per day for adults and £1 for OAP's and juniors
Control: Warden.Tel: 01706 373421
BK Rating: Difficult
E/A: North West
Comments: Drained and restocked by the Council in 1986. Public access

Hudson's Farm

Location: Rawcliff Road, St. Michael's on Wyre, near Garstang
Type and Size: Two small pools; one a specimen lake
Carp Stock: Well stocked with carp to 25 lbs
Category: Mixed Fishery
Other Species: Bream and tench
Permits: On bank or from farm
Cost: £2.50 per day mixed lake; £5 per day specimen lake. £65 per season mixed lake; £135 for both
Control: Tel: 01995 679654
BK Rating: Moderate
Baits/Methods: Boilies and luncheon meat are good baits
E/A: North West
Comments: Toilets. Disabled access

Junior Lodge

Location: Withnell Ford, near Chorley
Type and Size: Small lake
Carp Stock: Well stocked with carp to over 20 lbs
Category: Mixed Fishery
Other Species: Tench, roach and perch
Permits: In advance from Withnell A.C. Tel: 01254 890935
Cost: £35 per season; £12.50 juniors; £10 O.A.P's
Control: Withnell A.C.
Restrictions: 24 hour maximum stay. Bivvies limited
BK Rating: Not known
Baits/Methods: Legered boilies best
E/A: North West

Leeds - Liverpool Canal

Location: Jacksons Bridge, 12 miles from Liverpool
Type and Size: Small canal with little boat traffic
How to Find: Take the M58 or M57 from Liverpool, then the B5147 north, past Lydiate towards Halsall. After the church, turn right to Jacksons Bridge
Carp Stock: Stocked with carp, numbers and sizes not known
Category: Mixed Fishery
Other Species: Bream, tench, roach, and perch
Permits: Day tickets and annual tickets on bank, or from local tackle shops
Cost: £2 per day; £10 per year for juniors, OAP's and the disabled
Control: Jack Johnson. Tel: 0151 5264083 (Liverpool and District AA)

BK Rating: Difficult, until the carp grow and become established
E/A: North West
Comments: No close season

Main Lodge

Location: Manchester Old Road, Rhodes, near Middleton
Type and Size: Large lake
How to Find: From the end of the M 66 take the A 567 to Middleton. The lake is just past the shopping centre
Carp Stock: Well stocked with carp to upper doubles
Category: Mixed Fishery
Other Species: Pike, bream, roach and tench
Permits: Day tickets on bank
Cost: £2 (£1 for juniors)
Control: Middleton Angling Society
Restrictions: No keepnets or bloodworm
BK Rating: Moderate
E/A: Lancashire
Comments: Town lake reached by bus. Unhooking mats compulsory for big pike and carp

Mere Brow Lakes

Location: Near Tarleton, just off the A565 between Southport and Preston
Type and Size: Two lakes, total twenty acres
Carp Stock: Some carp to about 20lbs, exact number and sizes not known
Category: Mixed Fishery
Other Species: Roach and bream
Permits: Day tickets from office on site
Cost: About £2 per rod
Restrictions: No night fishing
BK Rating: Moderate
E/A: North West

Myre Fold Fisheries

Location: Royal Oak pub, off the A 59 near Blackburn
Type and Size: Two small farm pools
Carp Stock: Carp to doubles
Category: Mixed Fishery
Other Species: Tench, rudd and crucians
Permits: From the farmhouse
Cost: About £5 per day: reductions for half day
Control: Tel: 01254 813437
Restrictions: No night fishing; barbless hooks
BK Rating: Not known
E/A: North West

New Water

Location: Leigh, near Wigan
How to Find: Take the A579 from Wigan and turn right towards Leigh on the A578. Turn right into Smiths Lane and the lake will soon be seen on the left
Type and Size: Five acre lake
Carp Stock: Heavily stocked with carp to mid-doubles and several thousand little ones
Category: Mixed Fishery
Other Species: Roach, perch, tench, crucians, bream and pike
Permits: Day tickets on bank at about £2

Control: Tom Kelly. Tel: 01942 676291 (Leigh and District AA)
Restrictions: No night fishing; no boilies, bloodworm or joker; no keepnets
BK Rating: Easy
E/A: North West
Comments: No close season

Oldham Reservoirs

Location: Oldham
Type and Size: Two large reservoirs
How to Find: Near Oldham
Carp Stock: Some carp in Upper Strinesdale and Ogden Reservoirs
Category: Few Carp
Other Species: General coarse fish
Permits: Oldham United AC. A Dyson, 7 Raven Avenue, Chadderton, Oldham
Cost: Approx £1 per day; £10 per season
BK Rating: Not known, probably Difficult
Control: Club
E/A: North West
Comments: Tackle etc from Grundy's, 292 Manchester Street, Werneth, Oldham

Orrell Water Park

Location: West of Wigan, off junction 26 of the M6; Lodge Road, off the B5206
Type and Size: Long, narrow lake, stream-fed
Carp Stock: Quite well stocked with carp of around 8lbs, to lower doubles
Category: Mixed Fishery
Other Species: Bream, tench, roach, perch and gudgeon
Permits: Day tickets on bank
Cost: £3.20; £1.60 for OAP's and the unemployed during the week ; £1.05 for juniors
Control: Tel: 01695 625338
Restrictions: No night fishing; open from 6am; no groundbait
BK Rating: Easy
E/A: North West
Comments: There is another lake on site, which is not day ticket but is used for matches. Car park and toilets

Pennington Flash

Location: Leigh, near Oldham
Type and Size: Small lake
How to Find: Near Leigh, west of Manchester off the A580
Carp Stock: Some good carp
Category: Mixed Fishery
Other Species: General coarse fishing
Permits: Pennington Flash AA. Tel: 01942 673893
Cost: Day ticket - approx £1; season £5
BK Rating: Moderate
Control: Club
E/A: North West

Pilsworth Fisheries

Location: Pilsworth, Heywood
Type and Size: Seven lakes
How to Find: Take the M66 towards Bury from Manchester, and come off at junction 3
Carp Stock: Well stocked including plenty of doubles
Category: Mixed Fishery

Other Species: Mostly coarse fish
Permits: Day tickets - about £4
Control: Private. Tel: 01706 30619
BK Rating: Moderate
Baits/Methods: Normal carp fishing baits and methods
E/A: North West
Comments: This water is controlled by famous match fishermen Kevin and Benny Ashurst

Pine Lodge Coarse Fishery

Location: Off the A 59 Clitheroe by-pass, near Clitheroe
Type and Size: Several lakes - 14 acres of water
Carp Stock: Stocked with small carp
Category: Mixed Fishery
Other Species: Roach, bream, rudd, tench, chub, perch, golden orfe and gudgeon
Permits: On bank
Cost: £5 per day for 1 rod; £7.50 for 2 rods. Concessions for juniors and clubs
Control: Jeff Brookes. Tel: 01254 822211
Restrictions: Barbless hooks only; no night fishing
BK Rating: Not known
E/A: Lancashire
Comments: Open all year

Platts Lane Lakes

Location: Burscough, near Ormskirk
Type and Size: Five acre lake, very deep in parts
How to Find: Platts Lane, off the A59, just past Dean's Newsagents
Carp Stock: Some carp to about 10lbs
Category: Mixed Fishery
Other Species: Tench, roach, rudd, bream and crucians
Permits: Day tickets at Dean's Newsagents; tickets limited
Cost: £2; £1 for juniors
Control: Burscough AC
BK Rating: Moderate
E/A: North West

Red Rocks Fishery

Location: Potter Lane, Higher Walton, near Preston
Type and Size: 2 acre lake
Carp Stock: Well stocked with carp to mid-doubles
Category: Mixed Fishery
Other Species: Crucians, roach, bream, perch and chub
Permits: On bank
Cost: About £4 per day
Control: Bill Cooper. Tel: 01772 877277
Restrictions: No boilies; no nuts or groundbait
BK Rating: Moderate
E/A: North West
Comments: Toilets. Fishing hut. Disabled access

Redwell Carp Fishery

Location: Seven miles north east of Lancaster - there are signs to the fishery on the B6254 Carnforth-Kirkby Lonsdale road; near Arkholme and Carnforth
Type and Size: Three acre lake in attractive surroundings
Carp Stock: Well stocked with small carp, and some doubles to about 15lbs

Category: Carp Water
Permits: In advance from the house on the way in
Cost: £4 per day
Control: Private. Duncan Cummings. Tel: 015242 21979
BK Rating: Easy to Moderate
E/A: North West
Comments: Fishing is 7am to dusk only

River Calder

Location: Wigan area
Type and Size: Small river
Carp Stock: Quite well stocked with small carp, and a few doubles
Category: Mixed Fishery
Other Species: Most coarse fish and some trout
Permits: From local tackle shops
Control: Wigan AA. Secretary: W Gratton, 66 Balcarres Road, Aspull, Wigan
BK Rating: Moderate
E/A: North West
Comments: Possibly no close season in some areas

River Crossens

Location: Just east of Southport on the A565 Preston road
Type and Size: Narrow, shallow stretch of drain-type river
Carp Stock: Some carp to doubles
Category: Few Carp
Other Species: Bream, tench, roach, perch, pike, rudd and eels
Permits: Chorley Anglers, Chorley; Ted Carter, Preston and F Foster, Tarleton
Cost: Day tickets at £2 for adults and £1 for juniors and OAP's
Control: Southport DAA
Restrictions: No bloodworm!
BK Rating: Difficult
E/A: North West

Sabden Reservoir

Location: Whalley, near Accrington
Type and Size: Small reservoir
How to Find: Enquire from Secretary
Carp Stock: Some carp
Category: Few Carp
Other Species: Small trout
Permits: Accrington and District FC. A Balderstone, 42 Townley Avenue, Huncoat, Accrington. Tel: 01254 33517
Cost: Approx £4 per day
BK Rating: Moderate
Control: Club
E/A: North West

Smiths

Location: Manchester Road, Bolton
Carp Stock: Quite well stocked with good doubles and 20's to 23lbs (common) and 24lbs (mirror)
Category: Mixed Fishery
Permits: Bolton and District Angling Club - members only. Secretary: T McKee, 1 Lever Edge Lane, Great Lever, Bolton, Greater Manchester
Control: Club

BK Rating: Moderate
E/A: North West

Springview Lakes

Location: Taylers Lane, Springview, off the A 573 near Ince-in-Makerfield, Wigan
Type and Size: Two pools; 2 1/2 acres of water
Carp Stock: Well stocked with small carp
Category: Mixed Fishery
Other Species: Roach, rudd, tench, bream, chub and gudgeon
Permits: Possibly day tickets soon
Cost: Season tickets only at present at £15
Control: Tel: 01942 865540
BK Rating: Not known
E/ A: North West

Super Street Lodge

Location: Crowther St, Clayton - le - Moors, near Blackburn
Type and Size: Small lake
Carp Stock: Well stocked with carp to about 10 lbs
Category: Mixed Fishery
Other Species: Roach, perch, small bream. crucians and chub
Permits: In advance only from local tackle shops
Cost: £37 per season, £11 juniors and O.A.P's - to include other club waters
Control: Hynburn and Blackburn A.A. Tel: 01254 397448
BK.Rating: Moderate
E/A: North West

Swantley Lake

Location: Off the B6254, about eight miles north east of Lancaster
Type and Size: Two and a half acre lake, specially dug as a fishery a few years ago
Carp Stock: Well stocked with commons and mirrors to mid-doubles
Category: Mixed Fishery
Other Species: Roach, rudd and bream
Permits: Day and season tickets - for information and permits Tel: 01524 422146
Control: Lonsdale Angling Club - details from local tackle shops
BK Rating: Easy
E/A: North West

Thursland Farm A

Location: Thursland Hill Farm, Moss Lane, Thurnham, Lancaster
Type and Size: Small pond
How to Find: Off the A 588 near Galgate
Carp Stock: Well stocked with carp to about 10 lbs
Category: Mixed Fishery
Other Species: Roach and tench
Permits: Ticket machine on site; cost doubled if bailiff has to collect
Cost: £3.50 one rod; £6 two rods
Control: Private
Restrictions: No night fishing, no barbed hooks, no keepnets or lines less than 4lbs b/s
BK Rating: Not known
E/A: North West
Comments: Some basic accommodation offered - those staying may night fish

Twin Lakes

Location: Croston, near Chorley
How to Find: Take the B5249 from Chorley, then turn right at Croston onto the A581 and left just after the railway bridge. You will see the lake on the left
Type and Size: Small clay pit
Carp Stock: Recently stocked with very small carp
Category: Mixed Fishery
Permits: On site at £3 per day
Control: Graham Cooper. Tel: 01722 601093
Restrictions: No keepnets, bloodworm or joker
E/A: North West
Comments: Stocked mainly with small fish. Bar and hot meals from the site lodge

Walverden Reservoir

Location: Brunswick Street, Nelson, near Burnley
Type and Size: 10 acre lake
Carp Stock: Quite well stocked with carp to 20 lbs
Category: Mixed Fishery
Other Species: Bream, roach and tench
Permits: On bank
Cost: About £3 per rod. Half price for juniors and O.A.P's
Control: Tel: 01282 865500 ext. 444
Restrictions: No night fishing
BK Rating: Easy
Baits/Methods: Boilies and Chum Mixer are good baits
E/ A: North West

Wickenhall Fishery

Location: Ogden Lane, Wickenhall, Oldham, off the A640
Type and Size: Two small ponds
Carp Stock: Some small carp, and a few doubles
Other Species: Roach and bream
Permits: Day tickets on bank at £1.50
Control: T A Hughes, The Smithy, Smithy Green, Wickenhall Ogden Gardens, OL16 3TG
Restrictions: No night fishing; no groundbaiting
BK Rating: Fairly Hard
E/A: North West
Comments: No phone number given

Worthington Lake

Location: Worthington, a suburb of Wigan
Type and Size: Two acre pond
Carp Stock: Well stocked with carp to about 15lbs
Category: Mixed Fishery
Permits: Day tickets from local tackle shops
Control: Wigan - and District AA. Secretary: W Gratton, 66 Balcarres Road, Aspull, Wigan - includes other carp waters
Restrictions: No night fishing
BK Rating: Moderate
E/A: North West

Wrightington Lake

Location: Off the A5209 at Wrighton Hospital, between Ormskirk and the M6
Type and Size: 10 acre estate type lake
Carp Stock: Quite a number of carp to upper doubles
Category: Mixed Fishery
Permits: From local tackle shops - day and season tickets
Control: Wigan and District AA. W Gratton, 66 Balcarres Road, Aspull, Wigan
Restrictions: No night fishing
BK Rating: Difficult
E/A: North West

Wyreside Fisheries A

Location: Hampton Lane, Dolphinholm, Lancaster
Type and Size: Five man-made lakes, with more than twenty acres of water
Carp Stock: All five lakes contain carp, many of which are small, though there are some doubles to about 25lbs
Category: Mixed Fishery
Other Species: Roach, bream, tench, pike, and perch
Permits: Day tickets from the lodge
Cost: £7 for 2 rods
Control: Larry Fitzgerald. Tel: 01524 792093
BK Rating: Easy
E/A: North West
Comments: A pleasant and attractive complex to fish, with the chance of some big fish within a few years. Close season February 17th to April 10th. Bartons Lake is carp only. Self-catering lodges - send for brochure. Tel: 01524 791494/791830/792093. Trout fishing

LEICESTERSHIRE

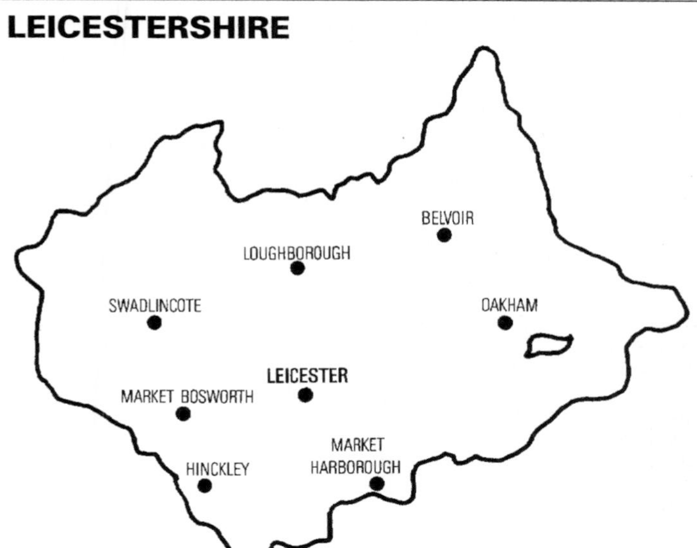

Ashby Canal

Location: A 5 road near Hinckley
Type and Size: Narrow, shallow canal
Carp Stock: Some carp to 15 lbs
Category: Few Carp
Other Species: Roach, tench, perch and bream
Permits: In advance only
Cost: About £10 per season
Control: Crown Leisure A A, 134 Rugby Road, Cublington, Leamington Spa CV32 7JQ. Tel: 01926 334508
BK Rating: Difficult
E/A: Severn Trent
Comments: Disabled access

Barlestone Lake

Location: Village of Barlestone, near Market Bosworth
Type and Size: One and half acre farm pond
How to Find: To centre of village, then right towards Nailstone; lake is on right behind Baxters Farm
Carp Stock: 110-130 carp to 16lb. Few doubles
Category: Mixed Fishery
BK Rating: Easy
Permits: Day tickets on the bank
Cost: £3 per day. £1.50 per half - day
Restrictions: No night fishing
E/A: Severn-Trent
Comments: Plenty of carp, most 6-9lb. Margin fishing (keeping well away from the bank) and surface fishing most successful

Barwell Lane Pit

Location: Barwell Lane, Barwell, near Hinckley
Type and Size: Small former quarry; very deep water
Carp Stock: Well stocked with carp to 25 lbs
Category: Mixed Fishery
Other Species: Pike, tench, bream, roach, rudd and perch
Permits: In advance only from local tackle shops
Cost: About £20 per season; £10 juniors and O.A.P's
Control: Hinckley A / C. Tel: 01455 239823
BK Rating: Not known
Baits/Methods: Boilies good for carp
E/A: Severn Trent

Beadles Pit

Location: Off Broome Lane, East Goscote, north of Leicester. Down long track next to railway line
Type and Size: 29 acre gravel pit
Carp Stock: 150 carp to 23lb. Average 8-14lbs
Category: Mixed Fishery
Other Species: Tench to 7lb. Pike to 25lb. Roach, bream, perch
Permits: Day tickets on bank £3
Control: Private
Restrictions: No restrictions
BK Rating: Moderate
E/A: Severn-Trent
Comments: Large open gravel pit with few features; fish are not at all hard to catch - once located

Belvoir Lakes

Location: Belvoir Castle, between Melton Mowbray and Grantham
Type and Size: Chain of small estate lakes
Carp Stock: Well stocked with carp to a good size
Category: Carp Waters
Other Species: Some coarse fish
Permits: Season tickets only from the Estate Office at Belvoir Castle
Control: Private
BK Rating: Easy
E/A: Severn-Trent

Birstall Carp Pool

Location: In centre of Country Park, near Birstall
Type and Size: Two and a half acre pool
Carp Stock: Heavily stocked with fish to upper doubles
Category: Carp Water
Other Species: Usual coarse fish
Permits: Season tickets £25 from Alan Smith, Broome AS. Membership open to all. Occasionally a waiting list for tickets
Control: Club
BK Rating: Easy - good winter water
E/A: Severn-Trent
Comments: Small pool with good head of carp, ideal for someone starting carp fishing

Bosworth Water Trust — A

Location: Half a mile west of Market Bosworth on the B585. Tel: 01455 291876
Type and Size: 20 acres of lake
Carp Stock: Some carp to doubles
Category: Mixed Fishery
Other Species: Usual coarse fish
Permits: Nigel and Jo Riley, at the site office before fishing
Cost: £1.50 per day - free to campers and members
Control: Private
BK Rating: Not known
E/A: Anglian
Comments: There is camping, and facilities for caravans near the lake, with toilets, showers and a snack bar. From the publicity, this 'leisure and water park' is more for sailing and board-sailing than for angling, but there are certainly some carp, so it might be worth a try

Charnwood Lake

Location: In Loughborough, two miles from the centre of the town
Type and Size: Lake of about eight acres and very deep
How to Find: Close to the A6 Loughborough-Leicester road. Go via Beeches Road, then turn right into Tuckers Road, and the lake is at the end, with a car park
Carp Stock: Well stocked with small carp, and a few to about 20lbs
Category: Mixed Fishery
Other Species: Roach, bream, chub, perch, pike and tench
Permits: Day tickets in advance only from local tackle shops
Cost: £2 per day; juniors £1; season - £20, juniors and unemployed £10
Control: J Stephens. Tel: 01509 267330
Restrictions: No night fishing
BK Rating: Difficult for the big carp; Moderate for the smaller ones
E/A: Severn-Trent
Comments: Some special swims for the disabled

Garden Farm Fisheries

Location: Barlestone
Type and Size: 2 acre lake
Carp Stock: Some carp to 20 lbs
Category: Mixed Fishery
Other Species: Bream and some other species
Permits: On site
Cost: About £5 per day
Control: Tel: 01455 291193
Restrictions: Night fishing by arrangement only
BK Rating: Not known
E/A: Severn Trent
Comments: Caravan and camping facilities. Full English breakfast available

Grand Union Canal

Location: Near Market Harborough
Type and Size: About five miles of canal
Carp Stock: Quite well stocked with carp up to 10lbs, some bigger fish
Category: Mixed Fishery
Other Species: Tench, bream, roach
Permits: Market Harborough Anglers. Seasonal Membership; day tickets from bailiffs on the bank, or in advance from Sports Shop, 7 St Mary

	Road, Market Harborough. Secretary: R Haycock, 16 Maurice Road, Market, Harborough
Cost:	Approx £5 per season; £1 per day
Control:	Club
BK Rating:	Moderate
E/A:	Severn-Trent

Groby

Location:	Off A50 at Groby - visible from the A50
Type and Size:	Small lake in centre of 'pick your own' farm. Watering pond (for strawberries) of one acre
Carp Stock:	Heavily stocked with carp to 20lb - 25+ doubles, most fish 2-8lb
Category:	Carp Water
Other Species:	Tench to 6lb, crucian carp
Permits:	Day tickets on bank - £4. Juniors £3
Control:	Private. Tel: 01162 874190
Restrictions:	No boilies, nuts, groundbaits, hemp. No line under 6lb. No hooks small than 14 - must be barbless. Night fishing by arrangement
BK Rating:	Moderate
E/A:	Severn-Trent
Comments:	Surface fishing at start of season gives the best chance of one of the bigger fish. During the season, mass baiting with casters, tares or any other allowed tiny bait gives the best results

Hall Farm Fishery

Location:	Klondyke Lane, Thorpe Satchville, near Melton Mowbray
Type and Size:	Two farm pools of about an acre each
Carp Stock:	Well stocked with doubles to over 20 lbs
Category:	Mixed Fishery
Other Species:	Roach, tench, chub, rudd, perch, bream and gudgeon
Permits:	On bank
Cost:	£4 per day
Control:	Tel: 01664 840315
Restrictions:	No night fishing; no keepnets; barbless hooks
BK Rating:	Not known
Baits/Methods:	Boilies are good for carp
E/A:	Severn Trent
Comments:	Toilet. Disabled access

Halstead House Farm

Location:	Halstead, off the B6047 Melton Mowbray road
Type and Size:	Small farm lake
Carp Stock:	Quite well stocked with carp to about 7lbs
Category:	Mixed Fishery
Other Species:	Roach, dace, gudgeon and a few tench
Permits:	On the bank or from the shop
Cost:	£3.50 per day; £2 for OAP's, juniors and the disabled
Control:	Tel: 0153 754239
Restrictions:	No night fishing. No keepnets, barbed hooks or groundbait
BK Rating:	Moderate
E/A:	Severn-Trent

Hartshorne Dams Carp Fishery

Location: Hartshorne, off the A514 near Swadlincote and Burton-upon-Trent
Type and Size: Three acre lake
Carp Stock: Well stocked with carp to upper doubles, and possibly larger
Category: Carp Water
Permits: AMR Country Clothing, Ashby de la Zouche; Melbourne Tackle and Gun, Melbourne; The Rodney Inn, Hartshorne (opening hours only); The Farmhouse, Manor Farm, Hartshorne. No tickets on bank - tickets must be purchased before fishing at £2.50 per day
Control: Private. Tel: 01283 215769
BK Rating: Moderate
E/A: Severn-Trent
Comments: There is also a 2½ acre general coarse lake on the site, and a £40 a season night syndicate on the carp lake

Hermitage Leisure Centre

Location: Hermitage near Coalville. Signposted for Leisure Centre
Type and Size: Old gravel pits of 10 acres
Carp Stock: Reasonable head of carp to 19lbs. 40% are doubles
Category: General coarse fishery
Permits: Day tickets: £2 on bank - night fishing by arrangement with warden
Control: Private. Tel: 01530 811215
Restrictions: No night fishing;
BK Rating: Moderate
E/A: Severn Trent
Comments: Lake contains a large island around which the fish often congregate; large numbers of water birds

Knossington Carp Lake

Location: Knossington, near Oakham
Type and Size: Small lake
How to Find: West of Oakham
Carp Stock: Well stocked with plenty of low doubles and fish of 8-9lbs
Category: Carp Water
Other Species: Crucians, bream, roach, tench
Permits: D H Preke. Tel: 01664 47305. Advance booking only
Cost: Approx £3 per day (£1.50 juniors)
Control: Private
BK Rating: Easy to Moderate
Restrictions: No night fishing, no keepnets,no groundbaiting
E/A: Severn-Trent

Lakeside Fishing

Location: Off the B 4109 between Hinckley and Wolvey
Type and Size: Very old 10 acre estate lake with islands
Carp Stock: Well stocked with carp averaging about 10 lbs; best is around 20 lbs
Category: Mixed fishery
Other Species: Crucians, bream, tench and perch
Permits: On bank
Cost: About £4 per day
Control: Tel: 01455 622090
Restrictions: Barbless hooks; children must be accompanied by an adult
BK Rating: Not known
Baits/Methods: Luncheon meat and boilies best
E/A: Severn Trent

Comments: Toilet. Disabled access. Picturesque 250 year old lake in the grounds of Leicester Grange Nature Reserve

Launde Abbey Pools

Location: Launde Abbey, off the Oakham-Leicester road
Type and Size: Four small Abbey pools, now restored, dredged and stocked
Carp Stock: Well stocked with commons to doubles
Category: Mixed Fishery
Other Species: Tench, roach, rudd, perch and chub
Permits: Day tickets on bank
Cost: £3.25; £2.50 for juniors and OAP's. Evening tickets from 5pm at £2.25
Control: Tel: 01572 86202
Restrictions: Fishing is dawn to dusk, but there is some night fishing by arrangement. No groundbaiting
BK Rating: Moderate
E/A: Anglian

Little Pit

Location: Hinckley
Type and Size: Five acre clay pit
How to Find: On Barwell Lane, Hinckley (opposite ASDA superstore)
Carp Stock: A few carp to a little over 20lbs
Category: Mixed Fishery
Other Species: General coarse fish
Permits: Hinckley and District AC. Secretary: Pat Donnachie. Tel: Hinckley 636121. Also available from Tony Horton's Fishing Tackle, Burbage. Tel: 01455 632269
Cost: £20 per year
Control: Club
BK Rating: Difficult
E/A: Severn-Trent
Comments: Typical deep clay pit, most success to surface and margin fishing

Mallory Park

Location: Mallory Park Fisheries, Kirkby Mallory LE9 7E. Tel: 01455 842931
Type and Size: Several lakes built in 1986 by Roy Marlow
Carp Stock: Well stocked with carp to 20lbs
Category: Mixed Fishery
Other Species: Most coarse fish
Permits: Marks and Marlow Ltd, 39 Tudor Road, Leicester. Tel: 01162 537714
Control: Private - two famous anglers, Ivan Marks and Roy Marlow
BK Rating: Moderate
E/A: Anglian
Comments: This is a conservation area, with ponds and Nature Reserve. Motor Sport racing, accommodation, buffet and bars nearby. Sponsors invited to help create conservaton areas for wildlife

Mill Farm A

Location: Gilmorton, 10 miles south of Leicester
Type and Size: Attractive four acre lake on a farm
How to Find: Turn right onto the A427 from junction 20 of the M1 going north, then take the first left turn to Gilmorton
Carp Stock: Fairly well stocked with carp to about 19lbs, many of which are small
Category: Mixed Fishery
Other Species: Roach, rudd, bream and tench

Permits: Day tickets on bank or from the shop - Tel: 01455 552392 for details
Cost: £3.50 one rod; £5 for two. Concessionary permits
Control: Private
Restrictions: Dawn to dusk only. Some summer night fishing by arrangement. No particles or groundbait
BK Rating: Easy
E/A: Severn-Trent
Comments: Some holiday accommodation at this very attractive lake - details from the phone number above. Bait and refreshments

Mill-on-the-Soar

Location: Mill-on-the-Soar Hotel, Sutton-in-the-Elms, just off the B4114 road, south west of Leicester
Type and Size: Three and a half acre lake with large island, fed by the River Soar
Carp Stock: Quite well stocked with carp to over 20lbs
Category: Mixed Fishery
Other Species: Chub, roach, rudd, perch and a few trout
Permits: £3 per day at the hotel reception desk
Control: Malcolm Cliff. Tel: 01455 282419
Restrictions: No night fishing - dawn till dusk only; no carp in keepnets
BK Rating: Moderate
E/A: Severn-Trent
Comments: Some access for the disabled; restocking and dredging is planned

Murphys Lake

Location: Next to both the Grand Union Canal and a Walkers Crisp Factory. Either down Canal Steeet, Thurmaston or by the back of Wanlip Country Club
Type and Size: Large gravel pit of 30 acres
Carp Stock: Few carp - fish caught to 27.8 - good chance of a 30lb+ fish. Maybe only 25 fish
Category: Mixed Fishery
Other Species: Specimen fish of all species
Permits: Season tickets £25.00 from Alan Smith, Broome AS. Membership open to all, but occasional waiting list for permits
Control: Club
Restrictions: None
BK Rating: Very Difficult - locating fish essential for success
E/A: Severn-Trent
Comments: Very large open gravel pit, very few features; once located fish are quite catchable. Also contains pike to 26lb+, bream to 10lbs+ and large tench, specimen fish of all species. Used by water skiers

Nanpantan Reservoir

Location: Nanpantan, near Loughborough
Type and Size: Reservoir about five acres in size
How to Find: Take the B5350 road to Loughborough to Nanpantan
Carp Stock: After draining, the lake was stocked with mirror carp many of which are now 5-9 lbs, with a few lower doubles and possibly one 20
Category: Carp Water
Other Species: Bream, tench, roach and perch
Permits: W H Wortley, 45 Baxter Gate, Loughborough. Tel: 01509 212697
Baits/Methods: Carp tactics and baits, including sweetcorn and luncheon meat
Control: Private
Restrictions: No groundbaiting. Thirty anglers only per day. No night fishing. Barbless hooks. Minimum 8lb line
BK Rating: Moderate

E/A: Severn-Trent
Comments: Granite block banks - unhooking mats recommended. Part of the lake is closed to anglers. Toilet block. Permits in advance only from Soar Valley Tackle, Woodbrook Road, Loughborough or W H Wortley. Information on 01509 234901

Peatling Pools

Location: Peatling Parva, just south of Leicester
Type and Size: Two small lakes, each with an island
Carp Stock: Well stocked with carp to over 25lbs
Category: Mixed Fishery
Other Species: Chub, roach, bream, rudd, tench and trout
Permits: On the bank at £3.50 and £4.50 for two rods
Control: Tel: 01533 478222
Restrictions: No night fishing - dawn till dusk only
Baits/Methods: A good water for surface fishing
BK Rating: Moderate
E/A: Severn-Trent

Sheepy Lake

Location: Sheepy Magna
Type and Size: Lake of seven acres
How to Find: Take the A444 between Sibson and Twycross and then the B585 to Sheepy Parva and Magna villages
Carp Stock: Well stocked with carp between 5 and 7lbs, mostly mirrors. A few doubles, and one possible 20
Category: Mixed Fishery
Other Species: Crucians, and some other coarse fish
Permits: Day tickets on the bank
Cost: Approx £2 per day
Control: Private
BK Rating: Easy
E/A: Severn-Trent

Spring Grange

Location: South Croxton, of the A607 north east of Leicester, and between Beeby and South Croxton
Type and Size: Two small lakes
Carp Stock: Well stocked with carp to 26lbs
Category: Mixed Fishery
Other Species: Bream, tench, roach, rudd, chub and barbel
Permits: Tickets in advance or on the bank
Cost: £5 for the large lake; £4 or the smaller. Reductions for OAP's, juniors and the disabled. Reduced rates for evenings
Control: Tel: 01537 50609
Restrictions: Barbless hooks only. Groundbait, peanuts, and dogs are banned (presumably all three cannot be used as baits!). No night fishing (dawn to dusk only). 4lb minimum line limit on large lake. Access for the disabled
BK Rating: Not known
E/A: Severn-Trent

Sulby Lily Pond

Location: Near Welford, on Leics/Northants border
Type and Size: Two acre silty pool
How to Find: Sulby is signposted just north of Welford on east side of A50
Carp Stock: Well stocked, a lot of small carp, but fish go up to about 20lb
Category: Carp Water
Other Species: Tench, small pike, roach and perch
Permits: Hinckley and District AC. Secretary: Pat Donnachie. Tel: 01455 636121. Also available from Tony Horton's Fishing Tackle, Burbage. Tel: 01455 632269
Cost: £20 per year
Control: Private
Restrictions: No night fishing
BK Rating: Moderate
E/A: Severn-Trent
Comments: Very weedy little water with lilies and silkweed

Walif Gravel Pits

Location: Near Willington
Type and Size: Large gravel pits
How to Find: Willington, near Derby
Carp Stock: Not known - some carp
Category: Few Carp
Other Species: Mixed coarse fish
Permits: Rising Sun public house, Willington
Cost: Approx £2 per day
Control: Derby Angling Association. J Callaghan, 3 Calvin Close, Alvaston, Derby DE2 OHX
BK Rating: Insufficient information
E/A: Severn-Trent

Wanlip Country Club

Location: Wanlip Road, Syston - near Leicester
Type and Size: Virtually square gravel pit of eight acres
Carp Stock: Carp to 27lb - most fish doubles. Possibly 10 twenties
Category: Mixed Fishery
Other Species: Tench to 7lb. Roach, perch and pike etc
Permits: Season tickets £25.00 from Alan Smith, Broome AS - enquire locally for details. Membership open to all, but occasionally waiting list for tickets
Control: Club
Restrictions: No restrictions
BK Rating: Hard
E/A: Severn-Trent
Comments: Long range tactics essential on this open water. Only features are gravel bars and right in the centre of the lake, the old causeway when it was dug. Water also used by water skiers. Keep rod tips low to avoid being cut off by the speed boats!

Welford Reservoir

Location: Welford, near Leicester
Type and Size: 20 acre reservoir
Carp Stock: Quite well stocked with good carp to double figures
Category: Mixed Fishery
Other Species: Bream, pike, tench, rudd and roach
Permits: British Waterways, Willow Grange, Church Road, Watford, or the

	bailiff,Mr W Williams, Welford Grange Farm, Welford
Cost:	Season tickets only at about £15
Restrictions:	No day tickets, and there may be a waiting list
BK Rating:	Moderate
E/A:	Severn-Trent

Willesley Lake

Location:	Near Measham, off the A453
Type and Size:	Estate lake of 23 acres, shallower at one end
Carp Stock:	Large numbers of carp to 23lb, 4 twenties, 2 twenty commons, good head of doubles
Other Species:	Usual coarse fish
Permits:	Day tickets on bank £3.50, or season tickets £20 from local tackle shops
Control:	Club Tel: 01530 270041 - Measham Tackle
Restrictions:	No night fishing; no floating baits. No day tickets on Sundays
BK Rating:	Easy to Moderate
E/A:	Severn-Trent
Comments:	Very heavily fished by match anglers due to large head of bream. No day tickets at weekends. Margin fishing productive in shallows

Willow Farm Carp Pool

Location:	Off Wanlip Road, Systan; through gravel working
Type and Size:	Three quarter acre pool
Carp Stock:	Plenty of carp to 19lb+, 10-15 doubles
Category:	Carp Water
Other Species:	Usual coarse fish
Permits:	Season tickets £25 on bank or from Michael Winterton. Tel: 01162 600937
Control:	Private
Restrictions:	No restrictions
BK Rating:	Moderate
E/A:	Severn-Trent
Comments:	Season ticket covers 10 lakes and several miles of Rivers Soar and Wreake. Most of the other lakes on the complex hold few carp to 20lb+

LINCOLNSHIRE

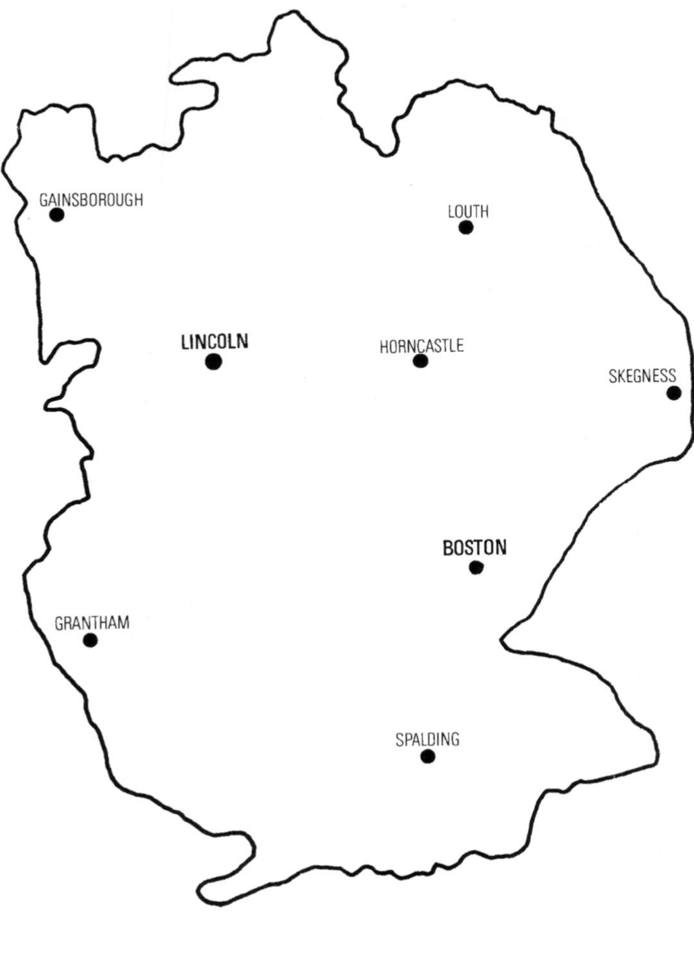

Ashby Park **A**

Location: Ashby Park, West Ashby, near Horncastle LN9 5PP. Tel: 01507 527966 or 01790 53321
Type and Size: Six lakes - about 15 acres of water in 52 acres of land
Carp Stock: Well stocked with carp to upper doubles
Category: Mixed Fishery
Other Species: Chub, rudd, tench, bream, pike, perch, roach, and eels
Permits: From Robin and Margaret Francis at the above address
Cost: Day £3.80; Year £84
Control: Private. Send for brochure
BK Rating: Not known
E/A: Anglian
Comments: Touring caravan site by lake; car parking at swims, ideal for disabled anglers; no close season; camping. Holiday accommodation for hire or for sale. Fishing in the R. Bain. Toilets and showers

Belleau Bridge Lake

Location: South Thoresby, west of Alford, off the A16 Louth to Spilsby road
Type and Size: Six acre shallow lake
Carp Stock: Quite well stocked with carp to about 15lbs
Category: Mixed Fishery
Other Species: Roach, tench, bream and eels
Permits: On the bank at £5 per day
Control: Tel: 01507 480225
Restrictions: No night fishing; no excessive groundbaiting
BK Rating: Moderate
E/A: Anglian
Comments: No close season. Cars can be driven to water's edge

Brickyard Fishery **A**

Location: South Somercotes, Louth
Type and Size: Four acre brick pit
How to Find: South Somercotes road, to the east of Louth
Carp Stock: Some carp to about 20lbs
Category: Mixed Fishery
Other Species: General coarse fish
Permits: Day tickets on site
Cost: Approx £3 per day
BK Rating: Moderate
Control: Private
E/A: Yorkshire
Comments: Small quiet caravan site - static vans for hire. Toilet block. Tourers welcome

Brookside Fisheries **A**

Location: North Scarle, between Lincoln and Newark
Type and Size: One acre pond with island
Carp Stock: Well stocked with quite a number of doubles to over 25lbs
Category: Mixed Fishery
Other Species: Koi, golden orfe, tench, rudd and roach
Permits: On bank at £3 per rod
Control: Tel: 01522 77234
Restrictions: No night fishing; no keepnets or groundbait
BK Rating: Moderate
E/A: Anglian

Comments: No close season; four caravans for hire; disabled anglers can take cars to the bank

Chapel Boating Lake

Location: Near Skegness
Type and Size: Lake of four acres
Carp Stock: Well stocked with carp. A 32lbs common was reported in *Angling Times,* January 1991, on boilie
Category: Mixed Fishery
Permits: John Cooke. Tel: 01754 72631
Cost: £3 one rod; for two £4
Restrictions: Open March 14th to the end of October only; no night fishing
BK Rating: Moderate
E/A: Anglian

Denton Reservoir

Location: Denton, near Grantham
Type and Size: Large reservoir
How to Find: Off the A607, four miles west of Grantham
Carp Stock: Well stocked with carp to 26lbs
Category: Mixed Fishery
Other Species: General coarse fish
Permits: Enquire locally
Cost: Approx £10 per year
BK Rating: Moderate
Control: Not known
Restrictions: None
E/A: Severn-Trent
Comments: We have been unable to find out where these permits can be obtained - try local tackle shops

Elmhurst Lake A

Location: Horncastle
How to Find: Elmhurst, near Horncastle
Carp Stock: Some carp to 15lbs
Category: Mixed Fishery
Other Species: Bream and tench
Permits: Tel: 01658 27533
Cost: On application
Control: Private
BK Rating: Insufficient information
E/A: Yorkshire
Comments: Caravan site - caravans to let. Lake described as 'picturesque'. No close season. Further information from owners on the number listed above

Four Ways Fisheries

Location: Langtoft Fen, Baston, near Market Deeping
Type and Size: 5 acre gravel pit
How to Find: Take the A 16 from Market Deeping towards Spalding, then turn left at Frognall. Turn left, then first right, and the fishery is on the right
Carp Stock: Well stocked with doubles to 28 lbs
Category: Mixed Fishery
Other Species: Tench, roach, perch and eels
Permits: In advance only
Cost: About £100 per season

Control: S.J.Skells. Tel: 01406 380473 / 01374 157308
Restrictions: Members only, no day tickets
BK Rating: Moderate
Baits/Methods: Boilies and sweetcorn are good baits
E/A: Anglian
Comments: Toilets. Space for caravans but no electricity. Probably open all year

Golf Lakes

Location: Golf Club, off the A158 at West Ashby about a mile north of Horncastle
Type and Size: Two lakes, of five acres and one and a half acres
Carp Stock: Some carp to 20lbs
Category: Mixed Fishery
Other Species: Tench to over 10lbs, roach, chub, bream and perch
Permits: In advance. Tel: 01507 526800
Cost: £10 per day
Restrictions: More than any other water we have! No night fishing (8am till sunset only); no keepnets, carp sacks, bolt rigs or hair rigs; barbless hooks. Float fishing only; no line of less than 5lb B/S
BK Rating: Not known
E/A: Anglian

Grooby's Pit

Location: Thorpe Culvert, off the B1195 near Spilsby
Type and Size: Two acre lake
Carp Stock: Not many carp, best about 12lbs
Category: Few Carp
Other Species: Tench, bream, roach and eels
Permits: Must be obtained from the house before fishing
Cost: £1.50 per day; 50p from 5pm to 9pm
Control: Tel: 01754 880216
Restrictions: Fishing is 6am to 9pm; no night fishing; no groundbait
BK Rating: Difficult
E/A: Anglian

Hall Farm Moat

Location: Hall Farm, Harpswell, near Gainsborough. Tel: 01427 73412
Type and Size: Farm moat of three quarters of an acre
How to Find: Off the A631 between Coringham and Harpswell
Carp Stock: Well stocked with carp of all sizes to 20lbs
Permits: Mixed Fishery
Cost: Approx £2 per day
BK Rating: Fairly Hard
Control: Private
Restrictions: No night fishing
E/A: Severn-Trent
Comments: The carp in this water are still growing - and now we have a moat, a stream and a dock in our guide!

Hill View Lake

Location: Hogsthorpe, near Skegness, PE24 5NR
Type and Size: Two lakes of two acres and three quarters of an acre
How to Find: Off the A52 road from Skegness to Malblethorpe, near Chapel St.Leonards
Carp Stock: Heavily stocked with carp, mainly small to 18lbs
Category: Mixed Fishery

Other Species: Tench and roach
Permit: On site. Details from owner. Tel: 01754 872979
Cost: £3 per day for one rod; £4.50 for two rods. Juniors, pensioners and disabled £1.50. After 5pm £1.75 for all
BK Rating: Easy
Control: Private
Restrictions: Barbless hooks only; no carp to be kept in keepnets
E/A: Anglian
Comments: Tackle can be hired. Tea, coffee and snacks. No close season. Ideal spot for the holidaymaker

Lakeside Fisheries

Location: Langworth, near Lincoln
Type and Size: 3 small lakes
How to Find: Take the A 158 from Lincoln towards Skegness. Turn right down Barlings Lane just after Langworth. The lakes are 1 mile on the left

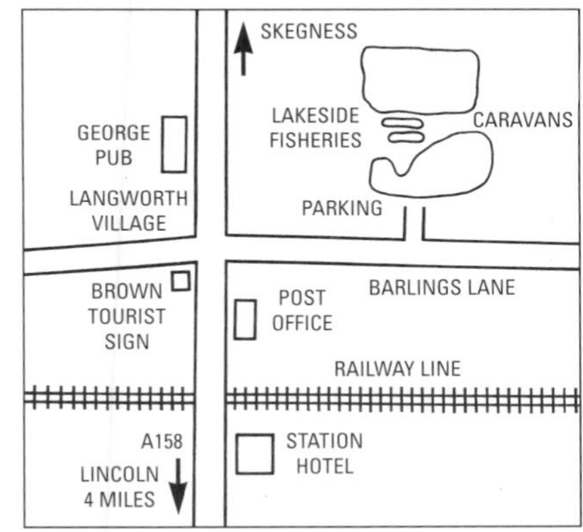

Carp Stock: Well stocked with carp to upper 20's
Category: Mixed Fishery
Other Species: Chub, roach, perch, rudd, tench, bream and golden orfe
Permits: On site
Cost: Match Lake £3 day; £5 night. Kingfisher Lake £5 day time. Bit - A - Chuck Lake £2 for accompanied children
Control: Tony Matthews. Tel: 01522 595933
Restrictions: No boilies or hemp
BK Rating: Easy
E/A: Anglian
Comments: Tourist caravan site. Open all year

Lake Helen **A**

Location: Lake Helen, Mill Lane, Sutterton, near Boston
Type and Size: Three acre lake
Carp Stock: Well stocked with carp to upper twenties
Category: Mixed Fishery
Other Species: Tench, bream, roach, rudd, crucians and golden orfe
Permits: Send for brochure. Tel: 01205 460681
Cost: £5 per day
Control: Private

BK Rating: Moderate
E/A: Anglian
Comments: One lakeside bungalow and caravan open all year. Barbless hooks. Dawn to dusk only

Lincolnshire Drains

Location: Spalding area
Type and Size: A number of Fen drains, including Vernatts
Carp Stock: Some carp to about 10lbs
Other Species: Pike, perch, rudd, bream and tench
Permits: Spalding Fishing Club - try local tackle shops, such as D T Ball, 1 Hawthorne Bank, Spalding or M Tidwells, Fen Lane, Spalding
Control: Club
BK Rating: Difficult
E/A: Anglian

Lowfields Country Holiday Fishing Retreat A

Location: Lowfields Grange, Eagle Lane, North Scarle, Lincoln LN6 9EN
Type and Size: Three small lakes, two and a half acres, one and a half acres and half an acre
How to Find: Off the A1133 Newark-on-Trent to Gainsborough road and south west of Lincoln
Carp Stock: Good carp to 20lbs+
Category: Mixed Fishery
Other Species: Perch, roach, bream, tench, eels, rudds and crucians
Permits: LCHFR, Lincoln. Tel: 01522 778717
Cost: On application
Control: Private. Paul and Andrea Anderson
Restrictions: No day tickets; no bivvies
BK Rating: Moderate
E/A: Severn-Trent
Comments: Formerly known as the Poplars and now surely our longest title!. Self-catering accommodation in beautiful surroundings, including some caravans. Holiday club ownership scheme. Baits on sale -Fishing included

Marshalls Lake

Location: Fulston, near Louth - enquire locally
Type and Size: Small farm pond
Carp Stock: Well stocked with carp to upper doubles
Category: Mixed Fishery
Other Species: Roach and rudd
Permits: Day tickets from bailiff on bank
Control: Private
BK Rating: Difficult
E/A: Anglian
Comments: There is no close season in Lincolnshire; night fishing permitted

North Kelsey Park

Location: North Kelsey, between Brigg and Caistor
Type and Size: Small lake
Carp Stock: Well stocked with commons to 18lbs and mirrors to 20lbs
Category: Usual coarse fish
Permits: For day tickets. Tel: 01831 132819
Cost: £3 per day
BK Rating: Moderate

E/A: Anglian
Comments: New water opened in October 1991, so not much known

Oham Lake

Location: Off the A 1104 at Maltby le Marsh
Type and Size: 2 acre lake
Carp Stock: Well stocked with carp to 20lbs
Category: Mixed fishery
Other Species: Crucians, bream, tench, roach and perch
Permits: On site
Control: 01507 450623
Cost: About £5 per day
BK Rating: Not known
E/A: Anglian

Richmond Lake

Location: North Hykeham, near Lincoln. Tel: 01522 681329
Type and Size: Large gravel pit of 80 acres
How to Find: To west of A46 at Richmond Drive near North Hykeham
Carp Stock: Plenty of doubles 23 1/4 lbs
Category: Carp Water
Other Species: Double figure bream, tench and rudd
Permits: On site
Cost: £2.50 per day approx
BK Rating: Easy
Control: Private
Restrictions: No night fishing
E/A: Anglian
Comments: No close season

River Glen

Location: Surfleet, near Boston
Type and Size: Fens type wide river
Carp Stock: Some carp to well over 20lbs; a 20lb mirror was caught in July 1992
Category: Few Carp
Other Species: Most coarse fish; a noted roach water
Permits: Try local tackle shops
Control: Club
BK Rating: Difficult
E/A: Anglian
Comments: There is said to be a shoal of carp which includes a number of twenties

River Witham

Location: Bardney area
Type and Size: Large 'fen drain' type river, noted for its match fishing
Carp Stock: Not many, but a record for the river was caught on maggots and light tackle in 1990 - it was a 23 1/2 lb mirror
Category: Few Carp
Other Species: Bream and most other coarse fish, including zander
Permits: Lincoln and District AA - enquire locally or in Lincoln
Control: Club
BK Rating: Very Difficult
E/A: Anglian

Rossways Water A

Location: 189 London Road, Wyberton, Boston. Tel: 01205 361643
Type and Size: One acre clay pit
How to Find: Main A16 road Boston to Spalding. 1 mile from Boston
Carp Stock: Well stocked with carp to 25 1/2 lbs
Category: Mixed Fishery
Other Species: Perch, roach, rudd, tench, bream
Permits: On site - day tickets by prior arrangement only
Cost: Approx £2.50 per rod; £4 for 2 rods
BK Rating: Very Difficult
Control: Private. Tel: 01205 361643
Restrictions: No nuts; no sacking, no groundbait; no particles
E/A: Anglian
Comments: Rod licences sold on premises. Night fishing by arrangement. Cafeteria, toilets, showers. Tackle and bait for sale. Attractive tree - lined pond. Possibly one fish of around 30lbs. Depth of 10-14 feet. Numbers limited, caravans on site for holiday stays. Open all year

South Holland Drain

Location: The B 1168 road near Holbeach St. Johns crosses the drain
Type and Size: Narrow Fenland drain
Carp Stock: Some carp to 30 lbs
Category: Few Carp
Other Species: Bream, tench, roach, pike and perch
Permits: In advance only from Ged's Tackle, Holbeach
Cost: About £4 per day; £10 per season
Control: Holbeach A/C. Tel: 01406 422020
Restrictions: No night fishing
BK Rating: Very Difficult
E/A: Anglian

Sudbrooke Pond

Location: Rookery Lane, Ancaster, near Sleaford
Type and Size: 2 acre pond with island
Carp Stock: Some doubles to 20 lbs
Category: Mixed Fishery
Other Species: Tench, roach and perch
Permits: On bank
Cost: £3 per day
Control: Tel: 01400 230388
Restrictions: No night fishing; barbless hooks
BK Rating: Not known
E/A: Anglian
Comments: Probably open all year

Swan Lake Leisure Park A

Location: Culvert Road, Thorpe Culvert, Skegness. Tel: 01754 881456
Type and Size: Two and a half acre caravan park lake
How to Find: Take the A52 from Skegness to Wainfleet. At Wainfleet, turn right onto the B1195 towards Spilsby. After about 1 1/2 miles, turn left down a lane and left again at the first crossroads
Carp Stock: Well stocked with carp, water record 26lbs
Category: Mixed Fishery
Other Species: Tench, roach and rudd
Permits: Weekly or daily, for site residents only

Cost: £3 per rod per day. £10 weekly per rod. £5 per week per rod for children from 12 to 16
BK Rating: Moderate
Control: Leisure Park
Restrictions: No night fishing. No groundbait. No floating baits
E/A: Anglian
Comments: The park is 7 acres in size with plenty of wildlife, and is only 5 miles from Skegness. There is a launderette and 4 caravans sleeping 7 or 8, and a four bedroomed cottage. No close season. Brochure from Mrs Caton

Sycamore Lake Carp Fishery A

Location: Willow Lodge, Willow Lakes, Newark Road, Foston, Granthm NG32 2LF. Tel: 01400 82190
Type and Size: Small and quite new, man-made lake of about three quarters of an acre and up to seven feet deep.
How to Find: Half a mile off the A1 between Newark and Grantham, and just outside the small village of Foston
Carp Stock: Well stocked with mirrors and commons between 2lbs and 12lbs
Category: Carp Only
Permits: On site
Cost: £4 per day, £3 for evening, to include two other lakes on site. Reductions for juniors and OAP's, and half price for those staying in the caravans on site
Control: Private
Restrictions: Barbless hooks; no keepnets or carp sacks. All nets to be disinfected at start
BK Rating: Easy
E/A: Anglian
Comments: Good fun fishery on pleasant site. Separate car park for day ticket anglers. 6 caravans to rent on site, with bait and tackle for sale, and usual caravan site facilities, ideal for a family holiday. No close season

Sycamore Lakes

Location: Burgh-le-Marsh, off the A158 road from Skegness
Type and Size: Three small clay pits
Carp Stock: All three are well stocked with carp to over 30lbs
Category: Mixed Fishery
Other Species: Tench, rudd, roach, golden orfe and perch
Permits: Day tickets on site
Cost: £4 or £5 for two rods. Reduced rates juniors, OAP's and the disabled
Control: Joy or Jose Giraldez on 01754 811411
Restrictions: No night fishing; 6am till dusk; no carp to be put in keepnets; all particle baits banned, except for sweetcorn
BK Rating: Moderate
E/A: Yorkshire
Comments: No close season; toilets, cafe and camping

Tattershall Park

Location: Tattershall Park Country Club, off the A153 between Sleaford and Skegness; near Tattershall Castle
Type and Size: Five acre estate lake
Carp Stock: Well stocked with carp to doubles
Category: Mixed Fishery
Other Species: Rudd and other coarse fish
Permits: Day tickets from the shop on site. Includes several other lakes and

	the River Bain
Control:	Tel: 01526 43162
BK Rating:	Moderate
E/A:	Anglian
Comments:	There are over 350 acres of water in ths country park, with big bream and pike in the other lakes. No close season

Tetford Country Cottages A

Location:	East Road, Tetford, near Salmonby, off the A158 from Skegness
Type and Size:	Two and a half acre lake with islands
Carp Stock:	Carp to 24lbs
Category:	Mixed Fishery
Other Species:	Tench, perch, roach and rudd
Permits:	On bank, or from the owners, Peg and Tony Buckman, Manor Farm, East Road, Tetford, near Horncastle LN9 6QQ. Tel: 01507 533276
Cost:	Day tickets £3; £4 for 2 rods
Restrictions:	Barbless hooks, not bigger than size 10. No keepnets at present as the water was very low in the summer of 1992. No nuts. No dogs
BK Rating:	Not known
E/A:	Anglian
Comments:	Open all year. Self-catering cottages. Toilet. Food

Trent Backwater

Location:	Off the A156 road between Gainsborough and Lincoln, at Fosdyke, near Torksey
Type and Size:	Arm of the River Trent, which is tidal
Carp Stock:	Not many, but possibly some large fish
Category:	Few Carp
Other Species:	Pike, roach, bream and eels
Permits:	£2 per day on bank
Control:	Workshop and District AA
Restrictions:	No night fishing
BK Rating:	Difficult
E/A:	Severn-Trent

Wagtail Lodge A

Location:	Off the A 1 at Marston, near Grantham
Type and Size:	Several good sized lakes
Carp Stock:	Well stocked with doubles
Category:	Carp Only (one of the lakes)
Other Species:	None in carp lake, but in others there are:- tench, orfe, rudd, barbel, catfish, bream, dace, chub, roach and crucians
Permits:	On bank
Cost:	£6 per day for carp lake; £4 mixed fishing; £3 juniors and O.A.P's
Control:	Tel: 01400 250720
Restrictions:	No boilies or groundbait
BK Rating:	Moderate
E/A:	Anglian
Comments:	Probably open all year. Self catering holiday chalets

West Ashby Lakes

Location:	West Ashby, near Horncastle
Type and Size:	Two gravel pits of five and two acres
How to Find:	On A153 just north of Horncastle
Carp Stock:	Many doubles up to 25lbs. Average 11lbs

Category: Carp Water
Other Species: Tench, chub, roach
Permits: On site - Tel: 01507 600473
BK Rating: Easy
Restrictions: No hair rigs; barbless hooks; no boilies; no particles (what is left?)
Control: Private
E/A: Anglian

Whisby Fishery

Location: Off the A46, south west of Lincoln
Type and Size: Two adjacent lakes of two acres and three acres
Carp Stock: Well stocked with doubles to over 20lbs
Category: Mixed Fishery
Other Species: Tench, grass carp, crucians, bream, roach and rudd
Permits: On bank
Cost: £3 per day; £2 for juniors, OAP's and the disabled; season tickets £55 and £45
Control: Gary Fasheavrne. Tel: 01522 682208
Restrictions: Night fishing by arrangement only - normally fishing is 7am until 9pm
BK Rating: Moderate
E/A: Anglian
Comments: Good access for the disabled; toilets, cafe and garden centre. No close season

Willow Lakes A

Location: Willow Lakes, Newark Road, Foston, Grantham NG32 2LF.Tel: 01400 82190
Type and Size: Three small lakes - Poplar is one and a quarter acres; Willow is one acre
Carp Stock: Some crucians and other species in Poplar; Willow stocked with 2,500 small mirrors and commons in 1990; Sycamore - carp to 14lbs
Category: Mixed Fisheries
Other Species: Tench, rudd, bream, roach, chub, perch
Permits: Day tickets on site
Cost: £3 per day; £2 for the evening. Reduced price for juniors and OAP's, and half price tickets for those renting the caravans on site
Control: Private
BK Rating: Easy
Restrictions: Barbless hooks; all nets to be disinfected at start
E/A: Anglian
Comments: There are 6 large caravans close to the lakes for rent, at prices ranging from £65 to £113 a week. They all have mains services and modern equipment, and are available from the middle of March until the end of October. The lakes are reed-fringed and attractive, and there is a further small carp fishery on the site (see separate entry). Tackle and bait available on site. No close season.

Woodlands Fishery

Location: Ashby Road, Spilsby, off the A115 Skegness road
Type and Size: Two very small man-made ponds
Carp Stock: Some small carp
Category: Mixed Fishery
Other Species: Crucians, tench, rudd, roach, perch and gudgeon
Permits: On site at £2 per day; evening tickets in the summer at £1.50
Control: Marie or Chris Sibley. Tel: 01790 54252
Restrictions: No night fishing
BK Rating: Not known
E/A: Anglian

Woodland Waters

Location: Off the A 153 between Peterborough and Ancaster
Type and Size: 20 acre lake, very deep in places
Carp Stock: Carp to upper twenties
Category: Mixed Fishery
Other Species: Big pike, perch bream, tench and roach
Permits: On bank
Cost: £4.50 per day; concessions £3. Season tickets
Control: Tel; 01400 230888
Restrictions: No nuts or hemp
BK Rating: Difficult
E/A: Anglian

MERSEYSIDE

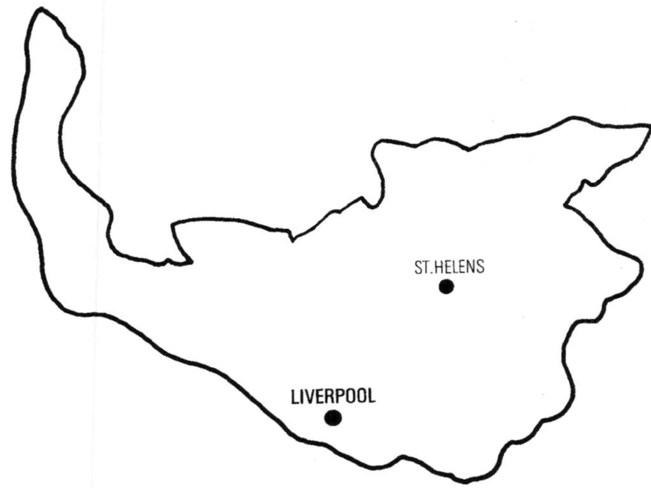

Arrowe Park Lake

Location: Arrowe Brooke Road, Birkenhead
Type and Size: 2 acre park lake
Carp Stock: Some carp to doubles
Category: Few Carp
Other Species: Tench, roach and bream
Permits: From the club
Cost: About £10 per season
Control: Ass. of Wirral Angling Clubs. Tel: 0151 334 3174
Restrictions: No night fishing
BK Rating: Difficult
E/A: North West

Barnacre Lake

Location: Barnacre Lane, Upton, near Birkenhead
Type and Size: Small lake
Carp Stock: Well stocked with carp to nearly 20 lbs
Category: Mixed Fishery
Other Species: Bream, crucians, tench, chub and barbel
Permits: On bank
Cost: About £5. Reductions for evenings
Control: Tel: 0151 677 1411
Restrictions: No night fishing; no keepnets; barbless hooks
BK Rating: Not known
E/A: North West

Burton Mere (b)

Location: Burton Manor, between Chester and Heswell (in the Wirral)
Type and Size: Four lakes
How to Find: 9 miles north west of Chester off the A540 road
Carp Stock: Heavily stocked with carp to 36lbs
Other Species: Perch, rudd, roach and tench
Permits: Tel: 0151 3530115
Cost: About £5 per day; syndicate
Control: Private
BK Rating: Easy
E/A: Welsh
Comments: Fomer home of Victorian Prime Minister Gladstone - his ghost must haunt the grounds! Mere averages 5 feet in depth. Float fishing close to the bank works well. Trout lake on site

Church Street Canal

Location: Church Street, St Helens
Type and Size: Industrial area canal; stretch of about 400 yards
How to Find: St Helens is north east of Liverpool
Carp Stock: Quite well stocked with carp to over 20lbs
Category: Mixed Fishery
Other Species: Roach, bream, perch and gudgeon
Permits: St Helens Angling Associaton. Details on bank or from local tackle shops. J Corkish, 65 Laffak Road, Carr Hill, St Helens WA11 9EH
Control: Club Tel: 01744 51046
BK Rating: Moderate
E/A: North West
Comments: There is a warm water outlet from a factory on this stretch and it has become very popular in the winter, when the water is warm enough to paddle in and other local waters are frozen. The canal gets very busy at this time. Plenty of matches but some good carp for pleasure anglers, and well worth a try - if you can get a place to fish - in icy conditons

Mellors Pool

Location: Whiston, near Liverpool
Type and Size: Small man-made lake with an island
How to Find: From junction 6 of the M 62 take Windy Arbor Road. Park opposite the garden centre
Carp Stock: Quite well stocked with carp averaging about 5 lbs
Category: Mixed Fishery
Other Species: Roach, perch, tench and crucians
Permits: On bank
Cost: £2 per day; juniors £1. £10 per season
Control: Whiston Village A.C. Tel: 0151 480 7917
Restrictions: No boilies or cereal groundbait
BK Rating: Not known
Baits/Methods: Bread good for carp
E/A: North West
Comments: Open all year

Mill Dam

Location: Near Kirkby, Liverpool
Type and Size: Small lake, recently cleared out and restocked
Carp Stock: Some carp, numbers and sizes not known
Category: Mixed Fishery

Other Species: Tench, roach, perch, and (they say) one pike!
Permits: From bailiff on bank
Cost: £7 adults; £3.50 juniors
Control: Kirkby Junior AC - community hall on banks of lake
BK Rating: Not known
E/A: North West

Newsham Park Lake

Location: Newsham Park, Tuebrook, Liverpool
Type and Size: Ancient odd-shaped park lake, about three acres
Carp Stock: Mixed Fishery
Other Species: Tench, roach and perch
Permits: None necessary - all fishing on the many Liverpool park lakes is free
Control: Liverpool City Council
BK Rating: Easy
E/A: North West
Comments: This lake was de-silted and restocked with over 50,000 fish in 1991. Platforms have been built for disabled anglers

Overflow

Location: Bidston Docks, Birkenhead (Wirral)
Type and Size: Formerly a six acre dry dock (now freshwater)
How to Find: Take the A553 from Birkenhead to St James's Church. Turn right, then first left to Bidston Incinerator, take next entrance and follow dockside - Overflow is the furthest water
Carp Stock: Carp to 10lbs+
Other Species: Big perch (3 - 4lbs) and eels of 4-6lbs
Permits: Free
Cost: Nothing
BK Rating: Moderate
Control: Docks/British Rail
E/A: North West
Comments: Carp caught on snaggy tip side - beware sunken cars. Maggots and worm work well on light tackle. Dock is 30 feet deep: we now have a stream and a Dock in our guide!

Peak Forest Canal

Location: Marple area (Greater Manchester)
Type and Size: Short, narrow canal
Carp Stock: Some carp, mainly in lock pools at Marple
Category: Mixed Fishery
Other Species: Tench and general coarse fish
Permits: Try local shops or County Palatine AA
Control: Club
BK Rating: Not known
E/A: North West

Sefton Park Lake

Location: A park in Liverpool
Type and Size: Four acre park lake, very busy and public
Carp Stock: Quite well stocked with small carp
Others Species: Tench, roach, crucians and perch
Permits: None necessary - free fishing and in other park lakes containing carp in Liverpool
Control: Liverpool City Council

BK Rating: Easy
E/A: North West
Comments: No close season

Whiston Mellors Lake

Location: Whiston, near St. Helens
Type and Size: 3 acre lake
How to Find: Opposite St. Michael's Church, Whiston
Carp Stock: Well stocked with carp to doubles
Category: Mixed Fishery
Other Species: Tench, roach, perch and bream
Permits: On bank
Cost: £2 per day
Control: Whiston Village A.C. Tel: Chris Mills, 0151 480717
Restrictions: No groundbait
BK Rating: Not known
E/A: North West

NORFOLK

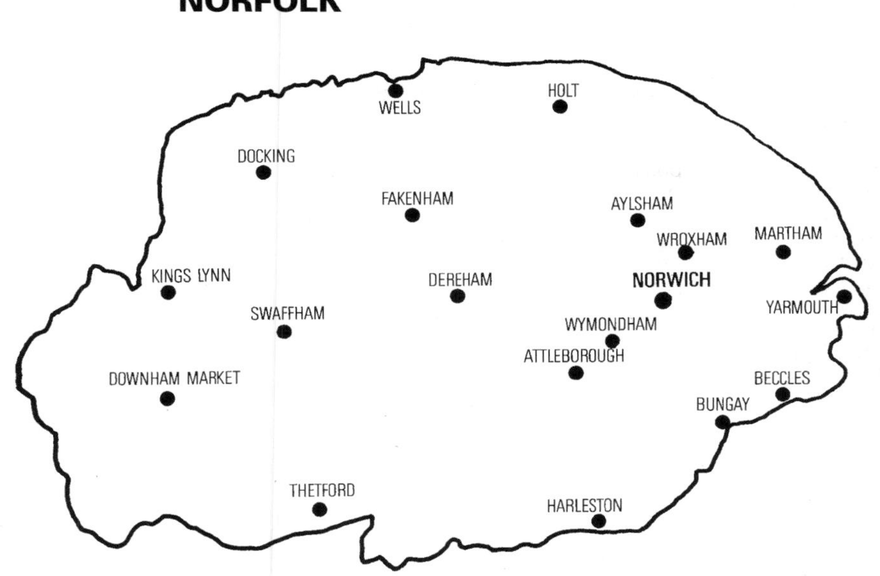

Aldeby Hall Farm Pits

Location: Aldeby Hall Farm, near Aldeby, Beccles
Type and Size: Four small pits
How to Find: Take the A146 from Norwich, and just before Beccles turn left to Aldeby. A mile after the village, find a track on the right going through a fruit farm, which is actually an old railway track; the pits are on the left in half a mile
Carp Stock: Some mirrors to 20lbs
Category: Mixed Fishery
Other Species: Crucians, bream, tench, rudd and roach
Permits: From bailiff on bank (day tickets), at £3
BK Rating: Easy
Control: Private
E/A: Anglian
Comments: The two pits on the left hold the carp; the others are mainly crucians with some rudd

Bartles Lodge — A

Location: Near the Mermaid pub, Elsing, near Norwich
Type and Size: One acre lake
Carp Stock: Carp to doubles
Category: Mixed Fishery
Other Species: Roach, rudd and tench
Permits: From the house opposite the church
Cost: About £5 per day
Control: Tel: 01362 637177
BK Rating: Not known
E/A: Anglian
Comments: Accommodation, bar and refreshments. Toilet

Bawburgh Lake

Location: Lodge Farm, Chapel Break Road, near Norwich
Type and Size: 20 acre gravel pit
Carp Stock: Well stocked with carp to doubles
Category: Mixed Fishery
Other Species: Pike, tench, chub, roach and bream
Permits: Tom Boulton's Tackle, Norwich
Cost: About £15 per season
Control: Great Yarmouth D.A.A. Tel: 01603 426834
BK Rating: Not known
E/A: Anglian
Comments: Fishing on the tiny River Yare included

Bedingham Pit

Location: Woodton, just off the B1332 between Bungay and Norwich
Type and Size: Five acre gravel pit
Carp Stock: Well stocked with quite a few doubles, and a number of 20's to nearly 30lbs
Category: Carp Water
Permits: This is a syndicate water, with informaton hard to obtain, but try local tackle shops in Norwich, Beccles and Bungay
Cost: Well over £100 per season
Control: Private
BK Rating: Moderate
E/A: Anglian
Comments: It may be possible to get details of how to obtain membership in the village of Woodton. This is a very good carp water and it would be worth some trouble to get into

Beeston Lake

Location: Neatishead, near Wroxham
Type and Size: Shallow three acre Broadland-type lake, with very clear water
How to Find: Take the A1151 from Norwich, and about a mile past Wroxham, turn right on the Neatishead road. Turn left at the Post Office, and the lake is 300 yards on the right
Carp Stock: Not many carp to low doubles
Category: Few Carp
Other Species: Very big tench and bream (the former British record bream of 13lb 9oz came from here), roach, rudd, eels and pike
Permits: Day tickets in advance only from the bailiff, A Jeckells. Tel: 01692 630688
Cost: £2; Only five tickets issued per day
Control: Private
BK Rating: Very Difficult
E/A: Anglian

Billingford Pit

Location: Billingford, near Swanton Morley
Type and Size: Three acre pit
How to Find: Take the A1067 from Norwich and turn left to Billingford at Bawdeswell. In the village, turn left towards Swanton Morley, and after 100 yards on the right there is a narrow track leading down to the pit
Carp Stock: A few big carp
Category: Few Carp
Other Species: Roach, perch and pike

Permits: Day tickets in advance only from local tackle shops, or Dereham District AS, Mr S R Allison, Pound Cottage, Cemetery Road, East Dereham. Tel: Dereham 694428. Membership is £10 for the season, to cover other pits and the river
Cost: Day tickets £2
BK Rating: Difficult
Restrictions: No night fishing
Control: Club
E/A: Anglian

Blickling Lake

Location: Blickling Hall, Aylsham
Type and Size: Estate lake of 20 acres
How to Find: Take the A140 from Norwich to Aylsham. Go through the town and take the Blickling road. Bear right, and this road leads to the car park at the northern end of the lake
Carp Stock: Well stocked with carp to double figures
Category: Mixed Fishery
Other Species: Famous for its big bream, also tench, roach and big pike
Permits: Day tickets from bailiff on the bank. Some season tickets from Mr B Cooper, Tel: 01263 734181
Cost: Day tickets £4
BK Rating: Moderate
E/A: Anglian
Comments: In the grounds of a famous stately home, this beautiful lake holds some fine fish. Barbless hooks; no night fishing; no keepnets

Booton Clay Pit

Location: Near the village of Booton, near Norwich
Type and Size: Clay pit of about four acres
How to Find: Take the Reepham road from Norwich and just before Reepham turn right towards Haveringland and Buxton. After a mile and a half you will find the pit on the left behind some trees.
Carp Stock: Only very few carp, but they are large. Two 30's were reported from this pit in 1984, but it is not known if these were genuine weights
Category: Few Carp
Other Species: Tench, roach, rudd, pike and bream
Permits: Day and season tickets from the bailiff on the bank
Cost: £3 per rod per day
Control: Private
BK Rating: Difficult
E/A: Anglian
Comments: An attractive lake, quite deep, with reeds and sandbars

Bradmoor Lakes

Location: Narborough, near Swaffham
Type and Size: Two gravel pits, one of two acres and the other five acres
How to Find: From Norwich take the A47 to Narborough. Beyond East Dereham and Swaffham, after two bridges over the River Nar, take lane on the right. The lakes will be seen on the left
Carp Stock: Very heavily stocked with mirrors to double figures. The crucian carp record was caught here
Category: Carp Water
Other Species: Crucians, bream, tench, roach and rudd
Permits: Membership of Swaffham Angling Club is necessary to fish this water - no day tickets. The Secretary, 30 Kings Street, Swaffham

Cost: Approx £16 per season
Control: Club
BK Rating: Easy to Moderate
E/A: Anglian
Comments: Very pleasant water, details of rules etc. from the Club Secretary. No particle baits

Bramley Lake

Location: Horsford, near Norwich
Type and Size: 12 acre lake
How to Find: Turn left at Horsford off the B1149 Norwich - Holt road. The fishery is in Dog Lane after a mile
Carp Stock: Well stocked with small carp to 5lbs
Category: Mixed Fishery
Other Species: Crucians, roach and rudd
Permits: From site office
Cost: £3.50 per day; juniors £2.50
Control: Private. Tel: 01603 409792
Restrictions: No boilies or cereal groundbait
BK Rating: Easy
E/A: Anglian
Comments: Other lakeside activities

Bridge Lake

Location: Lenwade, near Norwich
Type and Size: Two gravel pits
Carp Stock: Some carp, sizes not known
Category: Probably Few Carp
Other Species: Roach, rudd, bream, tench and pike
Permits: Limited annual permits from The City of Norwich AC, Mr Tom Boulton. Tel: 01603 426834. Waiting list
Control: Club
Restrictions: Please note that this is a syndicate water, although controlled by the Norwich Club - waiting list for syndicate membership
BK Rating: Not known
E/A: Anglian

Bure Valley Fishery

Location: Bure Valley Trout Lakes, four miles from Aylsham off the B1354 to Saxthorpe
Type and Size: Three acre gravel pit
Carp Stock: Quite well stocked with mirrors to over 20lbs
Category: Mixed Fishery
Other Species: Roach, perch, rudd and tench
Permits: In advance only, with booking essential, from David Green Tel: 01263 87666
Cost: £5 per 12 hour day session
BK Rating: Moderate
Control: Private
E/A: Anglian

Chapel Road Lake

Location: Chapel Road, Roughton, near Cromer
Type and Size: 1½ acre lake with islands
Carp Stock: Well stocked with carp to 20 lbs

Category: Mixed Fishery
Other Species: Tench, roach and perch
Permits: On bank
Cost: About £3 per day
Control: Tel: 01263 761369
BK Rating: Moderate
E/A: Anglian

Charity Lakes

Location: Common Lane, Great Witchingham, near Fakenham
Type and Size: Three gravel pits - 12 acres of water
Carp Stock: Well stocked with carp to 20 lbs
Category: Mixed Fishery
Other Species: Pike, bream, roach and tench
Permits: On bank
Cost: About £4 per day; £7 per night; £50 per season. Concessions
Control: Parish Council. Tel: 01603 872286
BK Rating: Not known
E/A: Anglian
Comments: Small lake best for carp. Disabled access

Chiswick Pit

Location: Farm near the village of Stow Bardolph
Type and Size: Small farm pond
How to Find: A47 from Norwich, then the A1122 to Stradsett. Turn right onto the A134 towards Kings Lynn. At Shouldham Thorpe turn left and a mile further on take a farm track on the left. The pond is on the left opposite the farmhouse
Carp Stock: Numbers not known but said to contain a reasonable number of mirrors and commons to double figures
Category: Mixed Fishery
Other Species: Rudd and tench
Permits: Day tickets must be obtained in advance from Stow Estates Office, Stow Bardolph. Tel: 01366 383194
Cost: Approx £2 per day
Restrictions: No night fishing - dawn to dusk only. Only three permits per day are issued
BK Rating: Moderate
E/A: Anglian

Cobbleacre Lake

Location: Off the A140 Norwich to Cromer road, nine miles north west of Norwich
Type and Size: Three and a half acre gravel pit with two islands, up to 18 feet deep in places
Carp Stock: Well stocked with mirrors and commons to 28lbs
Category: Mixed Fishery
Other Species: Bream to over 10lbs, roach, rudd, tench and perch
Permits: Day tickets on bank
Control: Private: Tel: 01603 754305
Cost: About £5 per day; £3 from 5pm till dusk; £8 for 24 hours
Restrictions: Night fishing by arrangement only. Barbless hooks
BK Rating: Moderate
E/A: Anglian
Comments: Toilet

Common Lakes

Location: Common Lane, Lenwade, off the A1067 Norwich - Fakenham road
Type and Size: Three gravel pits between two and five acres
Carp Stock: Some commons and mirrors, sizes not known
Category: Possibly Few Carp
Other Species: Roach, rudd, tench, perch, pike and bream
Permits: From bailiff on bank
Cost: £3 per day
BK Rating: Not known
Control: Great Witchingham Fuel Allotment Charity
E/A: Anglian
Restrictions: No night fishing - dawn to dusk only

Cranworth - Woodrising Carp Lake

Location: Near - Jubilee Farm, Cranworth, Dereham
Type and Size: Man-made farm pond of about an acre
How to Find: From Norwich take B1108 road to Watton. After Hingham take road on the right to Shipden. Follow the signs to Cranworth, and the lake is just after Jubilee Farm in the village

Carp Stock: Well stocked with commons and mirrors, mainly small but up to double figures
Category: Carp Water
Other Species: A few tench
Permits: Day tickets from Mr Bunning at Jubilee Farm
Baits/Methods: Normal carp fishing baits and methods
Control: Private Tel: 01362 820702
BK Rating: Easy
E/A: Anglian
Comments: Quite shallow, coloured lake, long and narrow

Denver Pit

Location: Sandy Lane, Denver, near Downham Market (not Denver, Colorado USA!)
Type and Size: One and a half acre gravel pit, with two islands and some weed
Category: Few Carp
Other Species: Catfish, tench, bream, roach, rudd and perch
Permits: In advance only from Bob Riches, 15 Sandy Lane, Denver
Cost: £3 per day; £4 for two rods
BK Rating: Difficult
E/A: Anglian
Comments: The wels are said to go about 7lbs, but there are reputed to be two other catfish varieties in the lake

Docking Village Pond

Location: Village of Docking near Fakenham
Type and Size: Clay pit of about an acre
How to Find: Take the A1067 from Norwich, and Docking is after Fakenham (A148-B1454)
Carp Stock: Quite well stocked with small commons up to 8lbs
Category: Mixed Fishery
Other Species: Crucian carp, roach and tench
Permits: From Roys Shop, close to pond. Day tickets must be bought on the same day
Cost: Approx £2 per day
Restrictions: Fishing 8.30am to 11pm only. No Sunday fishing. Eight tickets only issued each day

Baits/Methods: Normal baits and methods
Control: Private
BK Rating: Easy
E/A: Anglian
Comments: The commons are said to be wild carp, although with crucians present hybrids must be expected

Felmingham Mill Lake

Location: Felmingham Mill, off the B1145 road near Aylsham, about a mile from the village
Type and Size: Two small lakes
Carp Stock: Some double figure mirrors
Category: Few Carp
Other Species: Roach, perch, crucians, rudd and tench
Permits: Day tickets must be obtained before fishing from M Moore at the Mill House near the water. (Tel: Aylsham 735106). Tickets include fishing in the little Mill Stream for roach, trout, pike and a few grayling
Cost: £2 per day; £1 for children
BK Rating: Not known
E/A: Anglian
Comments: No night fishing

Felmingham Mill Lakes

Location: Felmingham, near Aylsham
Type and Size: 3 lakes about an acre each
How to Find: Take the A 140 / B 1145 from Aylsham to Felmingham Then turn left down the Mill House road
Carp Stock: Well stocked with carp to doubles
Category: Mixed Fishery
Other Species: Tench, perch, roach, rudd and bream
Permits: From the house
Cost: £3 per day; £1.50 juniors
Control: Private. Tel: 01263 735106
Restrictions: No boilies. No fish over 4 lb in keepnets
BK Rating: Not known
E/A: Anglian
Comments: Short stretch of the King's Beck stream included - roach, grayling, dace and brown trout

Felthorpe Lakes

Location: Brick Kiln Road, Felthorpe, near Norwich
Type and Size: Two pools of 3 acres and one acre
How to Find: Take the B 1149 from Norwich to Holt. After Horsford turn right into Brick Kiln Road
Carp Stock: Well stocked with upper singles and lower doubles
Category: Mixed Fishery
Other Species: Grass carp, crucians, tench, perch, roach, rudd and bream
Permits: In advance from Pond House, near the entrance to the fishery
Cost: £5 per day; £2.50 for juniors
Control: Tel: 01603 754408
BK Rating: Not known
E/A: Anglian

Fosters End Pits

Location: East Winch, near Kings Lynn - the pits are one mile down a track by the church
Type and Size: Eight acre pit and three tiny ponds
Carp Stock: Carp to double figures
Category: Few Carp
Other Species: Pike to over 20lbs, roach, rudd and crucians
Permits: Members only water of the Kings Lynn AA. Membership costs £12. Details from the Secretary
Control: Club
Restrictions: Members only
BK Rating: Not known
E/A: Anglian

Geens Pit

Location: Shropham, near Snetterton
Type and Size: Old pit of about one acre, shallow and wooded along one bank
Carp Stock: There are said to be only a few carp, but these are very large. A 34 pounder was reported in 1984, and since this is recorded as the lake record, it could well be genuine although we cannot be sure about this
Category: Few Carp
Other Species: Roach, rudd, tench and bream
Permits: Advance booking by telephone only to the owner,Mr Geen, Tel: Caston 735. Day tickets. Cost not known
Control: Private
BK Rating: Difficult
E/A: Anglian
Comments: We have listed a few waters of this kind, where very large carp have been reported caught. We cannot guarantee that these weights quoted are genuine, especially as all carp anglers know that the weights of many fish reported are exaggerated. If we can prove conclusively that any weights are genuine we will say so

Gimmingham Lakes

Location: Off the B 1145 Norwich to Mundesley road, near the mill at Gimmingham, North Walsham
Type and Size: Three small lakes, largest 3 acres
Carp Stock: Some carp to upper twenties
Category: Mixed Fishery
Other Species: Tench, rudd, roach, bream, perch and crucians
Permits: On bank
Cost: £2 per day; £3 for two rods; juniors £1
Control: Tel: 01263 720432
Restrictions: No boilies, trout pellets or cereal groundbait
BK Rating: Moderate
E/A: Anglian
Comments: Toilet

Glen's Pit

Location: Caston, Shropham, near Attleborough
Type and Size: One acre pit, quite deep in places
How to Find: Caston is just off the B1077 road between Attleborough and Watton. The pit is on the left hand side going into the village from the Attleborough side
Carp Stock: Quite well stocked with about 40 carp, most of which are doubles,

	with some bigger fish to about 34lbs
Category:	Mixed Fishery
Other Species:	Roach, rudd, perch, bream and eels
Permits:	Syndicate - information from J Green on 0195 3735
Control:	Private
BK Rating:	Very Difficult
E/A:	Anglian

Granary Lakes A

Location:	Granary Hotel, Little Dunham, near Dereham
Type and Size:	Three small interconnected long narrow lakes, plus a one acre lake near the hotel
How to Find:	Take the A47 Norwich - Dereham road, and 8 miles from Dereham turn right towards Little Dunham. Turn left, then right in village to the Granary Hotel
Carp Stock:	Carp to 20lbs in all lakes
Category:	Mixed Fishery
Other Species:	Crucians and tench
Permits:	Day tickets from hotel. Tel: 01328 701310. In advance only
Cost:	Approx £3 a rod - on bank for the three lake complex
BK Rating:	Moderate
Control:	Private
E/A:	Anglian
Comments:	Hotel accommodation with restaurant, swimming, golf, tennis as well as fishing

Great Massingham Village Pond

Location:	Great Massingham, between Norwich and Fakenham
How to Find:	Take A1067 Fakenham road from Norwich and then B1145 from it at Bawdeswell. Go through Litcham and after six miles take the road to Great Massingham. The pond is in the middle of the village
Carp Stock:	Well stocked with small commons
Category:	Carp Only
Permits:	From Post Office
BK Rating:	Easy
E/A:	Anglian
Comments:	These fish are said locally to be wild carp, but readers should note that there are very few wildies. John Wilson has confirmed that these are true wildies. No night fishing or fishing on Sundays. 2 anglers per day only

Great Melton Reservoir A

Location:	Lombe Estate, Hall Farm, Great Melton, Norwich NR9 3BW, 6 miles from Wymondham
Type and Size:	Five acre estate lake constructed 16 years ago, alongside a Nature Reserve
Carp Stock:	Well stocked with commons to about 10lbs
Category:	Carp Water
Other Species:	Possibly some brown trout, as it was a trout fishery until 3 years ago
Permits:	David Gregory, The Estate Office, address above. Tel: 01603 810135. These are confined to those who book holiday accommodation on the estate
Control:	Private
Restrictions:	No pets; some areas out of bounds to protect wildlife. Some fishing allowed from punts
BK Rating:	Not known, but probably Easy
E/A:	Anglian

Comments: Three cottages are to rent for self-catering holidays on this attractive estate, with fishing on two carp lakes, and the River Yare at Marlingford. Prices from about £200 per week, fishing included

Gunthorpe Hall Lake

Location: Gunthorpe Hall, Gunthorpe, near Melton Constable
Type and Size: Two acre estate lake
Carp Stock: Some common carp to double figures
Category: Few Carp
Other Species: Roach, rudd, perch, pike and tench
Permits: Day tickets by prior booking only from the Hall. Tel: 01263 861373. Only 7 tickets per day issued
Cost: £2 per day
BK Rating: Not known
Control: Private
Restrictions: No night fishing - dawn till dusk only. No Sunday fishing
E/A: Anglian

Hall Farm Pit

Location: Hall Farm, Burgh Castle opposite Burgh Hall on the road from Yarmouth
Type and Size: Half acre pit
Carp Stock: Well stocked with mirrors to double figures
Category: Mixed Fishery
Other Species: Crucians, roach, rudd and tench
Permits: Day tickets from the farm at the top of the field before fishing
Cost: £2 per day
Control: Private
BK Rating: Not known
E/A: Anglian

Haveringland Lake

Location: Haveringland, near Norwich
Type and Size: 14 acre dammed, shallow lake
Carp Stock: Carp to double figures
Category: Mixed Fishery
Other Species: Rudd, roach, bream, tench, and pike
Permits: Mr K Rustige. Tel: 01603 871302
Control: Private. Please note that you can only fish this water if you park a touring caravan on the park by the water
Restrictions: No fishing except for those with touring caravans on site
BK Rating: Not known
E/A: Anglian

Hevingham Lakes — A

Location: Hevingham, 8 miles north of Norwich
Type and Size: Man-made lakes of which there are two, both quite small
How to Find: From Norwich take B1149 towards Holt. About six miles fro Norwich take the second right marked 'Hevingham'. The fishery entrance is on the left about a mile further on
Carp Stock: Well stocked with carp, many of which are small but there are some doubles and also a few over 20lbs
Category: Mixed Fishery
Other Species: Crucians, roach, rudd, tench and bream
Permits: Day tickets in advance only from the owner who lives in the bungalow at the entrance of the fishery - Mr J C Matthewson Tel: 01603 754368

Cost: Free to those who stay. Otherwise £3; £5 for 2 rods
Baits/Methods: Normal carp fishing baits and methods
Control: Private
BK Rating: Moderate
E/A: Anglian
Comments: You can holiday here as the owner lets caravans to anglers. There are toilet and shower facilities. Touring caravans and tents are welcome and there is also a farmhouse to let. Prices according to season. No groundbait or keepnets

Highfield Fisheries

Location: Thorpe Abbots, off the A 413 Norwich to Lowestoft road
Type and Size: Two lakes of 3 acres and 1 acre
Carp Stock: Well stocked with carp to 20 lbs
Category: Mixed Fishery
Other Species: Tench, bream, roach, rudd, perch, crucians and gudgeon
Permits: On bank
Cost: £3.50 per day; £2 juniors and O.A.P's
Control: Tel: 01986 874869
Restrictions: No peanuts
BK Rating: Moderate
E/A: Anglian

Hilgay Lakes

Location: Hilgay, near Downham Market
Type and Size: Two lakes of 7 acres and half an acre
Carp Stock: Small carp
Category: Mixed Fishery
Other Species: Tench, crucians, roach and rudd
Permits: On bank
Cost: £3 per day; £2 juniors and O.A.P's
Control: Tel: 01366 385676
Restrictions: No boilies; no cereal groundbaits; no night fishing; barbless hooks
BK Rating: Not known
E/A: Anglian
Comments: Toilet

Holkham Hall Lake

Location: Off the A149 near Wells-next-the-Sea
Type and Size: 15 acre estate lake in the grounds of a big house which is open to the public
Carp Stock: Fairly well stocked, mainly with commons to upper doubles
Category: Mixed Fishery
Other Species: Tench, roach and perch
Permits: Day tickets from the Estate Office
Control: Private Tel: 01328 710227
Restrictions: No night fishing; dawn till dusk only; much of the bank cannot be fished after August 31st. No camping
BK Rating: Moderate
E/A: Anglian

Home Lake

Location: Bure Valley, Aylsham
Type and Size: 3 acre lake
Carp Stock: Said to contain 30 fish of around 20 lbs

Category: Mixed Fishery
Other Species: Roach, perch and eels
Permits: On bank
Cost: £5 per day; £7.50 for two rods. Half price for juniors
Control: Tel: 01263 587666
Restrictions: No nuts; no carp in keepnets
BK Rating: Difficult
Baits/Methods: Boilies are good
E/A: Anglian
Comments: Toilets and shop

Hoveton Hall Lake

Location: Off the A1151 Norwich road near Wroxham
Type and Size: Three acre Broadland lake
Carp Stock: Well stocked with carp from 10lbs to 20lb
Category: Mixed Fishery
Other Species: Roach and tench
Permits: Day tickets on bank
Cost: £2 per day from cottage by lake
BK Rating: Easy
E/A: Anglian
Comments: Ideal water for youngsters

Lakeside Fisheries

Location: Off the B 1146 road at East Bilney, near Dereham
Type and Size: Two lakes of 3 and 2 acres
Carp Stock: Carp to over 20 lbs; smaller (match) lake has thousands of little carp
Category: Mixed Fishery
Other Species: Bream, tench and roach
Permits: From site office
Cost: £5 per day; £3 juniors, O.A.P's and disabled
Control: Private. Tel: 01362 861-15
Restrictions: No boilies, Chum Mixer or cereal groundbait
BK Rating: Easy
E/A: Anglian

Ling Gravel Works

Location: Ling, near Norwich
Type and Size: Large lake
Carp Stock: Some carp to 20 lbs
Category: Mixed Fishery
Other Species: Pike to 40 lbs; bream to about 14 lbs; roach
Permits: Syndicate only
Cost: Enquire from control
Control: Tel: 01603 666861 (day) or 01603 487126 (evenings)
BK Rating: Not known
E/A: Anglian
Comments: Probably open all year. Former trout water.

Little Dunham Carp Lakes

Location: Little Dunham, near Swaffham
Type and Size: Five small ponds in an old railway cutting
How to Find: Take the A 47 from Swaffham towards King`s Lynn. At Necton, turn left before garage. Fishery is one mile on right
Carp Stock: Well stocked with carp to over 20 lbs

Category: Mixed Fishery
Other Species: Tench, rudd, roach and crucians
Permits: On bank
Cost: £3.50 per day, £50 per season
Control: Private. Tel: 01760 725286
Restrictions: No cereal groundbait
BK Rating: Not known
E/A: Anglian

Little Lake Land

Location: Wortwell, Bungay
Carp Stock: Some carp to double figures
Type and Size: Half acre lake, depths to 12ft
Category: Mixed Fishery
Other Species: Roach, perch, bream, tench
Permits: Mr A Hopkins Tel: 019866 46
Control: Private
Restrictions: No fishing except for those who park touring caravans at the lake
BK Rating: Moderate
E/A: Anglian

Little Melton Reservoir A

Location: Marlingford, Wymondham, near Norwich
Type and Size: Two acre estate lake
Carp Stock: Fairly well stocked with carp, sizes not known
Category: Carp Water
Other Species: Some very large brown and rainbow trout, this was previously a trout water
Permits: David Gregory. The Estate Office, Hall Farm, Great Melton, Norwich NR9 3BW. Tel: 01603 810135 - only for those booking the self-catering cottages on the estate
Control: Private
Restrictions: No pets; some areas may be out of bounds to protect wildlife. Some boat fishing allowed
BK Rating: Easy
E/A: Anglian
Comments: There are 3 cottages as holiday rents on this attractive estate with fishing on three lakes and the River Yare included

Lyng Easthaugh Pits

Location: Lyng, near Norwich
Type and Size: Two acre gravel pit
How to Find: Take the A1067 Norwich-Fakenham road, and turn left for Lyng at Lenwade village. Pits on the right in 1½ miles
Carp Stock: Well stocked with carp
Category: Carp Water
Other Species: A few coarse fish
Permits: Season tickets only - Dereham and Dist. A.C. Secretary, S Allinson, Sequenta, Cemetery Road, East Dereham. Tel: 01362 4828; the farm, Lyng, or local tackle dealers
Cost: Approx £10 per year
BK Rating: Easy
Control: Club
Restrictions: Members only
E/A: Anglian
Comments: The ticket includes other pits and river fishing. The big pit alongside may contain a few carp

Marlingford Mere

A

Location: Marlingford, Wymondham, Norwich
Type and Size: Twelve acre gravel pit, landscaped and now a fishery and wildlife reserve
Carp Stock: Well stocked with common carp about six years ago, numbers and sizes not known
Category: Carp Water
Other Species: Probably some
Permits: David Gregory, Estate Office, Hall Farm, Great Melton, Norwich NR9 3BW. Tel: 01603 810135; fishing only available to those booking the holiday cottages on the estate
Control: Private
Restrictions: No pets
BK Rating: Not known
E/A: Anglian
Comments: There are three cottages to rent for holidays on the estate, which is most attractive. Carp fishing on three carp lakes and the River Yare included. No day tickets or other permits

Martham Pits

Location: Close to the ferry on the River Thurne, near Martham village
Type and Size: A number of small, interconnected pits
Carp Stock: Mixed Fishery
Other Species: Well known as a tench fishery; also pike, bream, rudd, roach and eels
Permits: Molly's Sweet Shop, Black Lane, Martham. Tel: 01493 740366. Only 15 issued in advance each day
Cost: £2 per day
Control: Private
BK Rating: Difficult
E/A: Anglian

Mere Farm Pond

Location: Mere Farm, Saxthorpe
Type and Size: One acre farm pond
How to Find: Take the B1149 Holt road from Norwich to Saxthorpe. In village, cross the River Bure and straight across the crossroads. Mere Farm is one mile ahead on the left
Carp Stock: Well stocked with wild carp to 6lbs
Category: Mixed Fishery
Other Species: Roach and eels
Permits: From farmhouse; Tel: 01263 87883
Cost: £2 per day
BK Rating: Easy
E/A: Anglian
Comments: John Wilson tels us these carp are 'wildies' - and there are very few of those left in this country! Most fish which locals call 'wildies' are just long, thin commons

Nunnery Lakes

Location: Thetford
Type and Size: Five 5 gravel pits of 2-5 acres
How to Find: Enquire from local owner
Carp Stock: Well stocked with mirrors
Category: Mixed Fishery
Other Species: Tench, roach, perch, rudd

Permits: Annual syndicate only - apply in close season to Mr Lowndes, Nunnery House, Nunnery Place, Thetford with an SAE
Cost: On application
BK Rating: Moderate
Control: Private
Restrictions: No day tickets
E/A: Anglian

Pentney Carp Lakes

Location: Off the A 47 between Swaffham and King's Lynn
Type and Size: Two lakes of about 9 acres, joined by a channel
Carp Stock: Heavily stocked with many doubles, twenties and thirties
Category: Carp Water
Other Species: Possibly some
Permits: On site
Cost: £10 for 2 rods for 24 hours; £18 weekend; £60 per week
Control: Tel: 01860 841245 or 01284 762031
Restrictions: No peanuts
BK Rating: Moderate
E/A: Anglian
Comments: Specialist carp fishery. Showers / toilets, hot and cold food. Tackle shop. Bait for sale. Bait boats for hire

Railway Pit

Location: 3 miles from Attleborough
Type and Size: Tiny pit of about 1/4 acre
How to Find: Take the A11 from Norwich and 3 miles after Attleborough turn left at Old Buckenham crossroads. Cross the railway line, and the pit is on the left, surrounded by trees
Carp Stock: Some mirror carp, sizes and numbers not known
Category: Probably Few Carp
Other Species: Small tench, roach, perch and pike
Permits: FREE fishing
BK Rating: Not known
E/A: Anglian

Reepham Fisheries

Location: Just outside the village of Reepham, on the left of the road from Norwich
Type and Size: Three acre ex-trout lake
Carp Stock: Carp to over 20lbs
Category: Mixed Fishery
Other Species: Crucian, rudd and tench. There are also some ghost carp, koi and grass carp
Permits: From the bungalow, or on the bank
Cost: £5 per day
Control: Private. Tel: 01603 870829
Baits/Methods: Float and legering methods both work well
Restrictions: No night fishing, except by prior arrangement. Fishing from 6am until 10pm only. No keepnets, and carp to be retained for a few minutes in landing nets only for photographs. Barbless hooks. No boilies
BK Rating: Moderate
E/A: Anglian
Comments: Toilet. Disabled access

Ringland Lakes

Location: Ringland, near Norwich
Type and Size: Seven gravel pits
How to Find: From Norwich take A47 Dereham road and after two miles turn right down Longwater Lane by the Roundwell public house. Turn left at bottom of the hill, then keep left at the fork and a mile further on you will see a track on the right leading to the fishery
Carp Stock: Not a large number of carp but are said to be mostly large - from doubles to 30lbs, in the largest lake. This is called Days Waters and is the first along the track on the left
Category: Few Carp
Other Species: Perch, pike, bream, rudd, crucians and tench
Permits: Day tickets and also season tickets from the bailiff on the bank
Cost: Day tickets: approx £3. Season £24
Control: Leisure Sport Angling Tel: 01603 400730
BK Rating: Moderate
E/A: Anglian

River Wensum

Location: Below the mill in Norwich
Type and Size: Town river
Carp Stock: Plenty of carp to well over 20lbs, and 30's - escapees from a local fish farm
Category: Mixed Fishery
Other Species: Most coarse fish, including barbel
Permits: Clubs have some water in this area, but most is free fishing
BK Rating: Difficult, as fish must first be located, usually in the deeper, slower moving parts of the river
E/A: Anglian
Comments: It was only a flood which 'stocked' this river with carp, though there is no telling how many will survive. Other fish grow to good sizes in the Wensum, so the carp should do well

Rodally Pit

Location: In the centre of the village of Old Buckenham which is on the B1077 from Attleborough
Type and Size: Half acre shallow pond
Carp Stock: Some small commons
Category: Mixed Fishery
Other Species: Rudd and tench
Permits: FREE fishing
E/A: Anglian

Scottow Pond

Location: Scottow, near Swanton Abbot, and Coltishall
Type and Size: Five acre shallow, silty bottomed lake
Carp Stock: Well stocked with mirrors in 1983 - a rich lake so they should have grown well
Category: Mixed Fishery
Other Species: Good tench, pike and eels
Permits: Members only; no day tickets, from Mr Townsend, Hall Gardens,Scottow. Tel: 0169 269671
Cost: £10 per season
Control: Private
Restrictions: Members only

BK Rating: Not known, although it could be quite hard, as this water is very clear
E/A: Anglian
Comments: This water is just down the road from RAF Coltishall where PM was stationed during his National Service from 1949 - 51. He did try fishing it, and found it very difficult ... nothing but blanks!

Shallow Brook Carp Lake

Location: New Costessey, near Norwich
Type and Size: 2 1/4 acre lake about 12ft deep
How to Find: From Norwich take the A47 Dereham road into New Costessey. Turn right at the traffic lights into Norwich Road, and a half a mile further on the lake is on the left just after the river bridge
Carp Stock: Plenty of commons and mirrors to 20lbs
Category: Mixed Fishery
Other Species: Roach, perch, tench, crucian carp and rudd
Permits: Day tickets from farm shop before fishing
Cost: £5 per day: £3 - half day: £2 - evening. Season tickets also available. For details contact Tel: 01603 747667
Control: Private
Restrictions: No night fishing unless you buy a season ticket; day tickets are from dawn to dusk
BK Rating: Easy
E/A: Anglian
Comments: Car park close to lake. Facilities for wheelchair anglers. Permit includes roach, dace and chub fishing in a stretch of the little River Tub nearby

Shropham Pits

Location: Shropham, near Attleborough
Type and Size: Two pits, from five to ten feet deep
How to Find: Take the A11 from Norwich to 4 miles past Attleborough, and pass the White Lodge pub on the left. After another 1 1/2 miles, turn right at a sign marked 'By road'. At the crossroads turn right over a bridge, and take the first road on the left. The pits are 300 yds on the left
Carp Stock: Some carp to double figures
Category: Probably Few Carp
Other Species: Pike, tench, roach, rudd, eels, bream and crucians
Permits: Members only water of Wymondham and District AC. Membership from The Secretary, Mr T Binks, 25 Rosemary Road, Norwich. Tel: 01603 405341, or from the bailiff in the house opposite the pit entrance
Cost: £15 per season
Control: Club
BK Rating: Difficult
E/A: Anglian

Sovereign Lake

Location: Narborough, near King's Lynn
Type and Size: 8 acre gravel pit
How to Find: The lake is off the Narborough by - pass on the King's Lynn to Norwich road
Carp Stock: Some big carp to 20 lbs
Category: Few Carp
Other Species: Tench, perch, rudd, pike and eels
Permits: On bank
Cost: £3 per day
Control: Tel: 01760 337285
BK Rating: Difficult

E/A: Anglian
Comments: Cars can be parked close to swims

Stonegate Lake

Location: Off the B1145 Aylsham to Cawston road, turning left under the old railway bridge. The lake is on the right
Type and Size: Shallow three acre lake
Carp Stock: Some mirrors and commons to a good size
Other Species: Perch, rudd, crucians, bream and pike
Permits: Members only water of the Yarmouth, Gorleston and Dist A.C. Apply to the Chairman, Tony Giacomelli. Tel: 01760 44323, or from Tom Boulton. Tel: 01603 426834
Cost: £14 per season, to include fishing at Bawburgh Lake, Granary Lakes, and the Muckfleet Dyke
Control: Club
E/A: Anglian

Stradsett Lake

Location: Stradsett, near Kings Lynn - from Stradsett, turn right onto the A134, and the lake is also on the right, one mile further on
Type and Size: Eight acre lake, about 7ft in depth
Carp Stock: Some carp, sizes not known
Category: Mixed Fishery
Permits: Members only water, and a specialist syndicate, to which only members of Kings Lynn AC can apply. To join the club, apply to the Secretary
Cost: Kings Lynn AC costs £12 to join, and then there is an extra fee to join the Stradsett Syndicate
Control: Club
BK Rating: Moderate
E/A: Anglian

Swangey Lakes

Location: Near West Carr, Attleborough
Type and Size: Two gravel pits of 4½ acres and 1½ acres
How to Find: Take the A11 from Norwich, and on the Attleborough by-pass turn right to West Carr. After half a mile turn left when the road forks, and then right in 100 yards, continue through a ford across the river, and the fishery entrance is on the left
Carp Stock: Well stocked with carp to 20lbs and catfish to 25lbs
Category: Carp Water
Other Species: Crucians, tench, rudd, roach, perch, bream
Permits: Day tickets on bank from bailiff. Further enquiries from M and M Enterprises. Tel: 01953 452907
Cost: £5 per day, half price for juniors, £10 for 24 hours. Concessions
Control: Private
Restrictions: No peanuts. No carp in keepnets
BK Rating: Easy
E/A: Anglian
Comments: The lakes are 30ft deep in places. Unhooking mats compulsory

Swanton Morley Fisheries

Location: Swanton Morley, near East Dereham
How to Find: From East Dereham take the B1147 road, signposted Bawdeswell past the Papermakers public house and the church. Bear left at the T-junction then sharp right. Pass Waterfall Farm on your left and the entrance to the lakes is 400 yards on the right. Do NOT use the works entrance
Carp Stock: Not many carp; sizes unknown
Category: Few Carp
Other Species: Pike, perch, rudd and tench
Permits: Day tickets must be obtained in advance from: Rod and Gun, Norwich Street, Dereham; Mrs V Marsham, Waterfall Farm, Swanton Morley (Please enclose SAE). After 8am tickets can be obtained from Waterfall Farm. Season tickets from Waterfall Farm
Cost: Approx £2 per day (Juniors/OAP's/evening fishing £1)
Restrictions: No night fishing. Fishery is open from sunrise to sunset. Do NOT go to the working site or works lake
Control: Redland Angling Scheme
BK Rating: Difficult, as there are few carp
E/A: Anglian

Taswood Lakes

Location: Flordon, Tasburgh, Norwich
Type and Size: Five man-made lakes of one to 3 1/2 acres
How to Find: From Norwich take the A140 and take the right fork to Flordon in Newton Flotman. After 1 1/2 miles turn left to Tasburgh.
The lakes are on the left in 200 yards
Carp Stock: All the lakes contain some mirrors, the numbers of which are not known. The biggest lake holds some 20's to 30lbs
Category: Mixed Fishery
Other Species: Crucians, roach, rudd, bream, tench, perch, pike, some grass carp in the pond near the house
Cost: Day ticket cost £5 or £6. Night £7. Booked in advance
Control: Private - owner lives on property. Tel: 01508 470919
BK Rating: Moderate
E/A: Anglian
Comments: Owner sells koi carp, goldfish and other pond fish on site

Tatts Pit

Location: The Willows, Downham Market
Type and Size: Tree-lined pit of about an acre
How to Find: Take the A47 Dereham road from Norwich, then the A1122 to Downham Market, then follow the Wisbech road and look out for Downham Tackle on your right. Just before the shop, turn left, and the pit is 100 yards on the left at 'the Willows'
Carp Stock: Some mirrors, sizes not known
Category: Possibly Few Carp
Other Species: Tench and crucians
Permits: In advance only from Downham Tackle, Railway Road, Downham Market. Tel: 01366 384338
Cost: £3 per day
Control: Private
BK Rating: Not known
E/A: Anglian

Taverham

Location: Costessey No.2 and No.3 pits, Taverham, near Norwich
Type and Size: Ski Pit (No.2) - twelve acres, up to 20ft deep. The Carp Lake (No.3) - six acres, and 8 to 15 feet deep
Carp Stock: No.2 has a small number of carp to double figures. No.3 also has very few, but mirrors betwen 28lbs and 30lbs are caught each season
How to Find: Take the A1067 Fakenham road from Norwich to Taverham, and turn left at the crossroads into Sandy Lane. Go straight ahead at the next cross roads, and over the River Wensum bridge. The pits are on the left, with the car park by No.2. No parking on the roadside
Category: No.2 - Difficult: No.3 Very Difficult
Other Species: Tench, bream, roach, eels, perch and pike to 23lbs
Permits: Day tickets from tackle dealers, or season tickets from, The Secretary, Mr Cyril Wigg, 3 Coppice Avenue, Norwich. Tel: 01603 423625, and *must* be purchased in advance - no tickets on the bank
Cost: £2 Day - Season £20
Baits/Methods: Advanced carp fishing baits and techniques needed for these big hard to catch carp
Control: Club - Norfolk and Suffolk Anglers Consultative Council. Tel: 01932 564872
Restrictions: No night fishing
BK Rating: No.2 - Difficult; No.3 - Very Difficult
Comments: The big carp in No.3 are well known to carp sepcialists, so this is very much a specialist's water. Since there are very few of these fish they are obviously very hard to catch. There are some level swims provided near the car park for disabled anglers

Taverham Mills A

Location: Sandy Lane, Taverham, on the right just before the bridge over the River Wensum
Type and Size: Fifteen acre attractively matured man-made lake, dug in the '40's, with many islands, bays and peninsulas, and up to 12ft in depth. Heavily weeded in summer
Carp Stock: Plenty of carp with many doubles and twenties
Category: Mixed Fishery
Other Species: Tench, big bream and pike, roach and rudd
Permits: Day tickets limited in advance only from Norwich Angling Centre, Sprowston Road, Norwich. Tel: 01603 861014. Fax 01603 262082. Accommodation also available
Cost: About £5 per day
Control: Private
BK Rating: Moderate
E/A: Anglian
Comments: Self-catering holidays in holiday lodge - send for brochure

Thompson Water

Location: Merton, near Watton, Norwich
Type and Size: Shallow lake of 30 acres
How to Find: Take the B1108 road from Norwich to Watton and then the B1110 to Merton and Thompson, Take the track straight on to Peddars Way and the huge lake is on the left
Carp Stock: There have apparently always been some commons in this big lake, although not very many. It is reported to have been 'heavily stocked' (numbers not known) with mirrors in 1984 and they are also said to be caught in double figures
Category: Mixed Fishery
Other Species: Crucians, rudd, roach, bream, tench and pike

Permits: Day tickets from bailiff on bank. Information about the water from Merton Estate Office, Watton, Thetford IP25 6QJ. Tel: 01953 883370
Cost: Approx £3 per day
Control: Private
Baits/Methods: Usual carp baits and methods, though it may be wise to select baits which are less likely to be taken by the many other fish in the water
BK Rating: Difficult
E/A: Anglian

Tottenhill Pit

Location: Willow Place, Tottenhill, near King's Lynn
Type and Size: 2 acre matured gravel pit
How to Find: Take the A10 from King's Lynn towards Downham Market, turn left at the pub in Tottenhill, then right into Willow Place
Carp Stock: Quite well stocked with carp to 20lbs
Category: Mixed Fishery
Other Species: Rudd, roach, tench and crucians
Permits: In advance only from local tackle shops
Cost: £20 per seaon; £10 O.A.P's; £4 juniors
Control: King's Lynn A.A. Tel: 01553 671545
Restrictions: No night fishing; fishing starts 6am
BK Rating: Moderate
E/A: Anglian

University Broad

Location: Norwich University
Type and Size: Eighteen acre gravel pit
How to Find: In Norwich take B1108 Watton road and turn left onto Bluebell Road in Earlham. The lake will be seen on the right
Carp Stock: Good stock of carp over 20lbs
Category: Mixed Fishery
Other Species: Roach, rudd, tench, bream, and pike
Permits: Members only - University of East Anglia, Biology Department, U.E.A. Norwich. Annual permits only. Apply in writing with SAE
Cost: Approx £25 per year
BK Rating: Moderate
Control: University Tel: 01603 56161
Restrictions: Not known
E/A: Anglian
Comments: Only big still water within the city - up to 20 feet deep

Wades Pit

Location: Wymondham, near Norwich
Type and Size: Weedy pit of about an acre, up to seven feet deep
How to Find: Take the A11 from Norwich to Wymondham, and turn left after the railway bridge, and the pit is another half mile, on the left
Carp Stock: Some mirrors to middle doubles
Category: Few Carp
Other Species: Roach, perch, tench and crucians
Permits: Day tickets from bailiff on bank, season tickets and information from: Mr R Bartlett, 6 Vimy Ridge, Wymondham. Tel: 01953 605505
Cost: £1 (Juniors - 50p) for day tickets: £3 (Juniors £1.50) per season
Baits/Methods: Good float fishing water, ideal for youngsters
Control: Private
BK Rating: Easy for most fish, though we suspect harder for the carp, as there are not many of the bigger fish

E/A: Anglian

Walnut Tree Farm — A

Location: Lyng, off the A1067 Norwich Fakenham road, 12 miles north west of Norwich
Type and Size: Two recently opened and restored gravel pits of about 35 acres
Carp Stock: Well stocked with carp to 30lbs
Category: Mixed Fishery
Permits: William Bingham on site; enquire locally or at Norwich tackle shops
Cost: Not known
Control: Private
BK Rating: Not known
E/A: Anglian
Comments: Reported in the angling papers in July 1992 as having already produced a carp of 30lb 11oz in the first week of the season. However, the owners are said to be ready to import carp from Holland of up to 72lbs as soon as they can obtain the permission from MAFF, though the fish will not be eligible for British records. These are 'small lodges' for holidays, but we have been able to discover neither an address nor a phone number

Waveney Valley Lakes — A

Location: Wortwell, near Harleston, on the Suffolk border
Type and Size: Six mature gravel pits from 2-5 acres in size
How to Find: Take the A140 from Norwich to Pulham Market, then the B1134 to Harleston and the A143 to Wortwell. The entrance to the lakes is signposted in the middle of Wortwell
Carp Stock: All the lakes are well stocked with large carp. Plenty of doubles and 20's, and a number of very well authenticated 30's have been taken to 36lbs
Category: Carp Water
Other Species: Crucians, tench, roach, rudd, bream, perch, pike and eels
Permits: Day tickets sould be purchased from the site shop if open, if not, bailiffs call around. Day tickets cover 12 hours only. Night fishing allowed but another 12 hour ticket will be needed
Cost: £5 for one rod for 12 hours; two rods £6. Weekly + bivvy £40 for 1 rod; £65 for 2 rods
Control: Details from shop, or Tony Knox on Tel: 01986 788676
Baits/Methods: Advanced carp fishing rigs and methods and baits are needed at this heavily fished specialist carp water. Many boilies and multiple baits go in every day. Hard boilies, such as KM, work best
BK Rating: Moderate though some of the lakes can be easy for the smaller fish and lower doubles; the really big fish are quite dificult
E/A: Anglian
Comments: One of the best commercial carp fisheries in the country - and for this reason very well known for its twenties and thirties, and hard fished by many expert carp anglers. Tents can be pitched for long-stay holidays at an extra charge and you can also take your touring caravan. There are luxury lakeside caravans which must be booked well in advance, and these are ideal for a family holiday. There are top class shower and toilet facilities, and the shop sells carp bait, tackle and food. G E and D lakes are said to be the best for the really big fish, some of which are caught quite often and are well known to the regulars. No dogs. One of the comparatively few carp waters in the country which can be fished by everyone and where you are always in with a chance of a big fish. Sacking for 15 minutes only; unhooking mats compulsory. Day tickets only available on some lakes from November. Holiday cottages also to let in the area. Tel: 0137 9395

Walnut Farm Fishery

Location: Walnut Farm, near Attleborough
Type and Size: Pool about 1½ acres and a canal - shaped lake
How to Find: Turn left after the Little Chef on the A11 Attleborough bypass, left into Mill Road, and left again
Carp Stock: Carp averaging 5lbs - a few doubles in lake
Category: Mixed Fishery
Other Species: Roach, rudd, crucians, tench, bream, chub, perch and orfe
Permits: In advance only
Cost: £4 per day
Control: J.M.P. Tackle, Attleborough. Tel: 01953 455 282
Restrictions: No boilies or peanuts
BK Rating: Not known, possibly Easy
E/A: Anglian

Wensum Fisheries

Location: Costessey, Near Norwich
Type and Size: Attractive, wooded, old gravel pits of from 2-10 acres in size
How to Find: Take the A47 from Norwich, and after two miles turn right by the Roundwell public house down Longwater Lane. At the 'T' junction turn left, and then take a right fork in half a mile. The lakes are then 200 yards on the left, behind iron gates
Carp Stock: Clear Water Lake is well stocked with carp into double figures; Rainbow Pool contains a few carp
Category: Back Lake (the biggest) - roach, rudd and bream to over 9lbs (no carp); Roach Lake - roach, tench and bream (no carp); Clear Water Lake - tench and bream; Rainbow Pool - roach, tench and bream
Permits: Members only water of Norwich and Dist AA. Permits from the Secretary, Mr C Wigg, 3 Coppice Avenue, Norwich.
Tel: 01603 423625 (includes fishing on River Wensum)
Cost: On application
Control: Club
Restrictions: No night fishing
BK Rating: Clear Water - Moderate; Rainbow - Difficult
E/A: Anglian

Wereham Pit

Location: In the village of Wereham, opposite the George and Dragon Pub
Type and Size: Tiny, shallow, quarter of an acre pit
How to Find: Find Wereham, near Stradsett, off the A134
Carp Stock: Plenty of little carp
Category: Mixed Fishery
Other Species: Roach and pike
Permits: FREE fishing, ideal for young people
E/A: Anglian
BK Rating: Easy

West Lexham A

Location: West Lexham, near Kings Lynn
Type and Size: Beautiful moat
Carp Stock: Well stocked with carp to over 30lbs
Other Species: General coarse fish
Category: Mixed Fishery
Permits: Sue Allerton. Tel: (Swaffham) 01760 755252
Control: Private

Restrictions:	No fishing, except to those renting one of the self-catering holiday cottages on the site. Includes fishing on the River Nar
BK Rating:	Not known
E/A:	Anglian

Willsmore Water

Location:	Hayes Lane near Fakenham
Type and Size:	One and a half acre man-made lake
How to Find:	From Fakenham cross the River Wensum at Goggs Mill, then take Sandy Lane and Hayes Lane
Carp Stock:	Well stocked with carp to doubles
Category:	Mixed Fishery
Permits:	Fakenham AC (members only). Membership from G Parsons, 26 St Peters Road. Tel: 01328 4637
Cost:	Approx £4 entry fee - £10 per season
BK Rating:	Moderate
Restrictions:	No keepnets, no groundbaiting
E/A:	Anglian
Comments:	Membership also includes some other lakes and trout and coarse fishing on the River Wensum

Linear Fisheries Oxford

27lb 14oz
Hardwick Lakes

Wolterton Park Lake

Location: Wolterton Hall, 5 miles from Aylsham
Type and Size: Attractive estate lake, with an island and very clear water
Carp Stock: Some carp, sizes not known
Category: Few Carp
Other Species: A few big tench, eels and perch
Permits: Day tickets from the Head Gardener's Lodge, just inside the orchard which leads round the Great Hall to the lake
Cost: £3 per day
Control: Private
BK Rating: Very Difficult
E/A: Anglian
Comments: A very weedy, clear water which is very difficult to fish, as it seems to be sparsely stocked

Wood Lakes

Location: Stow, near Kings Lynn
Type and Size: Six lakes, largest 15 acres
How to Find: Take the A10 from Kings Lynn and turn right at Stow Bardolph, 500 yards before the bridge carry straight on at sharp bend. The lakes will be seen on the right shortly before Stow Bridge
Carp Stock: All well stocked with carp to over 25lbs
Category: Mixed Fishery
Other Species: Roach, rudd, tench, bream and pike
Permits: Day tickets from the reception kiosks, or on the banks from the bailiffs if the reception is closed
Cost: £4.50 per 12 hours (2 rods); £6 for 24 hours
Baits/Methods: Specialist carp fishing methods and baits needed for the better carp. Night fishing best, when there is less disturbance
Restrictions: No winter fishing from November 1st onwards
Control: Private. Tel: 01533 810414
BK Rating: Moderate
E/A: Anglian
Comments: Camping is allowed at extra cost. Touring caravans are also welcomed; family type water during the day. Best chance for the specialist is after dark

Woodrising Water Meadows

Location: Near Watton and Shippham
Type and Size: 3 acre lake
Carp Stock: Well stocked with carp
Category: Mixed Fishery
Other Species: Crucians, tench and roach
Permits: Day and season
Cost: Adults £3 per day; juniors £2; season tickets £40
Restrictions: No groundbait
Control: Tel: 01362 820702
BK Rating: Not known
E/A: Anglian
Comments: Lake available for matches. Open June 16th to March 14th

Worthing Pits

Location: Dereham, near Norwich
Type and Size: Two pits of 8 acres and 2 acres, the larger of which is open and has depths of up to 20ft
Carp Stock: Some carp to 20lbs
Category: Few Carp
Other Species: Roach, tench, perch and pike
Permits: Day tickets, in advance only, from local tackle shops, or Mr SR Allinson, Pound Cottage, Cemetery Road, East Dereham. Tel: 01362 694828
Cost: Dereham and Dist. AC membership, which includes these waters, several other pits, and stretches of the River Wensum behind the pits; cost £12 per season, half price for juniors
Control: Club
BK Rating: Not known
E/A: Anglian

NORTHAMPTONSHIRE

Barby Mill Pool

Location: Off the A 361 at Barby, near Daventry
Type and Size: 2 acre lake with island
Carp Stock: Quite well stocked with carp to nearly 20 lbs
Category: Mixed Fishery
Other Species: Roach, rudd, perch, tench, barbel, catfish, chub and gudgeon
Permits: On bank
Cost: £3.50 per day; £1.50 for under 14's
Control: Tel: 01788 579521
Restrictions: No carp over 2 lbs in keepnets; no night fishing; barbless hooks
BK Rating: Moderate
E/A: Severn Trent
Comments: Toilets

Bedford Road Weir

Location: River Nene, off the A 428 Northampton to Bedford road
Type and Size: Wide river with weirpool
Carp Stock: Plenty of doubles and a few twenties
Category: Mixed Fishery
Other Species: Numerous tench; bream, chub and roach
Permits: On bank
Cost: About £4 per day; reduced prices from local tackle shops. Concessions
Control: Northampton Nene A.C. Tel: 01604 770001
BK Rating: Moderate
Baits/Methods: Luncheon meat and sweetcorn are good baits
E/A: Anglian
Comments: Food etc. at the Britannia Inn

Biggin Lake

Location: Biggin Estate, Oundle, behind golf course
Type and Size: Six acre estate lake
How to Find: Oundle is east of Corby on the A427
Carp Stock: A few fish under 10lbs, but plenty of doubles to about 20lbs

Category: Carp Only
Other Species: None
Permits: B P Tackle,Cockingham Road, Kettering (Tackle Shop). Season tickets (in advance) only. Tel: 01536 81118
Cost: About £60
BK Rating: Easy
Control: Private. Tel: 01536 523084
Restrictions: No sacking except for quick pics. 72 hour maximum stay. Barbless hooks. No groundbait
E/A: Anglian
Comments: Well established, attractive water with plenty of cover on banks. Only fished for the past 6 years so it is thought that some of the big fish have never been caught

Biggin Pit

Location: Oundle Golf Course
Type and Size: Gravel pit of six acres
How to Find: On the outskirts of the town of Oundle
Carp Stock: Well stocked with carp to 20lbs
Category: Carp Water
Other Species: Few other fish
Permits: Robin Sharp, B P Tackle, Mill Road, Kettering
Cost: Syndicate - £100 per season and day tickets at £7.50
Control: Private
BK Rating: Easy
E/A: Anglian
Comments: Shallow, silty pit said to be good carp fishing. Quiet peaceful lake. Second lake about 3 acres on site also contains many small carp. Day tickets, bookable in advance - a very easy water

Billing Aquadrome

Location: Little Billing, near Northampton
Type and Size: There are a number of lakes on this holiday caravan and leisure complex, but only the Willow Pool (12 acres) is of much interest to carp anglers
How to Find: Take the A45 from Northampton and turn off to the village of Little Billing
Carp Stock: Very few, but have grown to great size in the past. The lake became famous in the 50's and 60's when a huge catch of twenties and a thirty were caught by Bob Reynolds, and in 1966 a 42 pounder was caught by Ray Clay. Still a few big fish but they are rarely caught
Category: Few Carp
Other Species: Pike, perch, roach, tench, bream
Permits: On site. Information Tel: 01604 45255
Restrictions: No night fishing. No fishing after mid-October
BK Rating: Super-Difficult
E/A: Anglian
Comments: Famous carp water now declined to the extent that carp are almost never caught there - although it was always very difficult. Crowds of thousands at weekends and bank holidays - hundreds of caravans, cafes and amusements etc. There may still be a few big fish and there was a low 30 caught there fairly recently

Bluebell Lakes

Location: Tansor, near Oundle
Type and Size: Three large gravel pits
Carp Stock: Well stocked with carp to over 30lbs
Category: Mixed Fishery
Other Species: Tench, bream, roach and pike
Permits: On site
Cost: About £6 per day; evening tickets and concessions
Control: Tel: 01945 780309 or 01850 783702
BK Rating: Moderate
E/A: Anglian
Comments: Toilet and hot meals. Probably open all year

Boddington Reservoir

Location: Byfield, 7 miles from Banbury
Type and Size: Big reservoir - 65 acres
Carp Stock: Some carp to a good size
Category: Mixed Fishery
Other Species: Pike, bream, perch, roach and tench
Permits: Season tickets from Principal Fisheries Officer, British Waterways, Willow Grange, Church Road, Watford, Herts Tel: 01923 226422. (There may be a waiting list)
Cost: £20 per season
Control: British Waterways
BK Rating: Not known
E/A: Thames

Brightwells Lake

Location: On the Ringstead to Addington road, between Thrapston and Kettering
Type and Size: Fifteen acre gravel pit
Carp Stock: Heavily stocked with many doubles to 24lbs, and several hundred small ones, placed in the water in 1991
Category: Mixed Fishery
Other Species: Tench, pike and roach
Permits: Season tickets only from Irthlingborough DAS; Peter Pratt, 7 The Shortlands, Irthlingborough
Cost: £20 per season
BK Rating: Moderate
E/A: Anglian

Canons Ashby Lakes

Location: National Trust estate on the B4525, half a mile from Moreton Pinkney
Type and Size: Two lakes of 6 acres
Carp Stock: Well stocked with carp to low doubles
Category: Mixed Fishery
Other Species: General coarse fish
Permits: Local tackle shops
Cost: About £20 per season
Control: Northampton Castle A.C. Tel: 01604 647305
Restrictions: No day tickets; no boilies, HP. baits or hair rigs. No ferrets!
BK Rating: Easy
E/A: Severn Trent

Castle Ashby Lakes

Location: Castle Ashby, near Northampton
Type and Size: Three estate lakes of various sizes
How to Find: Take a left turn off the A248 Northampton-Bedford road about 7 miles from Northampton
Carp Stock: Two of the lakes are quite well stocked with carp to mid-doubles
Category: Mixed Fishery
Other Species: General coarse fishing
Permits: Castle Ashby Estate Office, Castle Ashby, Northampton. Tel: 01604 712346. One lake recently opened as a specimen carp water - details from the estate office
Cost: £3 to £5 per day. Concessions
Control: Castle Ashby Estate
BK Rating: Moderate. Menagerie Lake - Very Easy for carp to 18lbs
Restrictions: No night fishing. Fishing is dawn till dusk only
E/A: Anglian
Comments: Toilets. Food and drink; bait. Facilities for the disabled

Clarkes

Location: Clarkes Pick Your Own Farm, Hannington, near Kettering - off the A43
Type and Size: Small farm lake of about an acre dug for irrigation and 16 feet deep
Carp Stock: Well stocked with carp to 25lbs, although many are small
Category: Mixed Fishery
Other Species: Usual coarse fish
Permits: Day tickets on site £3 per day
Control: Private
BK Rating: Moderate
E/A: Anglian

Corby Boating Lake

Location: On the outskirts of Corby, Cottingham Road
Type and Size: Town lake of 3½ acres
How to Find: In Corby
Carp Stock: Stocked with carp to 20lbs; a 33lb has been reported
Category: Mixed Fishery
Other Species: Roach, bream, tench, pike, rudd and catfish
Permits: Free fishing
Control: Council. Tel: 01536 203035 - Corby Tackle Centre
BK Rating: Easy
Restrictions: No night fishing; barbless hooks, no groundbaiting
E/A: Anglian

Cransley Hall A

Location: Off the Broughton bypass, about 3 miles from Kettering on the Northampton road
Type and Size: Estate lake
Carp Stock: Some carp to 20lbs
Category: Mixed Fishery
Other Species: Roach, tench
Permits: Cliff Smart's Angling Holidays, 29 Bridal Road, Burton Latimer, Northants NN15 5QP. Tel: 01536 724226/725453
Control: Bryan Perkins, Cransley Hall
BK Rating: Not known
E/A: Anglian
Comments: Bed and breakfast accommodation in 17th century hall, with

croquet,bowls and tennis, Cost about £36 per night, fishing included. Dinners at oak table in ornate dining room

Ditchford Lake

Location: Near Rushden
Type and Size: Two well matured gravel pits of about 6 and 30 acres
Carp Stock: Stocked with commons and mirrors most of which are doubles with a few twenties. Record 26lbs, from small lake; about 12 twenties in big lake with at least 4 twenty pound commons
Category: Mixed Fishery
Other Species: Most coarse fish
Permits: Rushden, Higham Ferrers and Irchester Angling Club. Season tickets only from Jack Leach Fishing Tackle, Church Street, Rushden
Cost: Approx £15 per season with a number of other good waters on the club ticket
Control: Club
BK Rating: Difficult
E/A: Anglian
Comments: Night fishing is allowed

Drayton Reservoir

Location: Daventry
Type and Size: 22 acre reservoir
How to Find: Half mile north of Daventry on the A 361
Carp Stock: 20,000 + carp, averaging 3 lbs
Category: Carp Water
Other Species: Roach, tench, perch and pike
Permits: On bank
Cost: £5 per day; £3 evenings; £2.50 concessions
Control: British Waterways. Tel: 01442 278717
Restrictions: No night fishing; no boilies; barbless hooks no bigger than size 12
BK Rating: Very Easy
E/A: Severn Trent
Comments: Open all year. Much match fishing. Huge catches of carp to over 200 lbs per day. Very heavily fished

Ecton Lakes

Location: Billing, near Northampton
Type and Size: New gravel pit of 40+ acres
Carp Stock: Low density - about 2 fish per acre, but plenty of 20's caught
Category: Mixed Fishery
Other Species: General coarse fish - some big pike
Permits: Jack Leach Fishing Tackle, Church Street, Rushden or Northampton Nene AC, M Eaton 12 Thorne Hill, Briar Hill, Northampton NN4 9SN
Cost: Approx £20 per season
BK Rating: Difficult
Control: Club
E/A: Anglian

Fineshade Abbey

Location: On the A43 between Corby and Stamford
Type and Size: Two small lakes, recently opened
Carp Stock: Some carp to doubles
Category: Mixed Fishery
Other Species: Roach, tench, perch and bream

Permits: Day tickets on site
Cost: Weekends 9am to 3.30pm - £5
Control: Private. Tel: 01780 83284 for bookings and information
Restrictions: Thought to be no night fishing; restricted fishing on weekdays
BK Rating: Not known
E/A: Anglian

Flecknoe Farm Fisheries

Location: Just outside Daventry
Type and Size: Two small lakes
Carp Stock: Well stocked with carp to doubles
Category: Carp Water
Permits: Season tickets only from FLecknoe Fisheries, Flecknoe Farm, near Rugby. Tel: 01788 891019. Brochure available
Cost: £75 per season; numbers limited
BK Rating: Not known
E/A: Severn-Trent

Foxholes Fisheries

Location: Crick, Northampton NN6 7US. Tel: 01788 823967. Off the A428 between, West Haddon and Crick
Type and Size: Four small lakes on fish farm. New 2 acre carp lake containing 50 carp from 10lbs to 22lbs
Carp Stock: Day Ticket Pool - mainly carp to 8lbs; Top Lake - carp only, most from 3 - 8lbs in weight; Bottom Lake - carp only, 5lbs to 12lbs; Middle Lake - some carp
Category: Day Ticket Pool - Mixed Fishery; Middle Lake - Mixed Fishery; Top Lake and Bottom lake - Carp Only; New Lake - Carp Only
Other Species: Day Ticket - crucians and tench; Middle Lake - tench, chub, perch, roach, crucians, bream, barbel
Permits: From Roger and Joan Chaplin at the above address
Cost: Day Ticket Pool - £2.50 for one rod, £5 for two rods, issued on bank by bailiff. Season tickets for Top, Bottom, Middle and New Lakes £40 for one weekday; £50 for 2 weekdays; £60 for 4 weekdays; £60 for Saturday plus one weekday; £65 for Sunday plus one weekday; £80 for Saturday and Sunday; £100 for 6 days a week
Restrictions: Barbless hooks; no keepnets; season ticket waters closed on Tuesdays; day ticket pool open every day; guest tickets allowed to season ticket holders
BK Rating: Easy
E/A: Severn-Trent
Comments: Shop and information office; ornamental fish for sale; conference room with seating for 50, and all conference facilities; can be booked for clubs or school trips at about £50 for an afternoon; lectures by staff at £10 per hour. Bookable on Tuesdays for business entertaining which may include fishing at £100 per day. Bookings also available on other days, with fishing for £50. Matches may be booked at £40 for Sunday mornings (15 pegs on Middle Lake). Leaflet with details on request. Demonstration nettings on some bank holidays at £1 per person. Annual open day with free fishing for tackle shop proprietors and angling correspondents. Fishery management courses...what more can you ask! We have not been invited to visit this fishery, but after such a good write-up, perhaps we shall be - Yes we were! We even have a free permit, thanks to owner Roger Chaplin

Gayton Pool

Location: Near Northampton
Type and Size: Small pool
How to Find: Enquire from Secretary
Carp Stock: Well stocked with carp
Category: Carp Water
Other Species: Some coarse fish
Permits: Gayton AC. S Barker, 91 Battmead, Bilsworth, Northants - members only
Cost: On application
BK Rating: Moderate
E/A: Anglian

Grand Union Canal

Location: Leicester Arm, near Watford Gap
Type and Size: Narrow canal
How to Find: Near Watford Gap services on M1
Carp Stock: Plenty of carp to middle doubles
Category: Mixed Fishery
Other Species: General coarse fish
Permits: Coventry AA - try local tackle shops
Cost: On application
Control: Club
BK Rating: Moderate
E/A: Anglian
Comments: Quite easy once fish are located. Coventry AA - P O'Connor, 48 Doncaster Close, Manor Farm, Wyken, Coventry CV2 1HX

Grendon Lakes

Location: Grendon, just off the A428 Northampton-Bedford road
Type and Size: Four lakes; Windsurfing Lake is 26 acres; Club Lake is about 10 acres
How to Find: From the A428 south of Northampton, turn left at Brafield-on-the- Green and right to Cogenhoe. At the T-junction turn right towards Grendon. Left in the village and left again at the next T-junction. The lakes are signposted on the left in about 400 yards
Carp Stock: Club lake well stocked with carp to doubles; Windsurfing Lake - some carp to 20lbs
Category: Mixed Fishery
Other Species: Roach, rudd, tench, bream and chub
Permits: Day tickets on bank
Cost: £2 per day; £1.50 for juniors, OAP's and the disabled. Half season - £35 and £20;season - £55 and £35
Control: Private, some sailing and windsurfing
BK Rating: Moderate
E/A: Anglian

Higham Wharf Lake

Location: Off the Higham Ferrers by-pass
Type and Size: Twenty year old gravel pit of about 120 acres
How to Find: The entrance is at the Ski-Club roundabout on the A45, Wharf Road, in Higham Ferrers and Pine Trees Village in Irthlingborough
Carp Stock: Not known, but not many. Fish to upper doubles caught, but there are probably some bigger fish
Category: Few Carp
Other Species: Roach, tench, bream, rudd, perch and pike
Permits: Irthlingborough AC - from local tackle shops

Cost: £20 per season
BK Rating: Difficult
E/A: Anglian
Comments: A night fishing ban, and long walks, make this lake a difficult proposition to all but the most determined

Hinton Fisheries

Location: Hinton-in-the-Hedges,near Brackley
Type and Size: Lake of 1½ acres
How to Find: Take the Hinton-in-the-Hedges road from Brackley
Carp Stock: Well stocked with carp, most fish between 5 and 12lbs, although there are plenty of doubles, and several twenties
Category: Carp Water
Other Species: Tench to 7lbs, crucians, roach, rudd, chub and trout
Permits: In advance in writing only from the owner, Trevor Smith, 24 Red Poll Close, Banbury, Oxfordshire. Information Tel: 01295 264483
Cost: On application
Control: Private
BK Rating: Moderate
E/A: Anglian
Comments: A second lake at this very pleasant fishery will be built this year. The fishery is in quiet farmland away from main roads, and is secluded by high hedges and a locked gate, to which only the members have a key. Usual rules, baits and methods. Hinton Fish and Fishing also supply a netting service, and have fish for sale, including double figure carp at very reasonable prices, with occasional twenties. Details from the owner at the number above. Hinton-in-the-Hedges has long been my favourite English place name - now I know what it looks like!

Irthlingborough Main Lake

Location: Irthlingborough - off the A605 Rushden - Kettering road, then turn left on the B751. After about 1½ miles turn left into a new housing estate, and then left again along a rough track, at the end of which is a car park
Type and Size: Typical Northants matured gravel pit of about ten acres
Carp Stock: Plenty of carp to about 20lbs
Category: Mixed Fishery
Other Species: Pike, bream, tench, roach, hybrids and perch
Permits: Irthlingborough and District AC. Secretary: Peter Pratt, 7 The Shortlands, Irthlingborough
Cost: £20 per season to include other waters; juniors and OAP's - £1
Control: Club
Restrictions: Members only
BK Rating: Moderate
E/A: Anglian
Comments: Attractive, reed-fringed lake, which is not heavily fished, and could contain some 'very big' carp, which have been seen on the surface

Jigsaw Lake

Location: Ecton, near Northampton
Type and Size: 8 acre gravel pit with many bars, islands and gullies
How to Find: Take the A 45 from Northampton and take the Grendon exit at Earls Barton. Turn right to the lake
Carp Stock: Well stocked with carp to over 20 lbs
Category: Mixed Fishery
Other Species: Pike to over 30 lbs, tench, roach and perch
Permits: In advance only from local tackle shops

Cost: About £25 per season; juniors and O.A.P's £10
Control: Tel: 01604 770001
BK Rating: Difficult
Baits/Methods: Boilies best for carp
E/A: Anglian

Ladybridge Lake

Location: Ladybridge Drive, Northampton
Type and Size: 3 1/2 acre lake with island
How to Find: Off the A 45 Northampton ring road
Carp Stock: Very heavily stocked with little carp; a few twenties
Category: Mixed Fishery
Other Species: Crucians and tench
Permits: On bank or from local tackle shops
Cost: About £3 per day; concessions
Control: Northampton Castle A.A.
Restrictions: No night fishing, or boilies
BK Rating: Very Easy
E/A: Anglian
Comments: Match fishing lake

Mid-Northants Carp Fishery

Location: Woodford Mill, Addington Road, near Ringstead
Type and Size: Three lakes of ten acres, six acres and one acre; gravel pits
How to Find: Turn left at the roundabout towards Ringstead from the A605 Higham Ferrers-Thrapston road, and at Ringstead take the left turn towards Great Addington. Woodford Mill will be seen on your right just after the bridge over the River Nene
Carp Stock: 'A' Lake - Well stocked with big carp including several 30's and at least two 40's . 'B' Lake - Mixed Fishery, double figure bream, catfish to 18lbs; 'C' Lake - grass carp and other species
Permits: Duncan Kay, 4 Sawyers Crescent, Chelveston, Northants. Tel: 01933 460115. In advance only. No day tickets; season tickets only
Cost: 'B' and 'C' Lakes, half mile of the adjacent River Nene, including membership of Higham Ferrers AC - £107 per year, January to January. 'A' Lake - £250 per season
BK Rating: 'B' and 'C' Lakes - Easy to Moderate. 'A' Lake - Moderate
Control: Private (Duncan Kay)
Restrictions: No long stay fishing, 48 hours maximum, 24 hours at weekends
E/A: Anglian
Comments: The Mid-Northants Carp Fishery is one of the most famous big fsh and carp waters in the country, with many 20's and 30's caught each season, and several 40's, which have been even been caught in the winter. The fishery is in a quiet and pleasant situation alongside the River Nene, but because of the huge fish it contains, and the fact that numbers of members are strictly limited, it is very hard to get into, and there is always a waiting list. The 'B' ticket, which includes Lake 'C' and the river is used as a waiting list for Lake 'A', the big carp lake, so you will need to apply for the 'B' ticket membership first, with the idea of hoping to get into 'A' the big carp water later. Full details from Duncan Kay, who controls the fishery, and who is well known as one of the leading big fish anglers in the country. This is private property, so do not go to the lakes without permission - if you are caught there without first getting permission to visit from Duncan, you are not likely to be offered membership - you have been warned! Rule 13 should be carefully noted: 'No climbing the trees is allowed' (there are virtually no trees, except a

few saplings to about 5 feet tall!) and also Rule 13b. 'The management takes no responsibility for any injury to members from trees falling on them!' Trees and bushes are being planted, and these will soon improve this already very pleasant fishery

Naseby Reservoir

Location: Naseby, between Kettering and Rugby, off the A50
Type and Size: 85 acre reservoir
Carp Stock: Well stocked with carp to over 20lbs
Category: Mixed Fishery
Other Species: Tench, rudd and other species including big catfish
Permits: MEM Fisheries Management Ltd, Bufton House, Walcote, Lutterworth, Leics LEI7 4JS. Tel: 01455 558559
Cost: £25 per season per rod. Two rods £55, night permit £85
Control: MEM Fisheries Management
Restrictions: No juniors
BK Rating: Moderate
E/A: Severn-Trent

Overstone Solarium

Location: Overstone, near Northampton
Type and Size: Two estate lakes of four acres and two acres
How to Find: Off the A4500 between Northampton and Wellingborough
Carp Stock: Fairly well stocked to 24lbs, mostly commons
Category: Mixed Fishery
Other Species: General coarse fish
Permits: On site, for caravan owners and tourers on site
BK Rating: Moderate
Control: Private. Tel: 01604 645265 Ecton Lane, Sywell
E/A: Anglian
Comments: Night fishing allowed. Day ticket water with caravans etc

Ransome Road Gravel Pit

Location: Near Northampton
Type and Size: Large gravel pit, about 30 acres plus
How to Find: On A508 near motorway junction 15
Carp Stock: Not many carp to 20lbs plus
Category: Few Carp
Other Species: General coarse fish
Permits: Northampton Nene AC - local tackle shops
Cost: Approx £10 per season
BK Rating: Difficult
Control: Club. Tel: 01604 770001
E/A: Anglian
Comments: Lake record 29lbs. Matured gravel pit. Details from Jack Leach Tackle, Church Street, Rushden

Red House Farm Fishery A

Location: Syresham, off the 43 between Silverstone and Brackley
Type and Size: Half acre farm pond
Carp Stock: Well stocked with carp to 18lbs
Category: Mixed Fishery
Other Species: Trout and catfish
Permits: Day tickets from bungalow on site. Tel: 01869 810306 (John Harper)
Cost: £4 per day
Control: Private

Restrictions: Fishing 5am to 11.30pm - no night fishing
BK Rating: Moderate
E/A: Severn-Trent
Comments: No close season. 3 self catering cottages to rent on the farm, close to the lake

River Nene

Location: Northampton, Ditchford, Peterborough, Oundle
Type and Size: River
How to Find: The River Nene runs from Peterborough to Northampton
Carp Stock: In some area well stocked. Average 11-12lbs. Some fish to 27lbs. Quite a few 20's. Biggest reported 27lbs from Billing stretch
Category: Mixed Fishery
Other Species: General coarse fish
Permits: Various clubs and local tackle shops. Jack Leach, Church Street, Rushden
Cost: Northampton Club - approx £10; Rushden Club £6
Control: Clubs
E/A: Anglian
Comments: Location is the problem, but simple methods and baits such as corn and luncheon meat will enable fish to be caught reasonably easily. Northampton Nene AC - M Eaton, 12 Thorne Hill, Briar Hill, Northampton NN4 9SN. Rushden AA - J Leach, Anglers Dept, Rushden, Northants. Many carp at Wellingborough, Ditchford and Higham areas, average size about 14lbs. Most fish now caught on boilies

River Nene

Location: Oundle Riverside Bridge
Type and Size: Narrow river
Carp Stock: Well stocked with carp to over 20 lbs, mostly commons
Category: Mixed Fishery
Other Species: Pike, tench, roach and perch
Permits: On bank
Cost: £2 per day
Control: Oundle A/C; details from 01733 65159
BK Rating: Difficult
E/A: Anglian

Rushton Lake

Location: Rushton, off the A6003 between Kettering and Corby
Type and Size: Medium-sized gravel pit
Carp Stock: Well stocked with small carp to doubles
Category: Mixed Fishery
Other Species: Big bream and roach
Permits: Local club, try local tackle shops in Kettering and Corby. Matches at the lake are booked by telephoning 01536 760986, so you might get some information on this number
Restrictions: Not known, but possibly no night fishing
BK Rating: Easy
E/A: Anglian
Comments: Matches take place each Thursday, with the draw at 5.30pm; entries and details from the phone number above

School Water

Location: Kimbolton, near Grafham Water
Type and Size: One and a half acres
How to Find: Kimbolton Castle
Carp Stock: Plenty of small carp to 5lbs
Category: Mixed Fishery
Other Species: General coarse fish
Permits: On site
Cost: Approx £2 per day
BK Rating: Easy
Control: Private
E/A: Anglian

Sharman Lake

Location: Sharman Road, off the A 428, Northampton
Type and Size: 3 acre gravel pit
Carp Stock: Well stocked with carp to about 25 lbs
Category: Mixed Fishery
Other Species: Bream, rudd, roach, perch and chub
Permits: On bank
Cost: £3 per day; £1.50 juniors, O.A.P's and disabled
Control: Tel: 01327 705692
Restrictions: No night fishing
BK Rating: Moderate
E/A: Anglian

Shelfley's Lake

Location: Ladybridge Drive, just off the A 45 ring road south of Northampton
Type and Size: Attractive lake with islands
Carp Stock: Well stocked with carp to 20 lbs
Category: Mixed Fishery
Other Species: Crucians and tench
Permits: On bank
Cost: About £4 per day; £15 per season. Concessions
Control: Martin Wood. Tel: 01604 647305
Restrictions: No night fishing; boilies or floating baits
BK Rating: Moderate
Baits/Methods: Luncheon meat and sweetcorn are best baits
E/A: Anglian

THE BEEKAY GUIDE TO 2000 BRITISH & EUROPEAN CARP WATERS

Is YOUR Water listed? If so, are the details correct?
If you spot omissions, inaccuracies, or know of any changes, please let us know by filling in the Waters Questionnaire at the back of this guide and return it to us at:

Beekay International
Withy Pool
Henlow Camp
Bedfordshire
SG16 6EA

Sibson Fisheries **A**

Location: New Lane, Stibbington, Peterborough
Type and Size: 14 acres of lakes
How to Find: Just off the A1 between Peterborough and Stamford
Carp Stock: Well stocked with carp to a good size
Category: Mixed Fishery
Other Species: Tench, bream, rudd, roach and trout
Permits: Details from the above address. Tel: (01780) 782621. Limited day tickets. Secretary - Sharon Denny. In advance only. Cost approx £4 per day, same for night. Season £50, book well in advance
BK Rating: Insufficient information
Control: Private
E/A: Anglian
Comments: Also two miles of river and holiday cottages at £20 per night. Trout lake. Bailiff David Mosiey also provides information. Tel: (01780) 78621 (Monday to Friday 9am to 5pm), 51 Church Lane, Stibbington. Membership limit 50 for coarse waters in advance only. Strict rules

Sulby Reservoir

Location: Welford, between Kettering and Rugby, off the A50
Type and Size: Huge reservoir of about one hundred acres
Carp Stock: Well stocked with mirrors to doubles
Category: Mixed Fishery
Other Species: Roach and bream
Permits: British Waterways, Willow Grange, Church Road, Watord, Herts. Tel: 01923 26722
Cost: Season tickets only (limited) at £20
Control: British Waterways
BK Rating: Moderate
E/A: Severn-Trent
Comments: These big BW reservoirs certainly contain carp, although they may be hard to find in such a huge area. There could well be some very big fish caught from them in the future

Sywell Reservoir

Location: Sywell Country Park, 6 miles from Northampton off the A45; between Earls Barton and Mears Ashby
Type and Size: 20 acre reservoir
Carp Stock: Some good carp, numbers and sizes not known
Category: Mixed Fishery
Other Species: Famous as a big tench water; also pike over 20lbs, perch and roach Members only water of Wellingborough and District AC. Season tickets about £5 from local tackle shops, or Wellingborough and District AC, Mr H Battison, 36 Church Way, Weston Favell, Northampton
Control: Club. Tel: 01604 810970
BK Rating: Difficult
Restrictions: No day tickets - members only
E/A: Anglian
Comments: Warden and local tackle shops. Very busy at weekends

Thorpe Fisheries

Location: Thorpe Waterville, near Thrapston
Type and Size: Two gravel pits of 40 acres and 25 acres
Carp Stock: Well stocked with carp to 25 lbs
Category: Mixed Fishery
Other Species: Bream, crucians, roach, tench and perch

Permits: On bank
Cost: About £5 per day; £2.50 juniors, O.A.P's and disabled
Control: Northampton Castle A.A. Tel: 01604 647305
Restrictions: No boilies or floating baits; no night fishing
BK Rating: Moderate
E/A: Anglian

Thrapston Gravel Pit

Location: Thrapston, near Kettering
Type and Size: Huge gravel pit of three hundred acres - 3 miles round
How to Find: Just off the A605 at Thrapston
Carp Stock: Unknown - some small fish but a few very big carp; small head of doubles, mostly commons from the river
Category: Few Carp
Other Species: General coarse fish
Permits: Permits from B P Tackle, Mill Road, Kettering
Cost: £20 per season or £3.50 per day
BK Rating: Super-Difficult
Comments: Possibly the biggest gravel pit in the country - and could contain some of the biggest fish. Carp have bred and some small carp have been caught recently. Heavily match fished with many boats. Poor access and very long walks

Weedon Road Gravel Pits

Location: Weedon Road, Northampton
Type and Size: Mature lake of about 15 acres
How to Find: In Northampton
Carp Stock: Low density - lake record 24lbs, but there are said to be bigger fish
Category: Few Carp
Other Species: General coarse fish - large tench
Permits: Northampton Nene AC - local tackle shops
Cost: Approx £10 per season
BK Rating: Difficult
Control: Club
E/A: Anglian
Comments: Northampton Nene AC. Secretary: M Eaton, 12 Thorne Hill, Briar Hill, Northampton NN4 9SN. Permits supplied

NORTHUMBERLAND

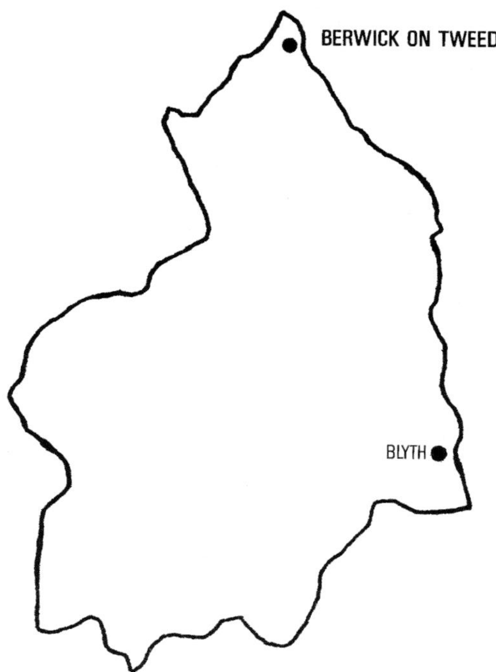

Ancroft Ponds

Location: Ancroft, on the B6525, five miles south of Berwick-on-Tweed
Type and Size: Two small ponds
Carp Stock: Some carp, numbers and sizes not known
Category: Mixed Fishery
Other Species: Crucians, roach, perch, tench and eels
Permits: Paul Armstrong. Tel: 01912 749399
Control: Club - BWAC
Restrictions: Weekly permits available for those residing outside 100 mile radius of Newcastle
BK Rating: Not known
E/A: Northumbrian
Comments: As far as we know, this is the most northerly water containing carp in England. Details are taken from the Angling Guide of the National Rivers Authority of the Northumbria Region; free copies can be obtained from the NRA at Eldon House, Regent Centre, Gosforth, Newcastle upon Tyne NE3 3UD. Tel: 01912 130266. This is an excellent guide in a way, but it doesn't give enough information; the size of the still waters is not given, the size and numbers of carp present are not mentioned and they don't tell us what BWAC means - they still haven't 3 years later!

Brenkley Pond

Location: Near Seaton Burn, between Newcastle and Cramington
Type and Size: Small pond
Carp Stock: Some carp, numbers and sizes not known
Category: Mixed Fishery
Other Species: Crucians, roach, perch, bream, tench, rudd and gudgeon
Permits: Mac Lycett. Tel: 0191 2373361
Control: Wansbeck and Cramlington AC; members only; details of membership from the phone number listed above
BK Rating: Not known
E/A: Northumbrian

Dissington Pond

Location: Ponteland, 7 miles north west of Newcastle, on the A696
Type and Size: Small pond
Carp Stock: Some carp
Category: Mixed Fishery
Other Species: Roach and perch
Permits: Paul Armstrong. Tel: 0191 2749399
Control: Club - BWAC
BK Rating: Not known
E/A: Northumbrian
Comments: There may be no close season in this and other ponds in Northumberland, Tyne and Wear, and Durham

NORTH YORKSHIRE

Acaster Malbis Lake

Location: Acaster, York
Type and Size: Lake of two acres
How to Find: Take the A64 south from York to the village of Acaster
Carp Stock: Quite well stocked with carp to about 20lbs
Category: Mixed Fishery
Other Species: Tench, roach, perch and bream
Permits: Day tickets from the office on the site, which is also a caravan site
Cost: On application
Control: Private
BK Rating: Moderate
Restrictions: No night fishing; fishing from 7am until dusk
E/A: Yorkshire

Bacon Factory Pond

Location: Sherburn - in - Elmet, near Tadcaster
Type and Size: Pond of 1½ acres
How to Find: A 162 from Tadcaster to Sherburn-in-Elmet. Fishery is on left after the roundabout
Carp Stock: Some carp to 20 lbs plus
Category: Mixed Fishery
Other Species: Roach, tench, perch and bream
Permits: On bank
Cost: £2 per day
Control: Wheatsheaf A.C. Tel: 01977 684 772
BK Rating: Not known
E/A: Yorkshire
Comments: Open all year

Balne Lake

Location: Off the A19 near Whitely Bridge, Selby
Type and Size: Five acre lake, quite shallow, surrounded by trees, and very weedy
Carp Stock: Very heavily stocked with mirrors between 5lbs and 10lbs
Category: Carp Water
Other Species: Roach
Permits: Season tickets only from local tackle shops - sometimes on the bank from owner
Control: Balne Moor AC
Restrictions: No night fishing; no carp sacks
BK Rating: Very Easy - multiple catches common
E/A: Yorkshire

Barlow Common Pond

Location: Barlow, near Selby
Type and Size: Four acre lake with an irregular bottom, and quite shallow
Carp Stock: Well stocked with small carp to about 10lbs,
Category: Mixed Fishery
Other Species: Roach, bream, tench, perch, chub and pike
Permits: Day tickets on bank
Cost: £2.50 per day. Season £18
Control: Selby District Council. Tel: 01757 617110
Restrictions: No nigh fishing. No keepnets
BK Rating: Easy
E/A: Yorkshire
Comments: This is a very weedy, shallow lake, which is a Nature Reserve, so part of the bank cannot be fished. Toilet

Birkdale Fishery

Location: Terrington, near York
Type and Size: Small, attractive lake in pleasant surroundings
Carp Stock: Well stocked with carp to 15lbs
Category: Mixed Fishery
Other Species: Tench, roach and bream
Permits: Day tickets on bank, or can be booked on 0165 384301
Cost: £3 per day plus £1 for extra rod
Control: Privately run by Wynn Jones
Restrictions: Night fishing by arrangement only
BK Rating: Moderate
Comments: Suitable for disabled anglers

Brickyard Fishery

Location: Off the A 61 at Hutton Moor, near Ripon`
Type and Size: Two small pools
Carp Stock: Well stocked with carp to 10 lbs
Category: Mixed Fishery
Other Species: Tench, perch, roach, gudgeon, golden rudd, chub and koi
Permits: In advance only from Ripon Angling Centre, 58-59 North St, Ripon Tel: 01765 604666
Cost: £5 per day; £3.50 evenings
Control: M. Scawthorn. Tel: 01765 640666
Restrictions: No night fishing; one rod only; no boilies
BK Rating: Moderate
E/A: Yorkshire

Brockholes Lake

Location: Drax, near Selby, North Yorks.
How to Find: Adjacent to the new link road between Goole and Drax
Type and Size: Lake approx 12 acres
Carp Stock: Exact figures unknown, many doubles, some 20's
Category: Mixed Fishery
Other Species: Bream, roach, tench, perch and pike
Permits: Season and Day - Season and Day/Night
Cost: £10 joining + £11 Day
Control: G Simms, 2 Oaklands, Camblesforth, Selby, N.Yorks Y08 8HH
Tel: 01757 618641
Restrictions: Juniors nightfishing must be accompanied by a senior
BK Rating: Difficult
E/A: Yorkshire
Comments: A very pleasant looking water, difficult to fish

Broken Brea **A**

Location: Off the B6217 at Brompton-on-Swale, near Richmond
Type and Size: Three acre man-made fishery; lake up to 15 feet in depth
Carp Stock: Stocked with 6,000 carp to 12lbs
Category: Mixed Fishery
Other Species: Roach, tench, bream, perch and gudgeon
Permits: On bank
Cost: £6; £3.50 for a morning or evening session
Control: Tel: 01748 825647
Restrictions: No night fishing; barbless hooks; no keepnets
BK Rating: Easy
E/A: Yorkshire
Comments: Cottages to rent for holidays; free fishing for those who stay at the cottages

Carlton Towers

Location: Off the A1041 south of Selby, and close to the M62
Type and Size: Ten acre lake in grounds of a stately home
Carp Stock: Not many, to upper doubles
Category: Few Carp
Other Species: Tench, roach, bream, perch and crucians
Permits: Carlton AC - season tickets only; enquire Tel: 01405 860791
Restrictions: Fishing the field bank only. No night fishing
BK Rating: Very Difficult
E/A: Yorkshire
Comments: Not much fished by carp anglers - a very attractive, shallow water with much weed and lilies

Catterick Lakes

Location: Allotment Lane, Catterick
Type and Size: Three gravel pits
Carp Stock: Heavily stocked with carp to over 20 lbs
Category: Mixed Fishery
Other Species: Roach, bream, perch and chub
Permits: Cafe, Allotment Lane
Cost: About £3 per day
Control: Leeds D.A.S. Tel: 01132 645500
Restrictions: No night fishing
BK Rating: Moderate

E/A: Yorkshire
Comments: One lake is a specialist carp fishery. River fishing on the River Swale included

Cawood Park — A

Location: Cawood, near Tadcaster
Type and Size: Three acre park lake
How to Find: From Tadcaster take the A162 towards Sherburn-in-Elmet, then turn left onto the B1223 towards Selby. After the village of Ryther, the lake will be found just before Cawood, on the right
Carp Stock: Well stocked with carp to 20lbs
Category: Mixed Fishery
Other Species: Large pike, roach, perch, chub, bream, pike, trout and tench
Permits: Day tickets from the site warden
Cost: Day £4; week £18; season £50
Control: Private. Details of fishing and caravans and bungalows to rent from Mr W G Archer, Tel: Cawood 450 or Site Warden, Tel: Cawood 8865
BK Rating: Not known
Restrictions: No keepnets except in matches. All trout to be returned immediately
E/A: Yorkshire
Comments: This is a caravan site and park, with luxury caravans and bungalows to rent. Licensed bar, children's boating pond and amusements. Trout fishing from March 25th. Open all year

Crag Pond

Location: Reynard Crag Lane, High Birstwith, near Darley, Harrogate
Type and Size: Small pond with island
How to Find: Turn off the A 59 to Darley
Carp Stock: Some carp to 8 lbs
Category: Mixed Fishery
Other Species: Chub, perch, tench and small roach
Permits: On bank
Cost: £5 per day; £3.50 juniors and 4 pm to dusk
Control: Richard Bartle, Tel: 01423 770334
Restrictions: No boilies, groundbait or night fishing
BK Rating: Not known - water opened in 1996
E/A: Yorkshire

Drax Lake

Location: Drax, near Selby - off the A1041 between Selby and Goole
Type and Size: Attractive lake of about 10 acres
Carp Stock: Well stocked with carp to low 20's, heavily weeded and surrounded by trees
Permits: Season ticket only - Mr G Simms, 2 Oaklands, Camblesforth, Selby
Cost: £10 joining fee, then £8 per season - reduced prices for juniors and OAP's
Control: Private
Restrictions: No sacks, weighing slings or radio-controlled boats
BK Rating: Moderate
E/A: Yorkshire
Comments: A very pleasant water, though weedy and lines of 15lbs. BS are recommended. All methods are successful

Dringhouses Lake

Location: Southern outskirts of York City
Type and Size: Three acre lake
How to Find: From York take the A1036 Tadcaster road. The lake is about three miles from the city centre
Carp Stock: Quite well stocked with a number of doubles to about 20lbs
Category: Mixed Fishery
Other Species: Pike, roach, rudd, chub and perch
Permits: Day tickets from house on site, must be obtained before fishing
Cost: On application - extra cost if not bought before starting to fish
Control: Private
BK Rating: Moderate
Restrictions: Night fishing on car park bank only
E/A: Yorkshire
Comments: Pleasant water with trees, but quite heavily fished

Ellerton Park

Location: Ellerton Park, Scorton, Richmond
Type and Size: 60 acre gravel pit, very deep in places
How to Find: Take the B 6271 from Catterick Bridge towards Northallerton, At Scorton, turn right and the fishery is in one mile
Carp Stock: Not many carp, but most are big - up to 20 lbs
Category: Mixed Fishery
Other Species: Pike, bream, roach, tench, perch and a few big barbel
Permits: On bank
Cost: £2 per day; juniors £1
Control: Tel: 01748 811373
Restrictions: No night fishing
BK Rating: Difficult
Baits/Methods: Legered boilies best
E/A: Yorkshire
Comments: A very hard water, best suited to the specimen hunter

Elvington Lake

Location: Elvington, near York
Type and Size: Lake of 3½ acres
How to Find: Take the B1228 from York towards Elvington to the south east of the city. The lake is just over 5 miles from York
Carp Stock: The lake is well stocked with carp, with plenty of small ones but many doubles to about 15lbs. Bigger fish are said to have been caught
Category: Mixed Fishery
Other Species: Bream, roach, rudd, tench, chub, perch. There are rumoured to be one or two barbel in the water
Permits: Day tickets from the house on the property - Mr S Britton, Lake Cottage, Elvington, York. Tel: 01904 608255. £3 for carp fishing
Control: Private
BK Rating: Easy
Restrictions: No night fishing, no groundbaiting
E/A: Yorkshire
Comments: No close season. Toilets and washing facilities. Prize winner for flowers in bloom

Fairview Lake

Location: In Broad Lane, Cawood Common, near Selby
Type and Size: Small lake
How to Find: Take the B1233 from Selby, and the lake is near the intersection with the B1222
Carp Stock: Well stocked with carp, sizes unknown
Category: Mixed Fishery
Other Species: Tench, rudd, perch and rainbow trout
Permits: Day tickets from the cottage on the banks of the fishery
BK Rating: Moderate
Control: Private
E/A: Yorkshire
Comments: A pleasant and attractive lake

Gowdall Pond

Location: New Gowdall, Hemingbrough, near Selby
Type & Size: Small pond of just over one acre, weedy and shallow
Carp Stock: Quite well stocked with carp to middle doubles
Category: Mixed Fishery
Other Species: Roach and bream
Permits: Day tickets on site
Cost: £2 per rod per day
Control: Private
Restrictions: No night fishing, day tickets only
BK Rating: Moderate
E/A Yorkshire

Grafton Mere A

Location: Prospect Farm, Marton-cum-Grafton, Boroughbridge
Type and Size: Man-made lake of 2½ acres, spring fed; three quarter acre lake
How to Find: This village is between York and Ripon. Take the B65265 from Boroughbridge to York. After 3 miles turn right to Grafton
Carp Stock: 8 doubles to 18lbs; 80 of 5-19lbs; 200 of 2lbs+, stocked in 1987
Category: Carp Only
Other Species: None
Permits: Pospect Farm. Tel: 01423 322045 (Roger Naish), must book by telephone
Cost: On application
BK Rating: Easy
Control: Private
Restrictions: Barbless hooks
E/A: Yorkshire
Comments: 100 yards from good pub. Bus service to York which is 16 miles. Three holiday cottages and bed and breakfast in 18th century working farm. Ideal centre for family holiday near Yorkshire Moors, dales and coast. Open all year. A one day catch of 306lbs (44 carp to 18lbs)

Green Lane Pond

Location: Scorton, near Richmond
Type and Size: 3 acre farm pond
How to Find: Farmhouse on track off the B 1263
Carp Stock: Well stocked with carp to doubles
Category: Mixed Fishery
Other Species: Tench, perch, roach, rudd and chub
Permits: From the farmhouse
Cost: About £5 per day

Control: Farm
BK Rating: Not known
E/A: Yorkshire
Comments: Open all year

Hay-A-Park

Location: On the outskirts of Knaresborough
Type and Size: Small gravel pit in two parts totalling three acres
Carp Stock: Reasonable head of carp averaging 10lbs, largest reported to date is 18lbs
Other Species: Bream, roach, rudd, tench, pike and perch
Permits: M and C Johnson Fishing Tackle, Briggate, Knaresborough. Tel: 01423 863065. Permits must be obtained before fishing
Control: Private. Knaresborough Piscatorials incorporating Dales AC
Baits/Metods: Normal carp tactics and baits
BK Rating: Fairly Easy
E/A: Yorkshire

Hollingwood Pool

Location: Leeming, behind the garden centre
Type and Size: Tiny pool
Carp Stock: Well stocked with carp to 5 lbs
Category: Mixed Fishery
Other Species: Tench
Permits: On bank
Cost: £4 per day; £2.50 juniors
Control: Tel: 01677 424706
Restrictions: No boilies; cereal groundbait; night fishing; barbless hooks
BK Rating: Easy
E/A: Yorkshire

Hoxne Farm Pond

Location: Sheriff Hutton Road, Strensall, York
Type and Size: Four small pools
Carp Stock: Mirrors and commons to 20lbs
Category: Mixed Fishery
Other Species: Usual coarse fish
Permits: Tel: 01904 490726
Cost: £2 to £3 per day
Restrictions: Fishing 7.30am till dusk only; barbless hooks
BK Rating: Moderate
E/A: Yorkshire

Knaresborough Lagoon

Location: Stockwell Lane, Knaresborough
Type and Size: Gravel pit of about 55 acres
Carp Stock: Some carp over 32lbs
Category: Few Carp
Other Species: Pike, bream and tench
Permits: Day tickets from tackle shops in Knaresborough and Harrogate
Control: Knaresborough Piscatorials incorporating Dales AC
BK Rating: Very Difficult
E/A: Yorkshire
Comments: A very clear water, and hard to fish. Recent restocking

Lightwater Valley Lake

Location: Lightwater Valley Theme Park, near Sheffield
Type and Size: 15 acre lake
Carp Stock: Well stocked with small carp to doubles
Category: Mixed Fishery
Other Species: Roach and bream
Permits: Day tickets on site at £2 per rod
Control: Private
Restrictions: No *day* fishing! Fishing is 6pm to 9am only
BK Rating: Easy
E/A: Yorkshire
Comments: Too many people on the park during the day, so only night fishing is allowed. Possibly no close season. Three rods allowed

Lingcroft Farm Pond

Location: One mile south off the York by-pass on the A19 towards Selby; farm is on the right
Type and Size: Small farm pond with large island - a former moat
Carp Stock: Heavily stocked with carp to 20lbs
Category: Mixed Fishery
Other Species: Bream, chub and roach
Permits: Season tickets from the farmhouse, cost £20
BK Rating: Easy
Control: Private. Tel: 01904 633146. No cereal groundbait. No carp in keepnets
E/A: Yorkshire
Comments: Much wildlife on this very pleasant fishery, so no litter and no left line, which damages wildlife. All proceeds from the fishery are donated to Fulford Church - this is a new one to us; could it start a trend?

Moulton Lane Pond

Location: Moulton Lane, North Cowton, off the A 167 between Croft-on-Tees and Dalton
Type and Size: Small pond with island
Carp Stock: Well stocked with carp averaging about 6 lbs
Category: Mixed Fishery
Other Species: Tench, roach, rudd, perch and bream
Permits: On bank
Cost: £3 per day; £2 juniors and O.A.P's
Control: Private. Tel: 01325 378345
Restrictions: No groundbait
BK Rating: Moderate
E/A: Yorkshire

Newhay Lake

Location: Newhay Carp Farm, near Selby
Type and Size: Three lakes
How to Find: Take the A63 from Selby, and at Hemingborough turn right to Newhay
Carp Stock: Well stocked with carp to 28lbs
Category: Mixed Fishery
Other Species: Bream, tench, chub, roach, perch and barbel
Permits: Day tickets on site. Tel: 01757 638383
Control: Private
Cost: £10, £15 for 24 hours; £25 for 48 hours
BK Rating: Moderate
Restrictions: Fishing times are from 8am till dusk; no keepnets or groundbait.

	Barbless or microbarb hooks
E/A:	Yorkshire
Comments:	No close season; some night fishing by arrangement

New Marske Reservoir

Location:	Grewgrass Lane, Langbaugh, near Redcar
Type and Size:	Small reservoir
Carp Stock:	Well stocked with doubles to 20 lbs
Category:	Mixed Fishery
Other Species:	Bream, perch, tench, crucians and gudgeon
Permits:	In advance only from Angler's Choice, Middlesborough or Redcar Angling Centre
Cost:	About £3 per day
Control:	Middlesborough A.C. Tel: 01642 815147
BK Rating:	Not known
E/A:	Yorkshire

Northingales Fish Ponds

Location:	Cawood, near York
Type and Size:	Two ponds of twelve acres and one acre
How to Find:	Take the A19 south from York towards Selby, and turn off on B1222 to Cawood
Carp Stock:	Both lakes contain some carp and the bigger one has fish to about 20lbs
Category:	Mixed Fishery
Carp Stock:	Tench, roach, bream, perch, dace, trout and gudgeon
Permits:	Day tickets from the house at the site, cost approx £1.50. Details from the owner. Tel: 01757 268414
Control:	Private
BK Rating:	Moderate
Restrictions:	One rod only. No night fishing. No juniors (under 16) unless accompanied by an adult. No groundbait
E/A:	Yorkshire
Comments:	Toilet

Oak Mere Fishery

Location:	Hill Farm, Skipwith, between York and Market Weighton
Type and Size:	Pond of less than two acres in size, only dug in 1989
How to Find:	From York take the A19 towards Selby and turn right onto the A163 for two miles. At the crossroads turn left towards Skipwith. Hill Farm is on the right after Skipwith
Carp Stock:	Some carp to over 10lbs
Category:	Few Carp
Other Species:	Tench, rudd, bream and crucians
Permits:	On the bank or from Hill Farm
Cost:	£3 per day; £2 after 5pm in summer; winter day tickets are £2
Control:	Anthony Patrick. Tel: 01757 288910
Restrictions:	Lots! No night fishing (dawn till dusk only); barbless hooks; one rod only; no groundbait, no keepnets for carp
BK Rating:	Difficult
E/A:	Yorkshire - they use this as a stockpond, which is perhaps why there are so many restrictions

Park View Lake

Location:	Off the A 166 at Sand Hutton, near Stamford Bridge
Type and Size:	5 acre lake
Carp Stock:	Well stocked with carp to nearly 30 lbs

Category: Mixed Fishery
Other Species: Roach, tench, bream, perch and pike
Permits: From local tackle shops
Cost: £25 per season; £12.50 O.A.P's and disabled; £10 juniors
Control: York D.A.A. Tel: 01904 783178
BK Rating: Not known
Baits/Methods: Legered boilies best
E/A: Yorkshire
Comments: Platform for the disabled

Primrose Valley Holiday Camp

Location: On the A165 Bridlington to Scarborough road
Type and Size: Small lake
Carp Stock: Well stocked with carp to 26lbs
Category: Mixed Fishery
Other Species: Usual coarse fish
Permits: On site; all information from Linford's Tackle Shop, Bridlington
Cost: £2 per day
BK Rating: Moderate
E/A: Yorkshire
Comments: Shallow boating lake, best fished early and late

Pumping Station Lakes

Location: Angram, Barlby, near Selby
Type and Size: Two lakes of about two acres each, both of which are fairly deep and weedy
Carp Stock: Well stocked with carp to double figures
Category: Mixed Fishery
Other Species: Coarse fish
Permits: None necessary - free fishing
Control: Council
Restrictions: No night fishing
BK Rating: Moderate
E/A: Yorkshire

Racecourse Lake

Location: Near Ripon
Type and Size: Pit of about 15 acres
How to Find: The fishery is about 1½ miles south of Ripon, in the middle of Ripon Racecourse
Carp Stock: Quite well stocked with carp which include a number doubles. A 28 has been caught
Category: Mixed Fishery
Other Species: Bream, rudd, tench, roach
Permits: Season tickets from Ripon Piscatorial Angling Association. Mainly membership only for locals but some tickets for those from outside the area. Details from the Secretary: Mr R Looney, 12 Lower Street, St Ripon, or P Godden, 3 Oak Road, Ripon, SAE required. Day tickets about £4 from Ripon Angling Centre, North Street, Ripon
Control: Club. Tel: 01765 605467
BK Rating: Moderate
E/A: Yorkshire

Raker Lake

Location: Wheldrake, off the B1228 south east of York
Type and Size: Newly opened fishery of three acres, mixed lake and small specialist carp lake
Carp Stock: Main lake stocked with carp to 7lb. Carp Lake stocked with carp to 14lbs
Category: Mixed Fishery
Other Species: Roach, rudd, bream, tench, chub, dace and perch in main lake
Permits: From self-service unit in car park at £3 per day
Control: Tel: 01904 448793
Restrictions: No night fishing; particle baits and keepnets not allowed on carp lake
BK Rating: Moderate
E/A: Yorkshire
Comments: Some access for the disabled; toilets

Red House Lagoon

Location: Close to the River Ouse at Moor Monkton, off the A59 north west of York
Type and Size: Large lake often flooded from the river
Carp Stock: Some carp, but few and far between
Category: Few Carp
Other Species: Bream, roach, tench, perch and a few pike and chub
Permits: Day tickets in advance only by sending a SAE to S Tomlinson, 57 Water Lane, Clifton, York YO3 6PW. Tel: 01904 638237
Cost: £3 per day
Control: York AA
Restrictions: No night fishing
BK Rating: Super-Difficult
E/A: Yorkshire

Ripon Canal

Location: Near Ripon
Type and Size: Small narrow canal, with little boat traffic
Carp Stock: Well stocked with carp to 10lbs
Category: Mixed Fishery
Other Species: Usual coarse fish
Permits: Tel: 01765 607114
Control: Club
Restrictions: Possibly no night fishing; used for matches at £1.50 per peg
BK Rating: Easy
E/A: Yorkshire

Roger's Pond

Location: Off the B 6265 near Ripon
Type and Size: 3 acre gravel pit
Carp Stock: Some carp to doubles
Category: Few Carp
Other Species: Crucians, dace, gudgeon and chub
Permits: In advance only from Ripon Angling Centre, Ripon
Cost: £4 per day
Control: Private. Tel: 01765 690422
Restrictions: No boilies
BK Rating: Difficult
E/A: Yorkshire
Comments: Open all year

Scarborough Mere

Location: In the town of Scarborough, off the Seamer Road
Type and Size: Eighteen acre mere
Carp Stock: Some carp to doubles
Category: Probably Few Carp
Other Species: Bream, tench, roach and pike
Permits: From bailiff on bank, or from Buckleys Tackle Shop, Leading Post Street, Scarborough, low cost
Cost: £2 per day. £18 per season plus £9 joining fee. Concessions
Control: Scarborough Mere Angling Club. Tel: 01723 353913
BK Rating: Probably Difficult for the bigger carp
E/A: Yorkshire
Comments: Refreshments on site during summer

Scrapyard Pond

Location: Drax, between Selby and Goole
Type and Size: Shallow ballast pit of about two acres
Carp Stock: Not very many, but some doubles to about 20lbs
Category: Few Carp
Other Species: Roach, perch and tench
Permits: British Rail Staff Association - enquire from the scrapyard or try G Harcome, 8 Upper Belmont Road, St Andrews, Bristol - possibly day tickets
Control: British Rail
BK Rating: Very Difficult
E/A: Yorkshire

Shearons Pond

Location: Goose Hill, Carlton, near Selby
Type and Size: Two acre lake, specially dug about 25 years ago
Carp Stock: Some coarse fish
Permits: Free to holders of a Yorkshire W/A licence
Restrictions: Night fishing is allowed
BK Rating: Very Easy
Baits/Methods: Good floater water, but any bait and method works well
Comments: Good lake all the year round, and ideal for a practice water

Staveley Lakes

Location: Staveley, between Harrogate and Ripon
Type and Size: Two lakes of three acres and two acres
How to Find: Take the A6055 from Knaresborough and turn left going north to Staveley
Carp Stock: Quite well stocked with carp to about 16lbs with a number of doubles. Fish of over 20lbs rumoured
Category: Mixed Fishery
Other Species: Tench, chub, rudd, perch and bream
Permits: Bradford City Angling Association. Season tickets from Mr H Briggs, 4 Brown Hill Close, Birkenshaw, Bradford, West Yorkshire
Control: Club
BK Rating: Moderate
E/A: Yorkshire

Thirsk Brick Ponds

Location: Newsham Road, Thirsk
Type and Size: Two small pools
Carp Stock: Some carp averaging about 8 lbs

Category: Mixed Fishery
Other Species: Pike, perch, tench and roach
Permits: In advance only from bailiff
Cost: About £2 per day
Control: The Dowlands, Newsham Road. Tel: 01845 522932
BK Rating: Not known
E/A: Yorkshire

Thorpe Underwood Water Meadows

Location: Thorpe Underwood between York and Harrogate - off the B 6265 near Green Hamerton
Type and Size: 3 acre lake
Carp Stock: Well stocked with carp to 10 lbs
Category: Mixed Fishery
Other Species: Roach, rudd, bream, tench and perch
Permits: On bank
Cost: £5 per day; £3 evenings and juniors
Control: Tel: 01423 331080
Restrictions: No boilies, or carp in keepnets; no barbed hooks
BK Rating: Moderate
E/A: Yorkshire
Comments: Toilets. Open all year

Three Lakes

Location: Selby
Type and Size: Lake of about eleven acres
Carp Stock: Well stocked with carp to over 33lbs
Category: Carp Water
Other Species: Reported are tench to 8lbs, eels to 6lbs, bream to 11lb, large perch, roach and trout
Permits: Private syndicate
Cost: £400 per year
Control: Private
Baits/Methods: Normal carp fishing baits and methods. Boilies good
Restrictions: No particle baits
BK Rating: Moderate
E/A: Yorkshire
Comments: Catches of up to a dozen fish a day reported. Over 60 twenties and 4 thirties

Tollerton Fishing Ponds A

Location: Just off the A19, 10 miles from York and three miles from Tollerton
Type and Size: Three small ponds
Carp Stock: Quite a number of doubles, with the record at 28lbs
Category: Mixed Fishery
Other Species: Tench, perch, roach, chub and pike
Permits: If you arrive before 7am you can start fishing, and pay on the bank; for arrivals after 7am you can buy your day ticket from the house
Cost: £3 per day from the house
Control: Private; Margaret Wackerman Tel: 01347 838115
Restrictions: No night fishing; dawn till dusk only; no groundbaiting; no keepnets for carp
BK Rating: Moderate
E/A: Yorkshire
Comments: Bed and breakfast at £10 per night, to include a day's fishing. Pleasant looking ponds, close together, with reeds etc

Twin Otters Fishery

Location: Womersley, off the A19 Doncaster Whitley road, near a transport cafe
Type and Size: Small lake, with an island, in private grounds
Carp Stock: Well stocked with carp, including 50 doubles to over 20lbs
Category: Mixed Fishery
Other Species: Crucians, rudd, roach, bream, perch, chub and tench
Permits: On the bank at £3 per day
Restrictions: No night fishing; no groundbaiting
BK Rating: Easy
E/A: Yorkshire

Welham Lake

Location: Norton Golf Club, Malton
Type and Size: Five acre lake
How to Find: Take the Welham road from Malton, and follow the sign to Malton and Norton Golf Club. The lake is in woodland to the right after entering the golf course
Carp Stock: Stocked with carp in 1988, sizes not known
Category: Probably Few Carp, though might become a Mixed Fishery
Other Species: Tench and eels
Permits: Permits only in advance before visiting. Booking advised, from Mike O'Donnell, Moorland Trout Lake, Pickering. Tel: 01751 73101
Cost: £8 per day (24 hours) - one rod only
Control: Private
BK Rating: Insufficient information
Restrictions: 8 anglers only per day. No permits on bank. Barbless hooks
Comments: A famous tench water, and very picturesque

Westerley Lake

Location: Wheldrake, six miles south east of York, off the B1228 road
Type and Size: Four acre lake
Carp Stock: Quite well stocked with carp to lower doubles
Category: Mixed Fishery
Other Species: Grass carp, bream, roach, rudd, perch and tench
Permits: On the bank at £2.50 per day. You can also get permits from the bungalow on the site, or from Springwell Garden Centre nearby
Control: Bruce Hairsine. Tel: 01904 448500
Restrictions: No night fishing - dawn to dusk only; no hemp or groundbait
BK Rating: Moderate
E/A: Yorkshire

Whitefield Reservoir

Location: Barrows Lane, Steeton, off the A629 Keighley - Skipton road
Type and Size: Small reservoir
Carp Stock: Some carp, numbers and sizes not known, but thought to be at least to double figure size
Category: Few Carp or Mixed Fishery
Other Species: Pike, roach, tench and perch
Permits: Keighley Angling Club - members only but open to all - Mr D Ward, 4 Compeigne Avenue, Keighley, North Yorkshire
Control: Club
E/A: Yorkshire

Willowgarth Fishery

Location: Carlton Miniott, near Thirsk
Type and Size: Two acre lake
How to Find: Turn left off the A19 north of York, go through Thirsk and just after Carlton Miniott turn left
Carp Stock: Well stocked with carp to mid-doubles; also ghost carp
Category: Carp Water
Other Species: Roach, perch and tench, and stocked annually with rainbow trout
Permits: Day tickets on bank
Cost: £5 March to end October; £3 November 1st to end February. Evening tickets half price
Control: Private
BK Rating: Easy
Restrictions: No night fishing - 6am to 9pm only
E/A: Yorkshire
Comments: Said to be Yorkshire's prettiest and most heavily stocked fishery. Car park and refreshment bar. One side suitable for disabled anglers. Groundbait, keepnets and nuts as baits are not allowed. No close season. Information from the owner Robin Fletcher. Tel: 01845 522827

Wistow Pit

Location: Broad Lane, Cawood Common, on the A1222 south of York
Type and Size: Very attractive three acre lake
Carp Stock: Well stocked with carp to low doubles, with possibly one or two just reaching 20lbs
Category: Mixed Fishery
Other Species: Tench, roach and bream
Permits: Day tickets on bank
Cost: About £2 per rod
Control: Private
Restrictions: No night fishing
BK Rating: Difficult
E/A: Yorkshire

Yorkshire Lakeside Lodges

Location: Outskirts of York, formerly known as 'Hoggy's Pond'
Type and Size: Large lake
How to Find: Edge of York
Carp Stock: Some carp to over 34lbs
Category: Mixed Fishery
Other Species: Tench
Permits: Tel: 01904 702346
Cost: On application
BK Rating: Difficult
Control: Private
E/A: Yorkshire
Comments: Full details from the phone number above

NOTTINGHAMSHIRE

Arches Lake

Location: East Retford, off the A638
Type and Size: Small, attractive lake near town
Carp Stock: Some carp to over 20lbs
Category: Mixed Fishery
Other Species: Roach, tench and bream
Permits: Sheffield Piscatorial Association; enquire from tackle shops in Sheffield
Control: Small club, with waters not heavily fished
BK Rating: Difficult, as there are not large numbers of carp
E/A: Severn-Trent

Attenborough North

Location: Long Lane, Attenborough, Beeston
Type and Size: Seven gravel pits from 13 acres to 43 acres
How to Find: Off the A6005 Beeston road through Attenborough village
Carp Stock: Not known - some carp to 13lbs
Category: Few Carp
Other Species: General coarse fish
Permits: Season tickets only
Cost: £21.00
Other Species: General coarse fish
Permits: Season tickets only
BK Rating: Not known
Control: Leisure Sport Angling, Staines Road, Chertsey, Surrey. Tel: 01932 564872

Restrictions: No night fishing
E/A: Severn-Trent
Comments: Site of Special Scientific Interest

Attenborough South (River Trent)

Location: Barton Lane, Long Eaton, Nottingham
Type and Size: Gravel pit of 114 acres; 2,500 metres of River Trent
How to Find: Station Road, Long Eaton. Take New Hythe Street, opposite Horseshoe Sports Tackle Shop for one mile to municipal car park
Carp Stock: There may be no carp in the lake, but carp to 31llbs have been reported from the River Trent area
Category: Few Carp
Other Species: Mixed coarse fish
Permits: Frank Russel 'Wotsits' Tackle Shop, 8 Archer Road, Stapleford, Nottingham. Tel: 011590 396096
Cost: £2
BK Rating: Very Difficult
Control: Leisure Sport Angling, Staines Road, Chertsey, Surrey Tel: 01932 564872
E/A: Severn-Trent
Comments: Main interest is in the river but it should be noted that this is regarded as a separate fishery, with fishing only allowed when no matches are taking place. Information from Gordon Plummer on Tel: 01602 3245

Besthorpe Fleet

Location: Tinkers Lane, Besthorpe, near Newark
Type and Size: 4 acre lake
Carp Stock: Some carp to doubles
Category: Few Carp
Other Species: Pike, tench, roach, bream and big eels
Permits: On bank
Cost: About £3 per day
Control: Collingham A.A. Tel: 01636 892280
BK Rating: Difficult
E/A: Severn Trent

Bestwood Pond

Location: Near Nottingham
Type and Size: Medium sized pool
How to Find: Enquire locally
Carp Stock: Well stocked, sizes not known
Category: Mixed Fishery
Other Species: General coarse fish
Permits: Notts AA - local tackle shops
Cost: On application
BK Rating: Insufficient information
E/A: Severn-Trent
Comments: Try local tackle shops for information, and also Nottingham and District Federation, W Belshaw, 17 Spring Green, Clifton Estate, Nottingham; and Notts AA, E J Collin, 224 Radford Boulevard, Nottingham NG7 5QG. Both supply tickets and information on other carp waters controlled by Nottingham clubs

Bleasby Lake

Location: Off the A38 between Mansfield and Sutton-in-Ashfield
Type and Size: 60 acre ancient lake, with much weed, and very shallow
Carp Stock: Not many carp, but they go to upper 20's
Category: Few Carp
Other Species: Most coarse fish
Permits: In advance only, low cost
Control: Members only water of Mansfield and District A. Secretary: A Quick, 138 Huthwaite Road, Sutton-in-Ashfield NG17 2GX
BK Rating: Very Difficult
E/A: Severn-Trent
Comments: This is a beautiful lake, but is very hard to fish, and very few carp are caught. In hot weather in the summer the weed makes the lake very difficult to fish, and you should only tackle this one if you are prepared for many long blanks

Butterley Reservoir

Location: Near Ripley
Type and Size: Medium sized reservoir
How to Find: No information. Try local tackle shops
Carp Stock: Well stocked, sizes not known
Category: Mixed Fishery
Other Species: General coarse fish
Permits: Ripley and District AA. From local tackle shops - day tickets
Cost: On application
BK Rating: Moderate
Control: Club
E/A: Severn-Trent
Comments: Little known - try locally, Ripley and District AA - R Turner, 2a Argyll Road, Ripley - ticket supplied

Coach House Pond

Location: The Coaching House, Tickhill, Bawtry
Type and Size: Very tiny estate pond
Carp Stock: Not many carp, but a possible 20
Category: Few Carp
Other Species: Tench and roach
Permits: On application from the house on the property - enquire locally for information
Control: Private
Restrictions: No night fishing, except by arrangement
BK Rating: Difficult
E/A: Severn-Trent

Daneshill Lake

Location: Daneshill Road, Torworth, Retford
Type and Size: 21 acre lake
How to Find: Just off the A1 north west of East Retford,near the main railway line
Carp Stock: Stocked in 1984 with 48 carp to 11lbs, but mirrors to 34lbs reported
Category: Mixed Fishery
Other Species: General coarse fish and pike to over 20 pounds
Permits: Day tickets on site
Cost: Approx £2 per day; £15 per season - night syndicate £55
BK Rating: Moderate
Control: Daneshill AC. Tel: 01909 770917 (day) or 01909 565787 (evening)

Restrictions: Night fishing reserved for syndicate. No inflatable boats
E/A: Severn-Trent

Erewash Canal

Location: Long Eaton area
Type and Size: Twelve mile canal
How to Find: Close to M1 from Long Eaton northwards
Carp Stock: Some good carp
Category: Mixed Fishery
Other Species: General coarse fish
Permits: Local tackle shops
Cost: On application
Control: Long Eaton AA and Long Eaton Victoria AS
BK Rating: Moderate
E/A: Severn-Trent
Comments: Once polluted, this canal is now restored and restocked, and it holds some good specimen fish. Long Eaton AA, W Parker, 75 College Street, Long Eaton, Notts; Long Eaton Victoria AS, D Kent, 18 Collingwood Road, Long Eaton, Notts. Permits available from both club secretaries

Grantham Canal

Location: Bottesford, to the west of Grantham
Type and Size: Attractive, very narrow and reeded canal stretch, with few boats
How to Find: Take the A52 Grantham to Bottesford road, then the Easthorpe road to Bottesford
Carp Stock: Some carp to over 10lbs
Category: Mixed Fishery
Other Species: Tench, bream and roach
Permits: Day and season tickets on bank, or from Matchman Supplies, Nottingham
Cost: £2 per day; £8 per season
Control: Bottesford DAA - Norman Chenoweth. Tel: 01159 335793
Restrictions: No night fishing
BK Rating: Difficult, at least until the carp are located
E/A: Severn-Trent

Harthill Reservoir

Location: Harthill, Worksop, off the A57
Type and Size: Two lakes of twenty acres and five acres, both heavily weeded
Carp Stock: Both stocked with a few big carp, most of which are doubles
Category: Few Carp
Other Species: Most coarse fish
Permits: Day tickets on bank - about £3
Control: Worksop and District AA. Secretary: R Whitehead, 72 Dryden Vale, Worksop. Tel: 01909 485176
Restrictions: No night fishing, and sailing in daytime
BK Rating: Very Difficult
E/A: Severn-Trent

Iron Mongers Pond

Location: Wilford, Nottinghm
Type and Size: Small man-made pond
Carp Stock: Said to be some carp, numbers and sizes not known
Category: Mixed Fishery
Other Species: Usual coarse fish
Permits: Day tickets from bailiff on bank

Control: Nottingham AA
BK Rating: Not known
E/A: Severn-Trent

Langold Lake

Location: Near Worksop
Type and Size: Big old gravel pit, very attractive, of more than 20 acres in size
Carp Stock: Not many but most are doubles with a possible 20
Category: Few Carp
Other Species: Most coarse fish
Permits: Day tickets from bailiff on site
Cost: £3 per day
Control: Private
Restrictions: No night fishing; no season tickets; two rods only
BK Rating: Difficult
E/A: Severn-Trent
Comments: A busy and heavily fished water, though as there are so few carp there are not many carp anglers

L. Lake

Location: Rainworth, Mansfield
Type and Size: 2 lakes, one of several acres
How to Find: Take the A 617 from Mansfield towards Newark. At Rainworth turn right towards the fishery
Carp Stock: Well stocked with carp to doubles
Category: Mixed Fishery
Other Species: Pike, tench, bream, roach, perch and crucians
Permits: On bank
Cost: £5 per day, £60 per season (£30 juniors and O.A.P's)
Control: Tel: 01623 490731
Restrictions: No boilies
BK Rating: Moderate
E/A: Anglian
Comments: Attractive estate lakes; toilets

Lound Windsurf Lake

Location: Chainbridge Lane, Lound, East Retford
Type and Size: Large lake
How to Find: Off the A638, north of East Retford
Carp Stock: Some carp to over 20lbs, including commons to 27lbs
Category: Mixed Fishery
Other Species: General coase fish
Permits: East Midlands Windsurf Centre on lake shore
Cost: About £80 per season
BK Rating: Moderate
Control: Private
Restrictions: None
E/A: Severn-Trent
Comments: Obviously, there will be windsurfing on this lake! Weedy at times

Manor House Fishery

Location: North Muskham, near Newark
Type and Size: Three lakes, North Muskham, near Newark and a stretch of the River Trent (largest 12 acres)
How to Find: Find North Muskham, which is north of Newark, near the A1

Carp Stock: Some good bags of small carp of under 5lbs are taken from the Trent in this area though there is always the chance of bigger fish. No.1 lake to 32lbs
Category: Mixed Fishery
Other Species: Roach, chub, bream, dace, tench, pike, bleak, gudgeon
Permits: Day tickets from the owner at his house on site. Walter Bower - Tel: 01636 702457
Cost: £3 per day
Restrictions: Fishing 6am to 7pm only
Control: Private
E/A: Severn-Trent
Comments: Toilet. Disabled access. Fishing on the River Trent included

Maythorne Mill Pool

Location: Maythorne, near Newark
Type and Size: One acre pool with island
Carp Stock: Well stocked with carp to over 20 lbs
Category: Mixed Fishery
Other Species: Bream, tench, roach and perch
Permits: On bank
Cost: About £5 per day
Control: Tel: 01636 812128
Restrictions: No boilies or groundbait
BK Rating: Not known
E/A: Severn Trent

Newark Dyke

Location: Just north of Newark-upon-Trent
Type and Size: Short cut off the main River Trent, much used for match fishig
Carp Stock: Not many, but fish over 20lbs have been caught
Category: Few Carp
Other Species: Chub, roach, barbel and gudgeon
Permits: Day tickets on bank
Cost: £3 per day - no season tickets
Control: Newark and District AA
BK Rating: Very Difficult
E/A: Severn-Trent

Nottingham - Grantham Canal

Location: Winding canal, between both towns - Nottingham and Grantham
Type and Size: Narrow, canal many miles in length
Category: Mixed Fishery
Other Species: Most coarse fish
Permits: Diffierent clubs - enquire from tackle shops in both towns
BK Rating: Difficult, until fish located, but in the heavily stocked areas it is quite easy
E/A: Severn-Trent

River Trent

Location: Dunham Bridge
Type and Size: Large river
How to Find: West bank near Dunham Bridge, off the A57 Lincoln-Sheffield road
Carp Stock: All sizes up to 22lbs (commons)
Category: Mixed Fishery
Other Species: General coarse fish
Permits: From local tackle shops, Sheffield and District AA, PO Box 218, Sheffield S1 1BU

Cost: £10 per season
BK Rating: Difficult
Control: Club
Restrictions: Heavily match fished
E/A: Severn-Trent
Comments: Tidal water

Sapphire Lakes A

Location: Norwell Lane, Cromwell, near Newark-on-Trent
Type and Size: Three lakes - 12 acres of water
How to Find: On the A1 just north of Newark; the Morwell road
Carp Stock: Heavily stocked with carp to 25lbs, best 30lbs. Many doubles
Category: Mixed Fishery
Other Species: Bream, and tench
Permits: On site. Tel: 01636 821131
Cost: £6 per day £6 per night; £75 per week. Winter ticket £75
BK Rating: Moderate
Control: Ken and Eunice Barker
Restrictions: Line below 10lbs BS banned in carp lake. Barbless hooks
E/A: Severn-Trent
Comments: A widely publicised fishery with big catches recorded - many doubles and some twenties. No close season. Booking advised for carp lake. Food on request. 2 caravans to let at £10 per night. Toilets

Shireoaks Hall Lake

Location: Shireoaks, just off the A57 between Worksop and Sheffield
Type and Size: 4 lakes of about 2 1/2 acres on estate
Carp Stock: Very heavily stocked with small carp to low doubles
Category: Carp Water
Permits: Day tickets on bank at low cost
Control: Private
Restrictions: No night fishing
BK Rating: Very Easy
E/A: Severn-Trent
Comments: Big catches common on standard baits. Bar and cafe on bank; ideal for beginners

South Muskham Fisheries (A1 Pits)

Location: South Muskham, near Newark-on-Trent
Type and Size: Six gravel pits, and stretch of River Trent
How to Find: Turn off the A1 at North Muskham. The entrance is by the rail crossing
Carp Stock: Very well stocked with many carp of up to 32lbs; many commons
Category: Mixed Fishery
Other Species: General coarse fish, pike to 20lbs and big bream
Permits: On bank
Cost: £5 per day and about £7 for night. Season tickets
BK Rating: Moderate
Control: Private. Tel: 01636 61208
Restrictions: No peanuts
E/A: Severn-Trent
Comments: These big gravel pits flood from the River Trent at times

Steetly Pool

Location: The village of Shireoaks, between Worksop and Sheffield
Type and Size: Four acre quarry, quite attractive
Carp Stock: Well stocked with small carp to about 10lbs, with one or two slightly bigger fish also present
Category: Mixed Fishery
Other Species: Roach, bream and tench
Permits: In advance only from Steetly Concrete Office, Shireoaks
Control: Steetly Concrete Co
Restrictions: No day tickets on bank; no Sunday fishing; one bank private; no night fishing
BK Rating: Moderate
E/A: Severn-Trent

Strip Ponds, Lakeside Fisheries

Location: Ranskill, off the A 638 between Retford and Bawtry
Type and Size: Canal type match water
Carp Stock: Very heavily stocked with carp to 5 lbs. A few doubles
Category: Carp Only
Other Species: None
Permits: From office
Cost: £3 per day
Control: Nigel Hawke. Tel: 01777 818524
Restrictions: Weekends only; no night fishing; no keepnets
BK Rating: Very Easy
E/A: Severn Trent
Comments: You should get a fish a cast! Other lakes on site. Toilets, showers and cafe

Willow Fishery

Location: Chain Bridge Lane, Lound, near Retford
Type and Size: Six small ponds
Carp Stock: Well stocked with carp to over 20 lbs
Category: Mixed Fishery
Other Species: Bream, tench, perch, roach and rudd
Permits: On bank
Cost: About £5 per day; £30 per season; concessions
Control: Tel: 01777 860036
Restrictions: No boilies or nuts
BK Rating: Easy
E/A: Severn Trent
Comments: Night fishing for season ticket holders only

Windmill Farm

Location: Windmill Farm, Spalford, near Newark. Tel: 01522 77305
Type and Size: Small farm lakes
Carp Stock: Well stocked with carp to doubles
Category: Carp Water
Other Species: Possibly a few
Permits: From the owner at the address above
Cost: £2 per day - £2.50 for night fishing
Control: Private
BK Rating: Not known
E/A: Severn-Trent
Comments: Tents and touring caravans allowed at this fishery - good facilities

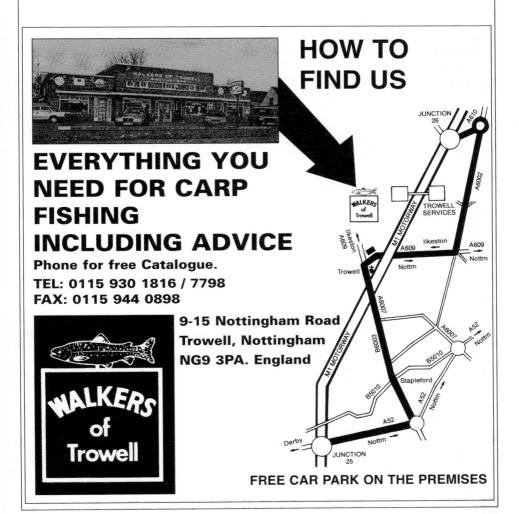

Windthorpe Pits

Location: Close to the A1, near Newark
Type and Size: 25 acre gravel pit, connected to the River Trent - very deep, with little cover
Carp Stock: Plenty of doubles, and possibly a few twenties
Category: Mixed Fishery
Other Species: Pike, roach, tench, bream and perch
Permits: Day tickets from the house close to the pit
Control: Sheffield Angling Club - season tickets from F Turner, 30 Mather Walk, Sheffield, or 142-144 Princes Street, Sheffield S4 4UW
Restrictions: Night fishing is allowed
BK Rating: Difficult
E/A: Severn-Trent

Winthorpe Lake

Location: Off the Newark-Gainsborough road, near Newark
Type and Size: 20 acre gravel pit
Carp Stock: Quite well stocked with carp to 22lbs
Category: Mixed Fishery
Other Species: Usual coarse fish
Permits: Sheffield and District AA. Secretary: F E Turner, 30 Mather Walk, Sheffield S9 4GL, or 142-144 Princes Street, Sheffield S4 4UW
Control: Club
BK Rating: Moderate
E/A: Severn-Trent
Comments: This water is very heavily match fished. The permit also includes some good fishing on the River Trent in the same area, with plenty of carp from 8lbs to 22lbs

Woodsetts Pond

Location: Woodsett, near Dinnington, off the A57 between Worksop and Sheffield
Type and Size: Five acre sand pit, locally known as 'The Quarry'
Carp Stock: Quite well stocked with carp to upper doubles
Category: Mixed Fishery
Other Species: Tench and roach
Permits: Day tickets on bank
Control: Worksop and Distrct AA. Secretary: R Whitehead, 72 Dryden Walk, Worksop
Restrictions: No night fishing
BK Rating: Very Difficult
E/A: Severn-Trent
Comments: This quarry is deep and weedy, which perhaps is why it is so hard, as it is quite well stocked with good sized carp

Woodsetts Quarry Pond

Location: Off the A57 Worksop to Sheffield road, near Worksop
Type and Size: Small disused quarry
Carp Stock: Said to be some carp; numbers and sizes not known
Category: Mixed Fishery
Other Species: Roach, bream and tench
Permits: Day tickets from bailiff on bank
Control: Worksop and District AA
BK Rating: Not known
E/A: Severn-Trent

OXFORDSHIRE

Boddington Reservoir

Location: Off the A 361 - 8 miles north of Banbury
Type and Size: 250 acre canal feeder reservoir
Carp Stock: Small number of carp to over 20 lbs
Category: Mixed Fishery
Other Species: General coarse fish including big pike
Permits: Fishery Officer, Willow Grange, Watford, Herts
Cost: On application
Control: British Waterways
Restrictions: No night fishing
BK Rating: Difficult
E/A: Severn Trent

Bullfield Lake

Location: Thrupp Lane, Home Farm, near Abingdon
Type and Size: 3 acre gravel pit
Carp Stock: Some carp to doubles
Category: Mixed Fishery
Other Species: Tench, roach, perch and pike
Permits: In advance from local tackle shops

Cost: About £3 per day; £20 per season
Control: Oxford and Abingdon A.A. Tel: 01865 391809
Restrictions: No night fishing
BK Rating: Not known
E/A: Thames
Comments: No fishing on the first lake you come to from the lane.

Clattercote Reservoir

Location: Near Claydon, 5 miles north of Banbury
Type and Size: 30 acre reservoir
Carp Stock: Well stocked with carp to doubles
Category: Mixed Fishery
Other Species: General coarse fish
Permits: Castaway Tackle, Banbury
Cost: £4 from shop; £6 from bailiff on bank
Control: Tel: 01295 254274. Banbury D.A.A.
Restrictions: No tins. No carp in nets
BK Rating: Easy
E/A: Severn Trent
Comments: Good beginners water.

Dorchester Lake

Location: Old Drayton Road, Dorchester - on -Thames, near Abingdon
Type and Size: Attractive 18 acre gravel pit with numerous islands
Carp Stock: Carp to well over 20 lbs
Category: Mixed Fishery
Other Species: Tench, roach, perch and bream
Permits: On bank
Cost: £3 per day; £22 per season - £10 juniors and O.A.P's
Control: Abingdon and Oxford A.A. Tel: 01865 391809
BK Rating: Not known
E/A: Thames

Dukes Lake

Location: Oxford
Type and Size: Four acre town lake
Carp Stock: Carp to doubles
Category: Mixed Fishery
Other Species: Tench, rudd and pike
Permits: North Oxford AC - Secretary, P Jackman, 1 Churchill Road, Kidlington, Oxford. Tel: 01865 79582
Control: Club
BK Rating: Moderate
E/A: Thames

Farnborough House Lake

Location: 6 miles north of Banbury
Type and Size: Shallow estate lake
Carp Stock: Small numbers to 30 lbs
Category: Mixed Fishery
Other Species: General coarse fish
Permits: Local tackle shops
Cost: £2 per day
Control: Banbury D.A.A. Tel: 01295 254274
BK Rating: Difficult

E/A: Severn Trent
Comments: East end of lake near house is best.

Guy Lakes

Location: Stanton Harcourt
Type and Size: Three beautiful matured gravel pits of 25, 20 and 15 acres next to each other
How to Find: Enquire from Head Bailiff

A fine 20 pound common from Guy Lakes.

Carp Stock: Yeomans - well stocked with carp to over 30 lbs.Unity - fairly well stocked with carp to upper twenties. Gaunts - soon to be stocked with fast growing carp
Category: Mixed Fishery
Other Species: Pike to 27 lbs, tench, chub, roach and rudd
Permits: Syndicate only from Linear Fisheries Head Bailiff. Tel: 01908 647320, Mobile 0585 327708 or on main Linear complex 2 miles away
Cost: £180
Control: Linear Fisheries, Oxford
Restrictions: No retaining fish or bent hooks
BK Rating: Yeomans - Moderate; Unity - Difficult
E/A: Thames
Comments: Open all year. One of the most attractive carp fisheries we know, up its own private drive with two locked gates. More than half of a £30,000 carp stocking scheme has already been spent recently by Linear Fisheries. Also includes 1/2 mile one bank of the River Windrush, with chub, barbel, trout, dace and roach. Brochure on request. Toilet. Watch out for the capybara.

Hardwick Carp Syndicate

Location: Linear Fisheries, Smiths Concrete, B 4449 between Stanton Harcourt and the A 415 Witney road
Type and Size: Open 15 acre gravel pit with a gravel conveyor on one side
How to Find: Opposite Manor Farm Lake and St.Johns Pool, next to the car park
Carp Stock: Heavily stocked with carp to 29 3/4 lbs. Many doubles and twenties.Some big commons to nearly 30 lbs

A beautifully-scaled mirror of 27-14 from Hardwick Carp Syndicate - part of the Shimano / Linear Fisheries complex.

Category: Carp Water
Other Species: Big chub and some other coarse fish
Permits: Syndicate membership £150 per year from Head Bailiff on bank or from 10a Rackstraw Grove, Old Farm Park, Milton Keynes, MK7 8PZ
No day tickets
Control: Linear Fisheries. Tel: 01908 645135 or Head Bailiff 01908 647320 Mobile 0585 327708
Restrictions: No retaining of fish and no bent hooks
BK Rating: Moderate
Baits/Methods: Boilies and floaters best
E /A: Thames
Comments On the Linear complex opposite the day ticket waters. Big multiple catches of doubles and twenties recorded. Membership vacancies. Toilet. Head Bailiff in attendance 24 hours a day. Open all year. Brochure on request

Hardwick Pits

Location: Hardwick, near Witney
Type and Size: Hardwick 1 - 70 acre gravel pit; Hardwick 2 - 60 acres
Carp Stock: One - about 60 carp, sizes not known. Two - said to be only 6 carp!
Category: Few Carp (very few!)
Other Species: Record chub and other coarse fish
Permits: Enquire at tackle shops in Witney and Oxford
BK Rating: Super-Difficult
E/A: Thames
Comments: As you can see, we know little about this one, except that the pits do contan a few carp and that some of them might be very big

Heyford Lakes

Location: Stanton Harcourt, near Witney
Type and Size: Two gravel pits of 10 and 8 acres
How to Find: Up a long track opposite States Lagoon on the B 4449 Eynsham to Hardwick road
Carp Stock: Well stocked with carp to over 30 lbs
Category: Mixed Fishery

Other Species: Bream, tench, chub, perch, roach, rudd, dace, crucians, eels, pike and gudgeon
Permits: Local tackle shops, especially States Tackle, 19 Fettiplace Road,Witney
Cost: About £20 per season, to include many other club waters. Extra for night fishing; concessions
Control: Newland A.C. Tel: Derek State, 01993 702587
Restrictions: See club booklet
BK Rating: Moderate
E/A: Thames
Comments: Open all year. Excellent club with very good waters. Club house with refreshments, hot food, etc.

Horse and Groom Inn — A

Location: Milcombe, near Banbury
Type and Size: Two lakes
How to Find: Just off the A361 between Banbury and Chipping Norton
Carp Stock: Carp to over 20lbs
Category: Mixed Fishery
Other Species: Tench and chub
Permits: Horse and Groom Inn, Milcombe. Tel: 01295 720471
Cost: On application
Control: Private
BK Rating: Insufficient information
E/A: Thames
Comments: 16th century inn, bed and breakfast, games room, skittle alley, 220 acres of rough shooting. Edge of Cotswolds. 18 hole golf course available

Linch Hill Fishery — A

Location: Standlake, Stanton Harcourt, near Oxford
Type and Size: Three gravel pits; largest fifty acres
How to Find: West of Oxford
Carp Stock: Some big carp to over 30lbs
Category: Mixed Fishery
Other Species: General coarse fish
Permits: Linch Hill Leisure Park, Stanton Harcourt, Oxford. Tel: 01865 882215
Cost: £2.50 to £8. Syndicate
BK Rating: Moderate
Control: Private
Restrictions: No night fishing
E/A: Thames
Comments: Accommodation - caravans and camping. Cafe and toilets

Lincoln Lake

Location: Standlake, near Witney
Type and Size: Small pool about 1½ acres, with an island
How to Find: Off the A 415 from Witney - the fishery is signposted on the right at Standlake
Carp Stock: Well stocked with doubles
Category: Mixed Fishery
Other Species: Tench, roach, pike and perch
Permits: On bank
Cost: £4.50 per day; juniors £2.25
Control: Private. Tel: 01865 300241
BK Rating: Not known
E/A: Thames
Comments: Open all year

Linear Fisheries, Oxford

Location: St. Johns Pool, Smiths Concrete, B 4449 between Stanton Harcourt and the A 415 Witney road

Type and Size: 18 acre matured gravel pit

How to Find: Take the A 40 west from Oxford, and turn left in 4 miles at the first roundabout. Follow signs to Stanton Harcourt but after Sutton keep straight on towards Hardwick. Linear Fisheries are the last lakes on each side of the road on the B 4449

Carp Stock: Well stocked with carp to 25 lbs

Category: Mixed Fishery

Other Species: Pike to 25 lbs, tench to over 9 lbs, perch and a few roach

Permits: On bank, in advance from local tackle shops, and from the Ferryman Inn at Bablock Hythe

Cost: £4 per rod for 12 hours; £6 per rod for 24 hours.Ticket machine - £1 coins needed

Control: Linear Fisheries, Oxford. Fishery Manager - Len Gurd. Tel: 01908 645135. Head Bailiff - Roy Parsons Tel: 01908 647320 Mobile 0585 327708

Restrictions: No sacking of fish. No bent hooks

BK Rating: Moderate

Baits/Methods: All normal carp baits and methods, including float fishing

E/A: Thames

Comments: Well run fishery by one of the country's leading coarse fishery companies. Purpose built car park with security lights. Toilet. Trout pellets for sale. Head Bailiff in attendance 24 hours a day. Pleasant, attractive lake with level banks. Open all year. Brochure on request. Two acre lake alongside. Linear is now sponsored by Shimano.

Manor Farm Lake

Location: Linear Fisheries, Smiths Concrete, B 4449 between Stanton Harcourt and the A 415 Witney road

Type and Size: 12 acre matured gravel pit

How to Find: Take the A 40 west from Oxford, and turn left in 4 miles on the B4449 at the first roundabout. Follow signs to Stanton Harcourt, but after Sutton keep straight on towards Hardwick. Linear Fisheries are the last lakes on either side of the road

A 40 pound 2 ounce fish from the Shimano / Linear Manor Farm Lake.

Carp Stock: Carp to 40¼ lbs
Category: Mixed Fishery
Other Species: Tench to over 10 lbs, bream to 13 lbs, pike to 25 lbs, chub to 6 lbs, and some roach
Permits: On bank, from local tackle shops and the Ferryman Inn at Bablock Hythe
Cost: £ 5 per rod for 12 hours; £ 7 per rod for 24 hours.Ticket machine - £1 coins needed
Control: Linear Fisheries. Fishery Manager - Tel: 01908 645135 Head Bailiff - Tel: 01908 647320 Mobile 0585 327708 also 01865 300872
Restrictions: No sacking of fish or bent hooks
BK Rating: Difficult
Baits/Methods: Specialist carp rigs and baits
E/A: Thames
Comments: A number of different thirties and twenties. Clear, weedy, and not easy to fish. Head Bailiff in attendance 24 hours a day. Open all year. Toilet. Brochure on request

Marlborough Pool

Location: On the A4 between Witney and Oxford
Type and Size: Mature gravel pit of eleven acres
Carp Stock: Well stocked with carp many years ago which have gone to over 20lbs
Category: Carp Water
Permits: Oxford Angling and Preservation Society. R Bateman, 16 The Gap, Marcham, Abingdon. Tel: 01865 391908. Season £32. No day tickets
BK Rating: Moderate
Control: Club
E/A: Thames
Comments: Quite a well-known carp water, quite heavily fished and in the past some well-known anglers have fished there

Milton Common

Location: Just off junction 7 of the M40; can be seen from the motorway
Type and Size: Three lakes of three, two and one and a half acres
Carp Stock: Quite well stocked with carp to 24lbs
Category: Carp Waters
Permits: From owner on site
Cost: Approximately £5 per day
Control: Private. Tel: 01844 278150
BK Rating: Moderate
E/A: Thames
Comments: We have heard that this fishery may stay open during the close season. Barbless hooks. No night fishing. Toilet

Orchid Lakes

Location: Abingdon Road, Dorchester OX1 7LP. Tel: 01865 341810 (between 9am and 7pm)
Type and Size: Lakes of 40 acres, 18 acres and 2 acres
Carp Stock: About 300 carp, most of which are over 20lbs, and 9 thirties. There are now said to be about forty 20's in the lakes and many thirties
Category: Mixed Fishery
Other Species: Tench, roach, perch, rudd and catfish to 30lbs
Permits: Day and season tickets at the above address
Cost: £5 for one rod; £10 for 2 rods. £10 per night. £75 per week
Control: Marsh Pratley. Tel: 01865 341810
BK Rating: Moderate
E/A: Thames

Gary Young caught this fabulous 37 1/2 pound common from Orchid Lakes in Dorchester on a KM Strawberry Oil boilie.

Comments: No close season. Cafe, toilets, washing facilities. Purpose-built bivvy swims. Concessions for long stay anglers

Oxford Canal (a)

Location: Banbury
Type and Size: Midlands canal, quite narrow
How to Find: On the outskirts of Banbury
Carp Stock: Plenty of carp to 15lbs+
Category: Mixed Fishery
Other Species: General coarse fish
Permits: Local tackle shops
Cost: On application
Control: Club
BK Rating: Moderate
E/A: Severn-Trent
Comments: Once you can find an area contaning carp, they are not hard to catch. Average 6-8lbs. Good winter fishing. Banbury and District AA, D Brewer, 42 Stanwell Lea, Middleton Cheney, Banbury, Oxon for tickets. A fish kill took place on the canal in the Banbury area in 1991

Oxford Canal (b)

Location: Lower Heyford to Northbrook, near Bicester
Type and Size: Narrow canal
Carp Stock: Well stocked with carp to 20 lbs
Category: Mixed Fishery
Other Species: Roach, perch, chub and gudgeon
Permits: On bank
Cost: About £3 per day
Control: Oxford D.A.A. Tel: 01865 776673
BK Rating: Moderate
E/A: Thames

Oxford Quarry

Location: Near Stanton Harcourt, Oxford
Type and Size: Gravel pit of 16 acres
How to Find: Lake is off the B449 road between Eynsham and Standlake
Carp Stock: Small number of carp to about 25lbs
Category: Few Carp
Other Species: Rudd, chub, tench, catfish, pike
Permits: Vauxhall Motors Angling Club, season tickets. Secretary: Mr B Matthews, 88 Langford Drive, Luton, Beds. Tel:01582 419489
Cost: On application
Control: Club
BK Rating: Difficult
E/A: Thames
Comments: One side shallow with gravel bars. Carp baits taken mainly by chub. Best method stalking individual fish often close in

Pickford Lake

Location: Oxford
Type an Size: Small town lake
Carp Stock: Well stocked with carp to 10lbs
Category: Mixed Fishery
Other Species: Tench
Permits: North Oxford AS (members only). Secretary: P Jackman, 1 Churchill Road, Kidlington, Oxford. Tel: 01865 79582
Control: Club
BK Rating: Not known
E/A: Thames

Pimlico Farm Lakes A

Location: Pimlico Farm, Tusmore, Bicester, OX6 9SL
Type and Size: Three lakes - 6 acres of water
Carp Stock: Well stocked with carp to 10 lbs
Category: Mixed Fishery
Other Species: Tench, roach, rudd and perch
Permits: On bank
Cost: About £5 per day
Control: Mr. and Mrs. J.Harper. Tel: 01869 810306
BK Rating: Moderate
E/A: Thames
Comments: Self-catering accommodation in attractive 'cottages'. Fishing free to guests. Send for brochure. Open all year. Facilities for disabled anglers. Free fishing for the disabled

Smiths Pool

Location: Linear Fisheries, Smiths Concrete, B 4449 between Stanton Harcourt and the A 415 Witney road
Type and Size: 10 acre open gravel pit
How to Find: Next to Hardwick Carp Syndicate on the Linear complex -a walk of about 300 metres from the car park
Carp Stock: Some carp to about 16 lbs
Category: Mixed Fishery
Other Species: Tench, chub, roach, rudd and bream
Permits: Season tickets from bailiffs on bank or from local tackle shops
Cost: £40. Some day tickets at bailiff's discretion - £4 for 12 hours, £7 for 24 hours

Control: Linear Fisheries. Head Bailiff. Tel: 01908 647320 Mobile 0585 327708
Restrictions: None
BK Rating: Moderate
E/A: Thames
Comments: Contains a reasonable number of carp, but is fished more for the other species. Open all year. Toilet. Head Bailiff in attendance 24 hours a day. Brochure on request

POWYS (Wales)

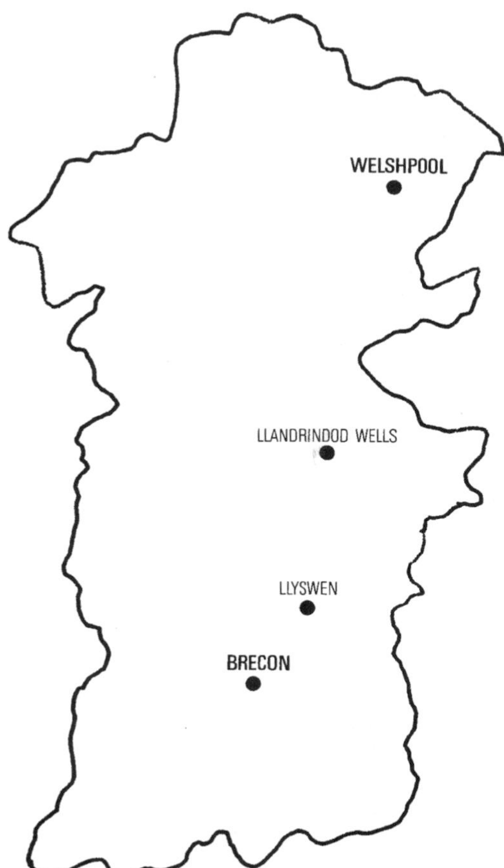

Llandrindod Wells Lake

Location: Edge of the town of Llandrindod Wells, central Wales

Type and Size: Dammed town lake with island, 16 acres

How to Find: Road leading from town centre goes round three sides of the lake

Carp Stock: Very heavily stocked, mostly mirrors. Many doubles and the occasional 20 pounder

Category: Mixed Fishery/Carp Water

Other Species: Roach, bream, pike, eels

Permits: Day and season tickets from the boathouse cafe on the lake. Night syndicate, details from the cafe

Restrictions: No night fishing unless you are a night syndicate member. No fishing on dam

Cost: On application

Baits/Methods: Fairly sophisticated carp methods and boiled baits used, but carp also caught on luncheon meat and floating baits, and on float tackle

Control: Day and season ticket, local Council
BK Rating: Moderate
E/A: Welsh
Comments: Town Lake with roads and many walkers, but still attractive. Often fishes well when the boats are being used!

Llyswen Carp Pools A

Location: The Dderw, Llyswen, Builth Wells
Type and Size: Three pools of three acres, two acres and two and a half acres
How to Find: Llyswen is on the A470 road between Brecon and Builth Wells
Carp Stock: The Orchard Pool nearest the farmhouse is quite well stocked with commons to about 10lbs and a few double figure mirrors to 20lbs. The other lakes are very heavily stocked with small commons to about 7lbs
Category: Carp Waters
Other Species: Tench, bream, roach, perch
Permits: Day tickets from the farm: Mr Eckley, The Dderw, Llyswen, Powys. Tel: 01874 754224
Cost: Orchard Pool £5 per day. Mill Pool and The Pool £4
Control: Private
BK Rating: Orchard Pool - Moderate. Mill Pool - Easy. The Pool - Very Easy
Baits/Methods: Boilies and particle baits; also floaters. Rigs and methods of all types will work and on the other pond the fish will take almost any bait as it is so overstocked
E/A: Welsh, Wye Area, 4 St John Street, Hereford. Tel: 01432 276313, or from tackle shops.
Comments: The Orchard Pool is a pleasant water surrounded by trees and reeds. The lakes are in the Wye Valley 10 miles south east of Builth Wells. Accommodation in three self-catering studio apartments on site - part of the house, sleeping four, three and two

Seven Oaks Park A

Location: Crewe Green, Coedway, between Shrewsbury and Welshpool
Type and Size: Small pool
Carp Stock: Some carp to 20 lbs
Category: Mixed Fishery
Other Species: Tench, roach and small bream
Permits: In advance from reception
Cost: £5 per day: Children free
Control: Tel. 01743 884271
BK Rating: Not known
E/A: Welsh
Comments: Probably open all year. Log cabins and caravans. Short stretch of the River Severn included, with chub and barbel

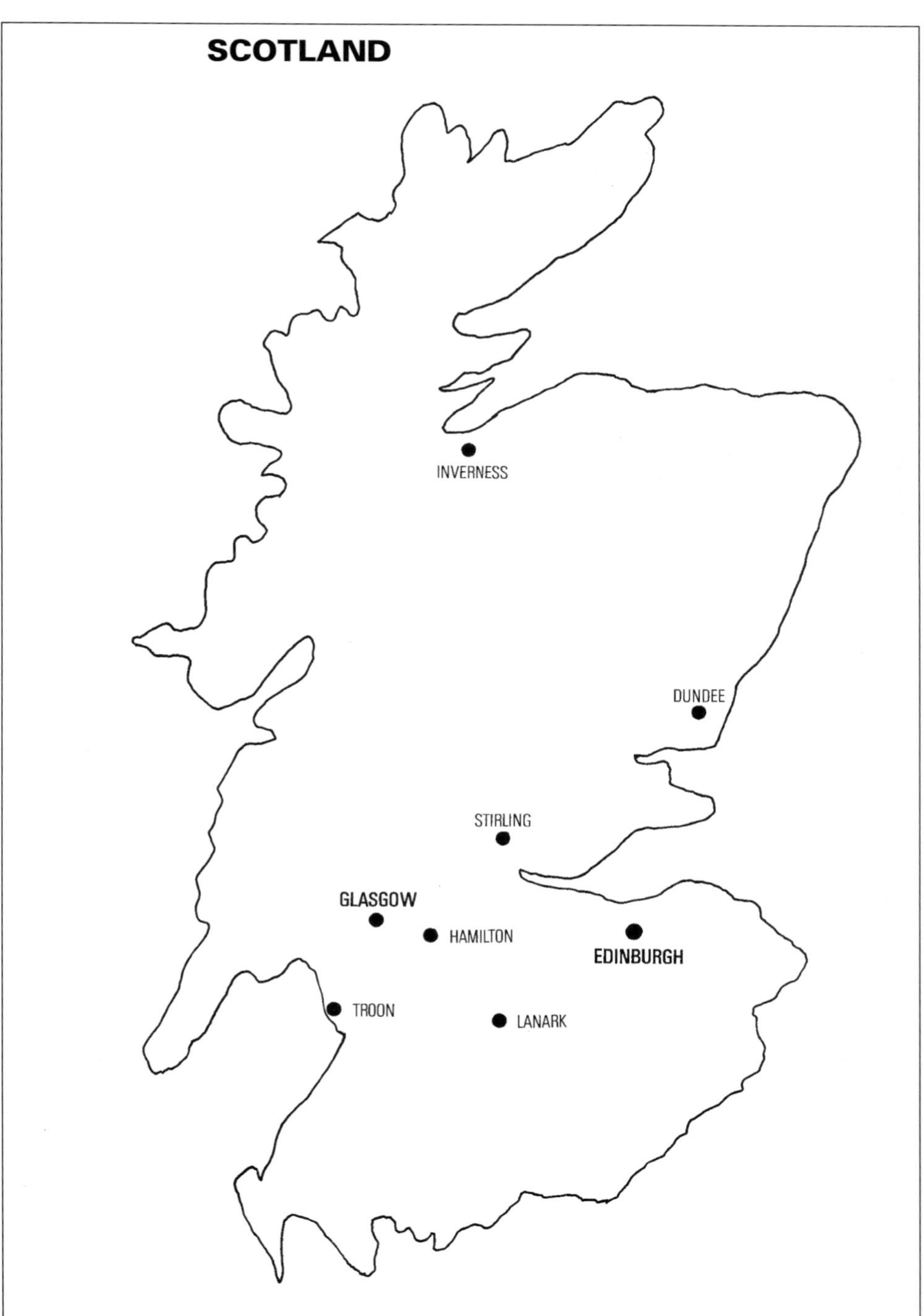
SCOTLAND
INVERNESS
DUNDEE
STIRLING
GLASGOW
HAMILTON
EDINBURGH
TROON
LANARK

Barhead Reservoir

Location: Just off the A77 south west of Glasgow, near Newton Mearns (Strathclyde)
Type and Size: There are several lakes here, and the small one contains carp
Carp Stock: Mirrors to low doubles
Category: Mixed Fishery
Other Species: Some coarse fish and trout
Permits: None necessary - free fishing
Control: Glasgow City Council
BK Rating: Not known
E/A: Scottish
Comments: No close season; quite a pleasant water which needs investigating

Clatio Loch

Location: Centre of the town of Dundee (Tayside)
Type and Size: Ten acre town lake
Carp Stock: Stocked with small carp in about 1988, and there are now fish up to about 6lb
Category: Mixed Fishery
Other Species: Roach, bream and perch
Permits: From Dundee City Council, at no cost
Control: Council
BK Rating: Easy
E/A: Scottish
Comments: No close season; a match water

Cowans Farm and Guest House — A

Location: Kirkgunzeon, Dumfries (Dumfries & Galloway)
Type and Size: One and a half acre man-made loch
How to Find: 9 miles south west of Dumfries, off the A711 Dalbeattie road
Carp Stock: Contains some carp
Category: Few Carp
Other Species: Roach, tench and rudd
Permits: Tel: 01387 76284
Cost: Day permits £2.50 per rod, free fishing to residents
BK Rating: Insufficient information
Control: Private
Restrictions: No keepnets. No groundbaiting
Comments: Bed and breakfast and evening meal in licensed guest house, 200 yards from loch. Other lochs and sea close by. No close season

Craighlaw Fisheries — A

Location: Near Newton Stewart (Dumfries & Galloway)
Type and Size: Lake of 6½ acres. There are two other lakes in the fishery, all of which contain carp
How to Find: First ask at the owner's: Palakona Bait Supplies, 30/32 Queen Street, Newton Stewart
Carp Stock: 150 fish to lower twenties
Category: Mixed Fishery
Other Species: Roach, rudd, bream and crucians
Permits: Day and weekly permits only from the owner at Palakona Bait supplies No tickets on the bank - you must obtain a permit before fishing
Cost: £5 per day; £10 for 24 hours
Control: Private
Comments: No close season. Comfortable accommodation in the owner's guest

house. Tel: 01671 402323. There are very few carp waters in Scotland and this is one of the newest. It should have a good future, as the SW of Scotland has a very mild climate. The lake is very attractive and has a lined bottom, which was built by the monks. In fact, this was a monastery fish pond, and the monks' fish house is still there. There are trees, with an island and a boat house. Depths are from 4 to 7 feet and there is some weed. Tackle shop

Culcreuch Castle Pool A

Location: Fintry, on the B818, 15 miles west of Stirling (Stirlingshire)
Type and Size: Two small lakes on estate
Carp Stock: Well stocked with mirrors to about 10lbs, and commons to lower doubles, which are said by locals to be wildies
Category: Carp Water
Permits: Scottish Carp Group, 57 Iona Way, Kirkintilloch, Glasgow. Tel: 0141-7767922
BK Rating: Moderate
Comments: Attractive lakes in the grounds of an hotel; members only, no day tickets

Duddingston Loch

Location: City centre of Edinburgh (Lothian)
Type and Size: 50 acre town lake, which is a bird reserve, and belongs to the Crown. Much of the bank cannot be fished
Carp Stock: Plenty of doubles to about 15lbs
Category: Mixed Fishery
Other Species: Roach, bream, and perch
Permits: Available free from Edinburgh City Council,or Mikes Tackle Shop, Portobello, Edinburgh
BK Rating: Difficult
Comments: No close season - size and restrictons make it difficult to find fish

Forth and Clyde Canal

Location: Kelvindale, north west Glasgow
Type and Size: Very wide, large canal
Carp Stock: Some very big carp to well over 20lbs
Category: Few Carp
Other Species: Roach, bream, perch and pike
Permits: None necessary - free fishing
BK Rating: Super-Difficult
Comments: No close season. Fish very difficult to locate in this big canal, but they have certainly never been caught

Glen Esk Caravan Park A

Location: Glen Esk Caravan Park, Edzell, Angus DD9 7YP, on the B966 eight miles north of Brechin
Type and Size: Three-quarter acre lake
Carp Stock: Well stocked with commons and mirrors to doubles
Category: Carp Water
Permits: On site
Control: Tel: 013564 523 / 565
BK Rating: Not known
Comments: No close season. Some caravans. Trout and salmon fishing available

Gooseloan Pond

Location: Kilwinning, 10 miles north of Troon, near the west coast (Ayrshire)
Type and Size: Old, deep quarry of about four acres
Carp Stock: Over thirty carp to about 20lbs
Category: Carp Water
Permits: Not known; enquire locally, possibly from farmers
BK Rating: Very Difficult

Hogganfield Loch

Location: City centre of Glasgow
Type and Size: 80 acre town lake, very busy and quite dangerous to fish at times!
Carp Stock: Well stocked with carp to about 20lbs
Category: Mixed Fishery
Other Species: Big bream and eels
Permits: None necessary - free fishing
Control: Council
BK Rating: Moderate
Comments: No close season, and night fishing is allowed. Thousands of water birds, and some people of dubious reputation, especially at night!

Kelhead Water, Annan

Location: Off the A 75 Carlisle - Dumfries road, two miles from Annan
Type and Size: 6 acre deep quarry
Carp Stock: Some carp to middle doubles
Category: Mixed Fishery
Other Species: Roach, tench, rudd, bream, pike, perch, gudgeon, eels and a few trout
Permits: In advance from cottage near the fishery entrance
Cost: £4 per day;
Control: Tel: 01461 700344
BK Rating: Not known
E/A: Scottish

Lanark Loch

Location: Public park in Lanark, on the A73 20 miles south east of Glasgow
Type and Size: 20 acre public lake
Carp Stock: Stocked with 500 carp of about 5lbs each in 1988
Category: Mixed Fishery
Other Species: Tench and bream
Permits: About £12 per season from Clydesdale District Council and local tackle shops
Cost: About £10 per season. Possible day tickets
BK Rating: Not known, but could be quite hard, as 20 fish an acre is a low stocking density
Comments: No close season - might be a good bet to catch a Scottish carp

Loch Libo

Location: Uplawmoor, Barrhead (Renfrewshire)
Type and Size: 20 acre shallow and weedy loch
Carp Stock: Well stocked with doubles to low twenties, and small commons
Category: Carp Water
Permits: Scottish Carp Group, 57 Iona Way, Kirkintilloch, Glasgow. Tel: 0141-7767922
Cost: About £30 per year
Control: Scottish Wildlife Trust
Restrictions: No fishing in some areas; limited number of anglers

BK Rating: Difficult
Comments: No close season

Monkland Canal

Location: Coatbridge (Lanarkshire)
Type and Size: Narrow canal
Carp Stock: Well stocked with carp to 5lbs
Category: Mixed Fishery
Other Species: Most coarse fish
Permits: Monklands DAC
Control: Tel: 0113 2645500
BK Rating: Easy
E/A: Scottish
Comments: No close season. No night fishing. Season £30. Concessions

Newton Lochan

Location: Gatehouse of Fleet, Galloway
Type and Size: 2 acre lake
Carp Stock: Carp to over 20 lbs, mostly small
Category: Mixed Fishery
Other Species: Pike, bream, roach, perch and tench
Permits: From the farmhouse
Cost: £3 per day; juniors £1
Control: Tel: 01557 840234
BK Rating: Not known
E/A: Scottish
Comments: Disabled access. Probably open all year

Strathclyde Water Park

Location: Hamilton (Lanarkshire)
Type and Size: 150 acre lake
Carp Stock: Well stocked with doubles to about 15lbs
Category: Mixed Fishery
Other Species: Roach and bream
Permits: From the Sports Centre at the lake, £4 per day
Control: Private
BK Rating: Moderate
Comments: No close season. Lots of people and match anglers

Torwood House Hotel **A**

Location: Glenluce, Newton Stewart, Witownshire (Dumfries & Galloway)
Type and Size: Two lochs
How to Find: Newton Stewart is to the west of Dumfries
Carp Stock: Little known, but does contain some carp to 20lbs
Category: Few Carp
Other Species: Tench, bream, roach, perch
Permits: From hotel: Tel: 01581 300469
Cost: Day tickets at £3.50 per day; £10 per week; £30 per season
Control: Torwood House Hotel
Comments: Accommodation in hotel, 200 yards from lochs. No close season. Pike and salmon fishing nearby. Some trout fishing. Barbless hooks. Toilets

SHROPSHIRE

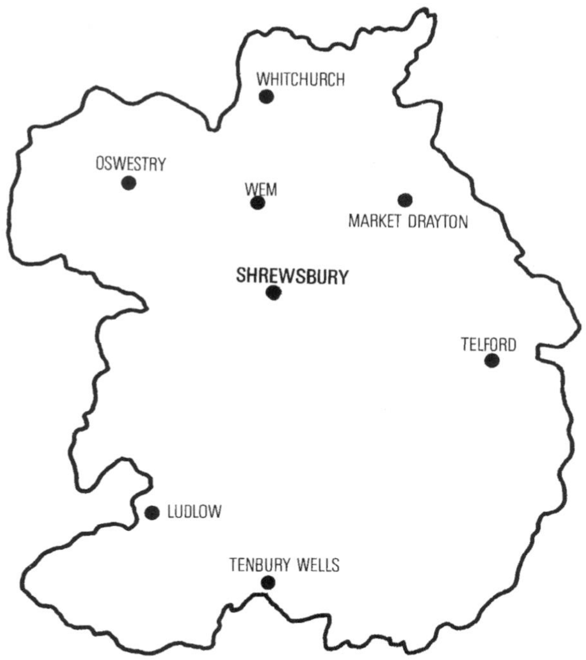

Apley Pool

Location: Near Telford at Lee Gomory
Type and Size: Small pool
Carp Stock: Heavily stocked to 10lbs
Category: Carp Only
Other Species: None
Permits: Telford Anglers Association, Malcolm Kelly. Tel: 01952 244272
Cost: On application
BK Rating: Easy
Control: Club
E/A: Severn-Trent

Bache Pool

Location: Near Ludlow
Type and Size: One and a half acre farm pond
How to Find: Turn off the B4365 from Ludlow towards Craven Arms and go through some narrow winding lanes, virtually getting lost!
Carp Stock: Very heavily stocked with many small commons and a few good mirrors and commons to 25lbs
Category: Carp Water
Other Species: General coarse fish
Permits: Day tickets on bank?
Control: Club
BK Rating: Easy, though hard for the big fish
E/A: Severn-Trent

Comments: Heavily fished, long narrow lake with lilies; shallow. Bigger fish very wary. Floaters good. A well known water to many Midlands carp anglers. Very opaque,'coloured' water. Big torches,Tilley lamps and loud radios common!

Bayliss Pools

Location: Shifnal, near Telford
Type and Size: No. 1: two acres; No.2: 2½ acres; No. 3: 3 - 6 acres
Carp Stock: No. 1: carp to 16lbs; No. 2: carp to 20lbs; No. 3: some carp to doubles
Category: Mixed Fishery
Other Species: Mixed coarse fish
Permits: On bank
Cost: £4 per day. Concessions
BK Rating: No. 1 - Moderate. No. 2 - Difficult
Control: Private. Tel: 01952 460530
E/A: Severn-Trent
Comments: No. 2 pool is said to be very deep and it fishes well in the winter. Information from Rod & Gun, 3 High Street, Dawley. Tel: 01952 503550

Beeches Pool

Location: Ironridge, near Telford
Type and Size: One acre pool
Carp Stock: Doubles to 16lbs and three twenties
Category: Mixed Fishery
Other Species: General coarse fish
Permits: On site
Cost: £2 per day approximately
BK Rating: Moderate
Control: Private
E/A: Severn-Trent
Comments: Try local tackle shops for permits and more information, such as Rod & Gun, 3 High Street, Dawley. Tel: 01952 503550

Boldings Pool

Location: Astley Abbotts, of the B4373 near Bridgnorth
Type and Size: Eight small pools
Carp Stock: Carp to upper doubles
Category: Mixed Fishery
Other Species: Tench, bream, chub, perch, roach and barbel
Permits: On bank between 6.30 and 8.30am; after 8.30am pay at house
Cost: £3 per day; £2 for juniors under 16
Control: Eddie and Sue Turner. Tel: 01746 763255
BK Rating: Moderate
E/A: Severn-Trent

Bomere

Location: In the town of Shrewsbury
Type and Size: Attractive lake of about five acres
Carp Stock: Probably only one or two, to upper doubles
Category: Few Carp
Other Species: Roach, tench, bream, perch and pike
Permits: Day tickets from local tackle shops
Control: Club
Restrictions: No night fishing
BK Rating: Super-Difficult
E/A: Severn-Trent

Bridge Pool, Patshull Park

Location: Patshull Park, Burnhill Green, Wolverhampton
Type and Size: Half acre pond max. depth 3m.
How to Find: Take the A454 Wolverhampton-Bridgnorth road to traffic lights by Mermaid pub, turn right signposted Pattingham, in village, bear right by church, after 1½ miles turn right into Patshull Park
Carp Stock: Mirrors and commons to 23 lbs
Category: Mixed Fishery
Other Species: Bream, roach and perch
Permits: Day tickets only
Cost: £4 per peg
Control: Private
Restrictions: No night fishing. Peanuts are banned; use of tiger nuts and soaked oil baits discouraged
BK Rating: Easy
Baits/Methods: Boiled baits best
E/A: Severn Trent
Comments: This is a mixed fishery, so not suitable for the dedicated carp angler, who might be competing with a 7 year old roach angler on the next peg. Open all year.

Brockton Grange A

Location: Brockton, near Much Wenlock. Tel: 019024 50000
Type and Size: Estate lake of about 20 acres. Alan Russell
Carp Stock: Well stocked with carp to over 20lbs
Category: Mixed Fishery
Other Species: Some coarse fish
Permits: From the Grange - about £50
Control: Private
BK Rating: Moderate
E/A: Severn-Trent
Comments: High class bed and breakfast accommodation in fine Victorian country house with 25 acres of attractive grounds and lake. Double £44 per night. This property is in Corvedale, one of Shropshire's finest dales, and convenient for Ludlow, Church Stretton and Ironbridge. No nuts

Brown Moss Mere

Location: Near Whitchurch off the A41
Type and Size: Lake of about three acres, very shallow and weedy
Carp Stock: Quite well stocked to doubles
Category: Mixed Fishery
Other Species: Roach, tench and bream
Permits: Day tickets on the bank at low cost
Control: Local club water
Restrictions: No night fishing
BK Rating: Moderate
E/A: Severn-Trent

Canal Reservoirs

Location: Great Sowdley, near Market Drayton
Type and Size: Small reservoirs off the canal
Carp Stock: Some carp, most small
Category: Mixed Fishery
Other Species: Perch, pike, roach, tench
Permits: Stoke-on-Trent AS. A Perkins, Muirshearlich, Fowlers Lane, Lightoaks,

	Stoke-on-Trent ST2 7NB. Enclose SAE
Control:	Club
BK Rating:	Difficult
E/A:	Severn-Trent

Castle Pool/Dandy Pool/Wide Waters

Location:	Little Dawley, near Telford
Type and Size:	Three separate small lakes, 2 - 3 acres each
How to Find:	Details from Telford Anglers Association. Tel: 01952 244272
Carp Stock:	Castle and Dandy well stocked with doubles to 20lbs; Wide Waters some carp to 25lbs+
Category:	Mixed Fisheries
Other Species:	Mixed coarse fish
Permits:	Telford Anglers Association
Cost:	About £3 per day; £20 per season. Concessions
BK Rating:	Castle/Dandy - Moderate; Wide Waters - Difficult
Control:	Club
E/A:	Severn-Trent
Comments:	We could find out very little about these waters, but the Telford Club Secretary should be able to help. Barbless hooks

Dorset Pools

Location:	Telford Way, Shrewsbury
Type and Size:	Two medium - sized pools
How to Find:	Off the B 5062 close to the R.Severn on the northern outskirts of Shrewsbury
Carp Stock:	Fairly well stocked with carp to 20 lbs
Category:	Mixed Fishery
Other Species:	Most coarse fish
Permits:	On bank
Cost:	£2 per day; £1 concessionary. Disabled anglers free, but must book in advance
Control:	Jock Patterson, bailiff. Tel: 01743 464916; mobile 0426 029198
Restrictions:	No boilies or groundbait
BK Rating:	Not known
E/A:	Severn Trent
Comments:	Open all year

Hawkstone Park Lake

Location:	Hawkstone Park, Hodnett, near Wem
Type and Size:	Park Lake, very narrow and about 1½ miles long!
Carp Stock:	The water is stocked with plenty of doubles and numerous twenties, both commons and mirrors to abut 28lbs
Category:	Carp Water
Other Species:	General coarse fish
Permits:	Hawk Lake Trust, Mr P Johnson 4 Soulton Crescent, Wem SY4 5HY
Control:	Hawk Lake Trust
BK Rating:	Difficult
Baits/Methods:	Normal carp fishing baits and methods
E/A:	North West
Comments:	With such an immensely long lake one of the main problems is obviously to find the fish, and it is this which makes the water hard, although it is quite well stocked with carp

Isle Estate

Location: Shrewsbury
Type and Size: Estate lake of about five acres
Carp Stock: One of the most heavily stocked carp waters in the country. Mostly small carp to 6lbs, but some fish present up to 20lbs
Category: Carp Water
Other Species: General coarse fish
Permits: Prince Albert AS, Secretary Mr C Clarke, 2 Avon Close, Upton, Macclesfield, Cheshire. Season tickets only
Cost: About £35 entry fee and approximately £35 per season. Members only
Control: Club
BK Rating: Very Easy
E/A: North West
Comments: One of those overstocked waters where the carp breed like rabbits. Fish can be caught by any method, and huge catches are recorded

Kingsnordley Pools

Location: Quatt, off the A442 just south east of Bridgnorth
Type and Size: 10 very small pools
Carp Stock: Well stocked with plenty of doubles to over 20lbs
Category: Mixed Fishery
Other Species: Bream, tench, roach, rudd, perch, gudgeon, barbel and goldfish
Permits: Day tickets on bank at about £3
Control: Tel: 01746 780247
Restrictions: No night fishing; no boilies; no groundbait
BK Rating: Moderate
E/A: Severn-Trent

Kyre Pool

Location: Tenbury Wells
Type and Size: Small lake
How to Find: Near Tenbury Wells
Carp Stock: Good carp to over 20lbs
Category: Mixed Fishery
Other Species: Pike and eels
Permits: S Lewis Fishing Tackle, Bewdley - day tickets
Cost: On application
Control: Private
BK Rating: Moderate
E/A: Severn-Trent

Middle Pool

Location: Wombridge, near Telford
Type and Size: $2^1/_2$ acre pool
Carp Stock: Carp to 20lbs, numbers not known
Category: Mixed Fishery
Other Species: Big bream
Permits: Season tickets from local tackle shops. No day tickets
Cost: On application
BK Rating: Moderate
Control: Telford Anglers Association. Tel: 01952 244272
Restrictions: No night fishing. No boilies
E/A: Severn-Trent

Mildenham Fishery — A

Location: Near Tenbury Wells
Type and Size: Disused canal, with no boats
Carp Stock: Some carp, numbers and sizes not known
Category: Mixed Fishery
Other Species: Rudd, roach, chub, dace and perch
Permits: Tel: 01299 250021 for details
Control: Private
BK Rating: Not known
E/A: Severn-Trent
Comments: Accommodation in Victorian farmhouse; some private river fishing also

Mill House Lakes

Location: Near Market Drayton
Type and Size: Two lakes
Carp Stock: Well stocked with carp to over 20 lbs
Category: Carp Water
Other Species: Bream and tench
Permits: Syndicate only
Cost: About £250
Control: Chris Bates, Mill House, Rosehill, Market Drayton. Shropshire TF9 2JF
E/A: Severn Trent

Moss Pool

Location: Forton, near Newport, Telford
Type and Size: Pool of about two acres
Carp Stock: Good head of doubles to 28lbs
Category: Mixed Fishery
Other Species: Bream and tench
Permits: On bank
Cost: Approximately £3 per day
BK Rating: Very Difficult
Control: Private
E/A: Severn-Trent
Comments: Try local tackle shops for permits and details. Rod & Guns, 3 High Street, Dawley. Tel:01952 503550

Neen Sollars Bungalow — A

Location: Between Cleobury Mortimer and Tenbury Wells
Type and Size: Estate lake of about an acre
Carp Stock: Some carp to about 10lbs
Category: Mixed Fishery
Permits: Fishing only available to those who rent the bungalow from the owner. Mr S R Jennings, 26 Moorpool Avenue, Harborne, Birmingham B17 9HN. Tel: 0121 4293262, weekdays after 7pm
Other Species: Roach, rudd and bream
Control: Private
Restrictions: Barbless hooks only; no keepnets
BK Rating: Not known
E/A: Severn-Trent
Comments: The accommodation is a chalet type self-catering bungalow with two double bedrooms, and a pull-down bed in dining room; sitting room, small kitchen and shower room etc. Covered verandah and summer house. Large garden, aviary and swing. Electricity included in price. Some acres of beautiful private woodland and pasture with the lake

and Mill Brook, with some stream fishing. 18 acre wildlife sanctuary with walks, and wildlife pool with log benches for picnics. Ideal for a holiday with children. Only guests have access to the land and fishing, which is included in the price. Private property - do not visit without permission

Nordley Ponds

Location: Nordley, near Bridgnorth
Type and Size: Three ponds of about an acre each
Carp Stock: Recently stocked with mixed coarse fish including some small carp
Category: Mixed Fishery
Other Species: Roach, bream and perch
Permits: Birmingham Anglers Association; members only
Restrictions: Probably no night fishing
BK Rating: Not known
E/A: Severn-Trent

Oswestry Lakes

Location: On the River Mor, near Oswestry
Type and Size: Small pools
Carp Stock: Well stocked with carp, sizes not known
Category: Mixed Fishery
Other Species: Most coarse fish
Permits: Oswestry AA, M J Shilton, 24 Windsor Close, Oswestry SY11 2UY, Tickets available for visitors. Details also from J E Ellis, Regal Stores, Oswestry; Morton Lodge Hotel, Morton
Cost: Season tickets; at about £10 - no day tickets
Control: Club
BK Rating: Not known
E/A: Severn-Trent

Patshull Park A

Location: Patshull Park, Pattingham, Shropshire WV6 7BR
Type and Size: Church Pool - 12 acre estate lake
Carp Stock: Well stocked with carp to 35lbs. Many 20lb commons
Category: Carp Water
Other Species: Tench, bream, roach, and some pike to over 30lbs
Permits: All information from the Patshull Park Hotel at the address above. Tel: 01902 700100; information on fishing from Fishery Manager Tel: 01902 700774. Syndicate only
BK Rating: Moderate
E/A: Severn-Trent
Comments: 48 bedroom hotel, golf, tennis and gymnasium; special breaks and conferences. Lakeside restaurant and coffee shop. Swimming and Beauty Centre(!) 280 acres of parkland not far from Wolverhampton. No peanuts. Open May 1st to March 15th

Rosehill Fishery

Location: Off the A41 at Rosehill, just south of Market Drayton
Type and Size: Two pools of six acres and two acres
Carp Stock: Some carp to middle doubles in large pool; carp to lower doubles in the newer small pool
Category: Mixed Fishery
Other Species: Crucians, roach, bream and perch in the large pool; barbel in the smaller pool
Permits: Day tickets on bank

Cost: £4 per day
BK Rating: Moderate
E/A: Severn-Trent

Shropshire Carp Syndicate

Location: Undisclosed
Type and Size: Small, attractive, secluded lake
Carp Stock: Well stocked with mirrors and commons to over 20lbs
Category: Mixed Fishery
Other Species: Ghost carp and big perch
Permits: Experienced anglers only can obtain details by telephoning 01909 450354 (daytime) or 01746 36443 (evenings)
BK Rating: Not known
E/A: Severn-Trent
Comments: Sounds like a pleasant syndicate; hot sandwiches and punt available. Night fishing allowed

Snailbeach Pool

Location: Off the A 438 road at Snailbeach, near Minsterley, south west of Shrewsbury
Type and Size: 8 acre former reservoir
Carp Stock: Well stocked with carp to about 10 lbs
Category: Mixed Fishery
Other Species: Roach, rudd, perch and gudgeon
Permits: In advance only from Shrewsbury Bait Centre. Tel: 01743 446759 or Sundane Tackle. Tel: 01743 361804
Cost: £2 per day; £10 per season
Control: L.M.S.A/C. Tel: 01743 359645
BK Rating: Not known
E/A: Severn Trent

Spring Lea Fishery

Location: Lea Cross, near Shrewsbury
Type and Size: Three lakes - 6 acres of water
How to Find: Take the A 488 road from Shrewsbury towards Bishop's Castle. After the Lea Cross pub at Hanwood, turn left on the Plealey road
Carp Stock: Well stocked with carp to doubles
Category: Mixed Fishery
Other Species: Crucians, tench, roach, rudd, bream and perch
Permits: On bank
Cost: About £4 per rod
Control: Tel: 01743 860972
Restrictions: No night fishing; no boilies. Barbless hooks
BK Rating: Not known
E/A: Severn Trent
Comments: Toilet. Disabled access

Stirchley Pools

Location: Hinksay, near Stirchley
Type and Size: Two pools of 1½ acres and 2 ½ acres
How to Find: These waters are near Dawley
Carp Stock: Small pool - carp to 10lbs; larger pool - some doubles to over 20lbs
Category: Mixed Fisheries
Other Species: Tench
Permits: Dawley Anglers Club. Tel: 01952 592899

Cost: About £2 per day
BK Rating: Moderate
Control: Club
E/A: Severn-Trent
Comments: All information from Dawley Anglers. Tickets from Rod & Gun,3 High Street, Dawley

Sutton Bank Fishery

Location: Sutton Bank, near Newport
Type and Size: 3 acre lake; short stretch of disused canal
How to Find: The fishery is on the left hand side of the A 519 between Eccleshall and Newport
Carp Stock: Both heavily stocked with carp to 8 lbs
Category: Mixed Fishery
Other Species: Tench, roach, chub, perch, orfe and gudgeon
Permits: On bank
Cost: Day tickets £3.50 for 2 rods; £3 for one rod; £1.50 evenings
Control: Private. Tel: 01952 813658
BK Rating: Easy
E/A: Severn Trent

Trench Pool

Location: Blue Pig Pub, Trench, near Telford
Type and Size: Large lake of 30 acres
Carp Stock: Some carp to over 20lbs
Category: Mixed Fishery
Other Species: Big pike, bream and tench
Permits: On bank
Cost: £2 per day
BK Rating: Moderate
Control: Telford AA. Tel: 01952 590605
E/A: Severn-Trent
Comments: Information from Rod & Gun, 3 High Street, Dawley. Tel: 01952 503550

Walcot East Lake

Location: Near Lydbury North, Ludlow
Type and Size: Seven acre lake
How to Find: Take the 49 Craven Arms road from Ludlow, and turn left on the B4368 to Little Brampton. Then take the right turn (B4385) to Lydbury North, and turn left into the estate at the Powis Arms
Carp Stock: A few carp to about 10lbs
Category: Few carp
Other Species: Bream, roach, perch
Permits: Birmingham Anglers Associaton, 100 Icknield Port Road, Rotton Park, Birmingham B16 OAP. Tel: 0121 454911. 9.30am to 1.30pm. 7pm to 9pm, weekdays. (Members only)
Cost: About £20 a season, whch includes all other BAA waters
BK Rating: Difficult, as there are few carp
Control: B.A.A
Restrictions: No groundbait of any kind
E/A: Severn-Trent
Comments: Not worth considering unless you want a general fishing day with the chance of carp

Walcot West Lake

Location: Walcot Hall Mansion, Lydbury North, near Bishops Castle
Type and Size: 19 acre estate lake
How to Find: Take the B 4368 road to Clun, and turn right towards Lydbury North. The fishery entrance is next to the Powys Arms pub
Carp Stock: Fairly well stocked with carp up to 15 lbs
Category: Mixed Fishery
Other Species: Tench, bream, roach, perch and eels
Permits: In advance from the Powys Arms
Cost: About £4 per day
Control: Enquire at the Powys Arms
BK Rating: Moderate
E/A: Severn Trent
Comments: Clive of India had these lakes constructed in the grounds of his hall in the 18th century

Whitchurch Lake

Location: Near Whitchurch
Type and Size: Small lake
Carp Stock: Well stocked with carp to about 10lbs
Category: Mixed Fishery
Other Species: Usual coarse fish
Permits: From J E Windsor, Black Park, Whitchurch
Cost: £5 per season
Control: Private
BK Rating: Not known
E/A: Severn-Trent

Withy Pool

Location: In the town of Telford
Type and Size: Medium sized town park lake
How to Find: Telford town park
Carp Stock: Carp to over 30lbs. Numbers not known
Category: Mixed Fishery
Other Species: General coarse fish. Catfish to over 20lbs
Permits: Dawley Anglers Club and Rod & Gun, 3 High Street, Dawley
Cost: On application
BK Rating: Difficult
Control: Club
Restrictions: No night fishing. No boilies
E/A: Severn-Trent
Comments: This lake could produce both big carp and catfish. Contact Mr Buttery, of Dawley AC . Tel: 01952 592899

Charity for Children who need Special Help

MARK

Sexually abused, aged 8.
Thrown out of school, aged 9.
Sent to Special school, aged 10.
No father, mother really can't cope.
Family in debt.
Left school, no qualifications,
no job, aged 16.
Before the Magistrates, aged 17.
What now?

JANE

Lives in poverty in Inner City area.
Goes to a Special school for
learning difficulties.
Reading age 8, actual age 15.
One of 6 children.
Parents can't afford new shoes,
often arrives at school hungry.
Never had a holiday in her life.
What chance?

WE HELP THEM

SECOND *Chance* is a registered charity for children who have special needs. Typically they may be victims of poverty, sexual or physical abuse, bereavement of a parent, physical disability, mental handicap, learning difficulty or any other experience needing help.

The charity works with them in all areas of their lives often through the medium of Angling, giving them added confidence to build a better life.

We would love to hear from anyone who would like to sponsor us, in any way, but particularly if you could help with fund raising functions, old and surplus fishing tackle, or your time to help.

For more information, list of suggestions on how to help or offers to help contact Doug Hulme, Director.

(Incorporating the Foster an Angler Charity – Angling's favourite charity)

Registered Charity No. 1001462

Patrons: Duke of Wellington KG. LVO., OBE., MC., Fiona Armstrong, David Bird, Bob Church, Hon. Edward Davies, John & Llin Golding MP, Sandra Halkon Hunt, Terence Lambert, Sir Cranley Onslow MP, Geoffrey Palmer, Anton Rodgers, Chris Yates.

Registered Address: Anchor Cottage, East Tisted, Alton, Hampshire, GU34 3RS

Woodcote Hall Pool

Location: Newport, near Telford
Type and Size: Three acre estate lake
Carp Stock: Well stocked with carp to upper 20's
Category: Carp Water
Other Species: Roach, bream, rudd, perch and tench
Permits: Season tickets only. Tel: 01952 503550
Control: Private
BK Rating: Moderate
E/A: Severn-Trent
Comments: Heavily fished water, said to be the best carp water in this area. Try Rod & Gun, 3 High Street, Dawley. There may possibly be some day tickets at £3 per day

SOMERSET

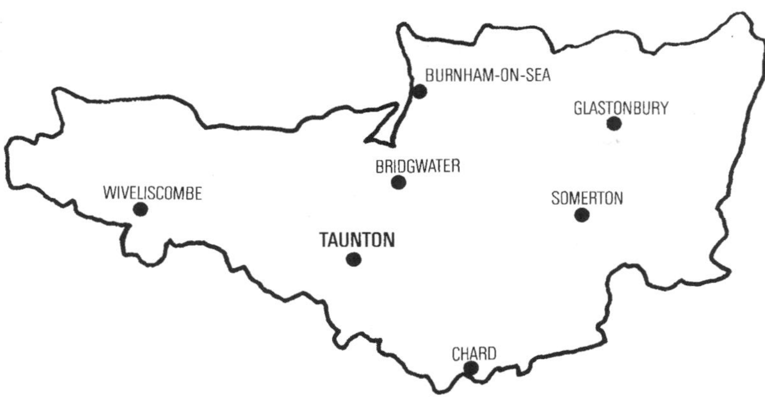

Apex Pond

Location: Burnham-on-Sea
Type and Size: Old pit of about five acres
How to Find: Go through Burnham-on-Sea and you will see the lake to the left of the road near houses
Carp Stock: Said to be well stocked with commons to about 6lbs
Category: Mixed Fishery
Other Species: Tench, rudd and pike
Permits: North Somerset Assciation of Anglers, and on the same tickets as Newton Pond. Secretary, R Newton, 64 Clevedon Road, Twickenham, Clevedon, Avon. Tel: 01275 856107
Restrictions: No night fishing
Control: Club
BK Rating: Fairly Easy
E/A: Wessex

Avalon Fisheries

Location: Westhay, near Glastonbury
Type and Size: Two medium-sized lakes
Carp Stock: Carp to 10 lbs
Category: Mixed Fishery
Other Species: Roach, bream, rudd, tench, perch and barbel
Permits: From fishing lodge
Cost: About £5 per day; reductions for evening tickets, juniors and O.A.P's
Control: Tel: 01458 841761
Restrictions: No night fishing; barbless hooks; no boilies or nuts
BK Rating: Not known
Baits/Methods: Sweetcorn and luncheon meat are best baits
E/A: Wessex
Comments: Toilet and disabled access

Bridgwater Bay Holiday Park A

Location: End of the Esplanade, Burnham-on-Sea
Type and Size: Small lake on holiday park
Carp Stock: Some mirror carp to 10lbs+

Category: Mixed Fishery
Other Species: Roach, rudd, tench and bream
Permits: Residents only, weekly tickets from reception at low cost
Control: Private
Restrictions: No close season fishing allowed
BK Rating: Moderate
E/A: Wessex
Comments: Large holiday camp with lodges, chalets, apartments and caravans. All modern facilities, including outdoor heated swimming pool, boating lake, snooker and pool room, tennis courts, shops, bars etc. Details and bookings from Hoseasons Holidays, Sunway House. Lowestoft NR32 3LT Tel: 01502 500500

Bridgwater - Taunton Canal A

Location: Bridgwater to Taunton, exit 24 of the M5
Type and Size: Narrow canal
How to Find: See local maps
Carp Stock: Some carp, mostly doubles to over 20lbs
Category: Mixed Fishery
Other Species: General coarse fish
Permits: Local tackle shops in Bridgewaer and Taunton. Bridgewater AA has some of the water
Cost: £2 per day in advance only
BK Rating: Dificult
Control: Club
E/A: Wessex
Comments: There are some big fish in this weedy canal. Near and between locks is often best. Could produce an upper 20. Self-catering cottages on the banks of the canal. Tel: 01278 662783 (Mrs Day)

Chard Reservoir

Location: Off the A 358 at Chafficombe, near Chard
Type and Size: 50 acre reservoir, tree lined and attractive
Carp Stock: Well stocked with carp to 20 lbs; many doubles
Category: Mixed Fishery
Other Species: Roach, tench and perch
Permits: Chard Angling Centre, in the town of Chard
Cost: £5 per day; £12 per season. Cheaper rates for juniors and O.A.P's
Control: Chard D.A.A. Tel: 01460 63771
Restrictions: Some areas cannot be fished
BK Rating: Moderate
Baits/Methods: Legered boilies best
E/A: South West
Comments: Part of the area is a Nature Reserve

Combwich Pond

(pronounced Come-itch - or something similar!)

Location: Combwich, near Bridgwater
Type and Size: Old clay pit of about 25 acres
How to Find: From Bridgwater take the A39 Minehead road and turn right at the War Memorial, Cannington. After about 1¼ miles you will see a track on the right, opposite Bowlan Farm, which leads to the car park
Carp Stock: Well stocked with both commons and mirrors which are said to average more than 15lbs in weight. There are many upper doubles and a number of 20's, some of which are commons
Category: Carp Water

Other Species: Tench, roach, rudd, pike and many thousands of eels

Permits: Bridgwater Angling Association - same ticket as for Dunwear Ponds, from local tackle shops, Veals of Bristol, and the Secretary, 7 Webbers Way, Puriton, Bridgwater, Somerset

Cost: £16 per year, open to all

Control: Club - Bridgwater Angling Association

BK Rating: Moderate to Difficult

Baits/Methods: All the most advanced baits, rigs and methods needed for this very hard water. Pastes and boilies are eaten by eels and it has been said that you may easily hook at least 100 eels per season, and lose many hooks in the snags and excessively irregular bottom of this lake, which was flooded at different times. Multiple (particle) baits are said to work best

E/A: Wessex

Comments: A very hard water where nearly all the success goes to the long-stay carp specialists. If you do get one it's likely to be big, with a very good chance of a 20 to 25lbs. Restocked with 7 pounders in 1991

Dunwear Ponds

Location: Dunwear Lane on the edge of the town of Bridgwater

Type and Size: Three clay pits known as the North Pond (about 4 acres); the South Pond (about 2 acres) and the Large Pond (about 20 acres)

How to Find: Turn off the A38 at the traffic lights towards Bridgwater Station (Westonzoyland Road). After nearly a mile turn right into Dunwear Lane and the car park will be seen only 400 yards along the lane on the right hand side. This is the ONLY entrance to the lakes

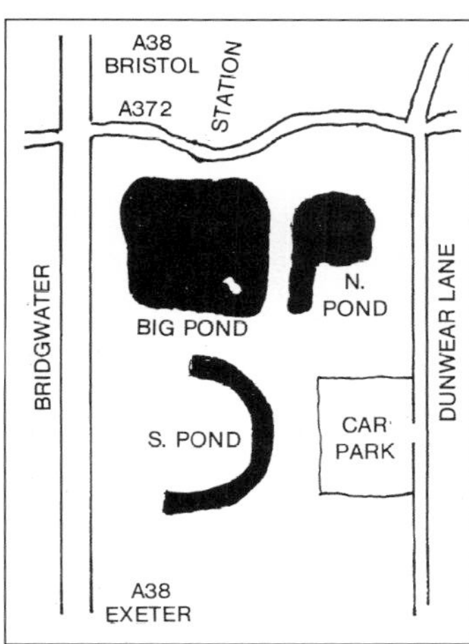

Carp Stock: North Pond well stocked with carp to about 18lbs, although a fish of about 24lbs has been reported from this lake. South Pond contains a few carp but most are doubles. Large Pond has a big stock of commons to about 8lbs and a few mirrors, which are very hard to locate, to about 19lbs

Category: North Pond - Carp Water, South Pond - Mixed Fishery, Large Pond - Mixed Fishery

Other Species: Roach, rudd, tench, pike, bream

Permits: Season tickets for this club water of the Bridgwater Angling Association are obtainable from Phil Dodd, Tel: 01278 444145, or

	from local tackle shops in Bridgwater and from Veals Fishing Tackle, Old Market, Bristol. Membership is open to all
Cost:	£20 per season which includes other waters
Restrictions:	No entry to water by any roads other than from the car park. No fishing on north bank of Large Pond
BK Rating:	North Pond - Moderate; South Pond - Moderate; Large Pond - Fairly Easy for the small commons. Difficult for the mirrors
Control:	Club
Baits/Methods:	Modern advanced carp rigs, methods and baits needed for most of these fish
E/A:	Wessex
Comments:	The Bridgwater club is an excellent club owning most of its own fisheries, but rules are strict, and anglers would do well to observe them. Best swim on the South Pond is the one next to the houses, past which you cannot go. This and the North Pond are hard fished by carp specialists, many of whom come from other parts of the country and spend days and nights in bivvies. Water is very busy during summer and crowded with children etc. Autumn fishing is much more peaceful. The Large Pond has islands and is split up by many reed beds which grow out into the lake along old, now flooded, paths. It is also very weedy with a thick growth of weed over most of the bottom. The club also has other ponds containing carp

Durleigh Reservoir

Location:	Durleigh Road, Bridgewater
Type and Size:	80 acre reservoir
Carp Stock:	Some carp to doubles
Category:	Mixed Fishery
Other Species:	Pike, roach, bream, hybrids, tench and rudd
Permits:	In advance from fishing lodge
Cost:	About £5 per day
Control:	Tel: 01278 424786
Restrictions:	No night fishing
BK Rating:	Moderate
E/A:	Wessex
Comments:	Toilets

Howley Street Pond

Location:	Howley Street, near Chard
Type and Size:	Half acre pond
Carp Stock:	Some carp to about 10lbs
Category:	Mixed Fishery
Other Species:	Tench, bream, roach and perch
Permits:	Day tickets from Chard Angling Centre, The Old Bakehouse, 2 Holyrood Street, Chard
Cost:	£3
Control:	Club
BK Rating:	Not known
E/A:	Wessex

Newtown Pond

Location:	Centre of the ton of Highbridge, west of A38
Type and Size:	Clay pit of seven acres
How to Find:	Take the Burnham-on-Sea road from Highbridge, turn left into housing estate; lake is on the left surrounded by houses
Carp Stock:	50 doubles, mostly mirrors. One or two lower 20's. 150 commons,

	mostly under 10lbs; fish said to be going back
Category:	Carp Water/Mixed Fishery
Other Species;	Pike, roach, rudd, bream, eels
Permits:	Newsagent in Highbridge High Street, Veals of Bristol,Old Market, Bristol
Cost:	Approximately £15 per season
Baits/Methods:	Boilies and multiples. Normal carp legering methods and rigs
Control:	Club. North Somerset Association of Anglers. Open to all
Restrictions:	No night fishing between 10.30pm and 5.30am; one rod only; no floating crust
E/A:	Wessex
BK Rating:	Moderate
Comments:	Town water quite noisy and busy, mostly 10-15 feet deep; little weed. Club Secretary: Mr R F Newton, 64 Clevedon Road, Tickenham, Clevedon, Avon, who will supply all information and possible details of day tickets

Oxenlease Farm A

Location:	Wiveliscombe
Type and Size:	Two farm ponds of an acre and half an acre
How to Find:	From Taunton take the A361 (3227) road west, where you will see a right turn to Wiveliscombe, by the Rock Inn to Waterrow - follow the fish sign for 4 miles
Carp Stock:	Good number of carp to 20lbs
Category:	Mixed Fishery
Other Species:	Tench, roach, rudd and bream
Permits:	Free fishing to those who stay in one of the six caravans on the site. Information from Mrs Rottenbury Tel: 01984 623427 (caravan site open Easter until end of October). Day permits for non-residents
Control:	Private
BK Rating:	Moderate
E/A:	South West

Perry Street Pond

Location:	Perry Street, near Chard
Type and Size:	One and quarter acre matured pit
Carp Stock:	Well stocked with carp, included a number of doubles to about 18lbs
Category:	Mixed Fishery
Other Species:	Tench, roach, rudd, bream and perch
Permits:	Season tickets only from Chard Angling Centre, The Old Bakehouse, 2 Holyrood Street,; Chard Cycle Centre, Holyrood Street. £12 per season. Concessions
Control:	Club. Tel: 01460 63771
BK Rating:	Difficult
E/A:	Wessex
Comments:	A pleasant little pond, but the doubles have been hooked a lot, and are not easy to catch

River Parrett A

Location:	Upstream from Bridgwater
Type and Size:	Short river
How to Find:	Bridgwater to Somerton
Carp Stock:	Unknown but commons caught recently to 21 1/2 lbs
Category:	Few Carp
Other Species:	Most coarse fish
Permits:	Bridgwater Angling Club - local tackle shops
Cost:	On application

BK Rating: Difficult due to location problems
Control: Club
E/A: Wessex
Comments: This river, the Huntspill, the King Sedgemoor Drain, and other rivers in the area all contain carp to about 25lbs - if you can find them! Try backwaters, mill pools, islands or any other features - and be prepared to do some walking! Try also the Milk Factory at Bason Bridge on the River Brue; Mark; and Edington. Holiday accommodation: self-catering lodges alongside River Huntspill, also bed and breakfast in main house with bar. Tel: 01278 781612 or 784264 for details and brochure

Screech Owl Ponds

Location: Close to the M5, and next to the River Parret, just outside Bridgwater
Type and Size: Small interconnected clay pits, heavily reeded - about eight acres of water
Carp Stock: In the past, carp to 20lbs have been reported
Category: Mixed Fishery
Other Species: Rudd, tench, bream and eels
Permits: From local tackle shops
Cost: About £3 per day
Control: Club Tel: 01278 444145
BK Rating: Difficult
E/A: Wessex
Comments: A hard to fish water because of the profuse reed hedges which split up the water areas. A Nature Reserve, with one bank out of bounds to anglers. No night fishing

The Sedges **A**

Location: Near Taunton
Type and Size: Two small lakes
Carp Stock: Carp to over 20 lbs
Category: Mixed Fishery
Other Species: Roach, tench, bream, chub and perch
Permits: Included in price
Control: Tel: 01278 445221
E/A: Wessex
Comments: Holiday caravans for hire - send for brochure

Thorney Lakes **A**

Location: Thorney Farm, Muchelney, Langport
Type and Size: Two lakes, one of two acres
Carp Stock: Well stocked with carp to 20lbs
Category: Mixed Fishery
Other Species: Carp, tench, roach, rudd and bream £4 per day; £2 winter. Concessions
Permits: Ann and Richard England, at the above address. Tel: 01458 250811
BK Rating: Moderate
E/A: Wessex
Comments: Camping and touring caravans: one free permit for each caravan. Barbless hooks. No nuts or boilies

Viaduct Fishery

Location: Cary Valley, Somerton TA11 6L. Tel: 01278 274022
Type and Size: Two lakes of five acres
Carp Stock: Some carp to double figures - best about 18lbs
Category: Mixed Fishery

Other Species:	Bream, tench, rudd, roach and perch
Permits:	Restricted membership obtainable from Tim and Lisa Chapman at the address above. Write or phone for brochure
Cost:	£4 per day; £3 half day
Control:	Private
BK Rating:	Not known
E/A:	Wessex
Restrictions:	No nuts or boilies. Barbless hooks; no keepnets
Comments:	There is a lodge, where drinks and refreshments are sold, as well as fresh and smoked trout, and pick your own strawberries! There are also two trout fly lakes, and one novices any-method trout pond. The trout fisheries are open all the year; normal close season applies for the carp fishing. Best trout to date is 9lbs 3ozs

Walrow Ponds

Location:	Near Bridgwater
Type and Size:	Small pits
Carp Stock:	Well stocked with carp to 10lbs or so, but some to 22lbs
Category:	Mixed Fishery
Other Species:	Bream, roach, rudd, tench and perch
Permits:	From local tackle shop. Secretary, Bridgwater AA. L A Williams, 7 Webbers Way, Puriton, Bridgwater TA7 8AS
Cost:	About £20 per season; to cover all the other Bridgwater club fisheries, most of which contain carp
Control:	Club
BK Rating:	Easy
E/A:	Wessex
Comments:	Also on N.Somerset AA ticket. Tel: 01275 856107

Westhay Lake

Location: Between Westhay and Shapwick, off the B3151 road near Glastonbury
Type and Size: Three and a half acre lake
Carp Stock: Well stocked with carp to 28lbs
Category: Mixed Fishery
Other Species: Tench, roach, rudd and crucians
Permits: All information and permits from Alan Tedder on 01278 456429 / 841761
Cost: £4 per day; £3 per night
Control: Private
BK Rating: Moderate
Comments: This fishery opened on June 16th 1991. Many of the fish came from a water called The Beeches, near Bridgwater, which is now closed. Tidy, well run carp fishery

SOUTH GLAMORGAN (Wales)

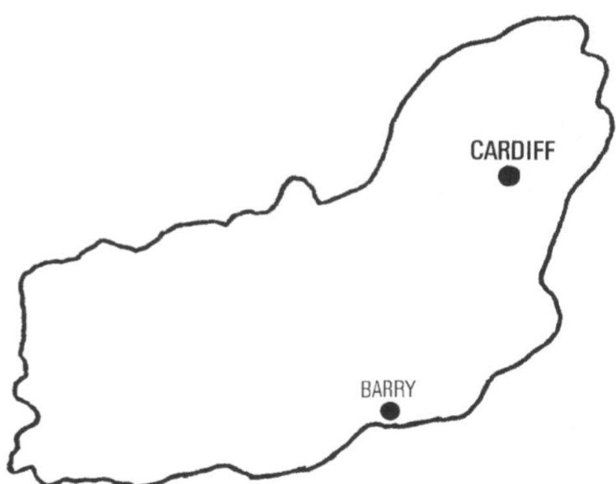

Barry Reservoir

Location: Barry Docks, Barry, near Cardiff
Type and Size: Five acre shallow lake with reeds but little weed
Carp Stock: Well stocked with small commons, and a few double figure mirrors
Category: Mixed Fishery
Other Species: Eels, roach and rudd
Permits: Members only water of Glamorgan AC. Secretary: P Mason, 8 Denys Close, Dinas Powis, South Glamorgan
Cost: About £30 per season
BK Rating: Fairly Hard
Restrictions: No night fishing; no day tickets
E/A: Welsh

Cafarfatha Park Lake

Location: Brecon Road, Merthyr Tydfil
Type and Size: Three acre town park lake with islands
Carp Stock: Well stocked with small carp, and a few upper doubles
Category: Mixed Fishery
Other Species: Eels, rudd and roach
Permits: Day tickets from bailiff on bank. Season tickets from local tackle shops
Cost: £2 per day; £12 per season
Restrictions: No night fishing; fishing from one bank only
BK Rating: Easy
E/A: Welsh

Darren Park Lake

Location: Frederick Street, Ferndale, near Porth
Type and Size: Pond of half an acre
Carp Stock: Some carp to 20 lbs
Category: Few Carp
Other Species: Perch, roach, bream and tench
Permits: In advance only from local tackle shops
Cost: About £18 per season
Control: Glycornel A.A.
BK Rating: Difficult
E/A: Welsh

Hendre Lake

Location: Hendre Road, Cardiff, off the A48
Type and Size: Six acre town lake with island
Carp Stock: Quite well stocked with doubles to about 20lbs
Category: Mixed Fishery
Other Species: Roach, tench and bream
Permits: Day tickets from Gary Evans Fishing Tackle, Cardiff or Newport, in advance only. Night syndicate, members only
Cost: £2 per day; £15 per season
Control: Private
Restrictons: No night fishing for non-members
BK Rating: Easy
E/A: Welsh

Kenfig Lake

Location: Kenfig, between Port Talbot and Porthcawl
Type and Size: 90 acre lake, shallow and weedy
Carp Stock: Some carp to over 10lbs
Category: Mixed Fishery
Other Species: Pike, bream, tench, roach, rudd, brown and rainbow trout
Permit:: Kenfig Hill and District AA. S Evans, 110 Quarella Road, Bridgend
Cost: About £20 per season; no day tickets, members only
Control: Club. Tel: 01656 785938
BK Rating: Difficult, as this is a very big lake
E/A: Welsh

Marshfield Reens

Location: Near Cardiff
Type and Size: Small lake
Carp Stock: Well stocked with carp to over 10lbs
Category: Mixed Fishery
Other Species: Tench and some other coarse fish
Permits: Bute AA - season tickets from L V Powell, 76 Clare Road, Grangetown, Cardiff
Control: Club
BK Rating: Moderate
E/A: Welsh

Roath Park Lake

Location: Roath Park, Cardiff
Type and Size: Park lake of about four acres
Carp Stock: Quite well stocked with carp to upper doubles
Category: Mixed Fishery
Other Species: Tench, roach, rudd
Permits: On bank
Control: Cardiff Corporaton
BK Rating: Moderate
Restrictions: No night fishing
E/A: Welsh

SOUTH YORKSHIRE

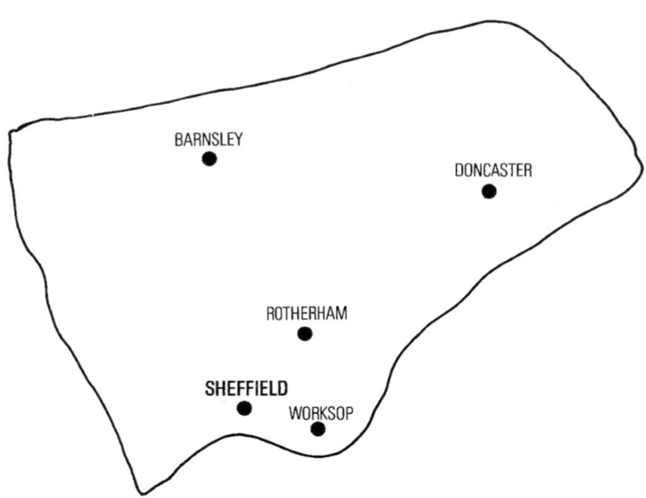

Askern Lake

Location: Askern, near Doncaster
Type and Size: Park lake of eight acres with an island
How to Find: Take the A19 from Doncaster to Askern. The lake is by the road on the right, in the town centre
Carp Stock: Lakes 1 and 2 contain a fair number of small carp. Lake 3 which is 8 acres, is well stocked with good carp to 29lbs
Category: Mixed Fishery
Other Species: Perch, roach, tench, crucians and pie
Permits: From bailiff on site
Cost: £2 per day, half price for juniors and OAP's. Boat hire at £2.15 for four hours
BK Rating: Moderate
Control: Council
Restrictions: No night fishing
E/A: Yorkshire
Comments: A busy town park lake, with tarmac banking which is very suitable for disabled anglers. Fishing allowed from boats

Bank End Coarse Fisheries

Location: Blaxton, near Doncaster
Type and Size: Two lakes of 4½ and 3½ acres
How to Find: Take the A614 Bawtry to Thorne road, then the B1396 from Blaxton. The lakes are on the right about 1½ miles from Blaxton
Carp Stock: These lakes were stocked in 1989 with carp to 12lbs; there are also carp to 20lbs
Category: Small lake - Carp Water; larger lake - Mixed Fishery
Other Species: Bream, tench, roach, rudd and perch
Permits: Day tickets on site

Cost: £4 per day
BK Rating: Insufficient information
Control: Private. Tel: 01302 770224
Restrictions: No night fishing. No hemp or tares
E/A: Severn-Trent
Comments: There are big tench and bream here, so every take will not be from a carp. Car parking on banks, with swims built to allow wheelchairs for the disabled. Tackle shops in Doncaster have details

Barlow Coarse Fishery

Location: Barlow, near Chesterfield
Type and Size: Two small lakes
How to Find: From Chesterfield, take the B 6051 towards Sheffield. The fishery is in 5 miles on right, after the Trout Inn
Carp Stock: Well stocked with carp to over 20 lbs
Category: Mixed Fishery
Other Species: Koi, roach, bream, tench, chub, perch, rudd and gudgeon
Permits: On bank
Cost: £4 per day; £3 juniors, O.A.P's and disabled
Control: Private. Tel: 0114 289 0543
Restrictions: No cereal groundbait or hemp
BK Rating: Moderate
E/A: Yorkshire
Comments: Toilet. No night fishing. Barbless hooks

Beedom's Fishery

Location: South Yorkshire, undislosed location
Carp Stock: Carp to well over 20lbs - at least five 20's and a thirty
Control: Club
Comments: Those who control this water do not want publicity, so no further details can be published. For information and an introduction to the controlling body, please contact Mr M A Beedom, 1 Martindale Walk, Carcroft, Doncaster DN6 8BX. Tel: 01302 330749

Blacker Dam

Location: Blacker Green Lane, Silkstone, near Barnsley, off the A628 Manchester road
Type and Size: Small attractive pond
Carp Stock: Thought to be quite well stocked
Category: Moderate
Other Species: Tench
Permits: Leeds and District ASA, members only but open to all - Secretary, Leeds and District ASA, c/o Leeds Anglers Club, Stoney Rock Lane, Leeds 9
Control: Club
E/A: Yorkshire

Bolton Brickponds

Location: Goldthorpe, Bolton-upon-Dearne, Near Barnsley
Type and Size: Three lakes, covering about 10 acres in all
How to Find: In Bolton-upon-Dearne, opposite the Council offices
Carp Stock: Well stocked with mirror and common carp to over 20lbs
Category: Mixed Fishery
Other Species: Pike, bream, tench, roach, perch, chub and trout
Permits: From the fishing hut on site, to be purchased before fishing. Only £3 per year, but day tickets needed in the trout season

BK Rating: Moderate
Restrictions: Night fishing by arrangement, but during the close season daytime only, and only using fly, worms, maggots or casters
Control: Community Miners Welfare. Tel: 01709 895263
E/A: Yorkshire
Comments: Toilets on site. Good facilities for disabled anglers

Bullhole

Location: Barnby Dun, near Doncaster
Type and Size: Offcut of the River Dun, about 3½ acres in size
How to Find: Go through Barnby Dun towards the power station. The pond is on the left beside the banks of the Don
Carp Stock: Some carp to double figures
Category: Mixed Fishery
Other Species: Most coarse fish
Permits: Mr J Thornton. Tel: 01302 886126
Cost: £10 per year, which includes three other ponds
BK Rating: Difficult
Control: Club
E/A: Yorkshire
Comments: No close season

Campsall Country Park

Location: Campsall, Askern, near Doncaster
Type and Size: Clay pit of about 11 acres
How to Find: Take the A19 from Doncaster to Askern, then a left fork to Campsall. Turn left to the lake before the Sports Centre
Carp Stock: Stocked with carp to mid-doubes
Category: Mixed Fishery
Other Species: Bream, tench, perch and rudd
Permits: Day tickets on bank
Cost: £1.10, half price for juniors and OAP's
BK Rating: Not known
Control: Council
Restrictions: No night fishing
E/A: Yorkshire
Comments: This is a park fishery stocked in 1982. It is very deep and has an island. Many fishing platforms,and good for the disabled. Askern Miners Welfare actually control the water

Carlton Mill Pond

Location: Carlton-in-Lindrick, on the A609 just north of Worksop
Type and Size: Three acre mill pond - enquire locally for exact venue
Carp Stock: Some carp to over 20lbs reported caught
Category: Mixed Fishery
Other Species: Usual coarse fish, including tench
Permits: Enquire locally or on bank - small local angling club, but we have no further details
BK Rating: Not known
E/A: Severn-Trent

Crookes Valley Lake

Location: In the centre of Sheffield, at Crookesmoor
Type and Size: Four acre boating lake
Carp Stock: Some mirrors to about 12lbs

Category: Few Carp
Other Species: Tench, roach, perch and pike
Permits: FREE fishing
Control: Sheffield University Tel: 0114 2648178
BK Rating: Difficult as there are not many carp
E/A: Yorkshire
Comments: Flat concrete banks like many park lakes. Rowing boats etc. Open all year

Cumwell Canal Pond

Location: Cumwell Lane, between Thurcroft and Bramley
Type and Size: Two acres of canal-like open water
Carp Stock: Some carp to over 20lbs, number and sizes not known
Other Species: General coarse fish
Permits: Day tickets on bank at low cost
Control: Local council
Restrictions: No night fishing
BK Rating: Moderate
E/A: Yorkshire
Comments: Public area; a bit like a rubbish tip!

Cusworth Hall Lakes

Location: Cusworth House, Cusworth, near Doncaster
Type and Size: Two estate lakes of about four acres each
How to Find: Take the A638 from Doncaster for about 1 1/2 miles, and follow the signs for Cusworth Hall
Carp Stock: Well stocked with carp to 22lbs
Category: Mixed Fishery
Other Species: Crucians, roach, perch, rudd and tench
Permits: Day tickets on bank
Cost: £1.50 per day, half price for juniors and OAP's
BK Rating: Easy
Control: Doncaster and District AA
Restrictions: No night fishing
E/A: Yorkshire
Comments: Fine country house and grounds, with museum. Toilet facilities, a picnic area and good for the disabled

Delves Lakes

Location: Thorne, near Goole, off the A614
Type and Size: Two lakes of about two to three acres each
Carp Stock: Quite well stocked with carp to upper doubles
Category: Mixed Fishery
Other Species: Tench, roach, perch, bream and a few crucians
Permits: On the bank at about £2 per rod; £10 per year
Control: Tel: 01405 815308 or 01405 812958 Thorne and District AA
BK Rating: Moderate
E/A: Yorkshire
Comments: No nut baits

Elsecar Reservoir

Location: Elsecar Park, Hoyland Nether, near Barnsley
Type and Size: 12 acre reservoir
How to Find: Take junction 36 from the M1 to Hoyland, then follow signs for Elsecar. Turn left at the T junction, and at the Market Hotel turn

right towards Wentworth
Carp Stock: Carp to over 20lbs
Category: Mixed Fishery, although possibly Few Carp
Other Species: Pike, bream, roach and tench
Permits: Day permits from bailiff on bank. About £2 per day, reduced prices for disabled and free to pensioners
BK Rating: Difficult
Control: Elsecar Main Colliery Angling Society. Tel: 01226 746297
Restrictions: No night fishing. No fishing from the parkside foreshore
E/A: Yorkshire
Comments: Costs for these reservoirs and other waters in Yorkshire seem to be very low, so Yorkshire looks like a good county for anglers

Flash Lane Pond

Location: Flash Lane, Wickersley, Rotherham
Type and Size: Small lake of about two acres
Carp Stock: Some carp to about 20lbs
Category: Few Carp
Other Species: Roach, rudd, tench and perch
Permits: Enquire from local tackle shops or ask on bank
Control: Small local club
BK Rating: Difficult
E/A: Yorkshire

Fleets Dam

Location: Smithies Lane, off the A61 one mile north of Barnsley
Type and Size: Ten acre attractive reed-fringed lake
Carp Stock: Well stocked wtih carp, and now caught to 15lbs
Category: Mixed Fishery
Other Species: Tench, roach, perch and pike
Permits: Day tickets on the bank
Cost: £3.50 adults, £2.50 juniors; evening tickets from 4pm £2.50. Season £50
Control: Allan Hanson, Stanborough Fisheries. Tel: 01226 292579
Baits/Methods: Luncheon meat, sweetcorn and bread all work well, with standard methods, especially float fishing close in
BK Rating: Easy
E/A: Yorkshire
Comments: This is mainly a match fishery, with big weights taken, and many anglers are broken in carp whilst pole fishing. Most matches take place on Tuesdays, Wednesdays, Saturday and Sunday, on about half the lake

Graves Park Pond

Location: Left side of the A61, travelling south from Sheffield City centre
Carp Stock: Plenty of doubles to 18lbs
Category: Mixed Fishery
Other Species: Roach and perch
Permits: From bailiff on bank
Control: Sheffield City Council
BK Rating: Difficult
E/A: Yorkshire
Comments: Good for disabled anglers, with a cafe nearby

Hoyle Mill Dam

Location: Kingsley, Hemworth, near Pontefract.Find Hoyle Mill Road, near Hemsworth Water Park
Type and Size: Large lake
Carp Stock: Carp to double figures
Category: Mixed Fishery
Other Species: Roach, tench, bream, chub and big eels
Permits: Day tickets from bailiff on bank,at £2 each
Control: Hemsworth and District AA. Open to all. Details and membership from Stan Pollington, 2 Common Road, Kinsley, Pontefract. Tel: 01977 612556
BK Rating: Not known
E/A: Yorkshire

Howbrook Reservoir

Location: Off the A 61 between Sheffield and Barnsley
Type and Size: 4 acre reservoir
Carp Stock: Well stocked with carp to upper twenties
Category: Mixed Fishery
Other Species: Tench, bream, perch, rudd, chub, roach and eels
Permits: On bank
Cost: About £2 per day; £10 per season
Control: Steve Gregory. Tel: 01742 320981
BK Rating: Not known
E/A: Yorkshire

Lindholme Lake Fisheries

Location: Sandtoft, near Doncaster
Type and Size: One and a half acre carp lake
How to Find: The complex is off the Sandtoft Road, 14 miles from Doncaster and 7 miles from the M18 junction
Carp Stock: Well stocked with carp - sizes not quoted in brochure
Category: Carp Only
Permits: On site
Cost: Day - £3.50; evening from 5pm - £2; some season tickets at £40
Control: Brian Lindley on site or Tel: 01427 872015
Restrictions: No night fishing - open 8am to 10pm, or one hour after sunset; no keepnets; one rod only; children under 14 must be accompanied by an adult
BK Rating: Insufficient information
E/A: Yorkshire
Comments: Some places for disabled anglers; toilets, washroom; free hot drinks. Rod and line hire; tuition by arrangement. Food can be arranged. There is also an 18 acre general coarse lake, open from 16th June to 31st October and four acre trout lake, open March to September (fly only)

Long Pond

Location: Barnby Dun, near Doncaster
Type and Size: Offcut from River Don, about half a mile long
How to Find: Near Thorpe Marsh power station, which is just across the canal through Barnby Dun
Carp Stock: Well stocked with carp to over 20lbs, and several thirties are rumoured to have been caught recently
Category: Mixed Fishery
Other Species: Most coarse fish

Permits: On the same permit as Bullhole - Mr I Thornton. Tel: 01302 886126
BK Rating: Difficult
Control: Club
E/A: Yorkshire
Comments: No close season

Milton Ponds

Location: Milton Road, Hoyland, near Sheffield
Type and Size: Two small ponds
Carp Stock: Carp to upper doubles
Category: Mixed Fishery
Other Species: Roach, tench, chub, bream, perch and big eels
Permits: On bank
Cost: About £2 per day
Control: Hoyland A.C. Tel: 01226 745263
Restrictions: No boilies
BK Rating: Not known
E/A: Yorkshire

Pontefract Park Lake

Location: Pontefract Racecourse
Type and Size: 4 acre park lake
Carp Stock: Some carp to mid-doubles
Category: Mixed Fishery
Other Species: Bream, tench, roach, perch and pike
Permits: From ticket office
Cost: About £3 per day; evening tickets
Control: Wakefield Leisure Services. Tel: 01977 705165
Restrictions: No keepnets
BK Rating: Not known
E/A: Yorkshire

Pool Bridge Farm

Location: Crockey Hill
Type and Size: Small lake, long and narrow with island
Carp Stock: Well stocked with carp to 20lbs
Category: Mixed Fishery
Other Species: Chub, roach, perch, tench, rudd, dace and crucians
Permits: Day tickets on bank at £2
Control: Ron Fletcher. Tel: 01904 637854
Restrictions: No night fishing, no keepnets; no sweetcorn or hemp (what will they ban next!)
BK Rating: Moderate
E/A: Yorkshire
Comments: A new lake is being constructed, and will be stocked with carp to over 20lbs

Rother Valley Country Park

Location: Killamarsh, Sheffield
Type and Size: Public country park of about 20 acres
Carp Stock: Some carp stocked to about 2lbs
Category: Few Carp
Other Species: General coarse fish
Permits: Day ticket on bank at low cost
Control: Private

BK Rating: Very Difficult
E/A: Yorkshire
Comments: Many members of the public, boats and water-skiers; no night fishing

Roundwood Pond

Location: The Mill, Aldwalk, Rotherham
Type and Size: Mill dam of about 10 acres
Carp Stock: Quite a few doubles to about 25lbs
Category: Mixed Fishery
Other Species: Usual coarse fish
Permits: British Rail - try BR Staff Association, 8 Upper Belmont Road, St Andrews, Bristol, or enquire from tackle shops in Rotherham
BK Rating: Moderate
E/A: Yorkshire
Comments: This water was stocked with about 50 good carp in the early 70's, and there could be some even better fish than the 20's reported caught

Sheffield Canal

Location: Tinsley, in the centre of Sheffield
Type and Size: Typical city canal
Carp Stock: The carp were put in 1979, and these are plenty of small fish, with the occasional double and 20
Category: Mixed Fishery
Other Species: Roach, pike, rudd and bream
Permits: Local club - enquire at tackle shops. Day tickets on bank in some areas
BK Rating: Moderate - Easy in the locks
E/A: Yorkshire
Comments: Usual problems associated with fishing in cities and towns - most of them caused by other people!

Thurnscoe Reservoir

Location: Opposite Hickleton Main Colliery, off the A635 Barnsley-Doncaster road at Thurnscoe
Type and Size: Small reservoir
Carp Stock: Fairly well stocked with carp, sizes not known
Category: Mixed Fishery
Other Species: Pike, roach, tench and bream
Permits: From bailiff on bank
Cost: About £5 per season
Control: Hickleton Main Angling Club
BK Rating: Not known
E/A: Yorkshire

Tyram Lakes **A**

Location: Off the A614 at Hatfield Woodhouse, near Doncaster; just after the prison!
Type and Size: Three lakes of 30 acres, 25 acres and one acre
Carp Stock: All well stocked with carp over 30lbs
Category: Mixed Fishery
Other Species: Roach, bream, tench and perch
Permits: Details from the William de Lindholme Hotel on site
Cost: About £6 per day. Season tickets
Control: Tel: 01302 840886
BK Rating: Easy
E/A: Yorkshire

Comments: Accommodaton, food and drinks at hotel. No close season. No bait bans. Toilets. Barbless hooks

Underbank Reservoir

Location: Stocksbridge, Sheffield
Type and Size: 60 acre reservoir, very deep
Carp Stock: A few carp, some doubles and the odd 20
Category: Few Carp
Other Species: Trout and some coarse fish
Permits: Day tickets on bank at low cost
Control: Council
BK Rating: Very Difficult
Restrictions: No night fishing
E/A: Yorkshire

Wentworth Fisheries

Location: Wentworth, Rotherham
Type and Size: Three lakes - Mill Dam - 13 acres; Dog Kennel - 17 acres; Morley Pond - 10 acres
Carp Stock: Very well stocked with doubles to over 20 lbs
Category: Mixed Fishery
Other Species: Crucians, roach, perch, bream, tench and gudgeon. Mill Dam - pike
Permits: Season ticket only
Cost: £40 per rod (Mill Dam and Dog Kennel) £120 for 2 rods - Morley Pond exclusive carp anglers only
Control: Not known - we were sent these details, but no address or telephone number
Restrictions: No night fishing
BK Rating: Not known
E/A: Yorkshire
Comments: Opened 1996 / 97, stocked with 120 carp - doubles and twenties. A 35 lb common stocked in June 1996. Open June 15th to March 31st.

William De Windholme Lake

Location: On the A64 8 miles SE of Doncaster, between Hatfield Woodhouse and Bawtry
Type and Size: Ten acre lake
Carp Stock: Well stocked with carp between 5lbs and 15lbs
Category: Carp Water
Permits: Annual only from Neville Fickling, 27 Lodge Lane, Upton, Gainsborough DN21 5NW
Cost: £50 for 12 months
BK Rating: Easy
E/A: Severn-Trent
Comments: Close season fishing allowed within E/A rules; a good water to learn on. Water sports centre, can be busy at weekends

Willow Garth Fishery

Location: Shaftholme Lane, Arksey, near Doncaster
Type and Size: Four acre lake
How to Find: From Doncaster take the A19 to Bentley, then turn right onto Arksey Lane and Marsh Lane
Carp Stock: Well stocked with carp to mid-doubles
Category: Carp Water
Other Species: Roach, perch and tench, and stocked annually with rainbow trout
Permits: Day tickets on bank

Cost: £2 dawn till dusk; £1.30 4pm till dusk; £2.50 per night
BK Rating: Moderate
Control: Private
E/A: Yorkshire
Comments: Very pleasant water, sometimes heavily fished. Car park and refreshment bar. One side suitable for disabled anglers. Groundbait, keepnets and nuts as baits not allowed. No close season. Information from the owner, Keith Davis. Tel: 01302 974258

Wintersett Reservoir

Location: Two miles from Crofton village in between Wakefield and Doncaster
Type and Size: Wintersett is the small lake next to Wintersett Reservoir. The fishery also includes Cold Hindley Reservoir
How to Find: Take the A638 Doncaster road from Wakefield. About two and a half miles, take a right turn down Lodge Lane to Crofton Village. The lakes are about two miles beyond the village
Carp Stock: Quite well stocked with plenty of doubles, and mirrors to 27lbs
Category: Mixed Fishery
Other Species: Roach, perch, tench, bream and pike from the small Wintersett lake. Crucians from Cold Hindley
Permits: From bailiff on bankside
Control: Coal Industries Social Welfare Organisation
BK Rating: Moderate
E/A: Yorkshire

Wombwell Dam

Location: Wombwell, three miles south east of Barnsley
Type and Size: Five acre lake
Carp Stock: Well stocked with doubles and small fish, with a few to nearly 30lbs
Category: Mixed Fishery
Other Species: Roach, bream and rudd
Permits: Day tickets on the bank
Cost: £2.50 for adults; £2.50 for juniors, OAP's and the disabled
Control: Wombwell Angling Centre, Tel: 01226 750659 or Barnsley Angling Centre, Tel: 01226 742859
Restrictions: No night fishing; no boilies or nuts(!)
BK Rating: Easy
E/A: Yorkshire

Worsborough Reservoir

Location: Worsborough,near Barnsley
Type and Size: Large reservoir
Carp Stock: Not many carp, but some big ones
Category: Few Carp
Other Species: Bream, tench, roach, bream/tench hybrids, crucians, perch, pike, eels and trout
Permits: On bank
Cost: £2 per day. £10 per season
Control: Barnsley DAS. T Eaton, 60 Walton Street, Barnsley. Tel: 01226 203090
Restrictions: No night fishing; no keepnets; Sunday fishing for members only; no live baiting, hempseed, bloodworm or jokers(!)
BK Rating: Very Difficult
E/A: Yorkshire
Comments: Since there is no close season, the adventurous might like to try it, but carp are few and far between, and are rarely seen

STAFFORDSHIRE

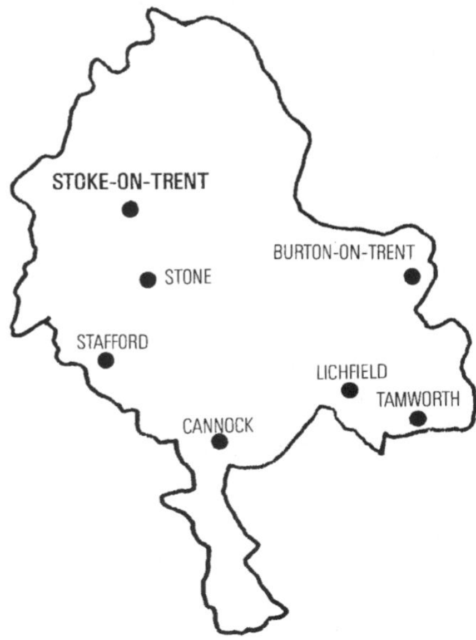

Anglesey Branch Canal

Location: White Horse Road, Brownhills, between Chasewater Reservoir and Freeth Bridge, on the A 5
Type and Size: Narrow canal but with some wide basins
Carp Stock: Quite well stocked with carp to 20 lbs
Category: Mixed Fishery
Other Species: Roach, perch, bream, pike and gudgeon
Permits: On bank
Cost: About £2 per day. Season tickets available
Control: Pelsall Social A.C. Tel: 01922 683234
Restrictions: No night fishing
BK Rating: Difficult
E/A: Severn Trent

Betley Mere

Location: Betley, on the A531, between Newcastle-under-Lyme and Nantwich
Type and Size: Ten acre shallow mere; a very attractive lake
Carp Stock: Well stocked with carp to about 25lbs
Category: Mixed Fishery
Other Species: Big pike, bream, tench and roach
Permits: From the house at the lake, or on the bank at weekends
Cost: £4 per day
Control: Frank Speed. Tel: 01270 820229
Baits/Methods: Boilies best for carp; long stay fishing often needed for success
BK Rating: Difficult
E/A: Severn-Trent
Comments: Night fishing is only allowed by special arrangement

Borrowpit Lake

Location: Sports Centre, Tamworth
Type and Size: 20 acre former gravel pit
Carp Stock: Well stocked with carp to doubles
Category: Mixed Fishery
Other Species: Tench, bream, roach and pike
Permits: On bank
Cost: About £2 per rod
Control: Lamb A/C. Tel: 01827 280593
Restrictions: No night fishing; no keepnets
BK Rating: Moderate
E/A: Severn Trent

Brookside Fishery

Location: Church Lane, Betley, near Nantwich
Type and Size: Small lake
Carp Stock: Well stocked with carp to over 20lbs
Category: Carp Water
Other Species: Roach
Permits: On bank
Cost: About £5 per day; £8 for two rods
Control: Tel: 01270 820528
Restrictions: No boilies, nuts or groundbait. No keepnets; barbless hooks
BK Rating: Moderate
E/A: North West
Comments: Toilets. Disabled access

Canwell Pool

Location: Canwell estate
Type and Size: Five acre estate lake
How to Find: Off the 453 Tamworth to Sutton Coldfield road
Carp Stock: Well stocked with carp to mid-20's
Category: Mixed Fishery
Other Species: General coarse fish
Permits: Sutton Coldfield AS. Secretary: Don Jones, Bricklyn House, Bulls Lane, Wishaw, Sutton Coldfield B76 9QN
Cost: £25 + possible joining fee
Control: Private
BK Rating: Fairly Hard
E/A: Severn-Trent
Comments: There is a long waiting list to join SCAS. A very quiet and attractive water

Central Forest Lake

Location: Central Forest Park, Stoke - on - Trent
Type and Size: 3 acre attractive park lake
Carp Stock: Well stocked with carp to 20 lbs
Category: Mixed Fishery
Other Species: Tench, roach, perch and bream
Permits: FREE FISHING
Cost: None
Control: Council Tel: 01782 202312
BK Rating: Not known
E/A: Severn Trent

Chasewater Lake

Location: Chasewater Park, Brownhills, Cannock
Type and Size: 20 acre lake
Carp Stock: Not many carp, but possibly a couple of 20's
Category: Few Carp
Other Species: Roach, rudd, bream, tench, perch and pike
Cost: About £3 per day
Control: Private
BK Rating: Very Difficult
E/A: Severn-Trent
Comments: A public water, and very busy. Only worth a try if you fancy something really hard, as this is certainly not a carp water

Cudmore Fisheries

Location: Whitmore, near the M6 and Newcastle-under-Lyme; the sign to the fishery will be seen one and a half miles from Whitmore on the Keele road
Type and Size: Six man-made lakes
Category: Carp Water
Carp Stock: Well stocked with carp to over 20lbs
Other Species: Chub, tench, roach and possibly some barbel
Permits: Day tickets on site from the lodge
Cost: £5 for two rods; £4 juniors OAP's and the disabled
Control: Cyril Brewster. Tel: 01782 680919
Restrictions: Boilies on one lake only
Baits/Methods: Sweetcorn and maggots, legered or float fished, and floaters also work well
BK Rating: Moderate
E/A: Severn-Trent
Comments: Open all year. Toilets. Disabled access

Deep Hay Pool

Location: Near Leek
Type and Size: Two small pools
Carp Stock: Mixed Fishery
Other Species: Roach, rudd, bream and tench
Permits: Members only water of Leek and Morland Fishing Club. H Emery, 20 Bosbourne Street, Leek; or enquire from local tackle shops
Restrictions: No day tickets; no night fishing
BK Rating: Moderate
E/A: Severn-Trent

Ellenhall Pools

Location: Eccelshall, near Stone
Type and Size: Four small farm pools
Carp Stock: Some carp, numbers and sizes not known
Category: Mixed Fishery
Other Species: Roach, tench, bream and perch
Permits: N Dale Tackle Shop, Albert Street, Stone
Control: Stone and District AS
BK Rating: Not known
E/A: Severn-Trent

Fisherwick Fly Fishing Lakes

Location: Whittington, near Lichfield. Tel: 01543 472515 / 472934
Type and Size: The Long Stream (500 yards); the Pump Pool (quarter acre); the Small Pool (quarter acre)
Carp Stock: Well stocked with carp to double figures
Category: Mixed Fishery
Other Species: Roach and perch
Permits: On site at the address above - discounts for annual membership
Control: Midland Game Fisheries
BK Rating: Not known
E/A: Severn-Trent
Comments: There are also three fly fishing lakes of 12 acres, 5 acres and 3 acres, and the Short Stream (fly fishing) - brown and rainbow trout in all these. Boats, tackle, rod licences, refreshments etc

Fisherwick Lakes

Location: Whittington, near Lichfield
Type and Size: Four small pools
Carp Stock: Well stocked with carp to doubles
Category: Mixed Fishery
Other Species: Perch, barbel, chub, tench and roach
Permits: From the lodge
Cost: About £5 per day; £40 per season
Control: Tel: 01543 472934
Restrictions: No night fishing; no cereal groundbaits; no keepnets; barbless hooks
BK Rating: Moderate
Baits/Methods: Boilies good for carp
E/A: Severn Trent

Fradley Canal

Location: Burton-on-Trent
Type and Size: Small canal
How to Find: Near Burton-on-Trent
Carp Stock: Plenty of carp when located - stocked with 5,000 small carp in 1990
Category: Mixed Fishery
Other Species: General coarse fish
Permits: Enquire in local tackle shops
Cost: On application
BK Rating: Easy, when fish are located
Control: Club
E/A: Severn-Trent
Comments: An early season catch in 1992 was reported as 7 fish to 12lbs in 4 hours, on legered boilies, using a 4lb line. For information try Burton-on-Trent AA - D J Clark, 7 Denton Rise, Burton-on-Trent DE13 OQB

Hamstall Fishery

Location: Hamstall Ridware, near Alrewas
Type and Size: Four small pools
Carp Stock: Well stocked with carp to 20 lbs
Category: Mixed Fishery
Other Species: Tench, bream, perch, roach and rudd
Permits: On site
Cost: £4.50 per day
Control: Geoff Payne. Tel: 01543 480744
Restrictions: No keepnets, groundbait or barbed hooks

BK Rating: Not known
Baits/Methods: Sweetcorn and luncheon meat are good baits
E/A: Severn Trent

Hanchurch Fishery

Location: Near Stoke - on - Trent
Type and Size: Ten lakes of from 1½ to 4½ acres
How to Find: Take the A 519 towards Eccleshall, and the fishery is on the right
Carp Stock: Well stocked with carp to upper twenties
Category: Mixed Fishery
Other Species: Bream, perch, tench, roach, crucians, chub and pike
Permits: Day tickets from lodge on one lake only. Season tickets for the rest
Cost: £6 two rods; £4 one rod. £35 per season £25 O.A.P's, juniors and the disabled
Control: Hanchurch F.C. Tel: 01782 642481
Restrictions: No boilies
BK Rating: Not known
E/A: Severn Trent

Hanley Park Lake

Location: Cauldon Road, Stoke-on-Trent
Type and Size: Shallow, three acre town park lake, attractive with two islands
Carp Stock: Some carp to doubles; double figure commons
Category: Mixed Fishery
Other Species: Roach, perch and bream
Permits: On bank
Cost: Half day £1.55 for adults; £1.25 juniors; season £13.50 and £8. Reductions for the disabled and unemployed
Control: Stoke-on-Trent Council, Leisure and Recreation Dept. Tel: 01782 202312
Restrictions: Dawn till dusk only; no night fishing
BK Rating: Moderate
E/A: Severn-Trent

Hopton Pools

Location: Hopton, near Stafford
Type and Size: Small lakes
Carp Stock: Some carp, sizes not known
Category: Mixed Fishery
Other Species: Tench and other coarse fish
Permits: Day and weekly tickets - Izaak Walton (Stafford) AA - T H Babbs, 4 Fieldside, Wildwood, Stafford
Control: Club
BK Rating: Not known
E/A: Severn-Trent

Izaak Walton Fishery

Location: Shallowford, near Eccleshall
Type and Size: Four small ponds
How to Find: Take the A5013 to Eccleshall, and after Chebsey turn into School Lane
Carp Stock: Well stocked with small carp
Category: Mixed Fishery
Other Species: Chub, crucians, bream, roach, tench and perch
Permits: On site
Cost: £3 per day; £4 for two rods. Juniors £2
Control: Paul & Brenda Jefferson. Tel: 01785 252 329
Restrictions: No boilies, dog biscuits(!), barbed hooks and keepnets

BK Rating: Easy
E/A: Severn Trent
Comments: Near Izaak Walton's cottage - a 1/4 mile stretch of the River Sow, mentioned in the Compleat Angler, is included

Lawton Hall Pool

Location: Off the A34 near Church Lawton, Kidsgrove
Type and Size: Very attractive estate lake
Carp Stock: Well stocked with carp to 28lbs
Category: Mixed Fishery
Other Species: Tench, bream, roach, perch and pike
Permits: Day tickets from Nick's Tackle Supplies, Kidsgrove or Anglers Den, Newcastle-under-Lyme; Tel: 01782 715155 or 01782 775871
Cost: £10 for a 24 hour ticket; some day tickets at £3; season £55 for dawn to dusk fishing. There is also a carp syndicate at £160 a year
BK Rating: Moderate
E/A: North West

Leighton Pool

Location: Wheatstone Park Farm, Chillington Lane, Codsall, near Wolverhampton
Type and Size: 3 acre pit with islands and lilies
Carp Stock: Well stocked with carp to mid-twenties
Category: Mixed Fishery
Other Species: Tench, roach, perch, rudd and crucians
Permits: On bank
Cost: £4 per day; £3 half day
Control: Tel: 01902 842156
Restrictions: One rod only. No boilies, bite alarms(!) or floating baits. No night fishing
BK Rating: Moderate
E/A: Severn Trent
Comments: Anglers must stop and ring bell at office near farm entry

Madeley Pool

Location: Moss Lane, near Newcastle - under - Lyme
Type and Size: 2 1/2 acre lake
How to Find: Take the A 525 from Newcastle to Whitchurch. In 4 miles turn right at the Offley Arms into Moss Lane, then first left
Carp Stock: Heavily stocked with carp averaging about 8 lbs
Category: Mixed Fishery
Other Species: Tench, small bream, crucians, rudd and roach
Permits: Free fishing
Cost: None
Control: Newcastle - under - Lyme Borough Council. Tel: 01782 750095
BK Rating: Easy
Baits/Methods: Legered boilies best
E/A: Severn Trent
Comments: Open all year. Pleasant town water

Millride Fishery

Location: Bognop Road, Essington
Type and Size: Several small pools
Carp Stock: Well stocked with small carp to 5 lbs
Category: Mixed Fishery
Other Species: Small bream, roach, tench, perch and gudgeon
Permits: On bank

Cost: £3 per day; £2.50 juniors and O.A.P's
Control: Tel: 01902 725165
BK Rating: Easy
E/A: Severn Trent

Park Hall Farm

Location: Park Hall Road, Weston Coyney, near Stoke - on - Trent
Type and Size: 5 acre lake
Carp Stock: Some carp to doubles
Category: Mixed Fishery
Other Species: Tench, roach, chub, perch and small bream
Permits: FREE FISHING
Cost: None
Control: Local council
BK Rating: Not known
E/A: Severn Trent

Pool House Farm

Location: Hunts Green, Tamworth
Type and Size: Old established one acre pool
How to Find: Off the A4091 towards Tamworth from Junction 9 on the M42
Carp Stock: Well stocked with many doubles
Category: Mixed Fishery
Other Species: Rudd, roach, tench, crucians, perch and chub
Permits: Day tickets in advance only from Mr C Heys, Pool House Farm, Brick Kiln Lane, Middleton, Tamworth B78 2BA. Tel: 01827 874856
Cost: £5 per day
Control: Private
Restrictions: Fishing 7am till dusk only; barbless hooks; no groundbait; no nuts
BK Rating: Moderate
E/A: Severn-Trent
Comments: An attractive pool with 22 fishing stages. Car park only 20 yards from bank. Also suitable for contests

Pretty Pigs Fishery

Location: Near Tamworth
Type and Size: 40 acre natural lake
How to Find: Near Shuttington village
Carp Stock: Well stocked with small carp, but fish up to possible 30lb
Category: Mixed Fishery
Other Species: General coarse fish
Permits: Birchmoor Angling Club. Secretary: Peter Mason, c/o Game Cock Inn public house. Tel: 01827 59783. Also day tickets available for small part of lake from Pretty Pigs public house on bank
Cost: About £3 per day. £80 per season
Control: Club
Restrictions: No fishing from one bank
BK Rating: Easy for small fish, large fish - Difficult, due to quantity of small ones
E/A: Severn-Trent
Comments: Lake formed by land subsidence and is mostly very shallow, river runs along one margin. Stalking best bet to sort out better fish

Serpentine Reservoir

Location: Knypersley, Stoke-on-Trent
Type and Size: Reservoir of 50 acres
How to Find: Knypersley is north of Stoke-on-Trent about half-way between Stoke and Congleton on the A27
Carp Stock: Not many carp in a very large water, but there are one or two big fish of well over 20lbs
Category: Few Carp
Other Species: General coarse fish
Permits: Cheshire Anglers' Association - members only. Secretary: G Brassington, 12 Highfield Drive, Nantwich, Cheshire
Control: Club
BK Rating: Very Difficult
E/A: Severn-Trent
Comments: Waters of this kind, which are large and contain only a very few big carp, are only recommended for experienced and successful carp anglers prepared to spend very long periods without catching, for the sake of a very big fish

Shelmoor Pool

Location: Off the A 518 at Gnosall, near Newport
Type and Size: 2 acre lake
Carp Stock: Quite well stocked with carp to 20 lbs, averaging 6 lbs
Category: Mixed Fishery
Other Species: Roach, perch, bream, crucians and gudgeon
Permits: On bank
Cost: £3.50 per day
Control: Tel: 01785 664616
Restrictions: No boilies
BK Rating: Not known
E/A: Severn Trent
Comments: Open all year

Shredicote Pools

Location: Mitton, just west of Penkridge off the A449
Type and Size: Two small attractive pools with trees, lilies etc
Carp Stock: Well stocked with carp to about 15lbs
Category: Mixed Fishery
Other Species: Tench, roach, perch and crucians
Permits: On the bank at £2 per day
Restrictions: None, and night fishing is allowed
BK Rating: Moderate
E/A: Severn-Trent

Shuttington Pool

Location: Near Tamworth
Type and Size: 11 acre natural lake
How to Find: Near Shuttington village
Carp Stock: Well stocked to mid-20's
Category: Mixed Fishery
Other Species: General coarse fish
Permits: Lambs Angling Club. Secretary: Mr Ghent, Hopleys, Ingram Pit Lane, Amington, Tamworth, Staff B77 3JA. Tel: 01827 51033
Cost: £20 + £5 joining fee
Control: Club

Restrictions: Unknown
E/A: Severn-Trent
Comments: May be a very long waiting list to join Lambs AC

Staffs - Worcester Canal

Location: Cross Keys, Penkridge, off the A449 between Stafford and Wolverhampton. The stretch is near the Cross Keys pub, off Filance Lane
Type and Size: Narrow canal with some boat traffic
Carp Stock: Quite well stocked with carp to doubles
Category: Mixed Fishery
Other Species: Perch, eels, tench, bream, crucians, chub and gudgeon
Permits: On bank at £2 per day
Control: Broomhill AS - Tony Cunningham. Tel: 01543 271775. Club membership at £5 (£2 juniors); from P Eldershaw Butchers on the A449, or from Tight Lines Fishing Tackle, Penkridge
BK Rating: Moderate
E/A: Severn-Trent

Stowe Pool

Location: Lichfield
Type and Size: Town lake of four acres
How to Find: In the centre of Lichfield
Carp Stock: Some carp to over 20lbs
Category: Few Carp
Other Species: General coarse fish
Permits: Day tickets on bank
Cost: £2 per day approximately
Control: Council
BK Rating: Difficult
E/A: Severn-Trent
Comments: A busy town lake

Westbridge Park Canal

Location: Weaver's Lane Bridge, Trent and Mersey Canal; off the A34 road between Stoke-on-Trent and Stone
Type and Size: Wide canal with some boat traffic
Carp Stock: Well stocked with carp to upper doubles
Category: Mixed Fishery
Other Species: Crucians, bream, roach, ruffe, gudgeon and chub
Permits: In advance only from Neil Dale Fishing Tackle, Albert Street, Stone. Tel: 01785 813708
Cost: £2 per day; weekly - £3 ; monthly - £4; annual - £15, to include three pools
BK Rating: Moderate
E/A: Severn - Trent

Westport Lake

Location: Tunstall, Stoke - on - Trent
Type and Size: Small lake between the railway and a canal
How to Find: Take the Tunstall-Burslem road from the A500 Stoke ring road, then the A527 at roundabout. The entrance to the lake is just along this road on the left hand side
Carp Stock: Well stocked with carp to about 25lbs
Category: Mixed Fishery
Other Species: Big, tench, bream and pike and some good roach

Permits: Day tickets on bank
Cost: £2 per day. Season tickets for 12 waters at about £15, £8 for juniors and £3.25 for the unemployed and the disabled
Control: Stoke-on-Trent Council control all these waters
BK Rating: Moderate
E/A: Severn-Trent

THE BEEKAY GUIDE TO 2000 BRITISH & EUROPEAN CARP WATERS

Is YOUR Water listed? If so, are the details correct?
If you spot omissions, inaccuracies, or know of any changes, please let us know by filling in the Waters Questionnaire at the back of this guide and return it to us at:

Beekay International
Withy Pool
Henlow Camp
Bedfordshire
SG16 6EA

SUFFOLK

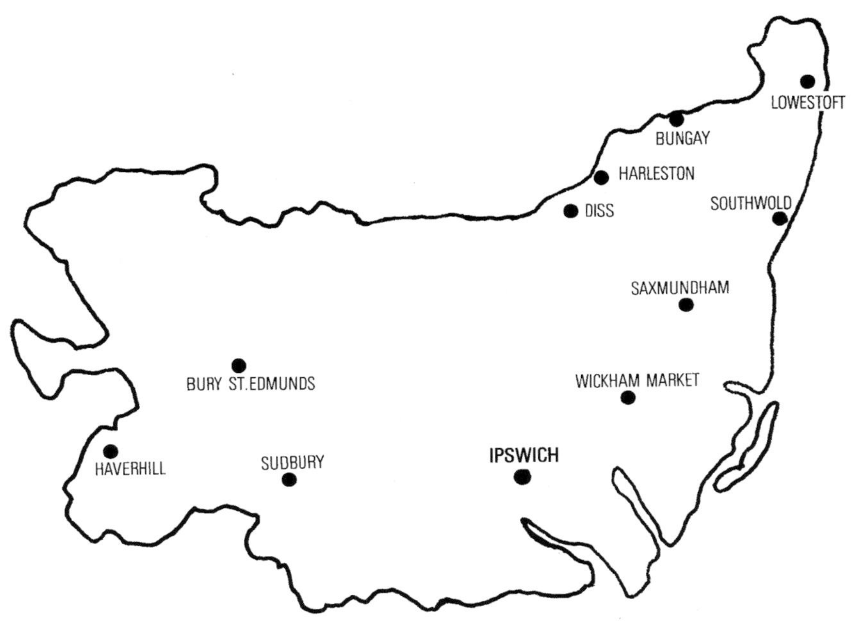

Aldeby Hall

Location: Aldeby, 4 miles north of Beccles, off A143, fronting River Waveney
Type and Size: Five pits totalling 4.5 acres
How to Find: Gillingham roundabout, A143 to Gt.Yarmouth, one mile road to Aldeby
Carp Stock: Well stocked
Category: Mixed Fishery
Other Species: Roach, rudd, tench, perch and bream
Permits: On bank
Cost: Adults - £5 per day 2 rods; concessions - £3. Season tickets.
Restrictions: No groundbaiting
BK Rating: Not known
E/A: Anglian
Comments: Rural. Car parking close to swims. Toilet and washing facilities. Night fishing allowed. Disabled access to some swims. Open all year to season ticket holders. Open for day tickets - Easter to end of October

Alderson Lakes

Location: Needham Market
Type and Size: Two former gravel pits of 9 acres
How to Find: Take the A 14 Ipswich to Norwich road, and at the A 140 exit turn left on the B 1078. After the R.Gipping bridge turn left
Carp Stock: Some small carp
Category: Mixed Fishery
Other Species: Tench, roach, bream, rudd and pike
Permits: In advance only from George Alderson, 19 Clover Close, Ipswich IP2 0PW (enclose S.A.E.)

Cost: £33 per season, plus £10 joining fee; £10 O.A.P's and juniors
Control: Gipping A.P.S. Tel: 01473 602828
BK Rating: Not known
E/A: Anglian

Barham Pits

Location: Claydon, near Ipswich
Type and Size: Two pits of 20 acres and 4 acres
How to Find: At Barham, 5 miles north of Ipswich, off the A45 Ipswich - Norwich road; Pest House Lane
Carp Stock: Some good carp in both waters
Category: Mixed Fishery
Other Species: General coarse fish; big pike
Permits: Members only. Gipping Angling and Preservation Society. Membership from G Alderson, 19 Clover Close, Chantry Estate, Ipswich
Cost: About £20-£25
BK Rating: Moderate
Control: Club
E/A: Anglian
Comments: The big lake is very attractive, with islands and bays. The club has other lakes and 10 miles of the River Gipping

Breakaway Pit

Location: Pesthouse Lane, Burham, near Ipswich
Type and Size: 3 acre gravel pit
Carp Stock: Some carp to over 20lbs
Category: Mixed Fishery
Other Species: Tench, roach, rudd and bream
Permits: In advance only from Breakaway Tackle
Cost: £2.50 per day; £4 two rods; £5 for 24 hours
Control: Breakaway Tackle, Ipswich. Tel: 01473 741393
Restrictions: No carp sacks
BK Rating: Moderate
Baits/ Methods: Boilies are a good bait
E/A: Anglian

Brandon Lake

Location: Close to the Little Ouse in Brandon, near Thetford
Type and Size: Man - made lake of about three acres
How to Find: In Brandon - Remembrance Park
Carp Stock: Some carp to double figures
Category: Mixed Fishery
Other Species: Roach, perch and bream
Permits: Day tickets before fishing from the Rod'n' Line tackle shop. Thetford. Tel: 01842 752930
Cost: £3 per day
BK Rating: Moderate
Control: Club
E/A: Anglian

Broome Pits

Location: Near Bungay, about a mile off the B1332 from Norwich
Type and Size: Four pits from one to four acres
Carp Stock: Mirrors to 20lb in Pit C and Pit D
Category: Mixed Fishery

Other Species: Crucians, roach, pike and big bream
Permits: Day tickets on bank
Cost: £2.50 per day. Season £20
Control: Bungay Cherry Tree AC - membership at £10 per season open to all, including numerous other waters in the area. Details from the Secretary, Mr I Gosling, 37 St Mary's Terrace, Bungay. Tel: 01986 892987/892982
BK Rating: Moderate
E/A: Anglian
Comments: The Club secretary has a leaflet on these waters. The two bigger pits are about ten feet in depth about one rod length from the bank

Bures Lake

Location: Bures, near Colchester
Type and Size: Beautiful wooded gravel pit of 4½ acres
How to Find: Take the B1508 into Bures from Colchester, and after the river bridge turn right past the church and along the Nayland road; 500 yards further on you will see the LAA entrance sign and gate
Carp Stock: A small number of big carp to over 20lbs
Category: Few Carp
Other Species: Many big tench to 6lbs, bream to 8lbs, roach, rudd, perch and pike
Permits: A members only water of the London Anglers Association - no day or season tickets, so to fish you will have to join the LAA, or one of the affiliated clubs. Details from LAA, Hoe Street, Walthamstow, London E7
Cost: £20 a year, to include many other fine waters all over the country
Restrictions: Members only
Control: LAA
BK Rating: Difficult
E/A: Anglian

Colston Hall Ponds A

Location: Colston Hall, Dennington, near Harleston
Type and Size: Two irrigation reservoirs of about an acre each
How to Find: From Harleston take the B1116 to Dennington, and turn left onto the A1120. In two miles turn down a lane to Colston Hall
Carp Stock: The pond nearest the house contains some carp. The other is about 6ft deep and is well stocked with mirrors to double figures
Category: Pond near house - Mixed Fishery; Other Pond - Carp Only
Other Species: Tench and rudd in the Mixed Fishery pond
Control: Tel: 01728 638375
BK Rating: Moderate
E/A: Anglian
Comments: Farmhouse bed and breakfast

Diss Mere

Location: In the town of Diss
Type and Size: 4 acre mere
How to Find: Take the A140/A 1066 from Norwich to Diss
Carp Stock: Some mirrors to double figures
Category: Mixed Fishery
Other Species: General coarse fish
Permits: Diss AC members only. Membership from 'Catch 22' Tackle shop, 23 Victoria Road, Diss. Tel: 01379 3272
Cost: About £7 per year
BK Rating: Difficult
Control: Club
E/A: Anglian

Ditchingham Pit

Location: Bungay Common
Type and Size: 3 acre gravel pit
How to Find: Bungay Common, off the B1332 alongside the River Waveney
Carp Stock: Well stocked with carp to doubles
Category: Mixed Fishery
Other Species: General coarse fish
Permits: Bungay Cherry Tree AC members only. Membership from Mr I Gosling, 37 St Mary's Terrace, Bungay. Tel: 01986 2982
Cost: About £10
BK Rating: Moderate
Control: Club
E/A: Anglian
Comments: Attractive lake. This club has much other fishing in the area

Flood Park

Location: Haverhill
How to Find: Opposite Sainsbury's superstore in Haverhill
Type and Size: 2½ acre clay pit
Carp Stock: About 50 fish to upper doubles
Category: Mixed Fishery
Other Species: Very large perch, roach, rudd and bream
Permits: Haverhill AC. Permits available from J & A Tackle. £15 per season. £7 Juniors and OAP's free
BK Rating: Moderate
E/A: Anglian
Comments: Carp are doing well and twenties are expected soon

Glemsford Lake

Location: Near Sudbury and Long Melford
Type and Size: Three gravel pits of 18, 14 and 3 acres
How to Find: Take the A1092 from Long Melford and then to Cavendish. The lakes are on the left, opposite Glemsford Road
Category: Few Carp
Other Species: General coarse fish
Permits: London Anglers Association - members only, open to all. Join through affiliated clubs or the LAA, Hoe Street, Walthamstow, London E17
Cost: About £15 a year
BK Rating: Difficult
Control: Club
Restrictions: No night fishing
E/A: Anglian
Comments: The LAA has many waters all over the south of England, including Bures Lake near Nayland, which contains a few 20lb carp

Great Lodge Farm Ponds

Location: Great Lodge Farm, Dennington, near Harleston
Type and Size: Four small farm ponds on private estate
How to Find: Take the B1116 from Harleston to Dennington, then left onto A1120. In 2 miles turn right onto the B1120 and a mile further on turn right down a track to the farm
Carp Stock: Mirrors to doubles
Category: Mixed Fisheries
Other Species: General coarse fish
Cost: Not known

BK Rating: Moderate
E/A: Anglian
Control: Not known

Gunssons Lake

Location: White House Farm, Sibton
Type and Size: One acre pond
How to Find: Off the A120, south-west of Southwold
Carp Stock: Well stocked with mirrors to doubles
Category: Carp Water
Other Species: Some tench and bream
Permits: Season tickets only from Mr Kitson. Tel: 0172 8260
Cost: On application
BK Rating: Moderate
Control: Private
Restrictions: Season tickets and touring caravanners only
E/A: Anglian
Comments: Shallow, coloured water, mainly for touring caravanners

Gunton Hall Lake A

Location: Corton, near Lowestoft
Type and Size: Two acre lake
How to Find: From Lowestoft take the A12 towards Great Yarmouth: Gunton Hall is on the right, just before Corton
Carp Stock: Some mirrors to double figures
Category: Mixed Fishery
Other Species: Tench, roach, rudd
Permits: Day tickets from Reception at Hall - must be booked in advance. Summer season and winter season tickets
Cost: On application. About £4 a day
BK Rating: Moderate
Control: Gunton Hall. Tel: 01502 720288
E/A: Anglian
Comments: This is a holiday centre; golf, tennis, archery and clay pigeon shooting for residents. For details telephone Gunton Hall. Attractive, weedy lake, quite shallow

Henham Dairy Pond

Location: Henham Park Estate, near Brampton
Type and Size: One acre estate lake only about three feet deep
Carp Stock: Heavily stocked with carp from 2 - 4lbs; some up to 16lbs
How to Find: From Beccles take the A145 to Blythburgh. Go through Brampton and after 2 miles turn left into Henham Park Estate. The pond is on the left hand side
Category: Mixed Fishery
Other Species: Crucians, tench, rudd and hybrids
Permits: Day tickets in advance only, after 6pm the day before fishing
Cost: £3.50 per day
Restrictions: No night fishing; one rod only; limited number of tickets
Control: Henham and District Angling Club Tel: 01502 518198 Mrs Fairs Tel: 01502 578672
BK Rating: Easy
E/A: Anglian
Comments: No Sunday tickets. 6 anglers per day

Holmans Pits

Location: Northfield Farm, Southery, near Downham Market. The pits are on the left off the B1386 Southery road, and probably just in Norfolk!
Type and Size: Three shallow pits of one to three acres
Carp Stock: Some carp, sizes not known
Category: Mixed Fishery
Permits: Members only water of Kings Lynn AC. Membership £12 to include many other local waters, from the Secretary
Other Species: Roach, rudd, bream, tench, perch and pike
Control: Club. Southery is Norfolk, so the pits may also be Norfolk
Restrictions: Members only
BK Rating: Difficult
E/A: Anglian

Ickworth Lake

Location: Horringer, near Bury St Edmunds, in the middle of the village
Type and Size: Five acre estate lake
Carp Stock: Some carp, sizes not known
Category: Probably Few Carp
Other Species: Roach, rudd and tench
Permits: From bailiff on bank
Cost: £3 per day
Control: National Trust
BK Rating: Difficult
E/A: Anglian

Lakeside Caravan Park A

Location: Saxmundham
Type and Size: Three acre lake
How to Find: Find Harleston and take the B1116 to Framlingham, then the B1119 Saxmundham road. At Rendham you will see signs on the left to the caravan park and lake
Carp Stock: A good head of mirror carp to double figures
Category: Mixed Fishery
Other Species: Roach, bream, perch and tench
Permits: Day tickets from bailiff who calls round. Information from the Manager. Tel: 01728 3344
Cost: About £3 per day
Control: Caravan site
BK Rating: Moderate
E/A: Anglian
Comments: Campers and touring caravans welcome

Loam Pond

Location: Sutton, near Woodbridge
Type and Size: Two small ponds
Carp Stock: Well stocked with carp to 20 lbs
Category: Mixed Fishery
Other Species: Crucians, bream, tench and rudd
Permits: In advance from The Rod and Gun Shop, Church St, Woodbridge
Cost: About £15 per season
Control: Woodbridge A.C. Tel: 01394 382337
Restrictions: No boilies; no night fishing
BK Rating: Not known
E/A: Anglian

Long Pond

Location: Stoke - by - Clare
How to Find: Alongside road between Cavendish and Clare
Type and Size: Two acre clay pit
Carp Stock: Well stocked with fish to upper doubles
Category: Mixed Fishery
Other Species: Roach, rudd, crucians, bream and tench
Permits: Enquire locally
BK Rating: Easy
E/A: Anglian
Comments: An idyllic lake

Marsh Farm Lakes

Location: Marsh Farm, Sternfield, near Saxmundham
Type and Size: Two small attractive lakes
Carp Stock: Well stocked with carp to 20 lbs
Category: Mixed Fishery
Other Species: Roach, rudd, tench and bream
Permits: From the farm shop
Cost: About £4 per day; £5 for two rods
Control: Tel: 01728 602168
Restrictions: No night fishing except by arrangement. No boilies, peanuts, tiger nuts or chick peas. No barbed hooks or keepnets
BK Rating: Not known
E/A: Anglian
Comments: Caravan site. Probably open all year

Mill Meadows

Location: River Stour, The Croft, Sudbury
Type and Size: Two miles of river
Carp Stock: Well stocked with carp to over 20 lbs
Category: Mixed Fishery
Other Species: Chub, roach, dace, perch, zander, pike and bream
Permits: Sudbury Angling Centre
Cost: £3 per day. £25 per season; concessions
Control: Sudbury D.A.A.
Restrictions: No bivvies
BK Rating: Moderate
Baits/Methods: Legered boilies good for carp
E/A: Anglian

Oulton Water

Location: Near Ipswich
Type and Size: Medium-sized reservoir
Carp Stock: Not many carp, but there are some big fish to well over 20lbs
Category: Few Carp
Other Species: Usual coarse fish
Permits: Try local tackle shops for information
Control: Not known
BK Rating: Very Difficult
E/A: Anglian

Redgrave Lake

Location: Redgrave Park, Botesdale, near Norwich
Type and Size: Huge estate lake with open bank - wooded at the dam end
Carp Stock: Only a few, but some big ones
Category: Few Carp
Other Species: Many bream to 8lbs, tench, roach, perch, eels and pike to 25lbs
Permits: Members only water. Apply to Redgrave Park, Redgrave. Tel: 01379 898206
Cost: £29.50 per year
Control: Private
Restrictions: Members only - no day tickets
BK Rating: Difficult
E/A: Anglian

Reydon No.1 Pit

Location: Lakeside Park Development, near Southwold off the A1095
Type and Size: Three acre reed - fringed gravel pit
How to Find: Take the A1095 from Southwold, and after going over a bridge, turn into the Lakeside Park estate road. The car parking area is behind the pit.
Carp Stock: Some carp to 27lbs
Category: Few Carp
Permits: Purdy's Newsagents, 31 High Street, Southwold. Tel: Lowestoft 724250. In advance only on day of fishing - also from Southwold tackle shops
Cost: £3.50 per day; juniors £1
Control: Southwold and Dist. Freshwater Angling Preservation Society, Secretary, Mrs B Reid. Tel: 01502 518198
Restrictions: No night fishing. One rod only. No fishing until 9am. No groundbait or uncooked seeds
BK Rating: Not known
E/A: Anglian
Comments: This lake is over 20ft deep in places. The club also has other waters. Half price for juniors. A new fishery has been constructed nearby, especially as a carp fishery, and known as Reydon No.4 Pit. Permits as above, and the water has been stocked with mirrors and commons to double figures. Open June 16th to March 14th

Roydon Sand Pit

Location: Roydon, near Diss
Type and Size: Little three-quarter acre pit, 25 feet deep in places
How to Find: From Diss take the A1066 to Roydon. Just before the service station, turn left down a lane to the house
Carp Stock: Small carp
Category: Mixed Fishery
Other Species: Tench, rudd, crucians
Permits: From the house next to the pit; Mrs Alasia. Tel: 01379 4409
Cost: About £3 per day
BK Rating: Easy
Control: Private
Restrictions: Not known
E/A: Anglian

Rushbrooke Lake

Location: Near Bury St Edmunds
Type and Size: Three acre lake
How to Find: Take the A45 from Bury towards Ipswich. In 2 miles turn right, then

second right to Wellnethan. The lake is on the left
Carp Stock: Carp to over 20lbs
Category: Mixed Fishery
Other Species: Tench, bream, roach
Permits: Members only - yearly from N Bruton. Tel: 01284 66074 or local tackle shops
Cost: On application
BK Rating: Moderate
Control: Private
Restrictions: No night fishing
E/A: NRA Anglian Region
Comments: Membershp also entitles members to fish West Stow Country Park, an 18 acre pit, which is a bird sanctuary (no night fishing) containing some carp to doubles - this water is near Lackford, off the A1101

Slaters Pit

Location: Near Oulton Broad
Type and Size: Small pit
Carp Stock: Well stocked with carp to about 15lbs
Category: Mixed Fishery
Other Species: Roach and tench
Permits: Not known - try local tackle shops
BK Rating: Thought to be Easy
Restrictions: Not known
E/A: Anglian
Comments: We have not been able to find out much about this one.. except that it is there, and it contains carp; any help would be appreciated

Starfield Pit

Location: Long Melford,near Sudbury
Type and Size: Gravel pit about 6 acres
How to Find: Take the A134 from Sudbury to Rodbridge Corner and turn left here towards Foxearth. Go through Liston and to the right of the chemical factory and take a track on the right through Liston Gardens. The pit is on the right at the bottom of the track
Carp Stock: Quite well stocked with mirrors to double figure size
Category: Mixed Fishery
Other Species: Bream, roach and pike
Permits: Day tickets in advance only from Mr N Mealham, 6 Springfield Terrace, East Street, Sudbury. Tel: 01787 77139. Season ticket/Club membership costs approxmately £15 from the Club Secretary as above
Cost: About £2 per day. Approximately £15 per season for club membership
Control: Long Melford and District Angling Association
BK Rating: Moderate
E/A: Anglian
Comments: Irregular shaped pit with some weed of 2 - 10 feet deep, with islands

Suffolk Stour

Location: Off the A137 near Manningtree
Type and Size: Wide shallow river, not far from the estuary
Carp Stock: Not many, but some up to 20lbs
Category: Few Carp
Other Species: Tench, roach and bream
Permits: On the bank at £2 per day. In advance at £1.50 from Viscount

	Tackle, Ispwich or Bridge Garage,Manningtree
Control:	Lawford AS. Richard Harbach. Tel: 01206 394452
BK Rating:	Very Difficult
E/A:	Anglian

Swale Pit

Location:	Waldringfield, near Woodbridge
Type and Size:	3 acre gravel pit
Carp Stock:	Very heavily stocked with little carp; a few doubles
Category:	Mixed Fishery
Other Species:	Crucians, bream, rudd and roach
Permits:	Rod and Gun Shop, 18 Church Street, Woodbridge - in advance booking advised
Cost:	About £3 per day
Control:	Tel: 01394 382377
Restrictions:	4 anglers per day only
BK Rating:	Very Easy
E/A:	Anglian

The Deep Hole

Location:	Frostend, one mile from Wrentham, near Lowestoft
Type and Size:	Small clay pit between 14ft and 20ft deep
How to Find:	Take the A12 from Lowestoft, go through Wrentham, and turn right just before the Wangford Plough pub. Pit is one mile, on the right
Carp Stock:	Some mirrors to double figures
Category:	Possibly Few Carp
Other Species:	Perch,chub, roach, rudd
Permits:	Members only water of the Southwold and Dist. Freshwater Preservation Society. To join apply to the Membership Secretary, Mr Barry Reid, 19 Sussex Road, Lowestoft. Tel: 01502 518198
Cost:	£17 a year, and £8 joining fee (juniors half price), which includes 5 other ponds
Control:	Club
Restrictions:	Members only
BK Rating:	Not known
E/A:	Anglian

Thorpeness Mere

Location:	Thorpeness, near Leiston
Type and Size:	Huge lake with many islands
How to Find:	Norwich - Bungay - Halesworth, then the A12 to Yoxford. Take the B1122 to Leiston, and the B1353 to Thorpeness
Carp Stock:	Some commons to 10lbs
Category:	Few Carp
Other Species:	Roach, rudd, eels
Permits:	Free (100 yards only)
Cost:	None
BK Rating:	Difficult
Control:	Thorpeness Estate Office. Tel: 01728 3555
Restrictions:	No fishing on most of the bank. No night fishing
E/A:	Anglian
Comments:	This is a 'children's playground' with 150 boats for hire - might do for a family day out. The lake is very shallow, only up to 2½ feet deep

Welmore Lake

Location: Near Downham Market
Type and Size: Two acre pond
How to Find: From Downham Market take the A1122, going west, and in Salters Lode, take the left turn and cross the Old Bedford River and the Old Delph
Carp Stock: Some carp to about 10lbs
Category: Mixed Fishery
Other Species: Roach, bream, perch and pike
Permits: In advance only from B Riches, 15 Sand Lane, Denver, Downham Market. Tel: 01366 383291
Cost: £3 per day
Control: Private
BK Rating: Moderate
E/A: Anglian
Comments: Usual baits successful. Surface fishing good in summer. Pleasant pond with an island, reeds and lilies

West Stow Country Park

Location: Just off the A1101 Bury St Edmunds - Mildenhall road. Just after the bridge over the River Lark, the country park will be seen on the right
Type and Size: 18 acre pit in a bird sanctuary. The lake has three islands and depths of up to 25ft
Carp Stock: Some double figure carp
Category: Probably Few Carp
Other Species: Tench, roach, perch, bream and pike
Permits: Members only. Permits from local tackle shops or from Mr N Bruton. Tel: 01284 66074
Cost: £15 per year, juniors half price. Also includes Rushbrooke Lake
Control: Club
Restrictions: No night fishing
BK Rating: Not known
E/A: Anglian

Weybread Fishery

Location: Mill Lane, Weybread, near Harleston
Type and Size: 2½ acre lake
Carp Stock: Well stocked with carp averaging 5 lbs
Category: Mixed Fishery
Other Species: Crucians, tench, bream, roach, chub and perch
Permits: In advance only
Cost: £3.50 per day; £4.50 for two rods
Control: Tel: 01379 588141
Restrictions: No boilies; no night fishing; no keepnets; barbless hooks
BK Rating: Not known
E/A: Anglian

Weybread Gravel Pits

Location: Weybread near Harleston, and quite near Waveney Valley Lakes
How to Find: Take the A140 from Norwich, and at Pulham Market take the B1134 to Harleston Then take the road to Weybread and after crossing the river the pits will be seen on either side of the road
Type and Size: Five gravel pits, one of which is very big
Carp Stock: The middle pit is very well stocked with mirrors; many are doubles and there are also some 20's. Club only pit is also well stocked with carp

Category: Middle Pit - Carp Water
Other Species: Crucians, roach, perch, tench, bream and pike
Permits: Day tickets in advance only from G Denny, The Tackle Shop, Harleston. Tel: 01379 852248; and the Cherry Tree public house in Harleston. Club membership Harleston and District Angling Club - details from tackle shop. Club Secretary: J Adamson, Yew Vila, Roydon, Diss - tickets
Cost: Day tickets £3 which includes the four pits but not the small club carp water. Club membership £7 per year (small club pit plus several miles of the Waveney), and an EXTRA £8 a year to include all five pits and the river
Restrictions: Club pit cannot be fished on a day ticket. Night fishing in all pits is for CLUB MEMBERS ONLY
BK Rating: Moderate
Baits/Methods: Advanced carp methods, baits and rigs usually needed for the larger carp
E/A: Anglian
Comments: Good gravel pit club fishery, with 20's possible. Worth joining the club for the small pit and the night fishing

White House Farm

Location: White House Farm, Rendham
Type and Size: Shallow half acre lake
Carp Stock: Some mirrors to 10lbs
Category: Mixed Fishery
Other Species: Roach, perch, crucians, and small tench
Permits: Mr Tate. Tel: 0172 8485
Control: Private
Restrictions: No fishing, except for those parking touring caravans on the land
BK Rating: Not known
E/A: Anglian

Wickhambrook Lake

Location: Wickhambrook, Suffolk
How to Find: About 2 miles outside village towards Newmarket
Type and Size: Narrow two acre clay pit
Carp Stock: Very heavily stocked with carp to mid-doubles
Category: Carp Water
Other Spcies: A few roach, rudd and bream
Permits: £7.50 on the bank per 12 hours for 2 rods
BK Rating: Very Easy
E/A: Anglian
Comments: Very prolific, 100 pound catches common, ideal water for beginner

Wickham Skeith Mere

Location: Village common of Wickham Skeith
Type and Size: Small common pond
How to Find: A140 from Norwich to Stoke Ash (27 miles) then turn right to Wickham Skeith
Carp Stock: Well stocked with small carp
Category: Carp Water
Other Species: Small pike
Permits: Free
BK Rating: Easy
E/A: Anglian
Comments: A free fishery ideal for youngsters or the family. Shallow and weedy

SURREY

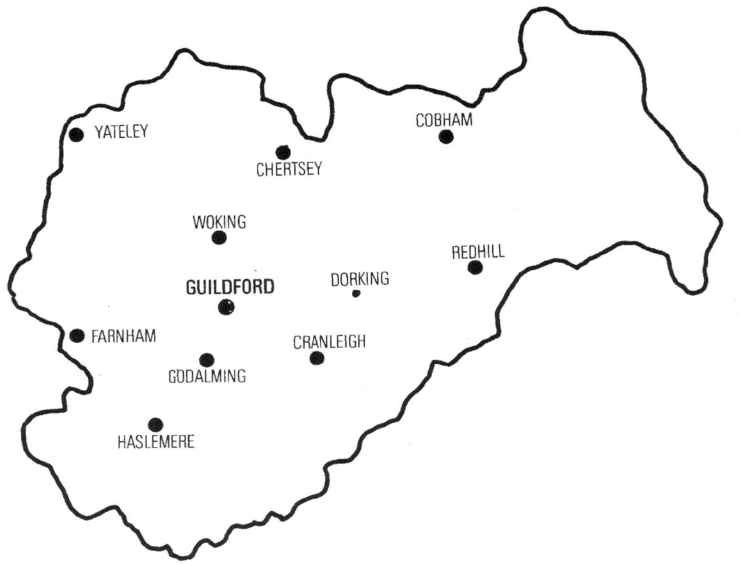

Ash Vale

Location: Lakeside Road, Ash Vale, Aldershot

Type and Size: Gravel pits. Lake 1 - 3 acres; Lake 2 - 1¼ acres; Lake 3 - 7½ acres

How to Find: From the A30 at Camberley, go to Frimley, then Frimley Green on the A321. After 3 miles take the Ash Vale road (A3013) then turn right onto Lakeside Road. The entrance to the fishery is under the railway bridge on the left

Carp Stock: Carp to 20lbs

Category: Mixed Fishery

Permits: Leisure Sport Angling, Thorpe Park, Staines Road, Chertsey, Surrey. Tel: 01932 564872. Season tickets only - no day tickets. Send for permit application form and enclose when sending in the form two passport size photographs of yourself. Ash Vale is included under 'unrestricted single water' permits. If you want to fish a number of Leisure Sport waters under this category, you can apply for a Group Water Permit to include all 21 of their waters

Cost: Single Water Permit, Ash Vale - About £14, Junior/OAP/disabled - £7, Group Water Permit for 21 venues (65 lakes and 15 stretches of river) - £29 . Junior/OAP/disabled - £14.50

Restrictions: No fires, no camping, no radios, no bright lights. Night fishing is allowed

Other Species: Crucian carp, tench, roach, rudd, perch. Pike in Lake 1

Control: Leisure Sport

BK Rating: Moderate

E/A: Thames

Comments: Send to Leisure Sport for the rule and guide book. Rules are strict in Leisure Sport waters and you will lose your membership if you break them

Badshot Lea Pond

Location: Badshot Lea, Farnham
Type and Size: Five acre lake
How to Find: Badshot Lea is on the outskirts of Farnham, about 3 miles from the centre of town,north of the Hogs Back
Carp Stock: Heavily stocked with carp to 10lbs, with a few doubles
Category: Carp Water
Othr Species: General coarse fish
Permits: Farnham Angling Society. Secretary: 70 Prince Charles Crescent, Farnborough, Hants
Cost: On application
Control: Club
BK Rating: Easy
E/A: Thames
Comments: Some carp died in 1996

Beaver Farm

Location: Off the A22 Eastbourne road, Newchapel, Lingfield, near East Grinstead
Type and Size: Four lakes
Carp Stock: Snipe Lake well stocked wtih carp, sizes not known; West Lake also has carp
Category: Mixed Fisheries
Other Species: Pike, rudd, roach, catfish, grass carp, zander and tench
Permits: From Beaver Farm Tel: 01342 834413
Cost: £5 per day, second rod £2; under 15's and OAP's half price weekdays only
Control: Private
Restrictions: No night fishing (8am to sunset); no keepnets, no radios
BK Rating: Not known
E/A: Southern

Bolder Mere

Location: Ockham, near Guildford - just off junction 10 of the A 25
Type and Size: 9 acre lake
Carp Stock: Carp to 20lbs
Category: Mixed Fisheries
Other Species: Bream, roach, perch, rudd and pike
Permits: In advance from cafe on site
Cost: About £3 per day
Control: Guildford A.S. Tel: 01483 574464
Restrictions: No night fishing
BK Rating: Moderate
E/A: Thames
Comments: Toilets and refreshments

Brittens Pond

Location: Jacobs Well,near Guildford
Type and Size: Old pond of about four acres, recently dredged and stocked
How to Find: Find Salt Box Road,Jacobs Well, Guildford, off the A320 towards Woking
Carp Stock: About 300 fish to 19½ lbs, some doubles, mostly small fish. Many of the carp are commons
Category: Carp Water
Other Species: Roach, rudd, tench and crucians
Permits: Guildford Angling Society. Day tickets from Guildford Angling Centre. Tel: 01483 574462
Cost: £35 per season. Day tickets about £5 per day

Control: Guildford Angling Centre
BK Rating: Easy
E/A: Thames
Comments: A heavily fished water. No floating baits; no night fishing - dawn to dusk only. Barbless hooks, size 12 or larger. Unhooking mat compulsory. No carp to be retained

Broadwater Lake

Location: Near Godalming
Type and Size: Lake of about 10 acres
Carp Stock: Very heavily stocked with many carp. Huge bags of small carp to 8lbs possible. Some doubles up to 20lbs
Category: Carp Water
Other Species: General coarse fish
Permits: Godalming Angling Society. Secretary: A Johnson, 86 Peper Harrow Road, Godalming, Surrey. Very long waiting list though juniors should get in at once
Cost: On application
Control: Club
BK Rating: Easy
E/A: Thames
Comments: A very easy water for small carp; it is hard to get through the small fish to catch the bigger ones, which are there. Club membership is hard to obtain

Chertsey

Location: Thorpe Road,near Chertsey
Type and Size: Gravel pit, 4½ acres
How to Find: Take the M25 to Staines and turn off at the A30 roundabout onto the A320 Staines-Chertsey road. Go to Egham, then Chertsey and take the right turn to Thorpe at the small roundabout. The entrance is on the right just before the M3 flyover
Carp Stock: Not known - the Leisure Sport guide book reports 'carp in excess of 20lbs'. We will assume it to be..
Category: Few Carp
Other Species: Bream, perch, roach, pike
Permits: Season tickets only from Leisure Sport, Thorpe Park, Staines Road, Chertsey, Surrey. Tel: 01932 564872
Cost: £20 per season. Juniors/OAP/disabled £10
Restrictions: No night fishing. No trespassing onto Thorpe Park property. No parking on M3. Cars must not be driven round lake
BK Rating: Difficult
Control: Leisure Sport Angling
E/A: Thames

Cobham Lake

Location: Cobham, near Walton-on-Thames
Type and Size: Small lake
Carp Stock: Well stocked with carp
Category: Mixed Fishery
Other Species: Pike, tench and bream
Permits: A members only water of Walton-on-Thames AS. Secretary: A Finlayson, 14 Harrow Road, West Bedfont, Feltham, Greater London
Cost: Season £30
BK Rating: Not known
E/A: Thames

Coleford Lake

Location: Mytchett, near Camberley
Type and Size: Attractive 36 acre lake
Carp Stock: Some big carp
Category: Mixed Fishery
Other Species: Pike over 30 lbs. Bream, rudd, hybrids and chub
Permits: Steve Sellings
Cost: About £5 to £7 per day
Control: Tel: 01252 518383
Restrictions: Barbless hooks
BK Rating: Difficult
E/A: Thames
Comments: Said to be mainly a water for big pike previously fished by a small syndicate

Cutt Mill

Location: Elstead, near Farnham
Type and Size: Estate lake of about seven acres
How to Find: Elstead is on the B3001 between Farnham and Milford
Carp Stock: About 200 carp, mostly doubles, and some twenties; lake record is 29lbs 12ozs
Category: Carp Water
Other Species: Mixed coarse fish
Permits: Farnham Angling Society - season tickets only. Secretary: 70 Prince Charles Crescent, Farnborough, Hants
Cost: About £30 per year plus a joining fee. Details on application
Control: Club
Restrictions: No long stay fishing - 48 hours maximum
Baits/Methods: You will need all the modern rigs, such as hair and bolt rigs and the most sophisticated baits and methods on this hard fished carp water
BK Rating: Moderate
E/A: Thames
Comments: This is quite a well-known carp water and is heavily fished by carp specialists. It is sometimes hard to find a place to fish as there are only about 20 swims on the lake; there are many trees and a marshy area. Recommended mainly for experienced carp anglers. It is a pleasant and attractive lake.

Epsom Stew Pond

Location: Off the B280 between Kingston and Epsom
Type and Size: Small, shallow, weedy pond
Carp Stock: Quite well stocked with small carp of about 3lbs, with a few up to 20lbs
Category: Mixed Fishery
Other Species: Tench, roach, perch, bream and pike
Permits: Day tickets on bank
Cost: £4 for adults; juniors and OAP's £2. £21 per season
Control: CALPAC; season and day tickets from D Wheeler, 314 Old Lodge Lane, Purley CR8 4AQ. Includes other waters Tel: 0181 6602766
BK Rating: Moderate
E/A: Thames

Firs Farm Lake

Location: Near Cranleigh
Type and Size: Newly dug lake of about 4 acres with two islands
How to Find: From Guildford take the A281 for 8 miles to a left turn into Wildwood

	lane, then turn right at the T - junction into Knowle Lane. In a mile you will see the Firs Farm on the right
Carp Stock:	Some small carp to about 7lbs - recently stocked
Category:	Mixed Fishery
Other Species:	Chub, perch, bream and some trout, as this was formerly a trout fishery
Permits:	Day tickets on bank
Cost:	£5 per rod, dawn till dusk; £3 for juniors, OAP's and the disabled
Control:	W Welch. Tel: 01403 822878
Restrictions:	No night fishing; no boilies
BK Rating:	Not known
E/A:	Thames

Frensham Great and Little Ponds

Location:	Frensham, between Farnham and Aldershot
Type and Size:	Big Pond is a very old, large lake of about 60 acres; Small Pond about 35 acres
Carp Stock:	Both quite well stocked - the Big Pond did have carp in it until recently to well over 30lbs, but most of these fish died in the late 80's
Category:	Mixed Fishery
Other Species:	Most coarse fish including tench, and pike
Permits:	From The Creel, Station Road, Aldershot. Tel: 01252 20871
Cost:	No day tickets
Control:	Farnham and District AS
BK Rating:	Difficult
E/A:	Southern

Gatton Manor Lakes

Location:	Off the A 29 at Oakley, near Dorking
Type and Size:	Two lakes of about 3/4 acre each
Carp Stock:	Some carp averaging around 5 lbs
Category:	Mixed Fishery
Other Species:	Pike, roach, perch and bream
Permits:	On site
Cost:	£2 per day
Control:	Paul Davidson. Tel: 01403 264644
Restrictions:	No night fishing
BK Rating:	Moderate
Baits/Methods:	Sweetcorn and boilies are good baits
E/A:	Thames

Goldsworth Water Park

Location:	Goldsworth Park, Woking - off the A425 near Knaphill
Type and Size:	20 acre lake on a housing estate
Carp Stock:	Some carp to doubles
Category:	Few Carp?
Other Species:	Roach, tench, bream, chub and perch
Permits:	Day tickets on bank, dawn till dusk only
Cost:	£3 for one rod, and £4.50 for two rods, with reductions for juniors, OAP's and the disabled; annual permits at £25, or £35 to include night fishing
Control:	Woking Water Activity Centre; Head Bailiff Brian Rich. Tel: 01483 764836 after 6.30pm. Other details from Woking Tackle Shop
Restrictions:	No night fishing on day tickets; no bloodworm (!); only 50 boilies per session (I expect they count them!)
BK Rating:	Moderate to Difficult
E/A:	Thames

Hawley Lake

Location: Near Camberley
Type and Size: 25 acre gravel pit
Carp Stock: Well stocked with carp - plenty of twenties and a few thirties
Category: Mixed Fishery
Other Species: Bream, tench, roach, perch and big eels
Permits: Belongs to the army; day tickets and annual permits at £17.50
BK Rating: Moderate
E/A: Thames
Comments: All information on this water, including location, can be obtained from Noel's Tackle, Tel: 01276 32488

Henfold Fisheries

Location: Blackbrook, near Dorking
Type and Size: Five small ponds
How to Find: Turn left one mile from Dorking on the A 24 to Horsham
Carp Stock: Well stocked with small carp to mid - doubles
Category: Mixed Fishery
Other Species: Roach, tench, bream, crucians, perch, orfe and eels
Permits: On bank
Cost: £6 per day; £10 for 2 rods. Reductions for juniors and O.A.P's
Control: Tel: 01737 843295
Restrictions: No boilies or particles
BK Rating: Not known
E/A: Thames
Comments: Toilets and snacks

Lodge Pond

Location: Off the A325 Farnham - Bordon road
Type and Size: Lake of about three acres
How to Find: Take the A325 from Farnham
Carp Stock: About 100 carp up to around 20lbs
Category: Carp Water
Other Species: Bream, tench, pike and roach
Permits: Farnham Angling Society. Some temporary membership (day) tickets from local tackle shops
Cost: Farnham AS membership about £41 per season plus an entry fee. Concessions
Control: Club. Tel: 01252 546592
BK Rating: Easy
E/A: Thames
Comments: A pleasant lake on Forestry Commission land

Newdigate

Location: New Barn Lane, Newdigate, near Dorking
Type and Size: Clay pits. Lake 1 - 8½ acres; Lake 2 - 3½ acres
How to Find: Take the A24 from Dorking, turn left onto Newdigate Road, then take left fork to T-junction in Newdigate village. Turn right, then first left at church. Bear left at next fork and the lakes are about 400 yards on the right, park in the car park only
Carp Stock: Good catches of carp reported to 8lbs (Lake 2); 5½ lbs (Lake 1). Much larger carp have been seen in Lake 1
Category: Carp Waters
Other Species: Pike, zander, tench and bream
Permits: Season tickets only from Leisure Sport, Thorpe Park, Staines Road,

	Chertsey, Surrey. Tel: 01932 564872
Cost:	£24 per season, junior/OAP/disabled - £12
Restrictions:	Night fishing permitted. Usual rules apply. No swimming or boating
BK Rating:	Easy. Guide book reports 'extremely good catches'
Baits/Methods:	Normal carp methods and baits
Control:	Leisure Sport Angling
E/A:	Thames
Comments:	Looks like a good water for some fairly easy catches of small carp, with the chance of something much bigger

Old Bury Hill

Location:	Lake View, Old Bury Hill, Doking
Type and Size:	Twelve and a half acre estate lake 200 years old, deep at one end, with lilies at the other - two other lakes
How to Find:	Near Dorking, just off the A25 Dorking-Guildford road
Carp Stock:	Plenty of mid-doubles; some good low 20's; best fish 30lbs
Category:	Mixed Fishery
Other Species:	Tench, bream, rudd, crucians, perch, roach, pike and zander
Permits:	Day tickets on bank; season tickets - Lake View, Old Bury Hill, Dorking. Tel: 01306 883621/877540
Cost:	One rod £8; two rods £12; juniors £4 and £5 respectively. Season about £100
BK Rating:	Moderate
Control:	Private
Restrictions:	No night fishing; no sacking; no particles
E/A:	Thames
Comments:	An attractive, fairly shallow lake. Large, hard boilies needed to avoid the big tench. Boats can be hired, but must be booked in advance. Refreshments and toilets on bank. No close season. Angling tuition

Priory Farm Lakes

Location:	Priory Farm, Nutfield
Type and Size:	Two attractive lakes of 2.5 acres each
How to Find:	Just off the A25 near Redhill
Carp Stock:	Very heavily stocked with carp to about 15 lbs
Category:	Carp Water
Other Species:	Tench, roach, rudd, perch and gudgeon
Permits:	Seasonal only
Cost:	On enquiry
Control:	Private. Tel: 01737 823304
BK Rating:	Hungerford Lake - Easy; Priory Lake - Moderate
E/A:	Southern
Comments:	Matches organised. Situated on an award winning P.Y.O farm with farm shop and plant centre. Refreshments and toilets close by. A good family centre

River Valley Fishery

Location:	River Valley, Sandhurst Road, Yateley, Camberley
Type and Size:	Gravel pit of 16 acres
How to Find:	This lake is in the same road as Tri - Lakes and the Leisure Sport Lakes
Carp Stock:	Well stocked with carp to 30lbs
Category:	Mixed Fishery
Other Species:	Rudd to 3½ lbs; perch, pike, tench
Permits:	On site. Day and night permits
Cost:	About £3 per day; approximately £4 per night
BK Rating:	Difficult

Control: Private
Baits/Methods: Usual carp baits and methods
E/A: Thames
Comments: Season tickets at about £30 for day; £40 for night. Very deep 47 year old lake, oldest in area, attractive with trees, bushes etc. For information telephone 01252 873865. There are also two smaller lakes and 1½ miles of the River Blackwater containing trout and chub

River Wey

Location: Byfleet and Wisley
Type and Size: Tributary of the River Thames
Carp Stock: Some fish to around 20lbs
Category: Few Carp
Other Species: Pike, dace, roach, chub, barbel, bream and perch
Permits: Byfleet AA - Mrs B Stilwell, 15 Ruston Road, Byfleet
Cost: £20 per season
Control: Club
BK Rating: Very Difficult
E/A: Thames

Send

Location: Send, near Woking
Type and Size: Two pits
Carp Stock: Well stocked with carp to over 30lbs
Category: Mixed Fishery
Other Species: Tench and perch
Permits: A members only water of Woking District AA - new members welcome. Details from the Secretary: D Powell, Maymont, Guildford Road, Knaphill, Woking
Control: Club
Restrictions: Members only, though some guest tickets for members' friends
BK Rating: Very Difficult
E/A: Thames

Shalford Park

Location: Ferry Lane, near the Ship Inn, off the Guildford to Godalming road
Type and Size: Canal-like stretch of the River Wey, with backwater and a joining stream
Carp Stock: Not many, sizes unknown
Category: Few Carp
Other Species: Chub, roach, perch, bream, pike, gudgeon and trout
Permits: On bank at £3 per day
Control: Guildford AS. Secretary: L Yarrow. Tel: 01483 574462
BK Rating: Very Difficult
E/A: Southern

Shawfield Lake

Location: Young's Drive, Ash, near Aldershot
Type and Size: Attractive matured gravel pit
Carp Stock: Well stocked with carp to 20 lbs
Category: Mixed Fishery
Other Species: Crucians, tench and perch
Permits: On bank
Cost: About £5 per day; half price juniors, O.A.P's and the disabled
Control: Farnborough and Dist. A.S. Tel: 01252 543470
Restrictions: No night fishing

BK Rating: Moderate
E/A: Thames

Shepperton Fishery

Location: Penny Lane, Shepperton
Type and Size: 20 acre gravel pit
Carp Stock: Well stocked with carp to over 30 lbs
Category: Mixed Fishery
Other Species: Pike, perch, bream, roach, tench and eels
Permits: From local tackle shops
Cost: About £25 per season - half price juniors, O.A.P's and disabled
Control: Leisure Sport Angling. Tel: 01932 564872
BK Rating: Moderate
Baits/Methods: Boilies best bait
E/A: Thames
Comments: Disabled access

Stillwater Lake

Location: Ash Vale, off the A321 about half a mile after Ash Vale station
Type and Size: Two lakes of 6 and 5 acres
Carp Stock: Well stocked with carp to over 20lbs
Category: Mixed Fishery
Other Species: Bream, roach and tench
Permits: In advance only from The Creel, Station Road, Aldershot
Restrictions: No night fishing; some bait restrictions
BK Rating: Moderate
E/A: Thames
Comments: Entry is through locked gate; you will be given a key when you buy your permit from Raison's

Surrey Lake

Location: Ten minutes from Junction 6 on the M25, near Reigate
Type and Size: Attractive lake of about two acres
Carp Stock: Well stocked with carp to 25lbs
Category: Mixed Fishery
Other Species: Tench
Permits: All details and permits on 0181-644 3669
BK Rating: Moderate
E/A: Thames

Swan Valley

Location: Darby Green Road, Yately
Type and Size: 4 small gravel pits
How to Find: Take the Yately road off the A 30, then turn right into Darby Green Road. The fishery is on the left.
Carp Stock: Large lake - well stocked with carp to 20lbs. Smaller lakes - carp to 6 lbs
Category: Mixed Fishery
Other Species: Tench, roach and perch
Permits: On bank
Cost: £4 per day for 2 rods; £6 all night; £10 for 24 hours
Control: Private
Restrictions: No nuts or keepnets
BK Rating: Easy
E/A: Thames
Comments: Information from Bracknell Angling Centre, 2a Fowlers Lane, Bracknell. Tel: 01344 425130

TriLakes

Location: Yateley Road, Sandhurst
Type and Size: Two gravel pits about 14 acres
How to Find: Take the Sandhurst road and turn into Yateley Road, at Yateley. Fishery is on the right just after the entrance to Yateley (Match Lake)
Carp Stock: Not very heavily stocked with carp, but there are a number of 20's and thirties, with the best mirror caught over 35lbs
Category: Mixed Fishery
Other Species: Tench, roach, rudd, perch, bream, chub, pike, trout
Permits: Must be obtained before fishing from the fishing hut by the entrance £7 per rod per day. C Homewood, TriLakes, Yateley Road, Sandhurst. Tel: 01252 873191
BK Rating: Difficult
Restrictions: No night fishing - open 8 am to sunset
E/A: Thames
Comments: This is a well-known commercial fishery which is often heavily fished, especialy at weekends. It is quite a pleasant water with many trees and bushes around the banks, and with islands. There are toilets, and a shop which sells bait, drinks, snacks and sweets and a licensed restaurant. A number of very big carp are caught each season. Fishing continues during the close season under special rules. Although most anglers are not carp specialists, the lake is fished by hard-line, and some well-known carp anglers, in the hope of a thirty. Long spells without takes can be expected

Twynersh Fishery

Location: Chertsey, near Thorpe Park, off Junction 11 on the M25
Type and Size: Two newish gravel pits containing carp
Carp Stock: Pit One - well stocked with small carp to 5lbs; Pit Two has carp to 20lbs
Category: Mixed Fisheries
Other Species: Tench, perch, roach, bream and pike
Permits: At the entrance gate
Cost: £4 per day for one rod; two rods is £6, Juniors £2.75 and OAP's £3
Control: Paul Rogers. Tel: 01931 570156
Restrictions: Fishing from two banks only. All carp to be returned at once; no night fishing; no nuts
BK Rating: Easy
E/A: Thames
Comments: There is another coarse lake on site, a trout lake, and a short stretch of the River Bourne

Willingshurst Lake

Location: Near Guildford, exact location not known; enquire locally
Type and Size: Small lake
Carp Stock: Well stocked wtih carp to about 14lbs, most of which are small
Category: Mixed Fishery
Other Species: Tench, roach and perch
Permits: Try local tackle shops for permits and information
BK Rating: Easy
E/A: Thames

Willow Pond

Location: Beaver Farm, A22 Eastbourne road, Newchapel, Lingfield, near East Grinstead. Tel: 01342 833144
Type and Size: Half acre specialist carp fishery

Carp Stock: Well stocked wtih carp, sizes not known
Category: Carp Only
Permits: Day tickets from Beaver Farm
Cost: £5 per day, second rod £2
Control: Private
Restrictions: No night fishing; no keepnets
BK Rating: Not known
E/A: Southern
Comments: Publicity from Beaver Farm gives no information on the sizes of the fish in their three ponds - there is a third one acre fishery on the farm which is stocked with perch, pike, bream and roach

Windhams Pool

Location: Off the A30 near Yateley
Type and Size: Two acre lake
Carp Stock: About 50 doubles
Category: Mixed Fishery
Other Species: Crucians, roach, tench and perch
Permits: In advance, book by phone. Tel: Camberley 874346
Cost: £3.50 to £4 per day
Restrictions: No night fishing
BK Rating: Difficult
E/A: Thames
Comments: Information from Noel's Tackle. Tel: 01276 32488

Wyndham's Pool

Location: Yateley
Type and Size: 4 acre lake, with big lily pads
How to Find: Turn off the A 30 at the Ely pub towards Yateley, and turn right to the fishery in half a mile
Carp Stock: Not many carp but most are doubles and twenties
Category: Few Carp
Other Species: Tench, crucians, roach, perch and pike
Permits: On bank
Cost: £2.50 per day for one rod; £3.50 for two rods. Reduced prices for juniors and O.A.P's
Control: Hampshire County Council. Tel: 01252 874346 (9am. to 8.30pm.only)
Restrictions: No night fishing except by arrangement; no groundbait, keepnets or carp sacks
BK Rating: Difficult
E/A: Thames

Wisley Common Ponds

Location: Wisley and Ockham Commons, Wisley
Type and Size: Several small common ponds
Carp Stock: Quite well stocked with carp, mostly small
Category: Mixed Fisheries
Other Species: Pike, perch and roach
Permits: FREE fishing. Tel: 01932 351409
BK Rating: Easy
E/A: Thames

Yateley

Location: Sandhurst Road, Yateley, near Camberley
Type and Size: Thirteen gravel pits varying in size from 34 acres to 12 acres
How to Find: Take the A30 from London to Camberley, then the A327 to Yateley, and turn right at the Royal Oak public house onto Sandhurst Road. Entrance to the west lakes is on the left and the car park to the east lakes is on the right
Carp Stock: Most of the lakes contain good carp. Lake 11, known as the Match Lake, has plenty of doubles and 20's. Lake 12, known as the Copse Lake, has a small number of big carp including a 30 which has been caught at 35lbs. On the west side of the road, the Car Park Lake (Lake 9) has produced fish of over 40lbs and the North Lake (Lake 4) contains a small number of large carp, to nearly 50lbs
Category: Carp Waters/Mixed Fisheries
Other Species: Crucians, tench, roach, rudd, pike, bream and catfish
Permits: This is a Leisure Sport Angling Special Venue. Season tickets only available, and they are limited, and issued on a 'first come - first served' basis. Apply to LSA, Thorpe Park, Staines Road, Chertsey, Surrey. Tel: 01932 564872
Cost: Day season - £34. Concessions £17. Night syndicate - £200
BK Rating: The waters vary but most must be regarded as Fairly Hard
Baits/Methods: Since these waters contain big fish, most of which have been caught a number of times, you will need all the most advanced carp fishing techniques and baits
Control: Leisure Sport Angling
E/A: Thames
Comments: Whilst some of these pits are really mixed fisheries, and some contain few carp, we have marked them as mainly carp waters, because of the huge size of some of the fish. Carp specialists fish these waters knowing that they may have very long waits, but may catch a very big fish. Because of the size of these fish, Yateley has become known as one of the top big carp fisheries in the country. It is fished by leading carp specialists, and in most cases long stay fishing and much patience is needed. Some of the lakes are actually just across the border in Hampshire

Yateley Green Pond

Location: Off the A 327 between Yateley and Eversley
Type and Size: Small village pond, attractive with lilies
Carp Stock: Well stocked with carp to upper doubles
Category: Mixed Fishery
Other Species: Tench, perch, crucians and rudd
Permits: FREE Fishing
Cost: None
Control: Yateley Town Council
BK Rating: Moderate
E/A: Thames

TYNE & WEAR

Big Water

Location: Seaton Burn, off the A1 just north of Newcastle
Type and Size: Not given in the E/A: Guide; we assume it is a lake
Carp Stock: Some carp; commons, mirrors and crucians, numbers and sizes no known
Category: Mixed Fishery
Other Species: Roach, rudd, tench, bream, eels and perch
Permits: Paul Armstrong. Tel: 0191 2749399
Control: Club - BWAC
Restrictions: Weekly permits for those living more than 100 miles radius from Newcastle
BK Rating: Not known
E/A: Northumbrian

Big Waters

Location: Wide Open, Newcastle-upon-Tyne
Type and Size: 20 acre shallow lake
Carp Stock: Well stocked with doubles to about 23lbs, both commons and mirrors
Category: Mixed Fishery
Other Species: Bream, tench and eels
Permits: Big Water Angling Club, Newcastle. Try local tackle shops for information
Cost: About £20 a season
BK Rating: Moderate
E/A: Northumbrian
Comments: Not carp fished much

Fellgate Ponds

Location: Lakeside Inn, near Gateshead
Type and Size: Two small clay pits
Carp Stock: Well stocked with commons, mirrors and leathers, doubles to 14lbs
Category: Mixed Fishery
Other Species: Dace, tench, roach, perch

Permits: Steve Sloan. Tel: 0191 4600200
Cost: About £2 per day
Control: George Atkin, 82 Glebe Terrace, Dunston, Gateshead NA11 9NQ
Restrictions: No night fishing
BK Rating: Moderate
E/A: Northumbrian

Killingworth Lake

Location: Killingworth, near Newcastle - A1056 road crosses the lake
Type and Size: 4 acre lake
Carp Stock: Some carp, numbers and sizes not known
Category: Mixed Fishery
Other Species: Tench, crucians, roach, perch, bream and pike
Permits: On bank
Cost: About £2.50 per day. £6 per season
Control: Tyne A.A. Tel: 0191 4600200
BK Rating: Difficult
E/A: Northumbrian
Comments: Disabled access

Leazes Park Lake

Location: Leazes Park, near the football ground, Newcastle
Type and Size: Small public boating lake of about two acres in size, with an island
Carp Stock: Well stocked with carp to about 15lbs
Other Species: Roach, rudd, tench, bream, perch and crucians
Permits: Day tickets from Roberts Tackle Shop, Newcastle - £2 per day
Control: Council. Tel: 0191 2620401
BK Rating: Moderate
E/A: Northumbrian
Comments: Barbless hooks. Toilet. Disabled access

Little Big Water

Location: Wide Open, off the B1318, just north of Gosforth
Type and Size: Pond of some kind - the E/A Guide doesn't say!
Carp Stock: Some commons and mirrors
Category: Mixed Fishery
Other Species: Roach, rudd, tench, bream, crucians, perch and eels
Permits: Paul Armstrong. Tel: 0191 2749399
Control: Club - BWAC
BK Rating: Not known
E/A: Northumbrian

Marden Quarry

Location: Whitley Bay, near Newcastle
Type and Size: Five acre pit
Carp Stock: Plenty of small commons and mirrors, up to about 15lbs
Category: Mixed Fishery
Other Species: Roach, rudd and perch
Permits: Big Water AC - day tickets from local tackle shops
Cost: £20 per season; day ticket £2
BK Rating: Easy
E/A: Northumbrian
Comments: No close season

ANGLING PROJECTS T.P.

"Get's kids hooked on Fishing - Not Drugs or Crime"

A view of the lake and education centre at Wraysbury, close to Heathrow Airport

Angling Projects offer courses on Angling and Conservation to any groups of youngsters.

Groups of between 8 and 15 youngsters can spend a day or stop over for a few days in our fully equipped centre. The centre has amenities for the disabled, as does the lake with its specially built fishing areas.

The facility is open to all schools, youth centres, scouts etc.

All facilities and education are entirely FREE.

Specialist angling courses can be arranged for carp and pike fishing.

All groups must be pre - booked and be accompanied by group leaders, teachers, or other responsible adult.

For further information or bookings - please contact : Les Webber at home between 6.30pm and 8.30pm any weekday on: 01734 431701.

Angling Projects appreciate the support from the following companies:

Anglers World
Holidays
46 Knifesmithgate, Chesterfield,
Derbyshire S40 1RQ

Leisure Sport Angling

Thorpe Park, Chertsey, Surrey KT16 8PN

BEEKAY INTERNATIONAL

Ryton Willows

Location: Ryton, west of Newcastle
Type and Size: Pond, lake or pit, who knows?
Carp Stock: Some carp
Category: Mixed Fishery
Other Species: Roach and perch
Permits: Limited day tickets available free from Ryton Public Library (also books!)
Control: Mr C Wouldhave (not Paul Armstrong this time!). Tel: 0191 4234603. Tyne Anglers Alliance
BK Rating: Not known
E/A: Northumbrian

Silksworth Lake

Location: Silksworth Sports Complex, New Silksworth, near Sunderland
Type and Size: Large lake, part of old mine workings
Carp Stock: Some carp to doubles
Category: Mixed Fishery
Other Species: Tench, bream, roach, rudd and perch
Permits: Some day tickets from nearby Sports Centre or on bank. Cost about £3 per day
Control: Sunderland FWAC; Mr Gordon Bennet. Tel: 0191 536 9755 or Mr Tony Kidd, 25 Toronto Close, Sunderland. Tel: 0191 5229070
BK Rating: Not known
E/A: Northumbria
Comments: Sports Centre Tel: 0191 5229119

Stargate Pond

Location: In the centre of Newcastle
Type and Size: One and a half acre gravel pit
Carp Stock: A few to over 20lbs
Category: Few Carp
Other Species: Roach, rudd and tench
Permits: £2 per day from Crookhill Post Office near lake, £15 per year
E/A: Northumbrian
Comments: Ryton DAC Tel: 0191 413127

WARWICKSHIRE

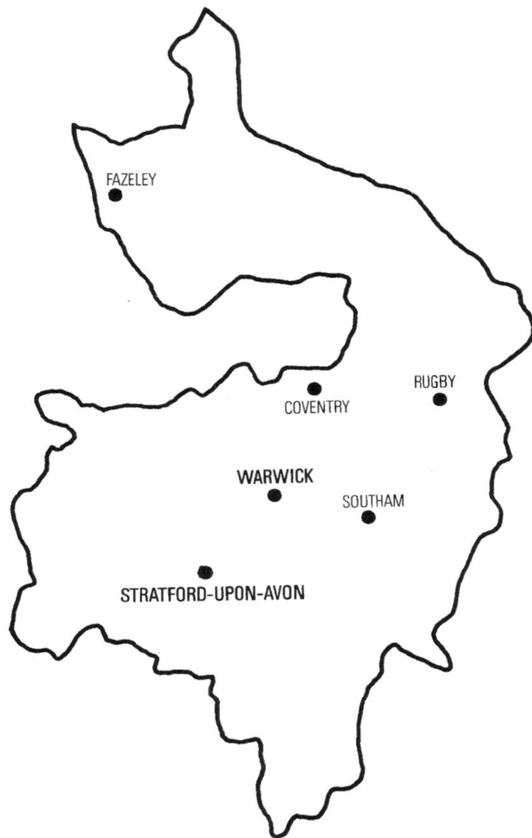

Bishops Bowl Lakes

Location: Bishops Itchington, Southam
Type and Size: Six small pools
How to Find: Off the B4451 south east of Leamington Spa
Carp Stock: Dinosaur's Dip - small carp; Mitre Pool - some carp; Blue Pool - carp to 20lbs
Category: Mixed Fisheries
Other Species: General coase fish, and some trout. Big pike, bream and tench
Permits: On site. Tel: 01926 613344
Cost: £3.50 per day approximately (6am to just after sunset); about £2 for a half day
BK Rating: Moderate
Control: Private
Restrictions: No night fishing
E/A: Severn-Trent

Comments: Best known for its trout lake, but the ponds mentioned are worth a try for carp. Matured limestone quarries, now a Nature Reserve. Mitre Pool 40 feet deep in places. Very pleasant surroundings

Clifton Lakes

Location: Clifton, near Nuneaton
Type and Size: A lake and 8 small pools
Carp Stock: Some carp to 30 lbs
Category: Mixed Fishery
Other Species: Tench, bream, roach, dace, perch, rudd, barbel, trout and eels
Permits: On bank
Cost: About £5 per day
Control: Tel: 01788 832719
Restrictions: Night fishing by arrangement only. No cereal groundbait
BK Rating: Easy
E/A: Severn Trent
Comments: Toilets and refreshments. Facilities for the disabled. Two miles of river fishing on the Warwickshire Avon

Foxholes Fishery

Location: Crick, near Rugby
Type and Size: Three lakes
How to Find: Off the A428 Rugby - Northampton road
Carp Stock: Some carp, sizes not known
Category: Mixed Fishery
Other Species: General coase fish including tench
Permits: R Chaplin, Great Arbour Close, Kenilworth. Information also from Banks and Burr, 27 Claremont Road, Rugby
Cost: On application
BK Rating: Insufficient information
Control: Private
E/A: Severn - Trent
Comments: Rugby Federation of Anglers also has some carp in Newbold Quarry (20 acres) near town centre. Tickets from Banks and Burr

Freemans Lake

Location: Wolvey, on the B4109 south of Hinckley
Type and Size: Small lake
Carp Stock: Heavily stocked with small carp, mostly commons
Category: Mixed Fishery
Other Species: Crucians, roach and big perch
Permits: Try tackle shops in Hinckley and Nuneaton
Control: Club
BK Rating: Easy
E/A: Severn-Trent

Grand Union Canal

Location: Hatton Locks, Hatton, near Warwick
Type and Size: Wide canal with many locks
Carp Stock: Carp to 20 lbs
Category: Mixed Fishery
Other Species: Roach, perch and bream
Permits: On bank
Cost: About £2 per day; £1 juniors and O.A.P's
Control: Warwick D.A.S. Tel: 01203 677214

Restrictions: No night fishing
BK Rating: Moderate
E/A: Severn Trent
Comments: Disabled access

Kingsbury Water Park, Gibsons Lake

Location: Fazeley, near Tamworth
Type and Size: Several old pits, one a specialist carp fishery of about three acres
How to Find: Follow the Tamworth road from Birmingham and take the road signposted 'Bodymoor Heath'. After one mile along this lane the fishery is on your left
Carp Stock: Few carp in some of the lakes. Carp lake well stocked with about 100 carp, plenty of doubles to over 20lbs
Category: Carp Water
Other Species: Tench, roach, rudd, bream, perch, pike
Permits: County Council Offices, Shire Hall, Warwick. No day tickets
Cost: Season tickets about £35 which cover 6 other gravel pits, including a good pike water
Control: County Council
BK Rating: Moderate
E/A: Severn-Trent
Comments: This water has been developed as a carp fishery since 1980, and the fish are said to be still growing well. Quite a pleasant setting

Monks Pool

Location: Weston Lane, Bulkington, near Bedworth
Type and Size: 3 acre lake
How to Find: Near the Weston Hall Hotel
Carp Stock: Well stocked with carp averaging about 5lbs - some upper doubles
Category: Carp Water
Other Species: Perch and roach
Permits: On bank
Cost: About £5 per day
Control: Tel: 01203 316892
Restrictions: No night fishing;no boilies; no keepnets; no barbed hooks
BK Rating: Easy
E/A: Severn Trent
Comments: Toilets

Napton Reservoir

Location: Napton, near Southam, Coventry
Type and Size: Two lakes, 20 acres and 4 acres
How to Find: Take the A425 from Warwick to Southam and then to Napton
Carp Stock: Few but large. Mirrors to over 20lbs
Category: Few Carp
Other Species: Bream, roach, tench and perch
Permits: From bailiffs on bank
Baits/Methods: Normal carp methods and baits
Control: Club - Coventry and District Angling Association. Secretary: P O'Connor, 48 Loxley Close, Wood End, Coventry. Tel: 01203 612880
BK Rating: Difficult
E/A: Severn-Trent
Comments: Most of the bigger carp are caught from the smaller lake, but both have a reputation as hard waters, probably because the carp stock is not large

Newbold Quarry

Location: On the edge of Rugby, about 1 1/2 miles from town centre
Type and Size: 25 acre quarry
Carp Stock: Well stocked with carp to double figures
Category: Mixed Fishery
Other Species: Tench and pike
Permits: From bailiffs on bank, or from Banks and Burr, 17 Claremont Road; C Donald, 155a Bilton Road
Cost: Day tickets £2; season tickets £15
Control: Club; Rugby Federation of Anglers, G Lawrence, 53 Manor Road, Rugby
BK Rating: Moderate
E/A: Severn - Trent

Snitterfield Fruit Farm

Location: Ingon Lane, Snitterfield, near Stratford-upon-Avon
Type and Size: Two small, deep pools
Carp Stock: Some carp to doubles
Category: Mixed Fishery
Other Species: Crucians, dace, roach, gudgeon, chub, roach, bream, tench and perch
Permits: In advance only from local tackle shops
Cost: £15 per season; £5 juniors, O.A.P's and disabled
Control: Royal Leamington Spa A.A. Tel: 01926 334185
Restrictions: No boilies; barbless hooks; no night fishing
BK Rating: Not known
E/A: Severn Trent

Warwick Canal

Location: South of Warwick
Type and Size: 12 1/2 miles of Grand Union Canal
How to Find: South of Warwick and Leamington Spa
Carp Stock: Good carp in reasonable numbers
Category: Mixed Fishery
Other Species: General coarse fish
Permits: Royal Leamington Spa AA.E G Archer, 9 Southway, Leamington Spa, and from local tackle shops
Cost: Day tickets about £2
BK Rating: Moderate
Control: Club
Restrictions: Not known
E/A: Severn-Trent
Comments: Carp are in this area in the River Leam, details from local tackle shops

WEST MIDLANDS

Blackhills Lake

Location: Wombourne, off the B1477 just south of Wolverhampton - enquire locally for exact location
Type and Size: Four acre lake on the edge of the golf course
Carp Stock: Very heavily stocked with small carp, and the occasional lower double
Category: Carp Water
Permits: Day tickets from the site office
Cost: About £2 per day
Control: Private
BK Rating: Easy
E/A: Severn-Trent

Blackroot Pool

Location: Sutton Park, near Birmingham
Type and Size: Park pool of 14 acres
How to Find: Six miles north of Birmingham on the A38 road to Lichfield
Carp Stock: Quite well stocked with carp which includes several 20's and two fish over 30lbs each
Category: Mixed Fishery
Other Species: Good pike and other coarse fish
Permits: From bailiffs on bank - about £2 per day
Control: Birmingham City Parks. Tel: 0121 325469
BK Rating: Very Difficult
E/A: Severn-Trent
Comments: Toilet. No night fishing

Blythe Waters

Location: Hampton Road, off the A 41 between Knowle and Copt Heath
Type and Size: Four lakes of from 2 - 4 acres
Carp Stock: Well stocked with carp to 20 lbs
Category: Mixed Fishery
Other Species: Crucians, tench, bream, roach, perch, gudgeon, eels and golden orfe
Permits: On site

Cost: About £6 per day. Evening tickets and concessions
Control: Fishery Office. Tel: 01675 443306
Restrictions: No keepnets
BK Rating: Not known
E/A: Severn Trent
Comments: Pegs for disabled. Toilets, snack bar and shop

Bonehill Mill

Location: Lichfield Street, Fazeley, Tamworth, B78 3QQ. Tel: 01827 288482
Type and Size: Three lakes totalling 20 acres
How to Find: Take the A5 to Tamworth and Fazeley village will be found just to the south of the town
Carp Stock: Very heavily stocked with many small commons mostly in the 2-5lbs range, with the occasional double figure fish. Some 20's to 25lbs
Category: Mixed Fisheries
Other Species: Bream, roach, pike, perch
Permits: Day tickets on bank
Control: Private
Restrictions: No night fishing: no nets or sacks: no groundbait, peanuts or tiger nuts: barbless hooks
BK Rating: Easy
E/A: Severn-Trent
Comments: Under new management - V Martin

Bracebridge Lake

Location: Sutton Park, Birmingham, off the A38 Lichfield road
Type and Size: Four acre park lake close to Blackroot Pool
Carp Stock: Few carp, but possibly some big ones
Category: Few Carp
Other Species: Tench, roach, bream and pike
Permits: Day tickets from bailiff on bank
Cost: About £2 per day
Control: Private
BK Rating: Very Difficult
E/A: Severn-Trent

Bridge Pool

Location: Patshull Park, Wolverhampton
Type and Size: Three acre lake next to the Great Lake at Patshull Park
How to Find: Take the A454 from Wolverhampton, turn right to Pattingham; take the Burnhill Green Road and you will see the fishery on the right in 1½ miles
Carp Stock: Quite well stocked with carp to doubles, many of whch came from the Great Lake
Permits: Day tickets from the lodge on site before fishing
Cost: £2.50 per day; £1.50 for juniors - 7.30am till dusk
Control: Patshull Park
BK Rating: Moderate
Restrictions: No night fishing; no groundbait or hemp
E/A: Severn-Trent
Comments: Easy access for disabled anglers; good float fishing water, with sweetcorn as bait - 4 feet to 9 feet deep,and separated from the big lake by a narrow causeway

Calf Heath Reservoir

Location: Junction twelve of the M6
Type and Size: Reservoir of 50 acres
How to Find: Come off the M6 at junction 12 and take the A5 road towards Telford
Carp Stock: Stocked by the club with thousands of carp. Several 20's and a 30 have been reported recently
Category: Carp Water
Other Species: Some coarse fish
Permits: Annual permit available from the bailiff's house on the A5 bank
Cost: About £4 per day
Control: Private. Tel: 01902 790570
BK Rating: Fairly Easy
E/A: Severn-Trent
Comments: This water is being developed as a carp fishery and is not far from the centre of Birmingham

Church Pool

Location: Patshull Park, Wolverhampton
Type and Size: Old pit, about 12 acres
How to Find: From Wolverhampton, take the A41 road west and then turn onto the A464. After the village of Tettenhall turn left to Pattingham. Here turn right to Patshull
Carp Stock: Well stocked with mirrors and commons to 25lbs. Many of the bigger fish are commons - which is rare! Mixed Fishery but almost reaches Carp Water status
Category: Mixed Fishery
Other Species: Bream, roach and tench, all of which reach large sizes
Permits: Lakeside Lodge Hotel, Patshull Estate. Tel: Pattingham 700100. Pattingham Anglers
Baits/Methods: Modern advanced carp fishing methods. Recent summer success has been floating pet foods such as Pedigree Chum Mixer. Boilies are also good, especially later in the year
Control: Private
Restrictions: No keepnets
BK Rating: Moderate
E/A: Severn-Trent
Comments: Fine catches of big carp to specialist carp anglers. It is in a very attractive setting but is quite hard fished. There are lilies and some weed, and some of the banks are tree-lined. The lake is over 15 feet deep in places. Good chance of a 20

Coleshill Pool

Location: Coleshill, near Birmingham
Type and Size: Two acre lake
Carp Stock: Quite well stocked with carp to 14lbs
Category: Mixed Fishery
Other Species: Tench, roach and bream
Permits: Tel: 0121 3511907
Control: Private
BK Rating: Not known, but used for match fishing
E/A: Severn-Trent

Cuttle Mill

Location: Wishaw, Sutton Coldfield, Birmingham, (Cuttle Mill Lane)
Type and Size: Carp pool 3.2 acres, coarse pool 2.75 acres
How to Find: Off the A4091 towards Tamworth, near the National Golf Centre
Carp Stock: Very heavily stocked with many doubles and many twenties. In 1991 3,111 doubles and 440 twenties were reported, plus three thirties
Category: Carp Water. Long Pool is Mixed Fishery
Other Species: Tench and roach
Permits: Day tickets from the owner, Tony Higgins, at the above address. Tel: 01827 872253
Cost: £13 per day for two rods, £10 from 25th October. Coarse pool £4.50 per day
Restrictions: No night fishing - fishing is from 7am till dusk. No barbed hooks. No keepnets. No seed, nut, bean or pea baits are allowed
Baits/Methods: Advanced carp rigs and methods needed. Recent successes have been on high protein boilies fished on the hair rig, and floating baits
Control: Private
BK Rating: Moderate
E/A: Severn-Trent
Comments: This is one of the best known commercial carp fisheries in the country, where anglers have good chance of landing 20's and probably 30's. Up to 31 doubles in a day have been reported, and as this is a commercial fishery it is obviously heavily fished. The house of the owner is right on the bank, and a small mill stream leads from the lake, which is in peaceful surroundings. Alongside the carp lake is another lake of 2.7 acres which is a Mixed Fishery. It contains plenty of carp to over 20lbs, and tench, roach, perch, chub, bream and dace. Details from the owners. Sleeping in cars permitted. Cafe

Earlswood Lakes

Location: Earlswood, Birmingham
Type and Size: Three estate lakes - 54 acres in all
Carp Stock: Two of the lakes contain some carp; sizes not known
Category: Mixed Fishery
Other Species: Big eels, roach, perch, bream, pike and tench
Permits: From bailiff on bank at £3 per day
Control: Private - Tel: 0121 7834233
BK Rating: Difficult
E/A: Severn-Trent

Edgbaston Reservoir

Location: Reservoir Road, Rotton Park, Birminghm
Type and Size: 20 acre reservoir in the city
How to Find: Turn into Monument Street from the A456 Hagley road in Ladywood, south west Birmingham. Reservoir Road is the fifth turning on the left
Carp Stock: Some carp to 20lbs
Category: Few Carp ?
Other Species: Roach, perch, bream and pike
Permits: Day tickets on bank; season tickets
Cost: £1.50 (£1 for unemployed)
Control: Birmingham City Council, Recreation Dept - Tel: 0121 4464659
BK Rating: Difficult
E/A: Severn-Trent
Comments: Cafe and other town facilities

Fen Pools

Location: North View Drive, Pensnett, near Brierley Hill
Type and Size: Three lakes, two quite large
How to Find: West Birmingham, near Dudley
Carp Stock: Some carp to over 20lbs, in Middle Pool and also some carp in Grove Pool
Category: Mixed Fishery
Other Species: Tench, bream and eels
Permits: Free fishing
Control: Private
BK Rating: Difficult
E/A: Severn-Trent
Comments: Unpleasant surroundings, between a factory and a housing estate!

Foxhills Fishery

Location: Pinfold Lane, off the A 34 near Walsall
Type and Size: Two small ponds
Carp Stock: Well stocked with carp to 20 lbs
Category: Mixed Fishery
Other Species: Roach, bream, perch and rudd
Permits: On bank
Cost: £4 per day; half day £2.50
Control: Tel: 0121 360 9160
Restrictions: No groundbait, barbed hooks or keepnets
BK Rating: Moderate
E/A: Severn Trent

Furnace Mill Fishery

Location: Lane off the A 4117 between Kidderminster and the Wyre Forest
Type and Size: Four small pools
Carp Stock: Some carp to 20 lbs
Category: Mixed Fishery
Other Species: Roach, rudd, bream, perch and chub
Permits: On site
Cost: £3.50 per day. Half day £2.50
Control: Tel: 01299 266160 (day;) 01746 862547 (eve.)
Restrictions: No night fishing; barbless hooks, no groundbait, nuts or beans
BK Rating: Moderate
E/A: Severn Trent

Heron Brook Fishery

Location: Near Wolverhampton, off the A41 near Tettenhall
Type and Size: Three acre lake with the River Penk flowing through the middle
Carp Stock: Some carp in the main lake, and the rest in the adjoining carp pool. These fish are mostly doubles
Category: Coarse Lake - Mixed Fishery; Carp Pool - Carp Only
Permits: Day tickets in advance only from Nigel Williams Fishing Tackle, Wolverhampton. Tel: 01902 744824 - phone call essential, or you may not be able to fish when you get there. Only 4 anglers a day on the Carp Pool
Control: Private
Baits/Methods: Boilies, luncheon meat and sweetcorn all do well on standard methods; floaters also take fish
BK Rating: Moderate
E/A: Severn-Trent

Himley Island Pool

Location: Himley Park, Dudley
Type and Size: Small estate lake
How to Find: Himley Park, near Wombourne
Carp Stock: Well stocked with carp to 20lbs
Category: Mixed Fishery
Other Species: Tench, crucians, bream and roach
Permits: Beddows Tackle Shop, Wombourne. Day tickets and night syndicate vacancies
Cost: On application
Control: Private
BK Rating: Moderate
E/A: Severn-Trent
Comments: Night carp syndicate members claim carp to mid-twenties

Lady Barbara's Pool

Location: Patshull Park, Pattingham, Wolverhampton
Type and Size: Six acre estate lake, and very attractive
Carp Stock: Plenty of doubles and a few 20's
Category: Mixed Fishery
Other Species: Tench, roach, bream and eels
Permits: Season tickets from Pattingham AC only - enquire locally
Control: Club
Restrictions: No day tickets; no night fishing
BK Rating: Moderate
E/A: Severn-Trent

Lifford Reservoir

Location: Tunnel Lane, Lifford, Birmingham
Type and Size: Small open reservoir
How to Find: Take the A441 from the centre of Birmingham, then Lifford Lane and Tunnel Lane
Carp Stock: Well stocked with carp to 20lbs
Category: Mixed Fishery
Other Species: Pike, roach, bream and perch
Permits: On bank
Cost: £2 per day; £1 for juniors
BK Rating: Moderate
E/A: Severn-Trent
Comments: Car park close to lake, and easy access for the disabled

Makin Fisheries

Location: Wolvey, north west of Birmingham
Type and Size: 12 lakes with a total area of about 30 acres
How to Find: Turn off the M6 at Junction 2 and go through Anstey and Shilton to Wolvey. In the village, turn into Bulkington Road, and you will see the signposts to the fishery in just under a mile
Carp Stock: Heavily stocked with carp to about 25lbs
Category: Mixed Fishery
Other Species: Tench, chub, barbel, dace, roach, golden orfe and trout
Permits: Day tickets on site
Cost: £6 per day; juniors, OAP's and the disabled £4. Reductions for winter fishing
Control: Private
Restrictions: Barbless hooks; no keepnets; no night fishing

BK Rating: Moderate
E/A: Severn-Trent
Comments: Snack bar and toilets; big fish of most species. Lakes One and Two open for trout fishing (fly and legered worm) from March 29th to June 15th

Netherton Reservoir

Location: Housing estate in Dudley
Type and Size: Ten acre public lake, with water ski-ing and many boats
Carp Stock: Not many carp, but those reported caught were doubles
Category: Few Carp
Other Species: Mixed coarse fish
Permits: Day tickets on the bank at low cost
Restrictions: No night fishing
Control: Private
BK Rating: Very Difficult
E/A: Severn-Trent

Packington

Location: Packington, near Meriden, Coventry
Type and Size: Two pits, Molands Mere and Gearys Level, totalling 35 acres
How to Find: Take the A45 from Birmingham and turn right at the sign for Maxstoke. Entrance is on your right
Carp Stock: Both waters are well stocked with doubles up to 28lbs
Category: Carp Water
Other Species: Large pike, roach, bream and rudd
Permits: Day tickets from the Lodge near the entrance before fishing. Season tickets. Tel: 0121 7422682
Cost: £4 per day, £60 per season; some summer evening and half day tickets
Control: Private
Restrictions: Night fishing for season ticket holders only
BK Rating: Fairly Hard
E/A: Severn-Trent
Comments: Well-known water, quite heavily fished and publicised

Park Lime Pits

Location: Near Walsall
Type and Size: Small disused pits
Carp Stock: Some carp, number and sizes not known
Category: Mixed Fishery
Other Species: Bream, roach, perch and pike
Permits: Walsall and District AS - day and season tickets, 38 Lichfield Road, Bloxwich, Walsall
Cost: Cheap tickets
Control: Club
BK Rating: Not known
E/A: Severn-Trent

Penns Hall Lake

Location: Sutton Coldfield, Birmingham
Type and Size: Long, narrow lake of about 10 acres
How to Find: Behind Penns Hall Hotel, Penns Lane, Sutton Coldfield
Carp Stock: Not many carp, doubles up to mid 20's
Category: Mixed Fishery
Other Species: Mostly bream and tench
Permits: Ansells Angling Club. Secretary: Mrs Rogers, Tel: 0121 7481200.

	Must join Ansells Sports and Social Club first
Cost:	Ansells AC £14 per year, Ansells S & S Club £8 per year
Control:	Private
BK Rating:	Difficult, because small numbers of carp
E/A:	Severn-Trent
Comments:	Town water, very popular with walkers

Pool Hall

Location: Lower Penn, near Wolverhampton
Type and Size: Five ancient lakes
How to Find: Take the Wolverhampton to Bridgnorth road and follow signs to Lower Penn
Carp Stock: Heavily stocked with many small carp, mostly commons, but a good number of doubles and twenties to 30lbs
Category: Carp Water
Permits: Day tickets from Pool Hall
Cost: About £4
Control: Private. Tel:0129 97485
Baits/Methods: All types of carp fishing baits and methods will catch on this easy water
BK Rating: Very Easy
E/A: Severn - Trent
Comments: Popular, heavily fished water. No night fishing. No boilies

Powells Pool

Location: Sutton Park, Birmingham
Type and Size: Large lake, also used for sailing
How to Find: Take the A5217 north from Junction 6 of the M6. Turn left onto the A452 at Erdington, and right on the B4531 Boldmere road at the first roundabout. The entrance to the park is opposite, with the pool and car park on the left
Carp Stock: Few large carp
Category: Few Carp
Other Species: Bream, roach, perch, tench, chub and big pike
Permits: On bank
Cost: £1.40 per day; 90p for juniors, OAP's and the unemployed
Control: Birmingham City Council
BK Rating: Difficult
E/A: Severn-Trent

Salford Park

Location: In Birmingham, near Spaghetti Junction
Type and Size: Twelve acre reservoir
How to Find: On the A38 towards the centre of Birmingham, close to junction 6 of the M6
Carp Stock: About 100 carp which average about 13lbs. There are several fish over 20lbs
Category: Mixed Fishery
Other Species: Roach, perch and tench
Permits: Day tickets available on bank; season tickets
Cost: £1.50 per rod
Control: Council. Tel: 0121 4464659
Restrictions: No night fishing
BK Rating: Fairly Hard
E/A: Severn-Trent
Comments: Hard fished and busy town fishery

Shatterford Fishery

Location: Arley, near Kidderminster
Type and Size: Three small lakes
How to Find: Take the Bridgnorth road to Arley
Carp Stock: Eric's some carp; Stuart's - carp to 20lbs; Knight's Folly - one acre lake stocked with doubles and contains fish to 25lbs+
Category: Eric's and Stuart's - Mixed Fisheries; Knights Folly - Carp Only
Other Species: Mixed coarse fish in Eric's and Stuart's
Permits: On site - day tickets
Cost: On application
Control: Private
BK Rating: Moderate
E/A: Severn-Trent
Comments: Knight's Folly is advertised as 'expecting to contain some very big carp'. We have heard that their waters have been netted and may not now contain carp

Solo Loop

Location: Loop of the Bimingham canal, near Dudley Road Hospital
Type and Size: Narrow and quite attractive canal arm
How to Find: Take the A45 Dudley Road, left into Winson Green Road, past the prison, then right into Lodge Road, and turn into the entrance on the right past the hospital
Carp Stock: Some carp to double figures
Category: Few Carp
Other Species: Roach, bream, tench, gudgeon and perch
Permits: Day tickets on bank at 70p
Control: Fisherman's Friend Tackle Shop in Birmingham
BK Rating: Difficult
E/A: Severn-Trent

Sutton Bank Fisheries

Location: Near Birmingham
Type and Size: Several small lakes
Carp Stock: Well stocked with carp to 20lbs
Category: Carp Water
Permits: Day tickets. Tel: 01952 811048
Cost: £10 to include a pub meal(!)
BK Rating: Moderate
E/A: Severn-Trent

Walsall Arboretum

Location: In the centre of Walsall
Type and Size: Four acre lake with islands etc
Carp Stock: Some carp to upper doubles, but fish hard to find
Category: Few Carp
Other Species: Roach, bream and tench
Permits: Day tickets at the lake
Control: Private
BK Rating: Difficult
E/A: Severn-Trent
Comments: A town lake not much fished for carp, but it could produce the odd good fish

Ward End Lake

Location: Ward End Park, off the A47 Heath Road, three miles east of Birmngham centre
Type and Size: Narrow, shallow park lake of about three acres
Carp Stock: Quite well stocked with carp to upper doubles
Category: Mixed Fishery
Other Species: Bream, tench, roach and perch
Permits: On bank; £1.40 per day and 90p for juniors
Baits/Methods: Boilies best for the carp
BK Rating: Moderate
E/A: Severn-Trent
Comments: Busy public park lake with much bankside disturbance

Wassell Grove Fisheries

Location: Wassell Grove Lane, Hagley, near Stourbridge
Type and Size: Three pools
Carp Stock: Some carp to 10lbs
Category: Mixed Fishery
Other Species: Tench, bream, rudd, chub and gudgeon
Permits: On bank;
Cost: About £5 per day; evening tickets available. Concessions
Control: Dave Anderson. Tel: 01562 885926
Restrictions: No groundbait; nuts or boilies. Barbless hooks only
BK Rating: Not known
E/A: Severn-Trent
Comments: Toilets and refreshment facilities

WEST SUSSEX

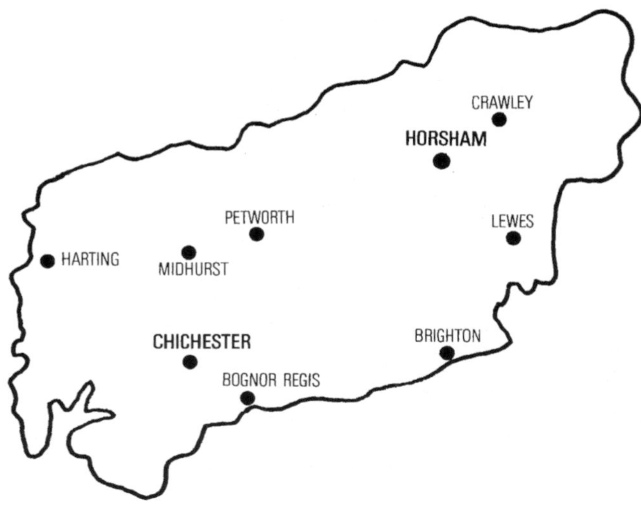

Borde Hill Lake

Location: Borde Hill Lane, two miles north of Haywards Heath, off the B3206
Type and Size: New three acre lake
Carp Stock: Some carp to lower doubles
Category: Few Carp
Other Species: Tench, perch and rudd
Permits: From the Fishery Kiosk
Cost: £5 per day; £2 for an extra rod
Control: David Buckley. Tel: 01444 417620
Restrictions: Fishing is sunrise to 11pm only
BK Rating: Difficult
E/A: Southern
Comments: Special facilities for the disabled, including reduced price weekday tickets and car park near lake. Contact Basil Farmer on Tel: 01444 247378

Buchan Park Fisheries

Location: Off the A246 Crawley to Horsham road, about 1½ miles from Crawley
Type and Size: Two lakes, one of which, Douster Pond, is about five acres and is very attractive, surrounded by trees and rhododendrons; this lake is 40 feet deep in places
Carp Stock: Well stocked with carp to doubles
Category: Mixed Fishery
Other Species: Bream, tench, roach, perch, pike, crucians and sunfish
Permits: Day tickets on bank
Cost: £3, or £2 in advance from Jack Frost Tackle, Crawley; or Ash Tackle Horsham
Control: Crawley AS. Secretary: Mr Kichols, 24 Rillside, Furness Green, Crawley, West Sussex
Restrictions: No night fishing - dawn till dusk only
BK Rating: Moderate
E/A: Thames

Chart's Plain

Location: Near the Abergavenny Arms, Copthorne
Type and Size: 3 acre lake
Carp Stock: Small carp, averaging about 5 lbs
Category: Mixed Fishery
Other Species: Roach, rudd, crucians, tench, perch and eels
Permits: On bank
Cost: About £5 per day; concessions
Control: Hazlewood Fisheries. Tel: 01342 715163
Restrictions: No night fishing; barbless hooks
BK Rating: Not known
E/A: Southern

Chichester Canal

Location: Near Chichester - runs from Chichester to Birdham Locks
Type and Size: Narrow disused canal about 10 miles long
Carp Stock: Well stocked with carp to about 10lbs, most of which are commons
Category: Mixed Fishery
Other Species: Tench, perch, pike and roach
Permits: Details from Mr Snook of Portsmouth and District AS, and also from Chichester Angling Association, Mr J Cooper,'Jaspers', Coney Road, East Wittering, nr Chichester, West Sussex
Control: Club
BK Rating: Moderate
E/A: Southern
Comments: PM claims the distinction of having stocked this part of the canal between 1946 and 1949! At the age of 16, this was the first water where he caught carp in any quantity. At the time, the lower part of the canal, known as Birdham Locks, was separated from the upper part towards Hunston and Chichester by a dam, constructed when the top lock collapsed. Fish could not get into the upper part, as it was at a higher level. The upper part was said to be almost devoid of fish since pollution from Chichester Canal Basin killed them during the 1939-45 war. The Birdham Locks section was packed with small commons, said by locals to be 'wildies' though I don't think they were! They had never been caught by 1946, as far as I know, as they were considered in those days to be 'uncatchable'. Once PM got them going on floating crust, which took 6 weeks, they were easy, and he caught up to 18 carp a day, mostly between 2lbs and 5lbs, with his best at 8lbs 3ozs. No-one else fished for carp. He put about 50 of these fish in the upper part of the canal, and is sure that the present stock descended from these fish, though he never fished the upper part of the canal. Later it was said that the Birdham Locks section was also polluted, and the fish had died, so whether there are still carp in the lower section we don't know - on the last visit a few years ago the water looked and smelt unpleasant, and there was no sign of any fish...though carp are notoriously hardy...

Crayfish Farm

Location: Pound Hill, Crawley, RH10 4TA
Type and Size: Four acre lake
How to Find: Ordnance Survey Sheet No.187; Reference 307 375
Carp Stock: Well stocked with carp; quite a number of doubles to about 23lbs
Category: Carp Water
Other Species: Perch and roach
Permits: The Owner, Old Hollow, Pound Hill, Worth, West Sussex. Season

	tickets only
Cost:	£245 per year
Control:	Private syndicate
BK Rating:	East
E/A:	Southern
Comments:	An attractive water. Barbless hooks only

Ditchling Pond

Location:	Ditchling Common
Type and Size:	Small pond on common land
How to Find:	Take the B2112 from Haywards Heath towards Burgess Hill - pond is just before the B2113
Carp Stock:	Small head of carp
Category:	Few Carp
Other Species:	General coarse fish
Permits:	Free fishing
Cost:	None
BK Rating:	Insufficient information
E/A:	Southern
Comments:	Very weedy free fishery

Dounhurst Farm Fishery

Location:	Kirdford, near Billingshurst
Type and Size:	Three small ponds
Carp Stock:	Stocked with carp to mid - doubles
Category:	Mixed Fishery
Other Species:	Crucians, tench, roach, rudd, gudgeon and eels
Permits:	In advance from control
Cost:	About £40 per season; some concessions
Control:	Henfield D.A.S. Tel: 01273 493441
Restrictions:	No night fishing; barbless hooks
BK Rating:	Moderate
E/A:	Southern

Furse Farm

Location:	Rudgwick, on the B2128, six miles north of Billingshurst
Type and Size:	Small lake
Carp Stock:	Well stocked with small carp to about 10lbs
Category:	Mixed Fishery
Other Species:	Tench, chub, perch, roach
Permits:	For all information and permits, Tel: 01403 822878; match bookings available
Cost:	£5 per day, juniors £3
Control:	Private
BK Rating:	Not known
E/A:	Southern

Hawkins Pond

Location:	Hammer Pond Road, Horsham
Type and Size:	Clay pit and former tin mine of 15 acres
How to Find:	In the town of Horsham - find Hammer Pond Road
Carp Stock:	Reasonable nuber of small carp, and about 30 doubles. Probably 3 carp to 28lbs, one of which is a common
Category:	Mixed Fishery
Permits:	Horsham and District AA. Secretary: G Kempson, 11 Clarence Road,

	Horsham, West Sussex
Cost:	About £28 a season - includes all club waters
Baits/Methods:	All baits but floaters good in summer. Hair rig best
Control:	Club
Restrictions:	No night fishing except for permit holders - fishing is from 4am to 11pm. No prebaiting. No litter
BK Rating:	Moderate
E/A:	Southern
Comments:	A beautiful lake surrounded by woodland. Average depth 8 feet

Hortons Pond

Location:	Small Dole, near Henfield
Type and Size:	Quarry of about 3½ acres, fringed by reeds
Carp Stock:	A few mirrors and commons, and many ghost carp
Category:	Mixed Fishery
Other Species:	Roach, rudd, tench and bream
Permits:	Blue Circle AC; ask for details at Cowfold Angling Centre, Henfield
BK Rating:	Not known
E/A:	Southern
Comments:	Good club water for beginners and juniors

Ivy Lake

Location:	Wyke, Chichester, just off the Chichester by-pass
Type and Size:	Five acre matured gravel pit
Carp Stock:	Quite well stocked with carp, including some doubles and a few 20's
Category:	Mixed Fishery
Other Species:	Roach, rudd, bream, tench and crucians
Permits:	Day tickets on bank
Control:	Private - Tel: 01243 787715
BK Rating:	Moderate
E/A:	Southern

Little Cansiron

Location:	Cansiron Lane, Holtye church, East Grinstead
Type and Size:	Two small farm pools
Carp Stock:	Well stocked with carp to 20 lbs
Category:	Carp Water
Other Species:	Tench
Permits:	On bank
Cost:	About £5 per day for 1 rod, £8 for 2 rods
Control:	Tel: 01836 564778
Restrictions:	No keepnets or barbed hooks
BK Rating:	Not known
E/A:	Southern
Comments:	Toilet. No fishing near power lines

Mill Farm Fishery

Location:	Off the A29 three miles south west of Pulborough at Bury Mill Farm
Type and Size:	Two lakes of about four acres, opened in 1992
Carp Stock:	Very well stocked with carp up to 30lbs
Category:	Mixed Fishery
Other Species:	Crucians, bream, roach and perch
Permits:	Day tickets on bank
Cost:	£5 or £8.50
Control:	01798 831617

Restrictions: Fishing 7am till dusk only; no barbed hooks, boilies, groundbait or keepnets
BK Rating: Easy
E/A: Southern
Comments: Attractive situation by South Downs. Closed Jan 1st to Easter

Milton Mount Lake

Location: Three Bridges, Crawley
Type and Size: Small lake
How to Find: Off junction 13 of the M23
Carp Stock: Well stocked with carp
Category: Carp Water
Other Species: Some other coarse fish
Permits: Crawley AS. Mr Kichols, 24 Rillside, Furness Green, Crawley
Cost: Season tickets approximately £20. Some day tickets at about £3
BK Rating: Moderate
Control: Club
E/A: Thames
Comments: Crawley AS also has carp on Tittermus Lake, Roffey Park Lake, Colgate, Buchan Park Lake and New Pond (listed). It is rumoured that this lake has been closed, so you will need to check locally

Newells Lake

Location: Monks Gate, Horsham
Type and Size: Clay pit of 4 1/2 acres
How to Find: Take the A281 from Horsham towards Brighton and after 3 miles the lake will be seen from the road
Carp Stock: Stocked in 1982 with 220 mirrors to 7lbs. Fish to 19lbs have been caught since
Category: Carp Water
Other Species: Tench, pike, roach and rudd
Permits: Season tickets only from the owner, Mr T Cotton, Newells Pond House, Newells Lane, Lower Beeding, Horsham. Tel: 01403 891424
Cost: £220 per year
Bait/Methods: Boilies on hair and bolt rigs
Control: Private
BK Rating: Easy
Restrictions: No keepnets or sacks. No particle baits.
E/A: Southern
Comments: No weed, open water, with an average depth of about five feet. Several carp a day possible, mostly small fish. Anglers' hut provided with book to record catches. Another lake of four acres - New Pond - costs £100 per season. Open June 16th to March 14th

New Pond

Location: Pease Pottage, near Crawley
Type and Size: Small tree-lined lake
How to Find: Near Crawley, off the A23
Carp Stock: Some carp, to mid doubles
Category: Mixed Fishery
Other Species: General coarse fish
Permits: Crawley AS, Mr Kichols, 24 Rillside, Furness Green, Crawley
Cost: Season - about £28
BK Rating: Moderate
Control: Club - no day tickets
E/A: Thames

Comments: Crawley AS also has other waters containing carp. No keepnets

Nunnery Lake

Location: Wyke, Chichester, part of the Chichester gravel pits, just off the by-pass
Type and Size: Ten acre matured gravel pit, with very clear water
Carp Stock: Well stocked with small carp and doubles to about 20lbs
Category: Mixed Fishery
Other Species: Roach, rudd, bream, pike and tench
Permits: Day tickets on bank
Cost: £3 per day
Control: Club
BK Rating: Moderate
E/A: Southern
Comments: A heavily fished water, and so not very easy to catch the fish, although they take well on the surface at times

Passies Ponds

Location: Coombes, near Shoreham and Steyning
Type and Size: Two lakes of 4 acres and a 'canal' match lake
How to Find: Take the A27 from Worthing, and turn left towards Coombes at Lancing. The lake is signposted on the right in about a mile
Carp Stock: Very heavily stocked with carp to 20lbs. Many small fish
Category: Mixed Fishery
Other Species: Tench, roach, rudd, crucians, chub and perch
Permits: Day tickets on site from service machine; evening tickets
Cost: £5 per day for two rods; juniors £3. Reduced prices in winter
Control: Private. Tel: 01273 465257
Restrictions: No night fishing except for local club members; barbless hooks only; no boilies; no hemp; no keepnets for large fish
BK Rating: Moderate
E/A: Southern
Comments: Some swims reserved for disabled anglers. Good baits are sweetcorn and luncheon meat. Open all year. Toilet

Petworth Park

Location: Petworth Park, Petworth
Type and Size: Seven acre estate lake in the grounds of a stately home
Carp Stock: A small number of carp to over 20lbs
Category: Few Carp
Other Species: A few big pike, tench, roach and perch
Control: Petworth Park
Restrictions: Fishing 9am till dusk only. Only 20 anglers per day. Petworth Park Estate Office
BK Rating: Difficult
E/A: Southern
Comments: This is a very beautiful estate, and the mansion is often open to the public; details from the Estate Office

Rivers Arun and Adur

Location: Arun from Pulborough northwards, Adur from Henfield near Brighton northwards
Type and Size: Some big carp
How to Find: The Arun runs from Littlehampton through Arundel to Pulborough; and Adur from Hove northwards
Carp Stock: Not known

Category: Few Carp
Other Species: General coarse fish
Permits: Local angling clubs and tackle shops
Cost: On application
Control: Clubs, CALPAC has fishing on these rivers and others, also canals and lakes. Send SAE to CALPAC, 93 Chapel Way, Epsom Downs, Surrey KT18 5TD
BK Rating: Very Difficult
E/A: Southern
Comments: As usual with rivers, location is the main problem. Try slower stretches, backwaters and bays. Carp to 20lbs+ have been taken in the middle and upper reaches of both rivers. Try also Pulborough AS. M Booth, 5 South Lane, Houghton, Arundel, West Sussex (Arun). Bines Bridge stretch good on River Adur - many big carp seen basking in weed. Floating crust good. Best legering results from 'Snatcher's Hole', above Bines Bridge

River Ouse

Location: Barcombe Mills, near Lewes
Type and Size: 33 mile long river
Carp Stock: A few good carp reported to about 20lbs, in the Barcombe Mills area, and possibly in the sections of the river
Category: Few Carp
Other Species: Sea trout (believe it or not!) and some big ones too; perch, bream, roach,dace, chub and pike
Permits: Old Mill Farm, Barcombe has day tickets. Other tickets from Ouse APS, Dr J L Cotton, Down End, Kingston Road, Lewes
Control: Private and Club
Restrictions: Some areas reserved for sea trout fishing; season tickets limited on club stretches
BK Rating: Very Difficult
E/A: Southern

Roosthole

Location: Hammer Pond Road, Horsham
Type and Size: Clay pit of 3½ acres
How to Find: The lake is in the town of Horsham, find Hammer Pond Road
Carp Stock: Quite well stocked with small carp and about 20 doubles, best fish 26lbs mirror
Category: Mixed Fishery
Other Species: Pike, bream, roach, rudd, perch
Permits: Season tickets from Horsham and District Angling Association. Secretary: G Kempson, 11 Clarence Road, Horsham
Cost: About £28 per year to include other club waters
Baits/Methods: Normal carp methods and all types of baits. Floaters work well
Control: Club
BK Rating: Very Difficult
Restrictions: No night fishing, fishing 4am till 11pm. Prebaiting banned. No litter
E/A: Southern
Comments: Very clear water and depths to 22 feet. Many snags. A peaceful lake, not heavily fished. Much larger carp are said to be in the water, but have not been caught, and the 22lb mirror has only been taken once in the last 5 years

Rother A.C. Lakes

Location: Near Midhurst
Type and Size: Three lakes and River Rother
How to Find: Enquire locally
Carp Stock: Some carp
Category: Mixed Fishery
Other Species: General coarse fish
Permits: Day tickets from Rice Bros, West Street; The Rother Inn, Lutener Road
Cost: Annual subscription about £10 with a £6 entry fee. Secretary: D Merritt, 17 Sandrock, June Lane, Midhurst
BK Rating: Insufficient information
Control: Club
E/A: Southern

Rowfant House Fishery A

Location: Old Hollow Lane, Turner's Hill, Crawley
Type and Size: 3 acre estate lake in grounds of old mansion
Carp Stock: Well stocked with carp to 20 lbs
Category: Mixed Fishery
Other Species: Bream, tench, roach, rudd, crucians and perch
Permits: On bank
Cost: About £6 per day
Control: Sporting Chance Tackle, Haywards Heath Tel: 01444 454095
Restrictions: No nuts or seeds. No fixed leads or barbed hooks
BK Rating: Not known
Baits/Methods: Boilies best bait
E/A: Thames
Comments: Food, drinks and accommodation

Southern Leisure Centre

Location: Wyke, near Chichester
Type and Size: Three fair sized gravel pits
How to Find: On the A27 from Chichester, to the south of the city
Carp Stock: Ivy, Nunnery and Triangle Lakes contain plenty of carp, up to upper doubles
Category: Mixed Fishery
Other Species: General coarse fish
Permits: On site. Tel: 01243 787715
Cost: Approximately £4 per day
Control: Southern Leisure Centre
BK Rating: Moderate
E/A: Southern
Comments: Very heavily fished in summer, and fishing can be difficult at times. Now taken over by Chichester DAS

Stemps Wood Pond

Location: On a farm near Bognor Regis
Type and Size: One acre farm pond in woodland
Carp Stock: Some commons, sizes not known
Other Species: Tench, rudd and crucians
Control: This pond is controlled by Bognor Regis AC, a member of the Hants and Sussex Anglers Alliance
BK Rating: Not known
E/A: Southern
Comments: A newly opened water, rebuilt and stocked from an overgrown derelict

farm pond by the hard work of members of the Bognor club

Tilgate Park Lake

Location: Crawley
Type and Size: Estate type of lake of ten acres
How to Find: Ordnance Survey Sheet No.187. Reference: 278 345
Carp Stock: Many small commons and a few double figure mirrors to about 22lbs
Category: Mixed Fishery
Other Species: General coarse fish, including large pike
Permits: From park keepers on bank - day tickets at £4
Control: Council
Restrictions: No night fishing
BK Rating: Very Difficult
E/A: Thames
Comments: A 'public'water; windsurfers, canoeists and dog walkers. There is even said to be a ghost which joins you in your bivvy! You need to find out the movements of the carp for success, not too easy with a casual aproach

Triangle Lake

Location: Chichester gravel pits, just off the by-pass
Type and Size: Six acre pit
Carp Stock: Well stocked with carp to about 17lbs
Category: Mixed Fishery
Other Species: Roach, crucians, rudd, bream and pike
Permits: Day tickets on site at low cost
Control: Private
Baits/Methods: Quite hard fished water, so sophisticated methods and baits needed; fixed lead methods and pop-ups work well
BK Rating: Moderate
E/A: Southern

Wintons Fishery

Location: Wintons Farm. Folders Lane, Burgess Hill. RH15 0DR
Type and Size: Three good-sized lakes
Carp Stock: Heavily stocked with carp to over 30 lbs
Category: Mixed Fishery
Other Species: Koi, and catfish to over 40 lbs
Permits: On site
Cost: About £10 per day. Membership also available
Control: Tel: 01444 236493 or 01444 23671 (evenings)
Restrictions: No night fishing except for members. No particles except sweetcorn.Barbless hooks only
BK Rating: Moderate
E/A: Southern
Comments: Probably open all year. Toilets with hot and cold water. Telephone. Cafeteria with hot meals

Woodmancote Place Fishery

Location: Off the A 23, 10 miles north of Brighton
Type and Size: Several lakes
How to Find: Telephone control for details
Carp Stock: Well stocked with carp to 30 lbs. One lake doubles only
Category: Carp Water
Permits: On bank

Cost: From £5 per day
Control: Tel: 01273 492941
Restrictions: Enquire from control
BK Rating: Moderate
E/A: Southern
Comments: Camping and caravans allowed

Wyke Lake

Location: On the Chichester by-pass
Type and Size: Gravel pit of about eight acres
How to Find: From Bognor Regis, take the Chichester road and turn left towards Portsmouth at the roundabout just before Chichester. The lake will be seen on the right - it is the third lake along
Carp Stock: Quite well stocked with carp to upper twenties, and one known 30
Category: Mixed Fishery
Other Species: Most other coarse fish to a good size
Permits: Chichester and District Angling Society. Membership Secretary: Mr C Few, Fisherman's Den, 5 Canada Grove, Bognor Regis, West Sussex. Season tickets only. Membership includes 3 other lakes and some stretches of river. The lakes all contain carp
Cost: £15 annual subscription plus a £10 entry fee. Juniors/OAP's about £6 entry fee and approximately £5 annual subsription. OAP's about £3 annual subscription only
Control: Club
BK Rating: Moderate
E/A: Southern
Comments: Chichester, Bognor Regis and Portsmouth clubs all have gravel pits in this area, most of which contain carp, including the Southern Leisure Centre. Enquire from tackle shops. Chichester AS also has Westhampnett lake, on the A27, a good doubles water

WEST YORKSHIRE

Brookfoot Lake

Location: Brighouse, off the A6025 Brighouse-Elland road - parking at the Grove Motel
Type and Size: Small lake
Carp Stock: Well stocked wtih carp, to about 20lbs
Category: Mixed Fishery
Other Species: Rudd, tench, perch, roach and pike
Permits: Day tickets from Calder Angling Supplies, Gooder Lane, Brighouse and Pondworks Angling Supplies, 364 Bradford Road, Bailiff Bridge,
Control: Brighouse Angling Association. M Riley, 30 Ravenstone Drive, West Vale, Greetland, Halifax. Tel: 01484 711063
BK Rating: Very Easy
Restrictions: No Sunday fishing; limited numbers. Carp must not be kept in nets
E/A: Yorkshire

Clayton Ponds

Location: Clayton Wood Road, Leeds
Type and Size: Two small ponds
How to Find: Off the Leeds ring road
Carp Stock: Some carp to double figures
Category: Few Carp
Other Species: Tench, roach, perch and big eels
Permits: Day and season tickets at low cost from Abbey Match Anglers, Commercial Road, Kirkstall, Leeds; and Headingly Angling Centre, Headingly
Control: Fox and Hounds Angling Club
BK Rating: Difficult
E/A: Yorkshire

DAF Trucks Pond

Location: Mirfield, just south of Dewsbury
Type and Size: Small pond
Carp Stock: Well stocked with small carp

Category: Mixed Fishery
Other Species: Usual coarse fish
Permits: Enquire locally, or from tackle shops in Dewsbury
BK Rating: Easy
E/A: Yorkshire

Doe Park Reservoir

Location: Denholme, between Halifax and Keighley
Type and Size: 20 acre resevoir
How to Find: Take the A629 from Halifax towards Keighley, and the fishery is at Denholme, on the right hand side of the road
Carp Stock: Some carp, sizes not known
Category: Few Carp
Other Species: Bream, tench, roach, rudd, pike, chub and trout
Permits: Day tickets from the keeper's house at Doe Park, and from Richmonds, 110 Morley Street, Bradford
Cost: £3 per day
Control: Bradford City Angling Association. Secretary: H Briggs, 4 Brown Hill Close,Birkinshaw, Bradford, West Yorkshire
BK Rating: Difficult, as there are not many carp
Restrictions: No night fishing (starts 7am). Fishing is from June 1st until the end of February. Entrance only from the marked gates
E/A: Yorkshire
Comments: Bradford City AA issues tickets for other lakes, the canal and rivers

Flanshaw Dam

Location: Flanshaw Lane, Flanshaw, Wakefield
Type and Size: Tiny park pond of about half an acre
Carp Stock: Quite well stocked with carp to about 10lbs
Category: Mixed Fishery
Other Species: Bream, tench, and roach
Permits: Day tickets from clubhouse on site; £1
Control: Wakefield Angling Club. Tel: 01924 827401 or 01924 369556 (clubhouse)
Restrictions: No night fishing; barbless hooks
BK Rating: Not known
E/A: Yorkshire

Folly Dam

Location: Woodhouse Road, Todmorden, near Halifax
Type and Size: One acre pool
Carp Stock: Some carp to doubles
Category: Mixed Fishery
Other Species: Perch, tench, bream, dace and gudgeon
Permits: In advance from local tackle shops
Cost: £20 per season, plus £10 joining fee; £10 for juniors, O.A.P's and disabled
Control: Todmorden A.S. Tel: 01282 428780
Restrictions: No night fishing
E/A: Yorkshire

Hemsworth Water Park

Location: Kinsley, near Wakefield, off the B6273
Type and Size: Two lakes of 4 1/2 acres and 1 1/2 acres
Carp Stock: Some carp to doubles
Category: Mixed Fishery
Other Species: Bream, tench, roach and chub

Permits: £2 per day on site
Control: Hemsworth Water Park. Michael Skues. Tel: 01977 612274
BK Rating: Insufficient information
E/A: Yorkshire
Comments: Special stands for disabled anglers. Larger lake used for water sports

Hill Top Reservoir

Location: Longlands Road, Hill Top, near Huddersfield
Type and Size: 11 acre reservoir
How to Find: Off the A62, seven miles south west of Huddersfield
Carp Stock: Some carp
Category: Few Carp
Other Species: Roach, perch, bream and pike
Permits: Day tickets from the Albion Inn, Longroyd Bridge, Slaithwaite
Control: Slaithwaite and District Angling Club
BK Rating: Difficult
E/A: Yorkshire

Horbury Quarry

Location: Horbury Junction, near Wakefield
Type and Size: 15 acres, very deep sand quarry
Carp Stock: Not many, but they go to upper doubles
Category: Few Carp
Other Species: Roach, bream, perch and pike
Permits: Season tickets only from Wakefield AC. Secretary: B D Harper, 29 Victoria Crescent, Horsforth, Leeds
Control: Club
BK Rating: Very Difficult
E/A: Yorkshire

Kettlethorpe Hall Lake

Location: Crigglestens, near Wakefield
Type and Size: Small pool with islands
Carp Stock: Some doubles
Category: Few Carp
Other Species: Crucians, roach, perch, bream, tench and chub
Permits: In advance only from local tackle shops
Cost: £14 per season; reduced prices for children, juniors, O.A.P's and disabled
Control: Wakefield A.C. Tel: 01924 258376
Restrictions: No night fishing; barbless hooks; no keepnets
BK Rating: Difficult
E/A: Yorkshire

Kippax Pond

Location: Brigshaw Lane, Kippax, Leeds
Type and Size: Small marshland pond
Carp Stock: Very well stocked with carp to upper doubles
Category: Mixed Fishery
Other Species: Roach and other coarse fish
Permits: Leeds and District ASA, members only, but open to all - The Secretary, Leeds and District ASA, 75 Stoney Rock Lane, Beckett Street, Leeds LS9 1TB - £30 per season
BK Rating: Easy
Restrictions: No night fishing; no day tickets; no Chum Mixers or similar baits(!)
Control: Club

E/A: Yorkshire
Comments: Over 100 carp rumoured to have been removed

Knotford Lagoon

Location: One and a half miles from Otley, near Leeds
Type and Size: 40 acre lake
How to FInd: The fishery is just off the A659 Otley-Pool road
Carp Stock: Not many carp, but a few large fish to well over 20lbs
Category: Few Carp
Other Species: Tench,roach, chub, perch and trout
Permits: Day tickets from Angling and Countrysports, Pool Road, Otley and Leeds tackle dealers, and the filling station at Pool. About £2 per day
Control: Club. Tel: 01532 663406/482373
BK Rating: Very Difficult
E/A: Yorkshire
Comments: No night fishing

Magdale Dam

Location: Honley,near Huddersfield, off the A616 Huddersfield - Holmfirth road
Type and Size: Medium-sized dam
Carp Stock: Plenty of carp to double figures
Category: Mixed Fishery
Other Species: Crucians, perch and rudd
Permits: Apply to Peter Budd, 39 Derwent Road, Honley, near Huddersfield. Tel: 01484 660258
Cost: £50 for the season, £10 for juniors. Free to registered disabled persons
Control: Holme Valley Piscatorials Association
BK Rating: Moderate
E/A: Yorkshire
Comments: This is a purpose built fishery, with ramps and stands for disabled anglers. Club membership is open to all

Millacre Pond

Location: Garforth, near Leeds
Type and Size: Small lake
Carp Stock: Well stocked with carp to doubles
Category: Mixed Fishery
Other Species: Bream, tench, roach, rudd and perch
Permits: On site
Cost: Not known
Control: Tel: 01532 867530
BK Rating: Not known
E/A: Yorkshire

New Miller Reservoir

Location: Off the A61, at Kettlethorpe, near Wakefield
Type and Size: About 70 acres, very pleasant but busy
Carp Stock: Not many carp, but some 20's
Category: Few Carp
Other Species: Most coarse fish,and some trout
Permits: Season tickets only, from local tackle shops. £14 per season. Concessions
Control: Wakefield AC. B D Harper, 29 Victoria Crescent, Horsforth, Leeds. Tel: 01274 672239
Restrictions: No night fishing. Barbless hooks. No keepnets

BK Rating: Super-Difficult
E/A: Yorkshire
Comments: Toilet

Nostell Priory A

Location: Nostell Priory, near Wakefield
Type and Size: Three lakes of 26 acres, 7 acres and 6 acres
How to Find: Just off the A638 Wakefield to Doncaste road
Carp Stock: All 3 lakes are well stocked with carp and fish of over 30lbs have been reported from all 3 lakes
Category: Mixed Fishery
Other Species: Bream, perch, and pike to over 30lbs
Permits: Day tickets and season tickets from the fishery shop. Information from John Austerfield or Tony Frost on 01924 863562
Cost: £3 per day. £2 for half day, from 7am to 1pm or 1pm till dusk. Season tickets £30 for top or bottom lake, or £60 for all three
Control: Head Bailiff, Foulby Lodge, Foulby, Wakefield. Tel: 01924 863562
BK Rating: Moderate
Restrictions: No keepnets; night fishing by arrangement
E/A: Yorkshire
Comments: In the grounds of a stately home owned by the National Trust. Fishing shop on lakeside. Touring caravans and tents welcome on the adjacent 30 acre woodland park. Tel: 01924 863938. Some close season fishing. Fish tackle and baits on sale

Nunroyd Pond

Location: Guiseley; Nunroyd Park, Guiseley - off the A65 Leeds-Ilkley road
Type and Size: Small park lake
Carp Stock: Some carp, sizes not known
Category: Few Carp
Other Species: Roach, tench
Permits: Membership from Abbey Match Anglers, Commercial Road, Kirkstall, Leeds
Control: Aireborough and District AA. Members only, open to all
BK Rating: Difficult
Restrictions: No night fishing. Barbless hooks
E/A: Yorkshire

Oulton Hall Pond

Location: Rothwell Sports Centre, Rothwell, near Leeds
Type and Size: One acre lake
Carp Stock: Some carp to about 10 lbs
Category: Mixed Fishery
Other Species: Roach, rudd, perch, chub, tench, bream and pike
Permits: Rothwell Sports Centre
Cost: About £2 per day
Control: Tel: 01132 824110
Restrictions: No fishing on about half of the bank
BK Rating: Not known
E/A: Yorkshire

Pastures Pond

Location: Allerton Bywater, just off the A639, between Castleford and Leeds, and close to the river
Type and Size: Shallow, 5 acre lake

Carp Stock: A very small number, though a common of over 30lbs has been reported
Category: Few Carp
Other Species: Most coarse fish
Permtis: From tackle shops in Castleford and Leeds
Control: Private
BK Rating: Very Difficult
Restrictions: Fishing from one bank only (nearest garage)
E/A: Yorkshire
Comments: No close season; very snaggy and difficult water

Pugney's Lake

Location: Crofton, near Wakefield
Type and Size: Very large, open park lake
How to Find: Take junction 39 from the M1, and at the roundabout take the Wakefield road, then the second right to Crofton; Pugney's Country Park
Carp Stock: Some carp, sizes not known
Category: Few Carp or possibly Mixed Fishery
Other Species: Bream, tench and perch
Permits: From reception at the entrance to the park - low cost day tickets
Control: Wakefield Metropolitan District Council
BK Rating: Not known
Restrictions: No night fishing
E/A: Yorkshire
Comments: There is windsurfing and sailing on the big lake. Club matches can be booked

Roberts Pond

Location: Behind Roberts Dye Works, Beechcliff, Keighley, off the Keighley to Skipton road
Type and Size: Small pond
Carp Stock: Some carp, number and sizes not known
Category: Probably Few Carp
Other Species: Bream, tench, roach, perch and pike
Permits: Keighley Angling Club, members only but open to all - Mr D Ward, 4 Compeigne Avenue, Keighley
Control: Club
E/A: Yorkshire

Roundhay Park Lakes

Location: Roundhay Park, 4 miles from Leeds
Type and Size: Two lakes, both of which contain some carp
Carp Stock: Some carp in both lakes, sizes not known
Category: Mixed Fishery
Other Species: Pike, perch, roach, tench, bream
Permits: Leeds and District AA. Secretary: G Copley, Anglers Club, Becket Street, Leeds LS9 1TB. Tel: 01132 663406
Cost: About £2 per day
BK Rating: Moderate
E/A: Yorkshire

Southern Washlands

Location: Outskirts of Wakefield
Type and Size: Two small lakes created by Wakefield District Council on a recently reclaimed site
Carp Stock: Some carp

Category: Mixed Fishery
Other Species: Bream, perch, roach and gudgeon
Permits: Day tickets from The Match Anglers Shop, off Westgate, Wakefield
Cost: £2 per day
Control: Wakefield MDC and Eastmoor AC - information on Eastmoor membership from Carl Young, 210 Stanley Road, Wakefield. Tel: 01924 373286
BK Rating: Not known
E/A: Yorkshire

Sugden End Reservoir

Location: Crossroads, Keighley
Type and Size: Large reservoir
How to Find: Off the A60 Bradford-Skipton road
Carp Stock: Some big carp
Category: Mixed Fishery
Other Species: General coarse fish; large tench
Permits: Keighley AC. L Brocklesby, 11 Eelholme View Street, Keighley (information only)
Cost: Day tickets -about £2. Season - approximately £10. From local tackle shops
BK Rating: Moderate
Control: Club
E/A: Yorkshire
Comments: The Keighley club also has other waters containing carp

Swillington Park

Location: Swillington Hall, near Leeds
Type and Size: Lakes of 3 acres, 2 acres, and two small ones
How to Find: Take the A 462 from Leeds towards Garforth. Fishery is on the right
Carp Stock: Well stocked with carp to doubles, mostly in one lake
Category: Mixed Fishery
Other Species: Tench, crucians, bream, rudd, perch, roach and chub
Permits: On site - season tickets only
Cost: About £50 per season; juniors £30
Control: Tel: 0113 286 9129
Restrictions: No night fishing; no keepnets; barbless hooks
BK Rating: Moderate
Baits/Methods: Boilies best bait
E/A: Yorkshire
Comments: Toilets. Disabled access. Probably open all year

Ulley Country Park

Location: Near Rotherham, off the A618 Pleasley Road
Type and Size: Large reservoir, 30 acres and very deep
Carp Stock: Some carp to mid-doubles
Category: Mixed Fishery
Other Species: Bream, roach, perch, pike and trout
Permits: Tickets from a vending machine in the car park. About £4 per day
Control: Rotherham MBC. Information on 01709 365332
BK Rating: Very Difficult
Restrictions: No night fishing
E/A: Yorkshire
Comments: This is part of Ulley Country Park, which is a nature reserve. Anglers leaving litter will be ordered by the rangers to leave the fishery; sailing on the lake

Walsden Lodges

Location: Ramsdenwood Road, Littleborough, Todmorden
Type and Size: Two small lodges
Carp Stock: Some carp, sizes not known
Category: Mixed Fishery
Other Species: Perch, roach, tench, chub and bream
Permits: In advance from local tackle shops - no day tickets
Cost: £20 per season, with a £10 joining fee. Reductions for juniors,ladies and O.A.P's
Control: Todmorden A/C. Tel: 01282 428780
BK Rating: Not known
E/A: Yorkshire

Wentworth Fishery - Greasborough Dam

Location: East Lodge, Greasborough
Type and Size: Two estate lakes
How to Find: Take the B6089 from Rotherham and after Greasborough, turn left at East Lodge and the fishery is 300 yards
Carp Stock: Well stocked with carp to 35lbs
Category: Mixed Fishery
Other Species: Big bream and tench, roach, big perch and trout to 10lbs
Permits: Season tickets only. Applications in writing only to: Fitzwilliam Wentworth Amenity Trust, Estate Office, Clayfields Lane, Wentworth,Rotherham S62 7TD
BK Rating: Moderate
Control: Estate
E/A: Yorkshire
Comments: A pleasant water with lilies and easy access. There is also a fly only trout lake on the site

Whitefields Reservoir

Location: Near Keighley
Type and Size: Reservoir
How to Find: Off the A60 Bradford-Skipton road near Keighley. Enquire at tackle shops
Carp Stock: Some carp in both waters
Category: Mixed Fisheries
Other Species: Tench, roach, perch, pike
Permits: Keighley AC. L Brocklesby, 11 Eelholme View Street, Keighley (information only)
Cost: Approximately £2 per day; about £10 per season. Tickets from local tackle shops
BK Rating: Moderate
Control: Club
E/A: Yorkshire
Comments: Large carp also in Sugden End Reservoir, Keighley AC

Workshop Lake

Location: Fairburn, off the A1 near Castleford; correct name is Newton lane Pond
Type and Size: Four acre snaggy lake
Carp Stock: Very well stocked wtih over 150 carp to 23lbs
Category: Mixed Fishery
Other Species: Usual coarse fish
Permits: Tel: 01924 863618. £13 + £5 for special carp permit
Control: Walton AC. Season tickets only; night fishing for members only. Tel: 01226 724771 (L Gray)

Restrictions: All carp to be returned immediately. Waiting list for carp fishing
BK Rating: Moderate
E/A: Yorkshire

Workshop Ponds

Location: Charles Roberts Factory, Horbury Junction, near Wakefield
Type and Size: Three acre weedy lake used as a water supply for the factory
Carp Stock: Quite well stocked to lower doubles
Category: Mixed Fishery
Other Species: Roach, rudd and bream
Permits: Charles Roberts Angling Club, hard to obtain - enquire locally
BK Rating: Moderate
E/A: Yorkshire
Comments: A heavly weeded works pond, attractive and used by match anglers

Yeadon Tarn

Location: Cemetery Road, Yeadon, between Bradford and Harrogate
Type and Size: Large lake, weedy in summer
Carp Stock: Quite well stocked with carp to double figures
Category: Mixed Fishery
Other Species: Tench, roach, bream, trout, perch and gudgeon
Permits: Day tickets. Headingley Angling Centre
Control: Aireborough and District Angling Association Tel: 01132 784445
Restrictions: No night fishing. No fishing from the Sailing Club jetty whilst sailing is take place
Baits/Methods: Luncheon meat said to be good for the bigger carp
BK Rating: Moderate
E/A: Yorkshire
Comments: Big open lake, used also for sailing. Level banks ideal for the disabled. Tickets about £2.50 per day

WILTSHIRE

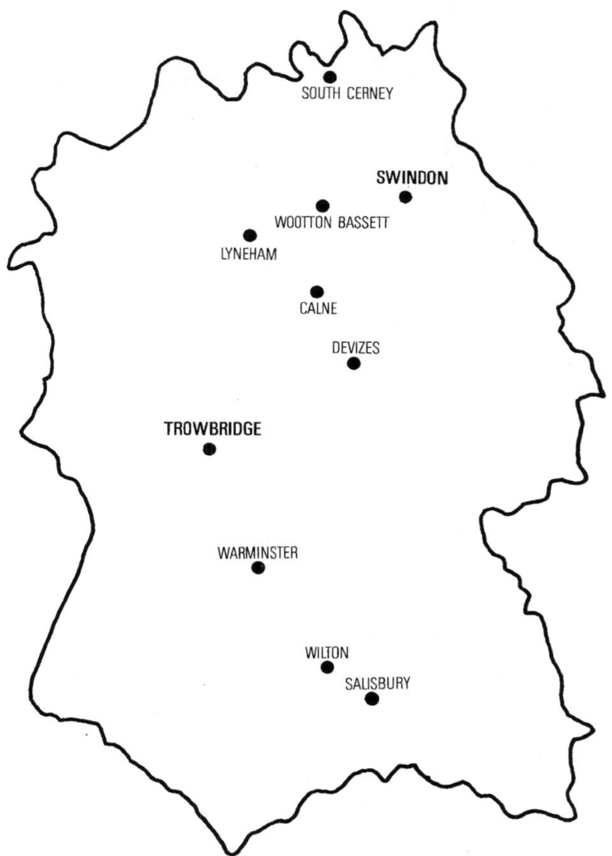

Barn Moor Lake

Location: Witherington Farm, Downton, Salisbury
Type and Size: 1 1/2 acre lake
How to Find: Take the right hand Alderbury turn off the A36 Salisbury-Southampton road. Take the first right turn and the farm is three miles further on, on the right hand side
Carp Stock: Well stocked with mirrors to 10lbs, and commons to 15lbs
Category: Mixed Fishery
Other Species: Tench and roach
Permits: Day tickets from owner on bank
Cost: £4 per day - half price for juniors and OAP's
Control: Private
Restrictions: No keepnets; no boilies or hgh protein baits (!)
BK Rating: Moderate
E/A: Wessex

Blackland Lakes

Location: Stockley Lane, off the A 4 near Quemerford between Chippenham and Marlborough
Type and Size: Two small pools
Carp Stock: Well stocked with carp to 30 lbs
Category: Mixed Fishery
Other Species: Perch, rudd, crucians, roach, bream and gudgeon
Permits: On bank
Cost: About £5 per day; £85 per season
Control: Tel: 01249 813672
Restrictions: No cereal groundbait; no barbed hooks
BK Rating: Not known
E/A: Wessex
Comments: Campsite and shop. Toilet. Disabled access

Bowood lake

Location: Bowood, near Calne
Type and Size: 20 acre estate lake
How to Find: Bowood Estate near Calne
Carp Stock: Some carp, including doubles
Category: Few Carp
Other Species: General coarse fish
Permits: Bowood Estate, Bowood, Calne
Cost: On application
BK Rating: Difficult
Control: Private
Restrictions: No fishing at the north end of the lake
E/A: Wessex
Comments: This beautiful lake contains big pike, and possibly a few big carp

Coate Water

Location: Coate Water Country Park, Marlborough Road, Swindon
Type and Size: Large old lake of about 70 acres
How to Find: Southern outskirts of Swindon
Carp Stock: Few original fish up to 23lbs. Recently stocked with a number of small carp. A 28 was caught in 1988
Category: Mixed Fishery
Other Species: Large bream, tench, roach, pike and perch
Permits: On bank; ticket machine
Cost: £1.20 per day - season night tickets for Swindon residents
Control: Thamesdown Borough Council, Euclid Street, Swindon.Tel: 01793 721173
BK Rating: Difficult
E/A: Thames
Comments: A big lake made famous by the writings of naturalist Richard Jefferies who lived on the bank. Boats and people - a 'public' water, £1 car parking. Toilets

Flamstone Cottage

Location: Bishopstone,near Salisbury
Type and Size: Small stream fed pool
How to Find: South west of Salisbury off the A354
Carp Stock: Well stocked with carp to 19lbs
Category: Carp Water
Other Species: Brown trout to 12lbs; tench, orfe, chub, roach and grayling - all large
Permits: Ealing Angling Centre. Tel: 0181-5673101

Cost: On application
Control: Private
Restrictions: Barbless hooks no larger than size 12, no keepnets
BK Rating: Easy
E/A: Wessex
Comments: An exclusive private specimen fishery. Standard baits. Carp by the island, near rushes

Hunters Moon Lodges A

Location: Henford Marsh, Warminster
Type and Size: Pleasant, small farmland lake
Carp Stock: Said to be some carp, number and sizes not known
Category: Mixed Fishery
Other Species: General coarse fish, and some trout
Permits: Fishing for residents only
Cost: On application at reception
Control: Private
BK Rating: Not known
E/A: Wessex
Comments: There are a number of well equipped timber built lodges for rent on the site round the lake. Booking details from Hoseasons Holidays, Sunway House, Lowestoft NR32 3LT. Tel: 01502 500500

Longleat

Location: Longleat, near Warminster
Type and Size: Three estate lakes
How to Find: Off the Warminster - Frome road
Carp Stock: Some carp to over 20lbs - stocked with 6,500lbs of small carp to 7lbs in 1990 - Top Lake; other lakes have very small carp
Category: Mixed Fishery
Other Species: General coarse fish
Permits: The Bailiff, Parkhill Cottage, Longleat Estate or on bank at £3
BK Rating: Moderate
Control: Longleat Estate, contact Pete Bundy. Tel: 01985 215082
Restrictions: No peas, beans or nuts. No boilies on middle or bottom lakes
E/A: Wessex
Comments: Watch out for the 'Lions of Longleat!'

Longwater A

Location: Eclestoke, Devizes
Type and Size: Shallow 6 acre estate lake
Carp Stock: Well stocked with carp to 20 lbs
Category: Mixed Fishery
Other Species: General coarse fish
Permits: In advance only from Mr. D. Hampton, Longwater. Season tickets
Cost: On application
Control: Tel: 01380 830095
BK.Rating: Moderate
E/A: Thames
Comments: High standard bed and breakfast. Touring caravans welcome

Lower Foxhangers **A**

Location: Lower Foxhangers Farm, Rowde, Devizes, Wilts. Tel: 01380 828245
Type and Size: This farm/guesthouse does not actually have its own fishing, but it is on the edge of the Kennet and Avon Canal, which contains some carp in this area
How to Find: Take the A361 from Devizes,and the road to the farm wil be seen on the right after a few miles
Carp Stock: Canal contains plenty of common and mirror carp to about 20lbs
Category: Mixed Fishery
Other Species: roach, perch, tench, crucian carp
Permtis: Devizes Angling Association, Secretary. T W Fell, 21 Cornwell Crescent, Devizes
Cost: Day and weekly tickets on application, and also from local tackle shops
BK Rating: Fairly Hard
Control: Club
E/A: Wessex
Comments: Bed and breakfast accommodation at farm, with good facilities - £28 per night for two. There are also 4 mobile homes to rent close to the canal, each of which sleeps four. Enquire from Colin and Cynthia Fletcher at the farm

Old Warden Castle

Location: Near Tisbury
Type and Size: Castle Lake
How to Find: Tisbury, near Wilton; off the A30 six miles west of Wilton
Carp Stock: Some carp
Category: Mixed Fishery
Other Species: General coarse fish
Permits: Tisbury AC, P Lever, 1 Maypole Bungalow, Ansty, Tisbury
Cost: On application
BK Rating: No information
Control: Club
Restrictions: Not known
E/A: Wessex

Petersfinger Lakes

Location: Two miles east of Salisbury just off the A36 Warminster road
Type and Size: Two large estate lakes in nature reserve
Carp Stock: Well stocked with good carp to 24lbs,including commons and mirrors
Category: Mixed Fishery
Other Species: Bream to 8¾ lbs, tench, perch and pike
Permits: Salisbury and Dist. Angling Club (members only). Membership Secretary, 9 New Zealand Avenue, Salisbury, Wilts SP2 7JX
Cost: £48 plus £15 registration fee - reduced prices for local OAP's juniors and members' wives
Control: Club. Tel: 01722 743192
BK Rating: Moderate
E/A: Wessex
Comments: This well known and very pleasant fishery is partly surrounded by trees and the surrounding nature reserve is owned by the club

Rowde Lake

Location: In the village of Rowde, near Devizes
Type and Size: Small pond of about an acre
Carp Stock: Fairly well stocked with carp to lower doubles

Category: Mixed Fishery
Other Species: General coarse fish, including large crucians
Permits: From house at lake, which is a caravan site
Cost: Day tickets to about £2 per day
Control: Private
BK Rating: Easy
E/A: Wessex

Silverlands Lake

Location: Lacock, near Chippenham
Type and Size: 5 acre open gravel pit
How to Find: Off the A350 between Chippenham and Melksham
Carp Stock: In the past, very few to 26lbs, but was restocked in 1987 - a 27 pounder was reported in late 1990
Category: Mixed Fishery
Other Species: Tench, roach, bream, pike
Permits: Robs Tackle, 22 Marshfield Road, Chippenham
Cost: Day and night- approximately £3; season about £45
Control: Private
Restrictions: Night fishing now allowed
BK Rating: Moderate
E/A: Wessex
Comments: A long walk - nearly a mile! - across fields. PM's 25$^{1}/_{4}$ caught here in 1971, is now dead - and the walk nearly killed him too! A 27 was reported from here in 1991. (Late news is that you can now drive to within 50 yards of the lake).

Steeple Langford Lakes

Location: Steeple Langford, near Warminster
Type and Size: Gravel pits
How to Find: Off the A36 ten miles north west of Salisbury
Carp Stock: Well stocked with carp to over 20lbs
Category: Carp Water
Other Species: General coarse fish
Permits: From baliff on site. Salisbury and District AC, R W Hillier, 29 New Zealand Avenue, Salisbury
Cost: On application
BK Rating: Difficult
Control: Club
Restrictions: Not known
E/A: Wessex
Comments: Salisbury AC also has other good carp waters

Sword Lakes

Location: Hayle Farm, near Calne
Type and Size: Two small pools
How to Find: Take the A 4 road from Calne towards Marlborough. Turn left at Hayle Farm Hotel
Carp Stock: Well stocked with carp to over 20 lbs
Category: Mixed Fishery
Other Species: Most coarse fish
Permits: In advance only from T.K.Tackle, Calne
Cost: £5 per day; concessions
Control: Tel: 01249 812003
Restrictions: No night fishing; no boilies
BK Rating: Easy

E/A: Thames
Comments: Toilets. Disabled access

Tockenham Reservoir

Location: Tockenham, near Lyneham
Type and Size: Reservoir of 8 acres, recently dredged
How to Find: Off the main Lyneham - Wootton Bassett road. Turn left just outside Lyneham. Down lane about 150 yards on right
Carp Stock: Stocked with about 600 carp of 2 - 4lbs and about 30 bigger fish to 20lbs. Good head of doubles including commons
Category: Carp Water
Other Species: Tench, bream, roach
Permits: Bristol and District Amalgamated Anglers, membership open to all: Season only. Secretary, J Parker, 16 Lansdowne View, Kingswood, Bristol BS14 4AW
Cost: About £20 per season
Restrictions: No night fishing
Baits/Methods: Normal carp fishing methods, boilies and floaters
Control: Club
BK Rating: Easy
E/A: Wessex
Comments: A very pleasant club water but hard fished especially during the summer. Carp harder to catch as season progresses. Stock fish said to be growing well and now averaging about 8lbs in weight

Wick Water

Location: Near South Cerney
Type and Size: Gravel pit of 7 acres
How to Find: Take the Cerney Wick road from South Cerney and turn right onto the Spine Road at the first crossroads. Wick Water is on the left shortly after the turn
Carp Stock: About 100 carp to low twenties
Category: Mixed Fishery
Other Species: General coarse fish
Permits: South Cerney Angling Club. Secretary, Fisherman's Rest, Broadway Lane, South Cerney (Send SAE)
Cost: £15 per season
Restrictions: No night fishing
Control: Club
BK Rating: Fairly Hard
E/A: Thames

Witherington Fishery

Location: Downston, near Salisbury
Type and Size: Two lakes of an acre and 1½ acres
Carp Stock: Well stocked with carp to 20 lbs
Category: Mixed Fishery
Other Species: Chub, perch, roach, bream and tench
Permits: From the lodge
Cost: About £5 per day; half price concessions
Control: Tel: 01722 710021
Restrictions: No keepnets; no night fishing; no boilies. Barbless hooks
BK Rating: Easy
E/A: Southern
Comments: Good disabled access. Toilets and refreshments. Put-and-take trout fishing

Wootton Bassett Lake

Location: Wootton Bassett, near Swindon
Type and Size: Small pond of about one acre
Carp Stock: Quite well stocked with carp to low doubles
Category: Mixed Fishery
Other Species: General coarse fish
Permits: Wootton Bassett Angling Club; members only; and you will need to live in the Wootton Bassett area. Secretary, T Strange, 15 Shakespeare Road, Wootton Bassett, Swindon, Wilts
Control: Club
BK Rating: Easy
E/A: Thames

EUROPEAN SECTION

We would urge all those who go to fish other countries to remember that they are the foreigners, and that they should behave well at all times. Buy all licences, and keep to all laws and rules; this way, you will help to give English anglers a good name. In some European countries, laws and rules are especially strict, and may be enforced by armed police and rangers.

If you cannot behave, and keep to all rules and laws when fishing abroad, you should not go to other countries; if you do, be well-behaved and friendly to local people and anglers, and you will help to restore the good name of English anglers - don't forget, it is their country, and whether or not you agree with their laws and rules, you must accept them and keep to them whilst you are there. Many fish in European countries are killed and eaten for food (just as English anglers kill sea fish and eat them!) and some English anglers even kill pike in England without even the excuse that they are to eat. If it is the custom to kill fish for food, then it is best to say nothing about it, however much you dislike the idea.

BELGIUM

A Government National Licence is essential to fish nearly all waters, cost approximiately 500BF(£10) and is available from Post Offices. Generally no night fishing but some night fishing is allowed on private waters and there is a close season from April 15th to June 1st

DENMARK

There is no close season for carp in Denmark, but there might be restrictions on a chosen water to protect other species. From 1 January 1993 all who go fishing with rod and line in fresh or saltwater, must have a national licence (Fisketegn). The licences costs approximately 100 dkr (£10) for a year, 75 dkr (£7) for a week and 25 dkr (£2) for a day. This licence does not in itself give permission to fish any water. There is no rod limit

The licence is obtained at the Post Office and from selected fishery managers and is strictly personal.

In some cases a licence is not required. This applies if the water has no connection to stream, river or beach which fish can pass, as often in trout fisheries with stocking of rainbow trout. People under 18 years and over 67 years do not need a licence.

To fish in freshwater in Denmark, you wil need permission, a ticket or membership. If you don't know who to talk to about it, try to ask the local tackle shop/petrol station/grocery or tourist office. Do not just fish, because there are no signs! ("Fiskeri Forbudt"). Very often a water is rented out to hunters who do not take any disturbance lightly.

There is not, as in France and Holland, a large number of public owned waters that a general licence can be bought for.

Catapults of any kind are forbidden to possess or use without permission from the police. The catapult is considered as a weapon and the permission costs approximately 900 dkr! Throwing sticks are legal without permission.

To bivvy up is considered as camping, and requires special permission from the water adminstrator.

Normally there are no problems in private waters. Night fishing is allowed but always check it out, as there might be a ban on a chosen water (often in trout waters).

Carp fisheries as known in England, do not exist in Denmark. The demand is simply not big enough.

Take all the extra carp tackle you need from home. Shops with a decent selection of carp tackle only exist in few numbers, mainly in Copenhagen.
Danish carp fishers return all their fish and use proper slings, sacks and unhooking mats. But still there are holiday anglers who consider all fish as food, especially in mixed trout/carp fisheries, where small carp are stocked.
Any baits can be used. Danish carp fishers use HNV boilies a lot. In heavily fished waters, birds have learned to eat boilies, so be warned! There is often a ban on baiting up in trout fisheries to protect the trout or to make the sport harder. In this case use stringers.
The Danish carp are of all kinds, both wild and king, and in all varieties. A standard Danish carp weighs between 5 and 10kgs, but fish up to16kg have been caught and there are rumours about a 20kg fish. Among Danish carp fishers the presumed maximum weight is 25kg. As the fishing pressure is very low on most of the waters no one really knows what is out there!

FRANCE

You must have a French National Licence, available from all fishing tackle shops to fish nearly all waters in France. Some are private and an extra permit will be required. In 1995, after years of considerable pressure (started by the English), the French government made night fishing for carp legal,but left it up to the regional departments whether night fishing should be allowed on their waters. Permissions often change from year to year so enquire first before fishing. Many of the successful and well known English anglers who caught big fish at Lake Cassien 'made their names' with 50, 60 and 70 pounders
A licence (stamp) is now obligatory for all private lakes in France and costs approximately 50fr (about £6)
If you are travelling to France to find a water you have not visited before, we strongly advise you to purchase the Michelin Motoring Atlas of France Scale 1:200 000.
It's A3 size and has a yellow cover and is obtainable at most W H Smith branches and on the ferries. If you are looking for camping sites, purchase the Michelin Camping Caravanning France book which has a green cover

On many French waters, night fishing is either restricted to certain areas, or totally banned as this sign clearly displays!

GERMANY

German anglers have to take a long written examination to obtain a fishing licence, but this is waived for foreigners. A Government licence is normally obtained by all before fishing - this costs about £6 a year from Post offices. There is no night fishing by law although owners of private waters can allow it, and many fish are killed and eaten. German rules and laws in relation to angling are very strict, so make sure you known what they are and that you keep to them. However, one law that you might choose to break is that all fish caught must be killed - the Green Party has managed to get laws passed that fishing is a cruel sport and all fish should be killed and not tortured by returning them alive! Most German anglers, unless fishing for food, do not agree with this law and return the fish alive; the choice is yours!

HOLLAND

You must not fish anywhere in Holland unless you hold 'Sportvisakte', the national licence which enables you to fish the whole year with two rods. You can fish most Dutch waters with this alone. It can be purchased at all Post Offices and most tackle shops. It only costs about £6 per year. For private waters, you may need another permit, from the club which controls it, or the person who owns the water. If you see the sign 'Verpacht Viswater' the water is *private* and you must get another permit. There is no close season in Holland

Night fishing is normally allowed by law during June, July and August. On many waters you cannot night fish in the other months. Some clubs allow night fishing outside the months listed.

The small private lakes in Holland rarely contain the big fish, and as they are private you should not fish this type of water. Many of the big Dutch carp are caught in canals and rivers, and as these are also the most heavily stocked carp waters in Holland, it is these you should fish.

A good map will show large expanses of water to the north of Utrecht, Den Haag (The Hague), and Amsterdam

All are excellent areas for carp, but the majority of Dutch stock are of the same strain,stocked year after year. This carp strain has about 25 per cent of 'wild blood' in it, which leads to a slower growth rate. This was caused by a group of anglers about 10 to 15 years ago, who said big mirrors and commons were too easy to catch, and that all the lakes should be stocked with wildies!

Normally the season starts in May and ends in October, depending on the winter. The last mild winters have provided carp fishing all year round.

As a result, the OVB (the Dutch organisation responsible for the stocking of all the waters in the country) has stocked with carp of this kind for the last 15 years. Luckily, about a year ago this policy was reversed, and the OVB started stocking again with 'Redmire-type' mirrors.

In short, most Dutch carp are now commons, and the majority of waters do contain beautiful long fish which will easily reach the 20lb mark, but will not often exceed 25lbs

Catching a bigger fish is difficult, as most of these are quite old, and are normally found only in the bigger lakes, canals and rivers.

Our Dutch informant tells us that ALL waters in Holland contain carp!

SPAIN

Unfortunately the licensing situation in Spain is rather complex. National licences are no longer available and a different licence is required for each of the autonomous regions which also impose their own regulatons. ICONA is the body responsible for issuing the licences although in

Andalucia (comprising most of the south of Spain) this function is undertaken by IARA
Tourist licences are available in most areas and although prices vary from region to region one can expect to pay about 1500 pesetas (£8). At the time of applying for one's licence it is also worth asking for a copy of the Boletin Oficial de las normal para la pesca. It is worth struggling through this paper, which is only available in Spanish, as it details all the current regulations regarding angling in that particular area. Local tourist offices often have a leaflet available in English which will give an extract of the more important rules. General rules normally applied include: two rods per person; fishing is allowed from one hour before dawn to one hour after sunset (this means no night fishing), no camping is permitted on lake or river banks. The night fishing rule is relaxed in some areas but only for the pursuit of Wels catfish (Silurus glanis); this does not apply to carp anglers. In some areas fishing in rivers a close season from April 15th to May 15th is imposed. Generally, carp fishing is carried out in the reservoirs or embalses and we do not known of any area that imposes a close season for coarse fishing here. Controlled fisheries or Cotos do exist and for these it is normally necessary to purchase an additional permit in advance. Elsewhere fishing is generally free. On Cotos the fisheries are controlled by bailiffs or Guardas,elsewhere licences are checked by the Guardia Civil who are armed police and do not take "No" for an answer. Treat them with the utmost respect and do exactly as they say or you could be in big trouble.... They are likely to check you at any time of the day or night; you have been warned!
The address of the local licensing authority can be supplied by either the local Tourist Office or police station or can be found in the Yellow Pages (Paginas Amarillas). When applying for the licence you will need to present your passport and the licence will normally be ready for collection the following day, sometimes later the same day.

ITALY

Although Italy is mainly known as good cat fishing country there are a lot of chances for carp lovers too. Because of the mild weather you can fish almost all the year with better catches in springtime and autumn. From the Alps lakes in the North to the warm dam in Sardinia you can chose between hundreds of unfished waters and unpressured carp and grass carp. The majority of the anglers know very well some famous venues as Salto or Mantova but there are many other different rivers and lakes holding very big carp.
Apart from the northern waters you can fish almost every time and everywhere with good chances. Winter fishing is often very good with biggest fish of the year. Please avoid end of April, May and first part of June because you can find carp spawning. Carp season is closed from 15th May to the end of June but you can always fish for carp if you do not sack any fish
Night fishing is not allowed as a national rule but very often, local laws are permitting night fishing for those who release the fish or fish for Silurus. You will find quite often "Not allowed but lack of control".. it means that fishing is not allowed but for personal experience, there is 95% of no risk due to lack of controls. To increase your safety (by Rangers) please avoid any fire and lights everywhere. During summer months the National Fire Department is struggling every day against big fires so they are very alerted.
Your fishing licence and FIPSAS (where needed) licence can be requested by the following armed police:
- Police-Bailiffs-Carabinieri-Guardia di Finanza-Guardia Forestale-

Regional Rangers and Volunteer Bailiffs. They are often armed but just for safety reasons. They work in two's or three's even with a boat. If you have any French experience you already know that they can confiscate your gear or give you a penalty.

Remember that fishing is always one hour before the sunrise to 30 minutes after the sunset! Generally bivvies and umbrellas are tolerated while classic tents are not allowed.

Foreign anglers are always welcome but remember that Rangers do not speak any English and they do not have to do it!

You must have with you a National licence type B (for foreign) available on request through main shops such as La Mincio or Fish Eye Italia (see telephone number list). You need a photo and the fee is approx 75.000 lt. each year, FIPSAS permission is requested on the National Federation waters (normally trout and pike water) but very often for good carp lakes. It will cost you 40.000 lt. each year approximately. Where requested you could need a third permission in case of private or exclusive waters. Anglers are usually allowed to fish with 2 rods but sometimes 3 are tolerated (i.e. Mantova's lake, Salto)

Some useful telephone numbers:

Here you can ask for licence or other information
La Mincio - Via Marengo Goito (Mantova) 037/604856
Trovatutto: Via Romana Zuccona 46030 San Biagia Mantova Tel: 0376/415057

Fish Eye Italia Via Loreto 7Recanati (Macerata) Tel: 071/981206
Ameria DeMatteis: Piazza Pietro Thoar 30 Roma Tel: 06/3371398
Minuti Paola Via Tosco Romagnola 848 S.Bendetto a Settino Pisa Tel.050/740156

AUSTRIA

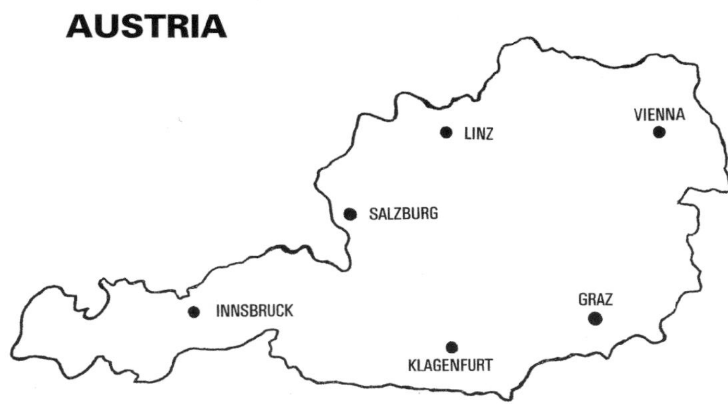

AA. Weissensee Lake

Location: Tachendorf at Villach - Spittal 100 route
Type and Size: 11 km lake with 99 m. maximum depth
Carp Stock: Well stocked with immaculate commons and mirrors. Several fish over 20 lbs, good chances of 30's. Big shoals of grass carp 20 - 35 lbs
Other Species: Monster pike, perch, trout and coarse fish
Permits: Local permission at the Tachendorf Tower
Restrictions: No night fishing No engine boat allowed(electrical only) to preserve this drinkable water. No free camping; no fires.
BK Rating: Easy to Moderate
Comments: Food and drink available at Tachendorf. A bridge divides the lake in two. The shallow part (2 - 5 m.) is full of weed but with more carp (smaller). Weed free areas (no fish finders allowed due to the clear water, polarized sunglasses are enough) location is very important for a light prebaiting (boilies and maize) and an accurate bait dropping. Many runs in daylight. The other side of the bridge is the open lake part with great depth. Rowing for 30 minutes allows you to reach the 'snag area' where you need heavier tackle, fish location and accurate bait dropping. Few chances to land a carp from the bank so you must row out and play the fish far from the sunken trees.

Gosselsdorfer See

Location: Off the A2 South Motorway at Karnten, near Klagenfurt
Type and Size: Old 80 acre lake, very weedy
Carp Stock: Very well stocked with carp to 40lbs
Category: Mixed Fishery
Other Species: Tench, grass carp and catfish
Permits: Wallerwirt, Seestrasse, Gosselsdorf. Tel: 04236 2168
Cost: 150 Austrian crowns per day; 350 per week
Control: Private
BK Rating: Very Difficult
Comments: Boat fishing essential; lake is full of lilies and is very difficult to fish. Night fishing is allowed. Austrian record carp of about 55lbs was caught from this lake

Irrsee

Location: Off the A1 motorway at Oberhofen, Oberösterreich
Type and Size: 147 acre lake
Carp Stock: Well stocked with carp to over 20lbs

Category: Mixed Fishery
Other Species: Pike and zander
Permits: J Hufnagl, Laiter 9, 4894 Oberhofen
Cost: 180 Austrian crowns per day; weekly permits also available
Restrictions: No night fishing, three rods allowed
Comments: Famous pike water; best pike caught is 57lbs. No livebaiting

Keutschacher See

Location: Karnten, Klagenfurt, off the A2 road
Type and Size: Lake of 110 acres
Carp Stock: Well stocked with carp to 35lbs
Category: Mixed Fishery
Other Species: Bream, tench, pike and catfish
Permits: Franzwagner, Plescherken
Restrictions: No livebaits; two rods allowed; night fishing is permitted
Comments: Very deep, warm water, with big, powerful fish

Millstatter See

Location: Off the A2 motorway at Karnten, near Klagenfurt
Type and Size: 180 acre lake
Carp Stock: Well stocked with carp to over 40lbs
Category: Mixed Fishery
Other Species: Most coarse fish
Permits: Verkenhrsburo Radentheim 9545, Haupstrasse 65. tel: 04246 2288 or Verkenhrsburo Dobriach 9873, Hauptpl 6. tel: 04246 7727
Cost: 250 Austrian crowns per week; bank fishing, nights allowed. Boat fishing also available, daytime only
Comments: Biggest known carp caught is over 50lbs

Ossiacher See

Location: Kärnten, Klagenfurt, off the A2 road
Type and Size: 370 acre lake
Carp Stock: Well stocked with carp to over 40lbs
Category: Mixed Fishery
Other Species: Most coarse fish and large catfish
Permits: Divided into sections, and permits; from Gerhard Kleindienst, Bodensdorf, Bundesstrasse 6. Tel: 09293 361
Cost: 60 to 100 Austrian crowns per day; also weekly permits
Restrictions: Night fishing is allowed; two rods; no livebaits
Comments: Well known as a big catfish water; carp fishing is more recent

Zeller See

Location: Off the A1 motorway near Salzburg
Type and Size: 120 acre lake
Carp Stock: Well stocked with carp to over 30lbs
Category: Mixed Fishery
Other Species: General coarse fish, with big pike
Permits: Stadtgem, Zell-am-See, Rathaus 2115 (We think this means the Town Hall!)
Control: Council
Cost: 100 Austrian crowns per day; guest permits for two weeks
Comments: Two rods are allowed. Most fishing is for pike, and this is regarded as one of the carp waters of the future in Austria. Best carp to date is about 40lbs

BELGIUM

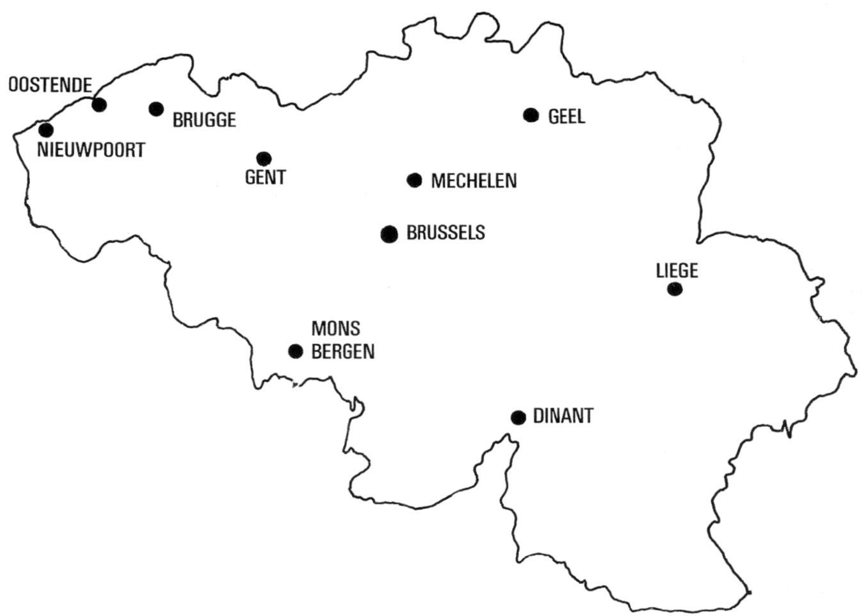

Albert Canal

Location: Flows westwards from Hasselt to Antwerp
Type & Size: A very large canal averaging 200 metres wide with a reasonable flow.
Carp Stock: Well stocked with carp throughout its whole length. Fish average 5-15kg with the occasional fish over 20kg.
Canal record is believed to be common of 24kg (53 pounds).
Permits: National Belgium licence available from all Post Offices.
Cost: Approximately 500BF (£10).
Restrictions: Officially no night fishing but few checks are carried out.
BK Rating: Moderate.
Comments: This huge canal carries a lot of barge traffic although the best fishing is often close in, away from the boats.
Always a good chance of a big fish.

Eghlegemvyver

Location: Hombeek, near Mechelen, a city about 40 miles north of Brussels
Type and Size: 92 acre rectangular sandpit
How to Find: Take the motorway from Ostend to Gent, then the road marked 'Brussels'. Near Brussels follow the ring road, and take the Mechelen exit. At Mechelen take the Hombeek exit
Carp Stock: Plenty of small carp, and a good number of 20's; best mirror taken was 31lbs and the best common 30lbs
Category: Mixed Fishery
Other Species: Pike to 41lbs, bream and big eels

Permits: On site
Cost: Day tickets £1.50 per rod; season - £18
Control: Private
Restrictions: You can only normally fish from March to the end of September, but the Chairman, Mr R Van Lint, may be able to give permission for fishing at other times. Night fishing only allowed at weekends in May and June
Comments: This big lake is not far from the pleasant city of Mechelen, and is not a long drive - nearly all motorway - from the port of Ostend

Herentals naar Bocholt Canal

Location: Flows eastwards from Bocholt, close to the Dutch border, to Herentals where it joins the Albert Canal.
Type & Size: Small canal averaging 40 metres wide and split into about 10 sections by sluices.
Carp Stock: Depends on section; upper sections lightily stocked, middle sections such as 7-8 relatively well stocked.
This canal, also known as the Kempish Canal, is home of the Belgium record mirror of 34 kilos (74 pounds) which lives in sections 6 - 7 or 7 - 8. Several sections hold carp to 20 kilos (44 pounds) with 6 - 7 and 7 8 holding the biggest.
Category: Carp Fishery.
Permits: National Belgium licence from post offices.
Cost: Approximately 500BF (£10).
Restrictions: Officially no night fishing. Maximum number of rods is two.
BK Rating: Difficult.
Comments: This canal is heavily used by barges. Middle sections warmed by power station outlet making it a reasonably good winter big fish water.

Kalkaert

Location: Between Middelkerke and Oostende
Type and Size: Chalk pit of about 20 acres
How to Find: Follow the coast road from Calais to Ostend
Carp Stock: Fairly heavily stocked with carp to 38lbs
Category: Mixed Fishery
Other Species: Big bream (to which our Belgian correspondent adds'..."and I know that carp anglers love them!")
BK Rating: Moderate
Control: Private
Permits: On site
Restrictions: Long stay fishing not allowed, though you may be able to make an arrangement with the bailiff, to stay longer; night fishng allowed (which is rare in Belgium)
Comments: Can be fished the whole year, but it is a busy camping site

Plassendaalse Vaart

Location: Near Nieuwpoort, in the Ostend area
Type and Size: Big canal, but the best carp area is near the sluices at Nieuwpoort
How to Find: Take the Nieuwpoort road, close to the coast from Calais or Ostend
Carp Stock: Well stocked with carp to all sizes; best caught so far was 47lbs(!)
Category: Mixed Fishery
Other Species: Roach, rudd, bream and eels
Permits: Government licence from any Post Office
Cost: £6 per season
Control: Government
BK Rating: Moderate

Restrictions: Night fishing during June, July and August only
Comments: Rod pods needed for the hard banks. Not a pleasant environment with many tourists. There are many similar canals in Belgium, of which this is a typical example; the canals go from the coast to Brussels, out towards the German border and back via Antwerp to Brugge (Bruges)

Restaurant de Goorhoeve

Location: One mile from Geel, which is 20 miles east of Antwerp
Type and Size: Four lakes
Carp Stock: Heavily stocked with carp to over 30lbs
Permits: Day and night tickets available on the bank - check price **before** paying!
BK Rating: Easy
Comments: The third lake is usually the best, with a good chance of catching many fish

Vossem

Location: Near Zaventem, the Brussels airport
Type and Size: Town park lake of about 45 acres
How to Find: From Brussels take the Zaventem road, and follow the signs to Vossem
Carp Stock: Many very small carp, with a few big ones to 30lbs
Category: Carp Water
Other Species: Some coarse fish
Permits: On site
Cost: £5 per day
Control: Private
BK Rating: Very Easy for the small fish, but Difficult for the big ones
Restrictions: No night fishing
Comments: Long range fishing not necessary - the closer you fish, the bigger fish you are likely to catch

Warm water outlets can make those long, mid-winter journeys worthwhile as KM displays with this 33 pound (15 kg) common from a Belgium canal.

Watersportbaan

Location: Gent, which is south east of Bruges towards Brussels, and is on the motorway
Type and Size: Not very large, long and narrow like a canal
Carp Stock: Heavily stocked with carp, including plenty of 20's
Category: Mixed Fishery
Other Species: Most coarse fish
Permits: Government licence at £6 from any Post Office
Control: Government
Restrictions: No night fishing
BK Rating: Fairly Hard

DENMARK

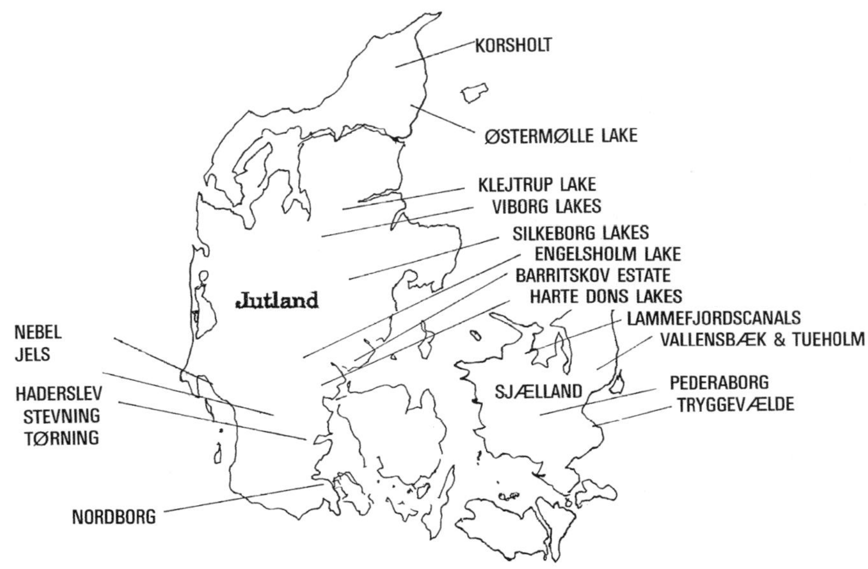

Barritskov Estate — A

Location: 25km east from Vejle (E45) in Jutland
Type and Size: Three very small shallow lakes. Approximately one acre each
How to Find: Take the road 23 from Vejle and look for the road signs after 25km
Carp Stock: Lots of small mirrors with some bigger to 25lbs. Average 4lbs
Other Species: In some other ponds there is a mixed carp/trout fishery
Permits: On the estate
Cost: 250 kr (£23 24 hours and 80 kr (£8) day in trout fishery
Control: Private, estate office. Tel: 75 69 11 77
Restrictions: None in carp lakes
Baits/Methods: Anything that lands in the water
BK Rating: Easy
Comments: Accommodation in small cabins around the lakes. Not a decent carp water. Mostly for inexperienced who don't mind easy fish in very small waters

Engelsholm Lake

Location: Near Nørup, 20 km west of Vejle in Jutland
Type and Size: 80 acres
How to Find: From Vejle (E45) drive west of the road 28, untl sign for Nørup
Carp Stock: Unknown, but old
Other Species: Pike to 35lbs, eels to 7lbs, trout
Permits: From the Q8 gas station in Norup
Cost: 50 kr (£5) per day
Control: Nørup-Randbol Angling Club
Restrictions: No fishing in bird sanctuary and in marked areas
Comments: A water unfished by carp anglers. The stream Vejle A starts here

Haderslev Lake

Location: At Haderslev in southern Jutland
Type and Size: Large 1100 acres mill lake. Many reed beds
How to Find: Located west of Haderslev City
Carp Stock: Unknown but old
Other Species: Pike,eels, bream, roach and perch
Permits: From Sportsmagasinet, Apotekergade 5 in Haderslev. Tel: 74 52 19 55
Cost: 25 kr (£2) per day and 100 kr (£10) per month
Control: Haderslev and Omegn Angling Club
Restrictions: Only bank fishing from public owned bank in eastern part. The areas are pointed out when obtaining the permit
Comments: The local carp fishing takes place in Stevning and Torning lakes as they are considered the only ones worth trying

Harte -Dons Lakes, Nørre Lake

Location: Near Kolding in Jutland
Type and Size: 90 acres. Very green water (algae)
How to Find: Use junction 63 on the E45/E20 and drive for Dons. Lake on your left
Carp Stock: Mirrors up to 25lbs but not many
Other Species: Pike, roach, tench, eel, perch and bream
Permits: From Steens Jagt and Fiskeri in Kolding,Helligkorsgade 1,6000 Kolding. Tel: 75 52 85 88. Permit covers three connected lakes
Cost: 30 kr (£3) per day, 150 kr (£14) per week, 300 kr (£28) per year
Control: Kolding Angling Club
Restrictions: Only bank fishing. No fishing for eels
Comments: Some carp fishing has been done here by locals for a number of years

Jels Lakes, Midt-Lake and Neder Lake

Location: Near Jels in southern Jutland
Type and Size: Midt-Lake 60 acres and Neder-Lake is 120 acres. Both are up to 30 feet deep but average is 15 feet. There is also a third small lake, that is closed for fishing
How to Find: The lakes are situated just outside the town of Jels
Carp Stock: Mirrors to 30lbs, but otherwise unknown
Other Species: Pike, perch, zander, trout, roach and bream
Permits: From Hotel Jels, Torvet 1, Jels, and from the tourist bureau (Tel: 74 55 21 10) and from the inn "Voldstedet" on the lake bank. From the last place, good advice from the landlord is given
Cost: 40 kr (£4) per day, 125 kr (£12) per week and 250 kr (£24) per year
Control: No returning of roach and bream. If disposal of fish is a problem contact the inn "Voldstedet" who will contact the controllers. The ban is due to a lake rescue programme that removes nuisance fish to restore a healthy balance in the lakes. Programmes like this are normal in Denmark and successful. Carp are not killed in these programmes
Comments: Not much carp fishing is being done here, but the rumours about them have travelled widely. Possibly a number of German anglers have discovered the lake

Klejtrup Lake

Location: North/east of Viborg and west of Hobro
Type and Size: Shallow 300 acre lake. Depth 10 feet
How to Find: 30 km from Viborg and 15 m from Hobro (E45). Drive to the town Klejtrup at the lake. Use road 579 from Hobro and go west until diverson to Klejtrup
Carp Stock: Unknown but old

Other Species: Pike, eel, perch and roach
Permits: Klejtrup kiosk, Viborgvej 3 in Klejtrup
Cost: 25kr (£2) per day and 100kr (£10) per year
Control: Klejtrup Fishing Association
Restrictions: Only bank fishing
Comments: This water has received no carp fishing pressure

Korsholt Put and Take

Location: Near Sindal, near Hjørring in north Jutland
Type and Size: A number of small lakes. Maximum three acres
How to Find: Take the E39 to Hjørring, then road 35 to Sindal. Drive through and turn left for Mosbjerg. The fishery is located at Mosbjergvej 135, on your left
Carp Stock: Good head of commons to 25lbs. Most smaller fish. The bigger ones live in a separate lake that special permission is needed for
Other Species: Pike and trout
Permits: On the estate
Cost: 125 kr (£12) per day per rod
Control: Private. Hans Olesen. Tel: 97 93 01 90
Restrictions: Not known, but some due to the trout fishing
Baits/Methods: All
Comments: Some very nice commons have been caught (eg see picture in ABU's Tight Lines from 1990)

Lammefjords Canal

Location: In the north western part of Sjoelland, near Holbæk
Type and Size: Two canals. North canal approx 13 miles long and 7-10 yards wide.South canal approx 9 miles long and 10-15 yards wide. Depth from two to five feet. The canal surrounds a very large area of dried out seabed. They end in the sea, protected by sluices
How to Find: Use road 21 from Holbæk and drive north. The road passes the dam on the seaside
Carp Stock: North Canal: Many wildies from 1 - 6 lbs, some fish up to 20lbs. South Canal: Not so many fish but larger, from 2 - 12lbs, some fish up to 25lbs
Other Species: Eels, rudd to 3lbs, roach to 2lbs and ide
Permits: From the grocery at Audebo (by the south canal on the main road) and from the tackle shop 'Lystfiskeren' in Holbæk
Cost: 25 kr (£2) per 24 hours and 200 kr (£19) per year
Control: Odsherreds Angling Club. Inge Christens. Tel: 53 45 91 87, Nattergalevej 1,4571 Grevinge
Restrictions: Maximum two rods. No bivvy on the dam. Only fishing from the dam bank. No digging in dam! No open fires. The rules are necessary to protect the grass and in turn the dam
Baits/Methods: All methods work well, Float fishing often the best. Sometimes lots of weed and weed cutting. Flow changes all day
BK Rating: Easy
Comments: The canals are visited by many anglers, but because of their size fishing pressure is very low, and in some areas nobody comes. Catches of 10 to 30 carp a day is normal. Fish tend to form small shoals

Nebel Lake **A**

Location: Near Vester Nebel, near Esbjerg in southern - Jutland
Type and Size: One larger and three smaller connected dug-out waters. In all 10 acres. Clear water. Mainly a trout fishery
How to Find: Take the E66 from Esbjerg and after approx 8 km, turn left for Vester Nebel. Drive to the town and ask your way the last 1 km
Carp Stock: Some fish up to 30lbs, both mirrors and commons. The number of

	fish is probably very low, perhaps only 20
Other Species:	Trout
Permits:	On site
Cost:	Approx 100 kr (£10) per day per rod
Control:	Private. Aksel Jensen, Vestervadvej 17, 6715 Esbjerg N. Tel: 75 16 94 95
Restrictions:	Carp must be returned. No night fishing. No pre-baiting
Baits/Methods:	Boilies work well
BK Rating:	Difficult
Comments:	The water has its number of regulars who catch well. As the fishing is very expensive very few fish only for carp. There is accommodation in cabins at the lakeside

Nordborg Lake

Location:	Near Nordborg on the island Als east of southern Jutland
Type and Size:	Long and narrow lake of 150 acres. Deep water close to the bank
How to Find:	Drive to Sønderborg and proceed to Nordborg. There are signs all over. Lake is situated on the north side of the town
Carp Stock:	Unknown, but an old stock has been supplemented recently
Other Species:	Pike, roach and bream
Permits:	From Nordals tourist office (in Nordborg). Tel: 74 45 05 92
Cost:	30 kr (£3) per day and 100 kr (£10) per week
Control:	Nordborg Angling Club
Comments:	The water is well known among match fishers but the carp fishing is very limited

Ostermølle Lake

Location:	Just outside Dronninglund town in north Jutland, approx 30 km north/east of Ålborg
Type and Size:	Five acre man-made lake with three islands. Depth from 2 to 6 feet
How to Find:	Lake situated just west of town. Small road leads by
Carp Stock:	Mostly commons to 20lbs but some mirrors to 22lbs. Many fish around 10lbs
Other Species:	Grass carp to 10lbs, crucian carp and eels
Permits:	From the tourist office in town and from Metax-Benzin, Slotsgate 55, Dronninglund
Cost:	20 kr (£2) per day and 100 kr (£10) year
Control:	Klokkerholm Angling Club
Restrictions:	Grass carp must be returned. Out of bounds area marked on ticket
Baits/Methods:	All methods. Boilies work well
BK Rating:	Easy
Comments:	A fairly new water, that has already seen some action, also from locals who eat the carp and see nothing good in returnng them. This part of the country is in many ways rather marginal! Birds love boilies. Carp anglers from all over Denmark visit the lake and the carp are beginning to be wary

Pedersborg Lake

Location:	Sorø in the south/west part of Sjoelland
Type and Size:	Long lake of 40 acres with depths up to 20 feet
How to Find:	Take the E20 road to Soro. The lake is situated in the north/west part of the town. There are two other and much larger lakes around the city
Carp Stock:	Unknown, but some mirrors to 14lbs and a few to 24lbs
Other Species:	Pike, zander, perch, eel, roach and bream
Permits:	From Boldhuset, Boldhusgade 1 (Tel: 53 63 24 94) in Sorø and from Krebsehuset, Ringstedvej 87 (on the E20) and from the local camping site
Cost:	25 kr (£2) per day

Control: Sorø Angling Club
Baits/Methods: All methods
Comments: These waters are still lightly fished. Carp have been present in the last 300 years together with catfish, but not much is known about the stocks

Silkeborg Lakes

(Silkeborg Langsø, Brassø, Juul sø)

Location: Around Silkeborg, 40 km from Århus (E45) in Jutland. The lakes are just a small part of a very big lake district all situated around Silkeborg. Maps on site will help you
Type and Size: Its hard to be precise, but the lakes cover thousands of acres of water and some lakes are deep (100 feet). Don't let the size of these lakes put you off
How to Find: See location
Carp Stock: Unknown but old. Mirrors to 22lbs have been caught recently. Not many fish
Other Species: Pike, perch, zander, trout, turbot, roach, bream, eel
Permits: From Silkeborg tourist office, Torvet 9, Silkeborg (Tel: 86 82 19 11)
Cost: 35 kr (£3) per day and 95 kr (£9) per week
Control: Silkeborg Angling Club
Restrictions: Only fishing from public banks
Baits/Methods: Boilies work well
BK Rating: Difficult
Comments: The lake district around Silkeborg is every year visited by a very large number of British anglers; not carp anglers though. The waters are therefore well investigated by British anglers

Tørning and Stevning Lakes

Location: West of Haderslev in southern Jutland
Type and Size: Mill ponds. Shallow and green. 80 acres in all
How to Find: From E45 take the junction 68 and drive west for Hammelev. Turn left and down in the valley
Carp Stock: Fish to 30lbs. Mirrors. Not many but high average weight
Other Species: Pike, eel, roach, bream
Permits: From the Torning water mill and from Harry Simonen (Torningvej 3, Vojens) who lives at the lake
Cost: Low
Control: Haderslev and Omegn Angling Club
Restrictions: No fishing in the woods
Baits/Methods: Boilies work well
BK Rating: Moderate
Comments: The waters have some fishing pressure, but are still not over-run by carp anglers

Tryggevaelde Stream

Location: South of the city Køge on Sjoelland at Strøby Egede
Type and Size: Stream, slow current. 15 yards wide. Average depth six feet. Very rich water
How to Find: Use the E20 or E47/E55 to get to Koge. From there use road 209/261 to get to Strøby Egede, where the stream meets the sea. On this relatively wide beat nearly all fishing is done
Carp Stock: Unknown, but few fish to at least 18lbs. The stream receives water from carp farms, and therefore also carp fry
Other Species: Perch to 4lbs, pike to 30lbs, sea trout to 20lbs, bream to 8lbs, roach to 3lbs and ide to 7lbs. Best time is from September till November and from February till May

Permits: From grocery in Stroby Egede (100 metres from water)
Cost: 35 kr (£3) per day
Control: Køge Angling Club
Restrictions: None in carp fishing
Baits/Methods: All
BK Rating: Difficult
Comments: Carp fishing is very hard and the fish landed are very few

Johan Edvardsson with a beautiful mirror of 30 1/2 pounds (14 kg).

Vallensbaek and Tueholm Lakes

Location: West of Copenhagen near Albertslund (Near Tåstrup)
Type and Size: Two shallow man-made lakes, fed by rainwater. Weed is scarce. Water is colour green. Max depth 7 feet,average 4 feet. Vallensbaek lake is 27 acres and Tueholm lake is 30 acres
How to Find: The E4 motorway cuts the joined lakes in two. Use the 'Albertslund' junction and drive west. On the north side of the motorway there is an entrance to the car park. The lakes are the largest in the area, so they should be easy to locate
Carp Stock: The carp were stocked several times starting in the early seventies. Nearly all fish are mirrors but some commons are present. Best fish around 30lbs. The stock consists of a older part with an average of 20lbs and a young part with an average of 10lbs
Other Species: Grass carp to 18lbs. Pike to 20lbs. Roach, bream, eel, perch, and crucian carp to 5lbs
Permits: From Shell Service, Albertslundvej 21 and Vestegnens Jagt & Fiskeri in Albertslund city, and from the cafeteria at the lakeside. No permits on bank!
Cost: 10 kr (£1) per day per rod
Control: VSS Fishing Clubs. Contract: Jørgen Krog. Tel: 43 62 37 25
Restrictions: Maximum 3 rods per angler. All kinds of carp must be returned. No use of bread. No fishing in certain areas (see map on ticket). No

CARP VIDEOS

CARP RIGS - Underwater- Kevin Maddocks	£13.99
WITHY POOL : Carp Water Supreme - Kevin Maddocks	£13.99
PRACTICAL CARPING 1: Julian Cundiff	£13.99
PRACTICAL CARPING 2: Julian Cundiff	£13.99
PRACTICAL CARPING 3: Julian Cundiff	£13.99
PRACTICAL CARPING 4: Julian Cundiff	£13.99
BIG CARP CHALLENGE 1: Mid Northants - Alan Taylor	£13.99
BIG CARP CHALLENGE 2: Horton - Alan Taylor	£13.99
FRENCH CARPING : An Introduction - Alan Taylor	£13.99
FRENCH CARPING 1: River Seine - Marc Ponsot & Friends	£13.99
FRENCH CARPING 2: Ton-Up, Lac Du Der - A. Taylor & Friends	£13.99
FRENCH CARPING 3: Chantecoq Facts - A. Taylor & Kevin Maddocks	£13.99
FRENCH CARPING 4: Big Carp, Orient - Kevin Maddocks	£13.99
FRENCH CARPING 5: Successful Failure - P. Regent & K. Bishop	£13.99
CARP FEVER 1: The Carp Revolution - Kevin Maddocks	£12.99
CARP FEVER 2: Rigs & Baits - Kevin Maddocks	£12.99
CARP FEVER 3: Baits & Rigs - Kevin Maddocks	£12.99
CARP FEVER 4: Off The Top & Down Below - Kevin Maddocks	£14.99
COLD - WATER CARPING: Kevin Maddocks	£13.99
ITALY : Basic Carping - Kevin Maddocks	£13.99
ITALY : Advanced Carping - Kevin Maddocks	£13.99
LONG RANGE CARPING: Phil Hyde & Clive Gibbins	£13.99
CARP TEACH - IN : Andy Little & Friends	£13.99
CARP FISHING: (Cuttle Mill) - Des Taylor	£13.99
STALKING CARP : (On Floaters) - Des Taylor	£13.99
EURO CARP QUEST 1: Fishabil - Kevin Maddocks	£12.99
EURO CARP QUEST 2: Brive - Kevin Maddocks	£12.99

BEST SELLERS

EXPEDITION BELUGA : (Sturgeon To 273lbs) - Kevin Maddocks	£13.99
CATFISH TOUR OF EUROPE : (Double Pack 2 x 60mins) - Kevin Maddocks	£19.99
BIG CATS OF THE VOLGA : Kevin Maddocks	£12.99
TENCH FISHING : David Maddocks	£13.99

All these videos can be purchased or ordered via your local tackle shop if you find this not possible, you can obtain them direct from Beekay - simply add £1 per item for P+P

Withy Pool, Henlow Camp,
Beds, SG16 6EA.
Tel: 01462 816960
Fax: 01462 817253

open fires and no fishing from boats

Baits/Methods: All methods works well

BK Rating: Moderate

Comments: This water is birthplace of many Danish carp anglers, and is therefore most heavily fished. The fish however are not as shy as one could fear. Beware that other kinds of anglers also fish here and that the large number of anglers attract thieves! As the noise from the motorway can be high, don't expect silence. Best places to fish are the areas where the fish can find some meat. Lot of boilie eating birds! You must often walk a long distance as no cars are allowed, so bring a trolley

Viborg Lakes (Nørre and Sønder Lake)

Location: In Viborg town in Jutland

Type and Size: Nørre lake is 280 acres and Sønder lake is 300 acres. Deep lakes with green water (algae) and large areas of lilies

How to Find: Easy location in town

Carp Stock: Old stock with a small number of fish to 40lbs. Average 15lbs. Both mirrors and commons

Other Species: Roach, bream, eels, pike

Permits: None necessary. Free fishing

Cost: None

Control: Viborg Tourist Office/the public

Restrictions: Only fishng from public banks. No camping, but night fishing is allowed

Baits/Methods: Boilies and particles work well

BK Rating: Difficult

Comments: A water with a long history of carp fishing. Most fishing takes place in Sønder lake (the southern one) in the areas with lilies. Many English and German carp anglers visit the water

FRANCE

AUTHON — A

Location: Authon, Normandy, about 50km south west of Chartres (exact location given at time of booking).

Type & Size: Two estate lakes totalling about 4 hectares (11 acres).

Carp Stock: Very heavily stocked with carp to over 20kg: average 10kg.

Other Species: Catfish to 50kg.

Permits: Booking essential, contact Chateau Du Lorey, 50570 Le Lorey, France. Tel: 0033-233456851. Fax: 0033-233453797 (English spoken).

Cost: One week self-catering approx £210 per person (inc. fishing, accommodation and ferry).

Restrictions: Only open 6 months of the year and the number of anglers is limited. Maximum of 3 rods, barbless hooks.

BK Rating: Very easy.

Comments: A fabulous carp water ideal for families or the non-stop angler (night fishing permitted). Colour brochure available.

Bazouges Sous Hédé

Location: Bazouges, Hédé, about 25 miles south of St Malo, near Combourg
Type and Size: Lake of about 40 acres
Carp Stock: Well stocked with carp with many upper twenty pound commons; best reported is 36lbs
Category: Mixed Fishery
Other Species: Usual coarse fish
Permits: We are told that this lake is 'on the Brittany licence' but you will have to enquire locally, as Brittany is not a French 'departément', and we cannot find out which 'county' this lake is in
BK Rating: Moderate
Comments: The fish are localised and you may not catch unless you locate them. The dam and south west bank by the lilies are the best ones. Open all year. May, June, September, and October are the best months. Fish not hard to catch once located, as the water is not heavily carp fished

Bieville

Location: Near Caen on the north coast (exact location given at time of booking).
Type & Size: Four sand pits: 40,28,17 and 10 acres.
Carp Stock: Heavily stocked with 10kg carp with a good number of fish 15-20kg.
Permits: Prior bookings essential, contact Chateau Du Lorey, 50570 Le Lorey, France. Tel: 0033.23345 6851. Fax: 0033. 233453797. (English spoken).
Cost: From £195 per peron, including ferry.
Restrictions: Maximum of 3 rods, no boats, barbless hooks. Closed in winter.
BK Rating: Very easy.
Comments: A well-run fishery with shower and toilet facilities, as well as a club house with fridge and cooker etc.

Beaumont-de-Lomagne A

Location: Beaumont-de-Lomagne, 40km north west of Toulouse, south west France.
How to Find: Leave the Bordeaux to Toulouse A62/E72 autoroute at Castelsarrasin exit and head south on the D45 then D14 to its junction with the D928. Turn right onto the D928 heading west and the lake is on the left hand side of the road as you enter Beaumont.
Type & Size: Man-made lake of approximately 28 hectares (70 acres).
Carp Stock: Heavily stocked with carp of all sizes up to 30kg.
Permits: French national licence plus 150fr per day or 900fr week.
BK Rating: Moderate.
Comments: Although this lake has the potential of producing excellent catches of big fish, it has a major disadvantage: when the lake becomes busy, the fish become less active. Night fishing permitted May to October. Boats not allowed. Good camp site, chalets available see advert.

Bort-les-Orques

Location: About 40 miles south west of Clermont Ferrand
Type and Size: Several rivers dammed forming a lake of approximately 1000 acres
How to Find: Take the E70 out of Clermont heading south west for about 20 miles, then turn left onto the 922 road and the lake can be seen at Bort
Carp Stock: Reasonable head of carp to at least 60lbs
Permits: Normal French national licence required
BK Rating: Moderate
Comments: This water holds huge carp. A lot of potential for the pioneering type of carp angler. Night fishing allowed. Water drops 30-40 feet by late autumn!

Kevin Maddocks with a Beaumont fish of 42 - 12 (19.4 kg) which fell to KM Strawberry Oil Palatant boilies.

Boulancourt — A

Location: In the Champagne area of France, east of Paris near Troyes (exact location given at time of booking).

Type & Size: Part of a fish-farm complex, classed as a Nature Reserve, of 110 hectares (270 acres).

Carp Stock: Probably the highest density of big carp anywhere in France; many tons of 20's, 30's and 40's up to nearly 60 pounds.

Other Species: Large grass carp, some catfish.

Permits: Booking essential, contract Chateau Du Lorey, 50570 Le Lorey, France. Tel: 0033-233456851. Fax: 0033-233453797. (English spoken).

Cost: £240 per person (fishing, ferry and self-catering facilities). Brochure offers several options.

Restrictions: Fishery only open 30 weeks of the year and the number of anglers is limited. Maximum of 3 rods, barbless hooks.

BK Rating: Very easy, best catch - one angler: 164 carp!

Comments: A fabulous carp water ideal for families or the non-stop angler (night fishing permitted). Colour brochure available.

Chalet Lake **A**

(Carp Fishers Abroad's Chalet Lake}

Location: 20 miles south of St. Avold Nr. Metz.
Type & Size: Very attractive 'Estate' lake of 20 acres with a Chalet standing on stilts in the water to one side.
Carp Stock: Heavily stocked with common and mirror carp to high forties. Average size: high twenties.
Category: Specialist managed fishery.
Other species: Big stocks of grass carp to mid thirties, koi to mid twenties and lots of Wels catfish to high sixties.
Permits: The fishery is run by Carp Fishers Abroad and is exclusively let by the week to parties of six or less in advance. For brochure and details, call either David Rance on 01952 585002 or Max Bond on 01473 327085.
BK rating: Moderate.
Comments: Chalet Lake is run by Carp Fishers Abroad. They have the complete package wiith a beautiful, secluded and private lake, expertly managed with big stocks of common, mirror, grass and koi carp in addition to monster catfish. The water has consistently produced spectacular catches of big fish for small parties of anglers who have a weeks holiday and no time for exploring unknown waters. No problems with night fishing, bivvies, bait etc. etc. One phone call will bring all you need to get your picture in the papers. A very high percentage of people who fish this water return the following year with the result that it gets booked up well in advance, so do book early.

Châteaux du Lorey **A**

Location: Normandy, in northern France
Type and Stock: Four small lakes on private estate
Carp Stock: Well stocked with carp to over 40lbs; record is 42lbs
Permits: Tel: 010 33 33 45 68 51 (France; English spoken)
Cost: About £35 per person per day, to include accommodation
Restrictions: Little fished; limited to six anglers
BK Rating: Moderate
Comments: Ideal for a famly holiday. Accommodation in house - all rooms with private bathroom and food included. Tranquil surroundings, and not far from the ferry ports

Chateaux Meillant Lake

(Carp Fishers Abroad's Chateaux Meillant Lake)

Location: 140 miles south of Paris, 20 miles from Bourges.
Type & Size: Beautiful 25 acre secluded estate lake set in a deciduous forest.
Carp Stock: Heavily stocked with common, mirror and grass carp to high thirties.
Category: Specialist managed fishery.
Other Species: Wels catfish.
Permits: This fishery is run by Carp Fishers Abroad. The fishing is let by the week to small parties and individuals strictly in advance. For Brochure and details, call either David Rance on 01952 585002 or Max Bond on 01473 327085.
BK Rating: Easy.
Comments: This is the latest water opened up and managed by Carp Fishers Abroad for English fisherman. If you are looking for a weeks holiday carp fishing with a few friends, on a beautiful, secluded lake, with no other fisherman and lots of action, then this is the one, Carp Fishers Abroad set out to provide reliable and consistent big carp fishing for anglers who want to be sure of being on the fish - people who haven't got the time to explore huge waters or wait all week for just one fish.

Etang de Biscarrosse et Parentis

Location: Biscarosse, close to the west coast about 40 miles south west of Bordeaux. Shown on all road maps
Type and Size: Dammed river forming a huge reservoir of several thousand acres. Sandy bottomed lake used for drinking water
Carp Stock: Quite well stocked with carp to 50lbs, plenty of 20's
Permits: French National licence from local tackle shops
BK Rating: Moderate
Comments: This water is partly on an air force base, and is regularly patrolled at night by military police

Etang de Boulet

Location: Feins, about 20 miles north of Rennes in northern France
Type and Size: Dammed river forming a very large, wedge-shaped lake
How to Find: The lake is on the D20, just off the N175 between Rennes and Mont St. Michel
Carp Stock: Lightly stocked with carp averaging over 20lbs; English anglers have had carp to at least 47lbs
Permits: Available from the cafe at Feins - French national licence
BK Rating: Difficult
Comments: A huge boom prevents windsurfers from entering the lake margins, but also causes problems where it is anchored to the bottom. Deeper areas produce the better fish. Hard boilies recommended because of crayfish. There was a fish kill in 1990, but it is still worth fishing

Alan Taylor with a French 44 pounder (20 kg) caught on KM Peach Oil Palatant.

Etang de cloyes sur Loire

Location: About 8 miles south from Chateaudun and 40 miles from Chartres
Type and Size: Old gravel pit of 60 acres near the river Loire
How to Find: Take the D955 from Alencon to Chateaudun
Carp Stock: Well stocked with commons and mirrors and a lake record of 51lbs (common carp)
Other Species: Coarse fish with very big zander over 25lbs
Permits: National French licence plus a day-ticket available on the site
BK Rating: Easy to Moderate
Comments: A lovely lake with a lot of nice commons. Carp fishing is allowed until 11pm

Etang d'Ecluzelles

Location: About 4 miles south of Dreux and 55 miles west of Paris
Type and Size: Dammed stream forming a lake of about 325 acres with varying depths
How to Find: Take the N12 from Alencon to Dreux
Carp Stock: Lightly stocked with some big carp to over 45lbs
Other Species: Coarse fish with big pike and big zander
Permits: French national licence required plus a day ticket from fishing tackle shops in Dreux
BK Rating: Moderate to Fairly Hard
Comments: A beautiful lake with big fish and not far away from Paris. Night fishing is not allowed

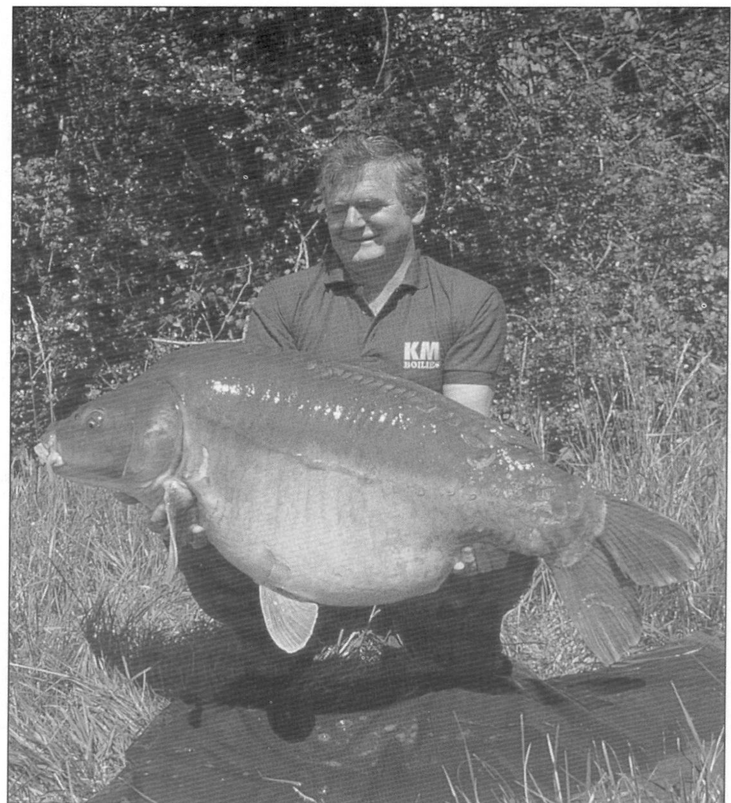

It's carp like this fabulous 55 pounder (25 kg), which fell to Kevin's Peach Oil boilies, that makes those French trips so worthwhile.

Etang d'Entressen

Location: Istres, north west of Marseilles (Bouche du Rhone)
Type and Size: Two lakes of 30 acres and 70 acres, both over 30 feet deep
Carp Stock: Well stocked with carp
Category: Mixed Fishery
Other Species: Tench, zander, gudgeon, roach, rudd, pike, perch and eels
Permits: AAP d'Entressen. Try locally or the Fed Departmentele des AA, 30 Boulevard de la Republique 13100, Aix-en-Provence
Comment: Easy access and little weed. Also very good for pike, perch and zander

Etang de Huelgoat

Location: Huelgoat to the east of Brest and south of Morlaix (Finistere)
Type and Size: 40 acre lake
Carp Stock: Very well stocked with carp
Category: Mixed Fishery
Other Species: Pike, perch, trout, eels and roach
Permits: Day tickets on site
Control: Societé Hydroelectrique des Monts d'Arree. Try Fed Depdes AAP, 1 rue de Poher, 29000 Quimper

Etang de Kerlouan

Location: To the north of Brest (Finistere)
Type and Size: Shallow lake of 30 acres
Carp Stock: Heavily stocked with carp
Category: Mixed Fishery
Other Species: Roach, tench, bream, eels, pike, dace
Permits: AAPP de Brest-lesneven; try the Fed Dep des APP, 1 Rue de Poher, 2900 Quimper
Comments: Rowing boats allowed

Etang de Miallet

Location: Miallet, on the River Cole, east of Nontron (Dordogne)
Type and Size: Long, narrow lake, about 35 acres in size
Carp Stock: Very well stocked with carp
Category: Mixed Fishery
Other Species: Tench, chub, bream, eels, roach, pike and zander
Permits: Day and weekly tickets locally
Control: The local angling associaton is at: Residence St-Front, Rue de Lys, BP33, 24002 Périgueux. Tel: 00 53 53 44 21
Comments: Wooded banks, but easy access; motor and rowing boats

Etang de la Gr de Cazine

Location: On the east side of la Souterraine between Châteauroux and Limoges
Type and Size: A dammed river forming a lake of about 100 acres
Carp Stock: Well stocked with doubles and 20's with a spinkling of 30's and the odd 40
Permits: Normal French national licence required, available from tackle shops in La Souterraine
BK Rating: Easy
Comments: This lake has ben carp fished for some time now by French anglers so advanced rigs and baits are most successful

Etang de la Vallée

Location: About 22 miles east of Orléans in the forest of Orléans
Type and Size: Beautiful lake of about 170 acres with a maximum depth of 16 feet
How to Find: At Orléans take the N152 along the river Loire until Châteauneuf sur Loire, then take the D10 until Combreux and turn left, you will see the lake in about a mile
Carp Stock: Lightly stocked with a good head of magnificent heavily scaled mirrors. An old record for the lake is 46lbs
Other Species: Bream, tench, pike and big zander over 22lbs, small catfish
Permits: French national licence obtainable in the local fishing tackle shops
BK Rating: Moderate to Difficult
Comments: Very hard boilies needed to beat the small catfish (Bullheads of America). The forest of Orléans is very beautiful. You can also fish the canal of Orléans with a number of carp to 20lbs and the nearby river Loire which is heavily stocked with commons and mirrors to 30lbs

Etang de Pirot

Location: In the Forest of Troncais, west of Moulins (Allier)
Type and Size: Very deep lake of about 200 acres, with the River Marmande flowing through it
Carp Stock: Very well stocked with carp
Category: Mixed Fishery
Other Species: Tench, roach, perch, pike and zander
Permits: Day, week and annual permits from local shops, cafes and tackle shops

TACKLE
TREV'S
WILMSLOW

THE MAIL ORDER SPECIALISTS

• BEST PRICES • BEST SERVICE • BEST TACKLE • BEST TRY US!

REELS • REELS • REELS • REELS • REELS

TOURNAMENT S5000T

FEATURES: TWIST BUSTER ROLLER, 7 BEARINGS, ALLOY SPOOL, POWER HANDLE WITH WOODEN GRIP. 450 YDS 12LBS LINE

THIS REEL OFFERS THE SERIOUS ANGLER ALL THE QUALITIES AND RELIABILITY NEEDED

THE ULTIMATE DISTANCE REEL. RRP£299 **OUR'S £225** DEALS ON 2 OR MORE....**SPARE SPOOLS £47.00**

EMBLEM S5000T & 5500T

FEATURES: TWIST BUSTER ROLLER, GYRO SPIN BALANCE, SMOOTH FRONT DRAG. 400 YDS 15LBS LINE

THIS REEL OFFERS THE SERIOUS ANGLER ALL THE QUALITIES AND RELIABILITY NEEDED

THE 5000T RRP£155 **OUR'S £110**
THE 5500T RRP£165 **OUR'S £117.99**
SPARE SPOOLS £22.50

SHIMANO AERLEX GT 8000

FEATURES: SIC ROLLER, AERO LINE LAY, POWER HANDLE WITH BIO GRIP. 350 YDS 17LBS LINE

RRP£99.99
OUR'S ONLY £84.99 EACH
SPARE SPOOLS £24.99

SHIMANO BIOMASTER GT 8000

FEATURES: SIC ROLLER, 3 BEARINGS, POWER HANDLE WITH WOOD GRIP, AERO LINE LAY. 350 YDS 17LBS LINE

RRP£129.99
OUR PRICE £110.00 EACH
SPARE SPOOLS £24.99

SHIMANO 6500 BAITRUNNER

FEATURES: ALLOY SPOOL, 3 BEARINGS AND BIO GRIP.
CAPACITY: 350 YDS 15LBS LINE

THE BIG BAIT RUNNER FOR THE BIG BAIT CASTER

RRP £139.99

NEW - SHAKESPEARE SIGMA SUPER

THIS REEL MAKES A PERFECT COMPANION TO OUR BAIT ROCKET ROD.
LINE CAPACITY: OVER 250 YDS 15LBS LINE
FEATURES: ALLOY SPOOL, 3 BEARINGS AND FRONT DRAG.

NORMALLY SELLS AT £42.99
OUR PRICE £34.99

SHIMANO BAITRUNNER REELS GT 8010 AND 6010

FEATURES: THE NEW METAL LIPPED SPOOL, EXTRA SPARE SPOOL, 4 BEARINGS AND BALANCE HANDLE.

THESE ARE PROBABLY THE TWO MOST POPULAR CARP FISHING REELS.

8010 GT RRP £114.99
6010 GT RRP £114.99

NEW ALL METAL CONVERSION

FITS SS9000, SS3000, EMBLEM'S AND P.M'S

MANUFACTURED FROM TOP QUALITY STAINLESS AND ALUMINIUM PARTS TO AVOID RUST AND CORROSION

£34.99 EACH
P&P F.O.C

ONLY £64-TWO OR ONLY £90-THREE

BAITING UP?

BOILLIE AND PARTICLE ROCKETS £5.99 & £7.99

SPECIAL OFFER: 1 FREE ROCKET WITH EVERY BAIT ROCKET ROD SOLD

BULK BOILIES

15mm & 20mm
NOW AVAILABLE
•Strawberry •Scopex
•Fish •Tutti Fruitti
•White Chocolate
5 Kilo bags........£25
10 Kilo bag...£39.99
50 + Kg......phone for price

These baits are of the highest quality and are normally sold with a different label at twice the price.

BULK LINE

GR60 – CLEAR/GREEN **£17.95** *(8/10/12 &15LBS)*

BERKELEY BIG GAME – CLEAR/GREEN/BROWN
ONLY £9.99 *(10/12 &15LBS)*

DAIWA SENSOR BLACK MONO –
ALL ONLY £5.99 *(6/8/10/12/15/18 & 20LBS)*

NEW PRO GOLD – the ultimate abrasion resistant line
6LBS **£14.95** – *8LBS* **£15.95** – *10LBS* **£16.95** – *12LBS* **£17.95** – *15LBS* **£18.95**

REELS • REELS • REELS • REELS • REELS

RODS • RODS • RODS• RODS

100% FUJI GUIDES

Custom built rods

100% FUJI GUIDES

CUSTOM BUILT DIAWA AMORPHOUS

THIS IS PROBABLY THE MOST POPULAR SERIOUS CARP ROD EVER MADE

12FT – 2.75 LBS TEST CURVE

Soft enough in the tip to play fish yet the butt section reveals incredible strength for achieving great distances. Custom built using only genuine Fuji components and assembled by master rod builders.

• 40mm ringing pattern (6 inc. tip) • 20mm NPS reel seat • Slim abbreviated handle

With Oxide rings **£149.99** with SIC rings **£174.99**

Don't be fooled by what others say. This blank has not been discontinued and will still be available for years to come.

HARRISON BALISTAS

100% FUJI GUIDES

MODEL	SPECIAL PRICE
12' 6" 3.5LBS	£125.00
12' 3LBS	£120.00
12' 2.75LBS	£120.00
12' 2.5LBS	£120.00
12' 2.25LBS	£120.00
12' 2 LBS	£110.00
12' 1.75LBS	£110.00

PRICES HELD FOR 1997
PLEASE PHONE FOR PRICE ON 2 OR MORE RODS
14 DAY MONEY BACK GUARANTEE IF NOT SATISFIED WITH QUALITY OF FINISH

NORTH WESTERN

100% FUJI GUIDES

MODEL	SPECIAL PRICE
12' 2.25LBS	£99.99
13' 2.5LBS	£99.99
12' 2.75LBS	£99.99

Custom built ***by us*** *to ensure that the looks are superb and the performance is excellent!*

ARMALITE MK2

100% FUJI GUIDES

TOP QUALITY ARMALITE BLANKS FROM CENTURY COUPLED WITH OUR HIGHEST QUALITY BUILD'S GIVE YOU THE MOST VERSATILE ROD MADE WITH PRICE'S YOU CAN AFFORD. WE WILL EVEN BEAT THESE PRICES FOR 2 OR MORE.

13' 3.5LBS	£164.99	12' 2.5LBS	£146.99
13' 3LBS	£159.99	12' 2.25LBS	£142.99
12' 3.5LBS	£156.99	12' 2LBS	£139.99
12' 3LBS	£153.99	12' 1.75LBS	£137.99
12' 2.75LBS	£149.99		

ARMALITE FAST TAPER RODS

13' 3.5LBS	£159.99
13' 3LBS	£157.99
12' 6" 3.25LBS	£155.99
12' 3LBS	£153.99
12' 2.75LBS	£149.99

NEW FROM CENTURY AK47 GEARBOX RODS

12' 6" 2.5LBS AND 3.5LBS
£175 EACH
These new rods cleverly use a geared butt section to enable two different tips to work well with it.

These rods were designed last year to give distance fishing new meaning. The success of the armalite range gave century the knowledge to produce a rod of untold reliability coupled with their experience of distance rod design they have produced the ultimate long range rod. Sensitive enough to be a pleasure to play fish on yet with enough power in the butt to impress the most experienced of caster's.

TREV'S ROCKET ROD SIMPLY THE BEST!

As reviewed by Julian Cundiff

100% FUJI GUIDES

This is a specifically designed rod for use with boily rockets. Not the usual beachcaster style, but a purpose built tool. 100% genuine fuji parts and British blank. Capable of putting rockets well over 100 yrds in a tight pattern.

• BEST PRICES • BEST SERVICE • BEST TACKLE • BEST TRY US!

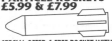

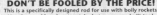

Control: AAAP 'La Fraternelle' de Cerilly
Comments: Privately owned. Easy access by car, and camping on the bank. Pleasant surroundings

Etang de Soustons

Location: About 100 miles south of Bordeaux
Type and Size: 1000 acres of natural lake near the Atlantic in the south west of France
How to Find: From Bordeaux take the N10 to Magescq, then take the D116 to Soustons
Carp Stock: Lightly stocked with carp to 50lbs
Category: Mixed Fishery
Other Species: Coarse fish with very big zander
Permits: French national licence taken in fishing tackle shop in the area
BK Rating: Fairly Hard
Comments: In a very touristic area; July and August are not the best for big carp fishing

Etang de Vert le Petit

Location: About 35 miles south of Paris and 10 miles from Corbeil-Essonnes
How to Find: Take the A6 from Paris to Corbeil-Essonnes, then the N191 to La Ferte-Alais
Carp Stock: Heavily stocked. An estimation of about 10 forties, 80 thirties and 200 twenties is not exaggerated. The lake records for 1991 are a leather of 44lbs, a mirror of 42lbs and a common of 40lbs
Other Species: Coarse fish with zander over 25lbs
Permits: National French licence and a day ticket available on site (19 francs in 1992)
BK Rating: Easy to Moderate (more and more difficult since 1990)
Comments: There are three lakes at Vert le Petit with big carp over 40lbs in all three. There are also beautiful carp in the River Essonne; a magnificent koi of 27lbs was caught in this river in 1991

Etang des Landes

Location: Central France, near Gouzon, 30km south west of Montlucon.
How to Find: From Paris/Orléans directions take the A71/E11 autoroute towards Clermont Ferrand. Turn off at Montlucon and head south west on the N145/E62 to Gouzon, then left on the D915. Etang des Landes is situated on the right hand side of the road, about 8km from Gouzon, access from Lussat.
Type & Size: A shallow lowland lake, fed by two or three small rivers, of about 40 hectares (100 acres).
Carp Stock: Heavily stocked with carp of 10-20kg and a few bigger fish to over 25kg.
Permits: This 'new' water is run by John Stent in England and was drained in the autumn of '96 to verify stock. Further details available from John Stent on 01895 477607.
BK Rating: Easy.

Etangs des Papillons A

Location: Mialett, Dordogne.
Type & Size: 3 lakes, 4 acres (Rouge): 3 acres (Bleu): 1.5 acres (Vert).
Carp Stock: All lakes heavily stocked to upper 30's. Rouge and Bleu stocked with large catfish.
Other Species: Pike, perch, roach, bream and black bass.
Permits: Exclusive Angling Holidays, 22 Willen Rd. Newport Pagnell, Bucks, MK16 ODF. Tel/Fax 01908 616886.
Restrictions: No particle baits.

BK Rating: Moderate.
Comments: Boilies and floaters good baits. Live bait, dead bait, liver for catfish. Caters for families or parties of 3/4/5 anglers. Each has a lake to themselves. Min. booking one week. Rouge and Bleu lakes very good for catfish; none are smaller than 26 lbs, the average weight is 38 lbs-at least 6 are over 50 lbs, with two over 60 lbs. Open March to 31st October. English carp fishing owner.

Etang du Puits

Location: About 14 miles south of Gien (45 miles from Orléans)
Type and Size: Beautiful lake of about 400 acres
How to Find: At Gien, take the D940 to Argent sur Sauldre, then right turn right and take the D948, about 4 miles after you will see the lake
Carp Stock: Lightly stocked with many thirties and a lake record of 41lbs, but bigger carp are living in this lake
Other Species: Bream, roach, tench and big pike
Permits: Available from tackle shop at Argent sur Sauldre, French national licence required
BK Rating: Moderate to Easy
Comments: A very beautiful lake in the forest with a maximum depth of about 30 feet. Possibility to fish in the nearby canal of Sauldre with carp to 25lbs

Etang du Touroulet A

Location: Touroulet, near Chalais, north east of Nontron (Dordogne)
Type and Size: Small lake of about 10 acres, up to 15 feet deep
Carp Stock: Heavily stocked with carp
Category: Mixed Fishery
Other Species: Roach, bream, tench, chub, perch and pike
Permits: Day and weekly tickets on site
Control: Private. Tel: 0033 5 53 62 07 90
Restrictions: Three rods only; bank fishing only; open from April to October
Comments: Camp site and restaurant. Accommodation - English owners

Etang le Puyrigaud

Location: Chalais, near Thiviers, 47km south of Limoges off the RN21.
Type & Size: Attractive 3 acre lake in private grounds.
Carp Stock: Well stocked with doubles and twenties.
Category: Mixed Fishery.
Other Species: Tench, zander, bream, roach, perch and gudgeon.
Permits: Doris or Graham Norman, Camping Le Touroulet 24800 Chanlais, Thiviers. Tel: 0033 553620790.
BK Rating: Moderate.
Comments: Fully furnished bungalow overlooking lake to rent with exlusive fishing. Secluded spot. English owners also own cafe next to Etang du Touroulet. Campsite and swimming beach. 5 minutes from Etang le Puyrigaud.

Etang Neuf

Location: Neuilly sur Eure, 45km west of Chartres.
Type & Size: Private lake of 10 hectares (25 acres).
Carp Stock: Approximately 700 carp, of which more than half are over 10kg and up to 20kg.
Other Species: Grass carp to over 10kg, some sturgeon and catfish.
Permits: Obligatory national stamp required (approx 50fr per year) in addition

	to owner's fees. Contact Didier Mosur on 0033-233739610.
Cost:	130fr for first night, then 80fr thereafter. Non-angling guests 20fr per 24 hours.
Restrictions:	Maximum of 4 rods. No pike fishing.
BK Rating:	Easy.
Comments:	A well-run water with good facilities including toilets and showers.

Etang St-Andre-des-Eaux

Location:	North west of St Nazaire (Loire-Atlantique)
Type and Size:	15 acre lake up to 40 feet deep, and weedy
Carp Stock:	Very good carp water, heavily stocked
Category:	Mixed Fishery
Other Species:	Roach, tench, pike, eels, bream and zander
Permits:	AAPP de St Nazaire; try Fed Dep des APP, 2 boulevard des Anglais, 44100 Nantes

Etang Tremelin

Location:	Near Rennes,in Brittany
Type and Size:	Lake of over 100 acres
How to Find:	At Montfort, west of Rennes, take the D30 to Iffendic, then the D61 south towards Phelan. The lake is 1 1/2 miles from Iffendic
Carp Stock:	Lightly stocked wtih carp to over 50lbs, average 20lbs
Permits:	On site
BK Rating:	Moderate
Comments:	A holiday-type complex, and quite busy at times. Other water sports take place, but there is a fishing only area

Fishabil A

Location:	Loscouet-sur-Meu, Brittany
Type and Size:	Originally a dammed stream built by monks, but in 1990 the lake was increasd in size to about 80 acres and the stream diverted. Most of the water is shallow, only 3 - 6 feet deep
How to Find:	Close to Rennes - as you approach Lascouet-sur-Meu the Fishabil centre is clearly signposted

KM with a typical low twenty from the prolific Fishabil complex.

Carp Stock: Originally there were only a few carp present to about 30lbs but in 1990 more than 35 tons of fish was stocked and most of these were carp. The majority are 15 - 25lbs with the occasional 30 and 40. One or two of over 50lbs have also been put in!
Permits: Available from the office on site. This is a private water so the normal French national licence is not required. Cost is about £30 for 24 hours for 4 rods - a bit expensive but this water is only an hour's drive from the ferry at St Malo. Petrol costs are low, and there are no toll roads on this route
Category: Mixed Fishery
Other Species: Catfish from Russia to over 100lbs have been stocked, with a number of 50 - 80 pounders; pike,zander,tench and black bass
BK Rating: Easy
Comments: Late in 1989 Fishabil S A purchased the property with the intention of creating a first class fishery, with no expense spared. Bore holes were drilled to obtain high quality water. The lake is managed by carp angler Raphael Farragi, who speaks good English and is extremely helpful to visitors. High quality accommodation is available by the lakeside, there is a tennis court, an anglers' cinema, horse riding and a coffee shop (no cooked meals). In 1991 Fishabil was the scene for the hightly acclaimed 'Euro Carp Quest' video, featuring Kevin Maddocks, and Bob Baldock. In three days more than 900lbs of carp including many 20's were caught and anyone contemplating a visit would find the video extremely helpful To book a room in advance write: Fishabil, Le Lac, 22230 Loscouet - sur - Meu, Brittany, France tel: 00 33 96252766

Grand Etang de Jugon

Location: North France, 20km from coast.
How to Find: From port of St. Malo take N137 to the N176/E401, then west to Jugon.
Type & Size: Dammed lake of approximately 81 hectares (200 acres).
Carp Stock: Lightly stocked with carp to 25 kilos.
Permits: National French licence.
BK Rating: Moderate.
Comments: This lake suffered a fish kill a few years ago but has recovered well.

La Ballastière de Laveyssière

Location: 15 miles south from Paris along the river Seine
Type and Stock: Old gravel pit of 70 acres with a maximum depth of 21 feet
How to Find: From Paris take the N7 to Dravel
Carp Stock: Well stocked with very big fish. A 56lb mirror was caught in 1991
Other Species: Coarse fish with big pike and big zander to 30lbs. Small catfish
Permits: Available from tackle shop in Draveil and Viry Chatillon. French national licence required
BK Rating: Moderate
Comments: Very hard boilies are needed to beat the small catfish. Along the River Seine the big carp come in to spawn. Possibility to fish the nearby River Seine where there are some very big carp. A carp of 33lbs is not a big fish for this area

La Poiteviniere

Location: Near Nantes in the Loire valley (exact location given at time of booking).
Type & Size: Chateau lake of 80 hectares (190 acres).
Carp Stock: Heavily stocked with carp of 10-20kg.
Permits: Prior booking essential, contact Chateau Du Lorey, 50570 Le Lorey, France. Tel: 0033.23345 6851. Fax: 0033.233454797. (English spoken).
Cost: Approximately £210 per person, including ferry, fishing and facilities.

Tangle free, easy action run control lever
5 Ball bearings in 5500/5600 models
Front main drag + polished metal spool rim
CAMCAD
DESIGNED TO PERFORM
At last, a breakthrough in RUN-CONTROL reels – CAMCAD. DESIGNED from basics to PERFORM perfectly every time.
From the tangle-free, easy-action run control lever to the front mounted multi-disc main drag, CAMCAD has been designed at all stages by anglers, for anglers.
Additional features include:
■ BALANCED FLYER AND HANDLE
■ OVERSIZED LINE-FRIENDLY ROLLER
■ RUN CONTROL MICRO DRAG
■ DOUBLE OSCILLATING GEAR SYSTEM FOR EASY CAST CROSS-WIND LINE LAY
■ POLISHED SPOOL RIM ON 5 BALL BEARING MODELS
■ ALL MODELS SUPPLIED WITH THREE SPOOLS
With a choice of 4 models and prices starting from £74.99 (model 3500) – Spoil yourself and check out the new CAMCAD at your local BROWNING stockist.
BROWNING
The Best There Is!
"The new BROWNING CAMCAD – the reel carp anglers have been waiting for, I'll have three!"
Tim Hodges
CATCHMORE CARP
Two SPARE spools with every reel

Restrictions: Maximum of 3 rods, no boats or barbless hooks.
BK Rating: Very Easy.
Comments: A well-run fishery with facilities.

Lac Amance

Location: Part of the famous Foret D'Orient group of lakes, 20km east of Troyes.
How to Find: From Calais, take the A26 to Reims and then towards Troyes. At Arcis (30km before Troyes) head east on the A441 towards Lesmont, then onto the D960 to Piney. Lake is signposted from Piney and is about 15km from the town.
Type & Size: Man made lake of about 600 hectares (1500 acres).
Carp Stock: Well stocked with fish of 15 kilos with a lake record of approximately 30 kilos.
Permits: Special local permit covers the three lakes of Orient, Temple and Amance. Yearly and vacation (one month) permits available from local bars and tackle shops.
BK Rating: Moderate.
Comments: Can get very weedy at times. Certain areas designated for night fishing. Closed during the winter months.

Lac au Duc

Location: Ploermel, south of Brittany, 40km from the famous Fishabil fishery.
How to Find: From St. Meen (Fishabil), take the D766/166 south to Ploermel; lake is about 2km north of town.
Type & Size: Lake of about 120 hectares (300 acres).
Carp Stock: Recent catches of carp to 23 kilos indicate good potential for this newly discovered venue.
Permits: National French licence.
BK Rating: Moderate.

Lac d'Aydat

Location: On the south west outskirts of Clermont Ferrand
Type and Size: A dammed river forming a lake of about 200 acres
How to Find: A little south of the N89/E70 road, about 30 minutes drive from Clermont
Carp Stock: Well stocked with all sizes of carp up to 55lbs
Permits: Day and week tickets available at shop on waterside
BK Rating: Easy
Comments: An ideal place to take the family. Pedaloes for hire and plenty of nearby campsites. Quite a popular water

Lac de Baron

Location: North east France, close to Belgium border.
How to Find: As for Lac des Vielles-Forges but stay on N43/A44 until Sedan, then take D977 south to le Chesne. Lake is two or three kilometres north of le Chesne.
Type: Large dammed lake.
Carp Stock: Well stocked with carp to at least 20 kilos.
BK Rating: Moderate.

Lac de Carces

Location: About 27 miles west from the Lake Cassien in the south of France
Type and Size: A lake of 235 acres formed by the damming of the River Caramy
Carp Stock: Lightly stocked with a good head of big fish. A 66lb carp was caught in 1983!
Other Species: Coarse fish with big zander to 25lbs

Permits: Available from tackle shop in Carces
BK Rating: Moderate
Comments: The warm climate of the south of France ensures a fast growth rate in this area. It was rumoured that this lake was drained in 1996, so it is advisable to confirm that the original stock of fish was returned

Lac de Castillon

Location: Near Castellane, 60km north west of Cannes, south east France. Not far from Lac de St.Cassien.
How to Find: From Cannes on the south coast head north to Grasse, then follow the N85 to Castellane. Turn right at Castellane onto the D955 and at 4km the lake can be seen on the left.
Type & Size: Dammed river forming a lake of approximately 600 hectares (1500 acres).
Carp Stock: Lightly stocked with good fish to a definite 30kg, maybe bigger.
Permits: National French licence.
BK Rating: Difficult.
Comments: A lovely water with lots of potential for the pioneering big fish angler.

Lac de Chambon

Location: Near Murol
Type and Size: Dammed secton of the River Creuse, several hundred acres
Carp Stock: Lightly stocked, fish to over 50lbs have been caught
Permits: French national licence,available from tackle shops
BK Rating: Difficult
Comments: The best areas are supposed to be where the river opens out into the lake. The depth fluctuates and some banks are steep

Lac de Chaumont

Location: East of the E17 road, just south of St Dizier, between Chalons and Chaumont
Type and Size: Natural looking lake of over 100 acres
Carp Stock: A good head of doubles and twenties, and there are certain to be fish of over 45lbs, though little is known of bigger fish
Permits: Available from the tackle shop in Chaumont; normal French national licence is needed
BK Rating: Moderate
Comments: As with all large waters, fish location is important, as they do tend to shoal. Multiple baits work well. Other water sports take place on this big lake

Lac de Gueriedan

Location: Brittany, west France.
How to Find: From the port of St. Malo take N137 south then N176/E401 west to Dinai, then south on the D766 and D166 to St. Meen. Head west on the N164 to Mur-de Bretagre; lake is about 3km west of town.
Type & Size: Dammed river approximately 40 hectares (100 acres).
Carp Stock: Recent catches of carp to 21 kilos indicate good potential for this 'new' water.
Permits: National French licence.
BK Rating: Moderate.

Lac de la Chaume

Location: About 30 miles south of Argenton-sur-Creuse
Type and Size: Lake of about 150 acres
How to Find: Follow the N20 south of Argenton, then take the D70 eastwards to Jeux. Half a mile from Jeux turn right down a track which leads to the lake
Carp Stock: Fairly heavly stocked with small fish but a good sprinkling of 30-40 pounders
Other Species: Coarse fish and some catfish
Permits: Available from the Mairie (Town Hall) at Azerables - about £15 for 24 hours with three rods
BK Rating: Easy to Moderate
Comments: Night fishing is permitted. Closed between November and March. Used for other water sports, but these are not a serious problem

Lac de la Foret d'Orient

Location: East of Troyes, to the south east of Paris (Aube)
Type and Size: Lake of over 5,000 acres which feeds a canal during the summer months
Carp Stock: Lightly stocked with carp of a very high average size; lots of 40's, many 50's, a few 60's and at least three fish (one a common) over 70 pounds
Category: Mixed Fishery
Other Species: Pike, tench, bream, perch, bleak, trout, chub, eels, roach
Permits: Special licence required, available from local bars and tackle shops
Restrictions: Boats allowed, but not with motors. Open from the first Saturday in April to the end of October
Comments: An excellent lake. There is no fishing allowed on over 50% of the lake and night fishing is restricted to three or four small areas

Kevin Maddocks with a 46 -10 (21.2kg) from Foret d'Orient.

Lac de la Liez

Location: At Langres, about 150 miles south west of Paris.
How to Find: From Reims take the E17 autoroute to its junction with the A31/E21 at Beauchemin, near Langres. Head east on the A31 for one junction, then go south on N19 to Langres. Lake is clearly signposted.
Type & Size: Dammed river forming a lovely lake of about 110 hectares (270 acres). Large areas of shallows but much of the lake is 5-15 metres deep.

Carp Stock: Well stocked with carp, many of which are 10-20kg. Lake record is approximately 30kg.

Permits: Special permit available from the bar near the dam or from local tackle shops.

BK Rating: Moderate.

Restrictions: In past years this lake has been closed for about 6 weeks around the May/June time so it is advisable to first check if you intend visiting the lake at this time. Night fishing is not allowed on the whole lake - only part of it.

Comments: This is a very attractive and pleasant water. Water sports are popular and a local angling club fishes the water. Guard de Peche checks are frequent.

Carp 'R' Us innovator, Ray Dale-Smith, proving that his products work well, with a fine winter common of 43 1/2 pounds (19.8 kg).

Lac de Lavuad-Gelade

Location: Four miles from Royere, south west of Aubusson (Creuse)

Type and Size: Big lake of over 600 acres

Carp Stock: Heavily stocked with carp

Category: Mixed Fishery

Other Species: Tench, perch and a few trout and pike

Permits: Enquire locally; the address for the local angling federation is: Maison de la Peche, 60 Av Louis-Laroche, BP 182, 23012 Gueret Cedex. Tackle shop: Sainte-Cricq, 65 Grande Rue, Aubusson

Restrictions: Rowing boats allowed.Maggot fishing permitted

Lac de Madine

Location: 40km southwest of Metz near Vigneulles.

How to Find: From Reims head south on the A4/E50 autoroute towards Metz. Leave the autoroute at the first junction after Verdun and take the D908 to Vigneulles and then onto Lac Madine.

Type & Size: Reservoir of about 1000 hectares (2500 acres).

Carp Stock: Heavily stocked with carp of 5-10kg with a sprinkling of 30's and 40's. According to rumours, two carp over 28kg were caught in 1990 but this has yet to be proven.

Permits: Available from the sports lodge at the north west corner of the lake and from local tackle shops.
BK Rating: Easy.
Restrictions: Large areas of no fishing and night fishing only permitted in two small areas.
Comments: Although regularly stocked with small carp this lake does have the potential of producing a huge carp. Some areas very snaggy (tree stumps).

Lac de Monampteuil

Location: To the south of Laon, in north France near the Belgian border (Aisne)
Type and Size: Artificial lake of 150 acres which feeds two canals
How to Find: Eight miles south of Laon
Carp Stock: Lightly stocked with carp up to mid 40's
Category: Mixed Fishery
Other Species: Pike, zander, perch, eels and other coarse fish
Permits: Association de Pêche et de Pisciculture, Laon, 4 Rue d'Ardon 02000 Laon. Tel: (23) 20 23 23 and from Oasis cafe adjacent to lake
Comments: Heavily stocked public water with very good fishing. Fishing from boats is allowed

Lac de Pres de St Jean (Lake Zup)

Location: In the centre of Chalon-sur-Saone
Type and Size: Town park lake of about 60 acres with depths to 40 feet
Carp Stock: Well stocked with carp to 40lbs, with 30's not uncommon. Stock also includes 'Mamur Carp' to about 100lbs, average weight about 10lbs. Lots of big grass carp
Permits: From Jackie Greset's tackle shop in the town. Night fishing permitted
BK Rating: Moderate
Comments: No boats present; has an overrated reputation, but it does give you somewhere to night fish legally when you are in the area

Lac de Salagou

Location: West of Montpellier, in the south of France
Type and Size: A dammed river forming an irregular-shaped lake about 4 miles in length
How to Find: Turn off the A9/E15 motorway at the southern, last, Montpellier exit. Follows the signs for Millau/Modeve on the 109 road. Just past the junction with the E9 (5 miles before Le Lodeve) you will see the sign posts to the lake
Carp Stock: Heavily stocked with thousands of commons and mirrors. The average size is 40's and a chance of a fifty
Other Species: Large trout, bream, pike and zander
Permits: French national licence from the tackle shop just over the first bridge as you enter Lodeve
BK Rating: Easy to Moderate
Comments: Location is very important in this huge water. Mussels are a problem, and some areas are very snaggy. Other places have shelving bottoms which are 'stepped' and these have proved difficult to fish. Hard boilies are recommended, popped up. A boat is very useful - take your own if possible, as they are very expensive to hire, and are not designed for carp anglers! Most of the lake is accessible from tracks. The ground is very rocky, making bivvy erection difficult. Because of the many snags, a good supply of terminal tackle is essential. Several videos featuring this lake are available

Lac des Closiers

Location: Dept of Loiret; north of Montargis, to the east of Orléans
Type and Size; Thirty acre lake
Carp Stock: Well stocked with carp to over 20lbs
Category: Mixed Fishery
Other Species: Roach, perch, bream, tench
Permits: This private lake is open to holders of a departmental permit; try the Federation departmentale des AAPP, 144 Rue des Anguignis, 45100 Orléans. Tel: 56 62 69
BK Rating: Moderate
Comments: There may be night fishing as this is not a public water

Lac des Vielles-Forges

Location: North east France, close to Belgium boarder.
How to Find: From Calais, take the A26 autoroute to Cambrai, then onto the N43 to Lonny and then north on the D40 for about 10km where the road passes over the lake.
Type & Size: Dammed lake of approximately 100 hectares (250 acres).
Carp Stock: Well stocked with carp to at least 20 kilos.
Permits: National French Licence.
BK Rating: Moderate.

Lac de St Cassien

Location: About 10 miles west of Cannes and the Mediterranean coast
Type and Size: Dammed streams forming a lake of about 1,500 acres, which is made up of three sections, south, north and west arms. Depths to 60 feet in the west and south arms, and more than 100 feet in the north arm
How to Find: The lake is close to the north side of the E80/A8 motorway and is shown on all road maps

Lake Cassien is one of the few French carp waters that is worth fishing in mid-winter, as Alan Taylor proves with this January common of 45 3/4 pounds (20.8 kg).

Carp Stock: Lake Cassien probably holds more big carp than any other lake in the world. Thirty pounders are 'small' by Cassien standards, with 40's, 50's and 60's being the target. Several carp over 70lbs have been caught. It was first stocked in 1964, and fish of a good size are put in every year

ARMALITE®
SPECIAL PERFORMANCE
the dream distance rod . . . for those with attitude!
The history and reputation of Armalite carp rods has been built on outstanding performance, unparalleled feel and distinctive appearance. In fact the pedigree of the Armalite is unquestionable.
Now for '97 is the latest generation — the 'Dream Distance Rod' Armalite SPs (Special Performance).
The result of an uncompromising attitude towards distance casting, reliability and close control, the Armalite SP has already smashed the 3½oz World casting record!
So now you can have the casting performance you need, combined with the fish playing reputation of an Armalite — without dreaming!
his is Peter Thain, a member of the Century Tournament Team, who at the Sports Cast International Championships, broke the 3½oz World fixed spool record with a cast of 245 yards using a standard Armalite SP 3½lb t/c rod!
ARMALITE SP
CARBON ARAMID Century
Century
It Makes the difference!

Category: Carp Water
Other Species: A few catfish and one, estimated to weigh about 150lbs, was caught by English angler Johnny Allen; also tench, pike and black bass. 1,000 small catfish were stocked in 1995
Permits: From Chez Pierre's restaurant on the banks of the southern arm, or from tackle shops in Cannes. Normal French licence required
BK Rating: Difficult
Comments: As far as Englinsh anglers are concerned, this mecca of carp waters was 'discovered' by Kevin Maddocks and Paul Regent in September 1984. Shortly after the lake was 'discovered' hundreds of English anglers visited the lake, and some historic catches were made.
The English were followed by the Dutch and then the Germans. In recent years the fishing has become much harder and now the water receives less pressure. The next few years will see only the more serious and dedicated carp anglers visiting the water, and more big catches will be made - but the best time has gone! For full details on Cassien, including an aerial photograph of the lake, see the book 'Carp Fever' by Kevin Maddocks. Night fishing is allowed on the whole of the lake

Lac de St Croix

Location: About 80 miles north of the Mediterranean coast,and north west of Cannes
Type and Size: A huge lake of more than 5,000 acres, formed by the damming of the river Vedon, depths up to 150 feet
Carp Stock: Lightly stocked with some large fish, which have been caught to over 55lbs
Permits: French national licence from tackle shops
BK Rating: Difficult
Comments: Very busy with holidaymakers. Lots of snags, but lots of potential also

Lac de St Pardoux

Location: About 15 miles north of Limoges
Type and Size: A dammed river forming a lake of about 600 acres
How to Find: Close to the west side of the N20 main road which runs from Limoges to Châteauroux
Carp Stock: Well stocked with carp at least 40lbs
Permits: Normal French national licence required
BK Rating: Moderate
Comments: This water has great potential as it has been fished hardly at all by English anglers

Lac de Vouglans

Location: Close to the Swiss border, north west of Lyon
Type and Size: The dammed River Ain, about 20 miles long with depths to 350 feet
How to Find: Take the N78 from Chalon-sur-Saone to Lons Le Saunier, and after 15 miles you will see the north end of the lake
Carp Stock: Well stocked with carp in the 10-30lbs range, lake record 55lbs
Permits: French national licence from tackle shops
BK Rating: Difficult
Comments: Lots of snags and very steep banks in places. It is advisable not to fish until carp are located, and although it is difficult you could get a very big fish

Lac du Causse

Location: South west France, near Brive, about 100km south of Limoges.

How to Find: From Paris take the autoroute south to Orleans, then the A71/E9 to Vierzon then turn off onto the A20/E9 through Chateauroux and Limoges to Brive-la-Gaillarde. Head west on the N89/E70 to Larche and turn left onto the D19; Lac du Causse is about 5km from Larche.

Type & Size: A beautiful dammed river, set in the rolling hills of the north Dordogne region, of about 120 hectares (300 acres).

Permits: National French license.

BK Rating: Easy.

Comments: Until emptied in 1995, this lake was well stocked with big fish from 15-25kg. Most of the fish were moved to another lake but a few, including one or two big ones, were returned. The lake was restocked with a good head of small carp and it will be some time before it returns to its former glory. This lake is featured in the video, Euro Carp Quest 2, presented by Kevin Maddocks.

A Lac Causse fish of 37 lbs (16.8 kg) for Whacker Catcher Alan Taylor.

Lac du Der-Chantecoq

Location: On the south west outskirts of St Dizier, about 120 miles east of Paris

Type and Size: A huge reservoir of 12,000 acres

How to Find: Take the D384 south west from St Dizier and the lake is situated on the right about 8 miles out

Carp Stock: Well stocked with carp to over 60lbs. Plenty of 30's and 40's. Special licence required. Available from local tackle shops and bars

Restrictions: Night fishing restricted to small areas of the lake

BK Rating: Moderate

Comments: For many years this place has produced some incredible carp catches and it still quite easy today. Fluctuates in size by more than 1000 acres throughout the year - full in the spring, low in the autumn. For further information on this water see the video 'French Carping 2 Ton-Up at Lac du Der' featuring Alan Taylor when more than 60 thirties were caught

JRC LUGGAGE, SLEEPING BAGS AND ACCESSORIES

ROD HOLDALLS AND QUIVER SLINGS

DELUXE HOLDALLS. Top of the range 3 rod holdalls that feature full length internal padding and fully padded extra large reel pouches. Extra large external pocket large enough to contain a one-man Titan bivvy and smaller pocket for banksticks or a pod. Fully padded adjustable shoulder strap and carry handle. Spline contains removable aluminium pole for easy bivvy storage.

Deluxe 3 Rod Holdall12' £99.99
Deluxe 3 Rod Holdall 13' £109.99
Deluxe 4 Rod Holdall 12' £119.99
Deluxe 4 Rod Holdall 13' £124.99
Deluxe 2 Rod Holdall 12' / 13' £89.99

STANDARD HOLDALLS. Most other companies would name this range deluxe as they feature a full length internal padded panel to protect rod rings. Other features include extra large reel pouches (big enough to accommodate long range reels), external brolly and bankstick pockets, and fully padded shoulder strap and carry handle.

2-Rod Std. 12' £64.99
2-Rod Std. 13' £69.99
3-Rod Std. 12' £74.99
3-Rod Std. 13' £79.99

DELUXE QUIVER SLING. Big enough to take a one-man Titan bivvy and 3 made-up rods. Rods are kept separate with individual butt pockets at the bottom and studded padded strap at the top. External pockets for landing net and banksticks and adjustable reel strap make this one of the best designed slings around .... RRP £44.99 *Our Price* **£39.95**

PADDED ROD SLEEVES .... 12' **£19.99** 13' **£21.99**
Eco Quiver £29.99
Combi Quiver with 2 sleeves 12' £79.99
Combi Quiver with 2 sleeves 13' £79.99

COCOON SLEEPING BAGS

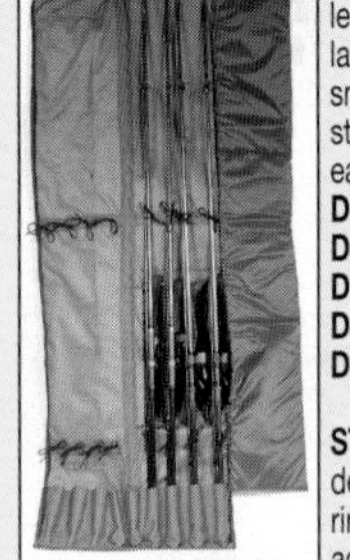

All JRC sleeping bags are straight sided (not mummy shaped) and have zips on both sides. They are all 6'3" long and 2'7" wide with the exception of the Super Cocoon 4 Season which is 6'9" long and 2'9" wide. All bags are supplied with compression sack.

Cocoon 3 Season (6'3"x2'7") £69.99
Cocoon 4 Season (6'3"x2'7") £99.99
Cocoon 5 Season (6'3"x2'7") £149.99
Super Cocoon 5 Season (6'9"x2'9") £169.99

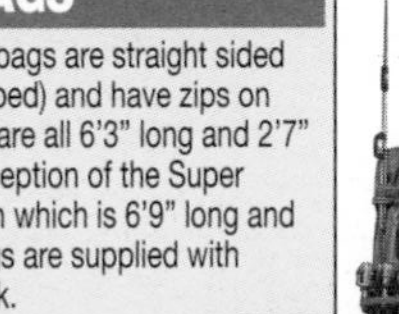

RUCKSACKS AND CARRYALL BAGS

CARRY COMBI RUCKSACKS

Featuring a removable top carryall and all the deluxe features you would expect from a JRC top-of-the-range product.

Rucksack Carry Combi £110
Mega Rucksack Carry Combi £129

CARRYALL RANGE

XL DELUXE CARRYALL
2 side pockets, 2 front pockets, double zip, padded shoulder straps and padded handles. 24" x 24" x 12"

LARGE DELUXE CARRYALL
As above but smaller. Size 20" x 20" x 10"

STALKER CARRYALL £29.99

All prices correct at going to press. Carriage on all large items £5 credit terms available. Mail order or shop callers welcome. Due to the constant upgrading of JRC Products specifications may change. Please phone for details of new JRC Products.

DELUXE 100 LITRE RUCKSACKS
100ltr Rucksack £89.95
100ltr with top flap £99.95

DELUXE 60 LITRE RUCKSACKS
60ltr Rucksack £69.95
60ltr with top flap £79.95

Stalker Rucksack £54.99

BEDCHAIR BAG (Deluxe)

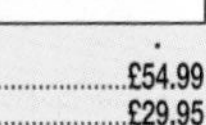

Large enough to accommodate all JRC chairs and bedchairs and most other makes. Deluxe bedchair bag with padded strap and bodyside with large external accessory pocket.

Deluxe Bedchair Bag £54.99
Eco Bedchair Bag £29.95

NEW JRC UNHOOKING MATS / REEL CASES

ZIP MAT / SLING / SCALES POUCH COMBIS
In our opinion the best designed (both for the angler and the carp) of its type. Supplied with carry bag.

Zip Mat Combi £34.95
Euro Zip Mat Combi £44.95
Safety Mat £27.95
Mega Catfish Safety Mat £39.99
Deluxe Buzz Bar Pouch £16.99
Weigh Sling £9.95

DELUXE REEL CASES
Perfectly shaped padded reel cases, specially made for carp reels.

Baitrunner size £6.45
Long Range Reel size £6.95

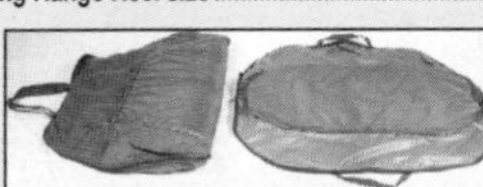

★ WE WILL MATCH ANY ADVERTISED CASH PRICE FOR GOODS IN STOCK ★

INTEREST-FREE CREDIT ★ INTEREST-FREE CREDIT ★

Lac du Mignon

Location: La Greve-sur-Mignon, north east of La Rochelle (Charente Maritime)
Type and Size: Small shallow lake of about 12 acres
Carp Stock: Very well stocked with carp
Category: Mixed Fishery
Other Species: Roach, tench, bream, rudd, eels, perch and pike
Permits: AAAP de La Greve enquire locally
Control: Information from the Fed Dep des APP, 43 Av Emile-Normandin, 17000 La Rochelle
Comments: Heavily stocked water, good fishing and much smaller than most French lakes. Rowing boats allowed

Lac du Temple

Location: Part of the famous Foret D'Orient group of lakes, 20km east of Troyes.
How to Find: From Calais, take the A26 to Reims and then towards Troyes. At Arcis (30km before Troyes) head east on the D441 towards Lesmont then onto the D960 to Piney. Lake is signposted from Piney and is about 10km from the town.
Type & Size: Huge, man made reservoir of more than 1200 hectares (3000acres).
Carp Stock: Relatively well stocked with carp to over 25 kilos although the average size is somewhat smaller.
Permits: Special local permit covers the three lakes of Orient, Temple and Amance. Yearly and vacation (one month) permits available from local bars and tackle shops.
BK Rating: Fairly hard.
Comments: This is a relatively newly-constructed water and its carp stock has not yet reached the huge proportions of the Orient & Amance fish! Certain areas are designed for night fishing. Closed during the winter months.

Lac Liton Rouge

Location: La Puisayé, Normandy, northern France
Type and Size: Small estate lake
Carp Stock: Well stocked with big carp to 51lbs
Category: Mixed Fishery
Other Species: Grass carp and catfish
Permits: Jean Louis Bunel, 35 Boulevard Arago, 75031 Paris. Tel: 010 331 43366821
BK Rating: Not known
Comments: Night fishing is allowed

La Darce

Location: Macon on the Saone
Type and Size: This 'lake' is part of the River Saone, and is over 40 acres in size
How to Find: Going south, go through Macon on the main road. Just before the end of the town turn left into the industrial estate
Carp Stock: Variable, as this depends on conditions in the river. When the river is highly coloured and fast, it is quite common for hundreds of carp to enter the Darce, and this also happens at spawning time, so the Darce always contains carp to over 40lbs - sometimes a few, sometimes many hundreds!
Other Species: Catfish to over 100lbs
Permits: French national licence from tackle shops
BK Rating: Moderate
Comments: Not a very attractive place as it is in the middle of an industrial estate, but many of the fish are commons of over 30lbs. Multiple (particle) baits work well

La Fert Vidame (Etang de Rouge)

Location: Puissay, west of Dreux, in Normandy
Type and Size: Dammed stream of about 12 acres
How to Find: Turn off the N12 at Verneuil, which is between Dreux and Alencon. Head south for about 5 miles to La Ferte Vidame
Carp Stock: Fairly heavily stocked with many doubles, quite a few twenties, some thirties and an occasional forty
Other Species: Some coarse fish, including grass carp to 30lbs
Permits: Available on site, or from J L Bunel's tackle shop in Paris
BK Rating: Easy
Comments: Night fishing is allowed, and the French licence is not required, as this is a private water. A nice looking lake, where the average angler can catch some good fish

La Folie A

Location: Excideuil, Perigord Vert, Dordogne; 20 miles north east of Perigueux
Type and Size: Lake of two and a half acres, spring fed, on private estate
Carp Stock: Well stocked with carp to 40lbs+
Category: Carp Water
Permits: Colin Maclean, Exclusive Angling Holidays, 22 Willen Road, Newport Pagnell, Bucks, MK16 OAF Tel: 01908 616886
Restrictions: No particle baits
BK Rating: Moderate
Other Species: Zander, pike, tench, and roach
Comments: Comfortable bungalow to rent weekly with fishing included; the house is right at the side of the lake and there is five acres of land, with woodland and an orchard. 3 bedrooms. Exclusive and peaceful holiday with good carp fishing, but La Folie is only available to those who respect the fish, the natural environment,and the French countryside and its people. Beautiful grape-growing region with a very warm climate and plenty of sun. Carp fishing English owners Open March 1st to November 30th. We have stayed here - it's beautiful!

Lake Aiguebelette

Location: In the French mountains, about 10 miles from Chambery
Type and Size: About 1350 acres with a maximum depth of 200 feet! It's one of the bigger natural French lakes in an area of outstanding beauty
Carp Stock: Lightly stocked with mirrors and commons. The lake record is a nice common carp caught in the 70's, 57lbs (110 cm long)
Other Species: Coarse fish with big pike to over 40lbs and big lake trout
Permits: Available from the tackle shop in the town of Aiguebelette
BK Rating: Moderate to Difficult
Comments: A big mountain lake, very deep with warm springs, very good for carp fishing. Much of the bank is privately owned and fishing spots are somewhat limited. There are several camping sites around the water. Fishing from a boat can be very successful

Lake Aussonne

Location: Eight miles from Toulouse in southern France
Type and Size: 20 acre lake
Carp Stock: Recently stocked wtih two and a half tonnes of carp from 20lbs to 40lbs in weight
Category: Carp Water
Permits: BBS European Leisure Ltd, 46 Beechwood Avenue, Ruislip, Middx

	HA4 6EJ. Tel: 01895 630516. Bookable in advance only by the week
Cost:	£125 per week, or £200 for two weeks, from Saturday noon to Saturday 10am. Accompanied juniors £75 or £125 for two weeks. £25 a week for non-fishing guests. Please note that this does not include accommodation, so you will need to take bivvies
Restrictions:	Three rods only. Night fishing allowed, as the lake is private. No sacking in the heat of the day; bivvy areas must be kept clean
BK Rating:	Not known
Comments:	Send to BBS for brochure and booking form. Restaurant and bar (open until 2am) on lake. English breakfasts. Washing and toilet facilities. Opened on May 30th 1992. Transport provided from local airport/railway station. Summer temperatures can reach 40 C!

Lake de Mervent

Location:	About 5 miles north of Fontenay Le Comte
Type and Size:	A lake of 300 acres formed by the damming of river Vendée
How to Find:	From Fontenay Le Comte, take the D65
Carp Stock:	Lightly stocked
Other Species:	All coarse fish
Permits:	From tackle shop at Fontenay Le Comte. French national licence
BK Rating:	Fairly Hard

Lake de Saint-Etienne Cantales

Location:	About 15 miles south west of Aurillac in the middle of France
Type and Size:	A big lake of 2,000 acres, formed by the damming of the river Cère
How to Find:	Take the N122 from Clermond-Ferrand to Aurillac, then take the N120
Carp Stock:	Lightly stocked with mirrors and commons to at least 25kg
Other Species:	All coarse fish with big zander and pike
Permits:	French national licence from fishing tackle shop at Aurillac
BK Rating:	Fairly Hard
Comments:	Much of this lake is over 30 metres deep but the northern end has some shallow areas. There is much speculation as to the ultimate size of the carp in this lake and fish of over 30kg are rumoured. An ideal water for the pioneering type of angler but night fishing strictly forbidden!

Lake des Fadès

Location:	In the middle of France, about 20 miles north-east of Clermont - Ferrand
Type and Size:	Lake of 1000 acres, very deep in some places, formed by the damming of the river Sioule (maximum depth of 180 feet)
Carp Stock:	Lightly stocked
Other Species:	Coarse fish and big predatory fish
Permits:	French national licence taken in tackle shop in the area
BK Rating:	Difficult
Comments:	A very beautiful lake

Lake des Vezins

Location:	About 15 miles south east of Avranches, 10 miles off the Atlantic coast and "Le Mont Saint-Michel"
Type and Size:	About 100 acres formed by the damming of the river Selune, a good French salmon river
How to Find:	From Avranches, take the N175, then at Pontaubault turn left and take the N176 to Ducey and take the D178 to Vezins
Carp Stock:	Lightly stocked
Other Species:	Coarse fish with big zander
Permits:	French national licence from fishing tackle shop at Avranches

BK Rating: Fairly Hard
Comments: A lot of common carp. Carp fishing is not very easy on the banks of this lake, it is easier with a boat

Lake de Vileneuve De La Raho

Location: Three miles south of Perpignan in the south of France near the Spanish border
Type and Size: About 400 acres in size, near the sea
Carp Stock: Well stocked with a lot of twenties and thirties
Other Species: Coarse fish. Big black bass
Permits: In the fishing tackle shop
BK Rating: Moderate
Comments: Very touristic area for family holidays

Lake of Apremont

Location: 10 miles from the Atlantic coast, 10 miles from La Roche sur Yon
Type and Size: Lake of 320 acres formed by the damming of the River Vie. Maximum depth is about 22 feet
How to Find: From Nantes take D178, at Aizenay take D107
Carp Stock: Well stocked with big carp to over 45lbs
Other Species: Coarse fish
Permits: Available from Aizenay and La Roche sur Yon. French national licence required
BK Rating: Easy to Moderate
Comments: Not far away from the French Atlantic coast; a good place for family holidays

Lake of Bourdon

Location: About 35 miles south east from Auxerre
Type and Size: About 475 acres with an average depth to 18 feet
How to Find: From Auxerre, take the D965 to St Fargeau
Carp Stock: Heavily stocked with carp to 40lbs
Other Species: All coarse fish and small catfish
Permits: Available from tackle shop in St Fargeau
BK Rating: Easy
Comments: Lovely lake. Very hard boilies, such as KM boilies, are needed to beat the small catfish

Lake of Eguzon

Location: About 13 miles south from Argenton sur Creuse. About 32 miles from the big town of Châteauroux in the centre of France
Type and Size: About 625 acres, formed by the damming of the River Creuse, with a maximum depth of 100 feet
How to Find: From Argenton sur Creuse, take the D913 to Eguzon
Carp Stock: Well stocked with big carp to over 45lbs
Other Species: All coarse fish with big zander to over 45lbs
Permits: Available from tackle shop in Eguzon. French national licence required
BK Rating: Moderate
Comments: The banks of this lake are very difficult. A boat is most useful when fishing this beautiful lake

Lake of Vassivière

Location: In the middle of France, about 20 miles from Aubusson
Type and Size: Dammed river forming a huge lake of more than 2700 acres with a maximum depth of 100 feet

Carp Stock: Well stocked with big fish to over 50lbs
Other Species: All coarse fish with big pike to 40lbs
Permits: Available from tackle shop in Royere. French national licence required
BK Rating: Moderate
Coments: Beautiful lake for spring holidays. Some English anglers have had tremendous success on this water with very big fish

Le Bourg

Location: Neuily s. Eure, a few miles north west of Chartres
Type and Size: 30 acre lake
How to Find: South La Ferte Vidame to Neuilly s. Eure on the D8 road
Carp Stock: Approximately 500 carp to 40lbs
Other Species: Roach and tench
Permits: On the bank
Cost: £10 first 24 hours, £5 every 24 hours thereafter
Control: Private
Restrictions: Six anglers maximum except by mutual agreement. Reservations - Tel:0016 33 73 96 10
Baits/Methods: All conventional baits and methods work
BK Rating: Easy
Comments: All fish to be returned unharmed

Les Baillargeaux A

Location: Near Montpon, in the Dordogne; on the River Isle north east of Bordeaux
Type and Size: Large lake
Carp Stock: Well stocked wtih twenties and thirties to 37lb
Category: Not known - probably some other coarse fish
Permits: Only for those who book accommodation - Jenette and Roger Gaunt, Les Baillargeaux, 24700 Montpon, France. Tel: 00 33 53 80 08 729 (cheaper after 8pm and weekends). English spoken
BK Rating: Not known
Comments: Full board or bed and breakfast in the farmhouse. Permit to fish waters in the Dordogne costs about £13 and applies to all public waters. Numerous other carp lakes in area; the one quoted offers special rates to guests, at an extra cost for fishing of £3.50 per day. B and B £70 weekly per person; full board £140; half board £125. Reduced rates for children

Les Ormes A

Location: Near Dinan, Brittany
Type and Size: Small pit of less than 10 acres
Carp Stock: Heavily stocked with doubles, and the occasional twenty
Permits: On site, but only for those who stay at the camp site
BK Rating: Easy
Comments: Ideal family venue, busy at times

Les Quis

Location: South east Paris.
How to Find: Organised trips by luxury coach.
Type & Size: Three lakes each in excess of 4 hectares (10 acres).
Carp Stock: About 1300 mirrors and commons - lots of 10-15 kilo fish. Some 20 kilos with a chance to catch a 25 kilo carp. Also catfish to over 25 kilos.
Permits: Information from Bernie Stamp or Terry O'Brien on 0181 857 1244 or 0181 857 7020.
Cost: £375 per week, includes travel, permits and insurance.
BK Rating: Easy.
Restrictions: No particles.

The NEW range of Kevin Maddocks carp attractors.

KM Boilies

The Kevin Maddocks range of shelf-life boilies were the very first to become popular in the U.K. and Europe. Our many years of producing ready-mades is only too clear when you pick up a packet – perfect shape, colour, texture, smell and taste. And most importantly - they catch a lot of fish too. Kevin Maddocks uses them on every trip at home and abroad and he wouldn't do that unless they were brilliant! They are available in 10mm Minis, 15mm Standards, 20mm Professionals and 25mm Donkey Chokers. The 10mm Minis are available in 200g packs at £3.99, the 15mm Standards are available in 200g Handy packs at £3.50 and 400g at £4.99. Professional packs cost £9.99 and are available in 15 or 20mm. For the price conscious angler and those travelling to other countries - 5kg Session carrier bag at £29.99 or a 10kg Euro carrier bag at £59.99. For full range of flavours see Boilie Flavours list.

KM Pop-Ups

The KM Pop-Ups have been on the market long enough now to be of the perfect quality - and that they are! Each pack contains 50 Pop-Ups and these are mixed in 15 and 20mm sizes. They are available in the ten KM Boilie flavours, plus the ever-popular Neutral (no flavour), so you can glug, spray or soak them in our range of Hookbait Enhancers or your very own exclusive flavours.

Price £3.99 a pack. For a full range of flavours see Boilie Flavours list.

KM Bait Perfector Sachets

A revolutionary range of 20 high-tech powder additives for carp anglers that strive to produce their own ultimate bait. The majority of the range consists of extremely high quality palatants, enhancers and stimulators which have been produced for us by technicians in one of Europe's finest laboratories. Each additive is carefully packed in totally encapsulated sachets at the source of production to ensure complete and essential freshness and recommended dosages are shown on the reverse of each sachet. A further information sheet is also available.

Price 99p per sachet

KM Base Mixes

1kg	**Boilie Mix**	**£4.99**
1kg	**Bird Food Blend**	**£5.99**
1kg	**Fishmeal Blend**	**£5.99**
1kg	**H.p.N.V. Compound**	**£6.99**
2.5kg	**50/50 Boilie Mix**	**£8.99**

KM Bait Perfector Liquid Flavours

This range of flavours is well proven and contains our most famous and successful flavours, such as the legendary Cream RM30 and Honey Syrup. The range is available in glass bottles (like all good flavours should be) in 30ml and 100ml. Flavours include: Strawberry Crush, Sweet Milk, Tutti Frutti, Clockwork Orange, Freshwater Crayfish, Sweet Corn, Choco Mint, Honey Syrup and Cream RM 30.

Prices are £2.49 and £5.99 respectively.

THE CUSTOMERS COME FIRST

Don't be fobbed off with inferior boilies just because that's all your dealer has in stock! He can easily place a phone order with us and have the bait in a few days. If you encounter difficulties, report this to us on 01462 816960 and we will make sure you get the bait you want.

Comments: A very successful commercially run fishery and one of the easiest big fish waters in France.

L'Étang de Catus

Location: In the dept of Lot, between Cahors and Gourdon
Type and Size: Attractive 15 acre lake
Carp Stock: Well stocked with carp to at least 20lbs
Category: Mixed Fishery
Other Species: Tench, perch and trout
Permits: Day, weekly and annual permits from the Fed départementale des APP, 40 Boulevard Gambetta, 46000 Cahors
BK Rating: Moderate
Comments: Smaller than many French carp lakes. Some information from the Town Hall (Mairie). Tackle shop Amat, 87 Rue Joffre; Boiyssou, Cahors

L'Étang d'Helfaut

Location: Pas-de-Calais, near Saint Omer, east of Boulogne
Type and Size: Four lakes totalling 18 acres
Carp Stock: Well stocked with carp to 20lbs
Category: Mixed Fishery
Other Species: Tench, bream, bleak, pike and perch
Permits: Season and annual permits; try the APP, 2 Residence de France, Rue Emile-Zola 62400 Bethune
BK Rating: Not known

Les Étangs de la Forêt de Rambouillet

Location: Rambouillet, south west of Versailles near Paris
Type and Size: Three attractive forest lakes of 7 to 15 acres each
Carp Stock: Very well stocked with carp,sizes not known
Category: Mixed Fishery
Other Species: Bream and perch
Permits: AAPP des Yvelines, 19 Rue du Docteur-Roux, 78520 Limay, or try the tackle shop in Rambouillet-Pommier, 27 Rue Felix-Faure
BK Rating: Easy
Comments: Public place with lots of people, but this is a good carp fishery near Paris

Les Étangs de l'Hirondelle, Becquerel et Grand Marais

Location: Pas-de-Calais, east of the town of Arras, at d'Ecourt-St-Quentin
Type and Size: Three lakes of 120 acres, up to 17 feet in depth
Carp Stock: Very well stocked with carp, numbers and sizes not known
Category: Mixed Fishery
Other Species: Tench, pike, perch and eels
Permits: Day and annual permits from the Town Hall (Mairie)
BK Rating: Easy
Comments: There are rowing boats on these lakes

Les Étangs du Stock et de Gondrexange

Location: About 7 miles from Sarrebourg along the canal of Houllieres about 60 miles east from Nancy
Type and Size: 1775 acres for the étang of Stock and 1400 for the étang of Gondrexange. The maximum depth for the two lakes is about 18 feet
Carp Stock: Heavily stocked with many thirties and a good number of forties. Etang du Stock holds the bigger fish, up to 60lbs
Other Species: Bream roach, perch and big pike over 35lbs
BK Rating: Easy to Moderate

Comments: The carp are mirrors, heavily scaled. Possibility to fish also the near by canal of Houilieres which holds a good stock of carp and Petit Etang du Stock which is more heavily stocked with carp to 55lbs. Petit Stock is abut 400 acres and receives a lot of pressure. A boat is essential for fishing Grand Stock

Les Sablieres de Les Planches

Location: Châteauroux (Indre)
Type and Size: Little 2 acre lake
Carp Stock: Heavily stocked with carp
Category: Mixed Fishery
Other Species: Roach, bleak, tench, zander
Permits: Day tickets from AAPP de Chateauroux, 19 Rue des Etats-Unis, 36000 Chateauroux
Comments: The smallest French water we have been able to find!

Lyon Canal

Location: In the big city of Lyon
Type and Size: Large canal used by huge barges and tankers
How to Find: The Lyon ring road passes over this canal which runs from the River Saone to the River Rhone
Carp Stock: Heavily stocked with fish up to 55lbs, many thirties are caught
Permits: French national licence from tackle shops in Lyon
BK Rating: Easy
Comments: This is a water for the adventurous, who don't mind boat traffic and human beings. Location is easy, as the carp congregate in groups and some very big fish can be seen

Marcilac la Croisille

Location: 25 miles east of Tulle
Type and Size: A dammed river forming a large lake in excess of 600 acres
How to Find: A little south of the main E70 road which runs from Tulle to Clermont Ferrand
Carp Stock: Moderately stocked with carp to at least 50lbs
Permits: Normal French national licence required
BK Rating: Moderate
Comments: This water definitely holds big carp but little else is known about it. Lots of potential for the pioneering type angler

Merceuil

Location: Four miles south of Beaune, between Dijon and Chalon-sur-Saone
Type and Size: Gravel pit of about 40 acres
How to Find: Turn off the A6/E15 motorway at Beaune, and head east on the D970. Follow signs to Bligny-les-Beaunes. The lake is alongside the motorway about 4 miles out of Beaune
Carp Stock: Lightly stocked with carp to over 35lbs
Permits: Available from Jackie Greset's shop in Chalon-sur-Saone (alongside the river a little downstream of the road bridge). French national licence required
BK Rating: Fairly Hard
Comments: Mussels and crayfish a problem. The old river course in the centre of the lake is productive. Very hard boilies (such as KM boilies) necessary to beat the crayfish

KM Hookbait Enhancer Dips

The KM Hookbait Dips were the first on the market. Not only are they the most successful in terms of sales but they are also the most effective. This year we have improved them even further with the addition of our new liquid palatant and the new flavours to match our boilie range.

150ml of liquid in a 250ml tub: £4.99.

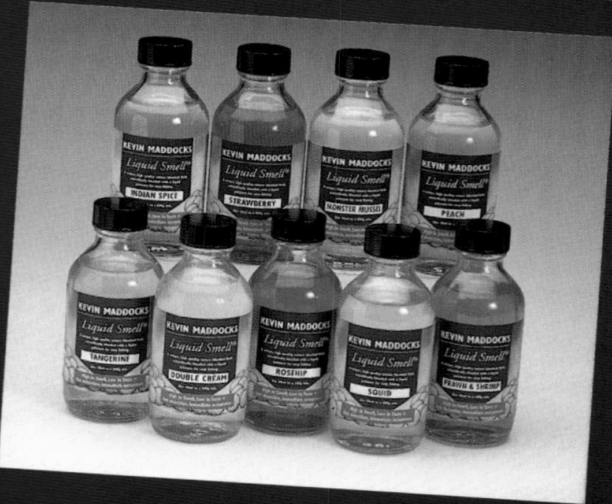

KM Liquid Smells™

The new KM Liquid Smells™ are probably the only flavours ever developed solely for carp fishing use (the majority being food-grade flavours simply re-packed). From inception to perfection, the emphasis on these fluids has been HIGH in smell, LOW in taste. The high smell ensures that carp detect your bait more easily, especially during the night or when they are at distance. The low taste ensures immediate acceptance as soon as the carp samples your bait. These new Liquid Smells™ represent a major step forward in the development of carp attractors. Make sure you get a slice of the action! Available in Strawberry, Peach, Rosehip, Squid, Indian Spice, Monster Mussel, Tangerine, Prawn & Shrimp, Double Cream

Price: £9.99 per 100ml glass bottle.

Quality Counts

We should like to point out, that we make no apologies for our boilies not being the cheapest on the market - it is a proven fact that high quality boilies catch more fish (and promote healthy growth) and we take pride in the fact that our boilies are of the very highest quality possible.

Withy Pool, Henlow Camp, Bedfordshire SG16 6EA. Tel: 01462 816960 Fax: 01462 817253

Mimizan

Location: Mimizan, close to the west coast, 60 miles south west of Bordeaux
Type and Size: Dammed river forming a lake of more than 200 acres
Carp Stock: Quite well stocked with long, lean commons to over 30lbs, with plenty of 20's
Permits: Local tackle shops; French national licence
BK Rating: Moderate
Comments: Strictly controlled, although night fishing is allowed in some areas

Monclar-de-Quercy

Location: Monclar, 15km east of Montauban, south west France.
How to Find: From the Bordeaux to Toulouse A62/E72 autoroute take the Montauban exit. From Montauban head east on the D8 to Monclar. The lake lies to the east of the town.
Type & Size: Dammed river forming a lake of about 16 hectares (40 acres).
Carp Stock: Little is known about the maximum size of the carp. The lake was originally stocked a long time ago and has received very little attention from carp specialists. Commons to over 15 kilos and possibly some big mirrors, but a good head of small carp too.
Permits: Special local permit available from tackle shops at Monclar.
BK Rating: Easy.
Comments: Ideal place for family; good camping site, swimming pool, miniature railway around lake.

Parc de Miribel-Jonage

Location: In the eastern outskirts of Lyon city.
How to Find: From Lyon take the E61 autoroute towards Geneve and Parc de Miribel is clearly sign posted.
Type & Size: A large, well landscaped city park featuring several lakes; the largest being approximately 40 hectares (100 acres).
Carp Stock: Well stocked with carp of 10 - 20kg and a good amount of bigger fish up to 30kg.
Permits: Available locally.
BK Rating: Easy.
Comments: Hugely underestimated by English carp anglers; a lake with lots of potential.

Parcours de Pêche

Location: Domaine des Forges,near Montmirail off the RD33 between Paris and Chalons sur Marne, and east of Paris
Type and Size: There are three lakes, not large, on the fishery, but the carp are in the Étang due 'Bois' Joli
Carp Stock: Heavily stocked with carp from 16-25lbs, though forty pounders are claimed
Category: Mixed Fishery
Other Species: Some coarse fish
Permits: Domaine des Forges, Les Forges 51270 Talus St Prix; Tel: 26 80 39 29
Cost: Day - 150 francs; 48 hours - 250 francs; week - 1,500 francs
Restrictions: Night fishing allowed for carp only
Comments: There are two other lakes on site: one is a trout lake, the other contains catfish to 100lbs and big pike. Separate permits and prices for these. The owners will book local accommodation if required

Pareloup

Location: Between Rodez and Millau
Type and Size: Dammed streams which form huge reservoir, several miles across, and 1,800 acres in extent
How to Find: The lake is about 3 miles to the south of the 911 road between Rodez and Millau - take the D993 towards Sales Curan
Carp Stock: A good head of low doubles, some 20's, 30's and 40's and a reported 57 pounder
Permits: French national licence from the tackle shop in Millau
BK Rating: Moderate
Comments: Location is of paramount importance - don't bother to fish until you spot carp; mussels and crayfish a bit of a problem. Boat recommended - an ideal water for the pioneering big fish man

Reservoir de Bouzey

Location: North west France, 10km west of Epinal.
How to Find: From Nancy head south on the N57 to Epinal and then south west onto the D460. The reservoir is on the left hand side of the D460 about 10km out of Epinal.
Type & Size: Dammed river forming a lake of approximately 80 hectares (200 acres) made up of two arms.
Carp Stock: Lightly stocked with carp averaging 15 kilos and a sprinkling of larger ones to at least 25 kilos.
Permits: National French licence.
BK Rating: Moderate.

Reservoir de Charmes

Location: 10km north of Langres, which is 150 miles south of Paris.
How to Find: From Paris take the E17 autoroute to its junction with the A31/E21 at Beauchemin, near Langres. Head east on the A31 for one junction, then north on N19 to Rolampout, then the D121 to Charmes. Lake is clearly signposted.
Type & Size: Dammed river forming a reservoir of 90 hectares (220 acres). Depth averages 5-10 metres.
Carp Stock: Average size of carp is quite high with many 20kg fish present. Lake record is 32kg.
Permits: Special licence available from bars around the lake and from local tackle shops.
BK Rating: Moderate.
Restrictions: Night fishing is usually allowed on about 50% of the lake.
Comments: Can become busy at times, water is shared by local angling club but worth a try because of the huge fish that this lake holds. Regular Guard de Peche checks are carried out.

Reservoir de Chazilly

Location: Chazilly/Ste-Sabine, north west of Beaune (Cote d'Or)
Type and Size: Very deep reservoir of 200 acres
Carp Stock: Well stocked with carp
Category: Mixed Fishery
Other Species: Pike, perch, roach, tench and bream
Permits: APP. 'La Gaule de l'Auxois' at the village of Ste-Sabine; Fed Departementale, 6 rue Charles-Dumont, 21000 Dijon
Comments: Annual permits; boat fishing allowed. No other water sports apart from fishing. Also smaller reservoir nearby, Reservoir du Tillot, 50 acres and very attractive; well stocked with carp

NOW THAT YOU'VE FOUND THE LAKE, LET US HELP YOU BANK THE FISH!

THE NEW WITHY POOL RIG SIZE 6 & 8

DEVELOPED AND EXTENSIVELY USED BY KEVIN MADDOCKS DURING 1996. THIS IS A BUOYANT BAIT ONLY RIG. PERFECT FOR FISHING OVER DECAYING LEAVES, WEED OR SILT. THIS RIG SEEMS TO HOOK THE MOUTH REGARDLESS OF WHICH DIRECTION MR. CARP APPROACHES THE BAIT

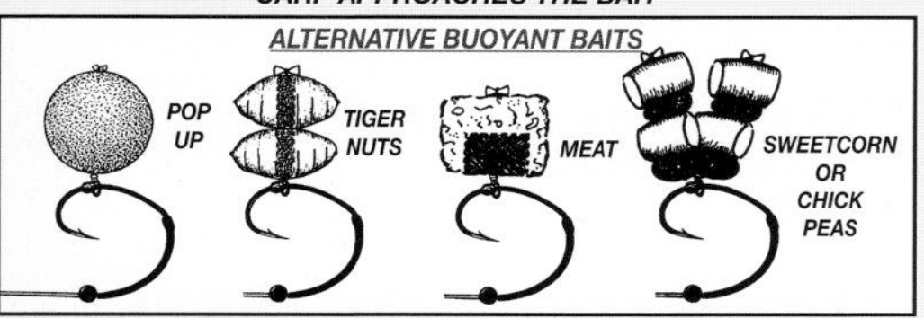

THIS RIG UTILISES THE NEW 'NAILER' HOOK AND THE FAMOUS GHOUL HOOKLINK. BAIT MAY BE ATTACHED BY USE OF AN ELASTIC BAIT BAND OR TIED ON WITH DENTAL FLOSS.

AMNESIA 'D' RIG SIZE 4, 6 & 8

TIED IN COMBI-LINK FASHION WITH OUR NEW ULTRA LEDKOR

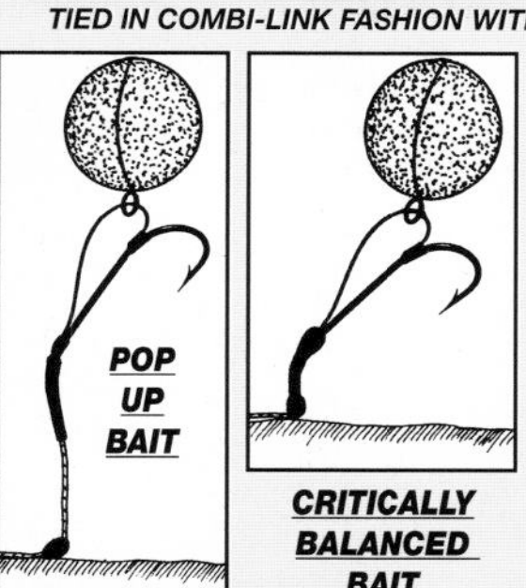

CRITICALLY BALANCED BAIT

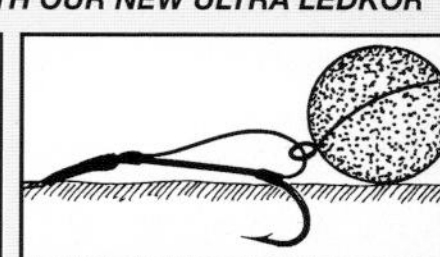

BOTTOM BAIT

IF THE CARP TRIES TO EJEC ANY OF THESE PRESENTATIONS THIS ULTR SHARP HOOK WILL TURN OVER AND SNAG THE INSID OF THE MOUTH. THE SMALL PIECE OF SHRINK TUBE AID THIS TURN OVER EFFECT.

THE MINI 'D' ANCHOR RIG SIZE 4,6 & 8

THIS RIG IS AN ANTI-EJECT RIG COMBINING ONE OF KEVIN NASH'S FAVOURITE MINI 'D' LOOP STYLE RIGS AND THE FRANK WARWICK ANCHOR RIG. UTILISING THE ULTRA STRONG CENTURION 2000 HOOK AND A LEDKOR ULTRA COMBI-LINK, THIS RIG CAN BE USED IN MANY DIFFERENT WAYS FOR POP-UPS

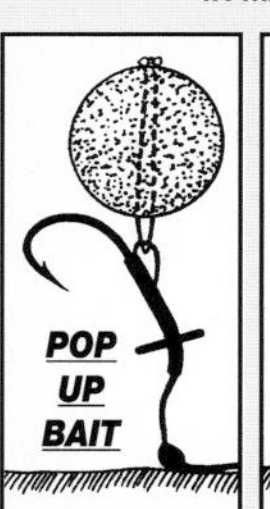

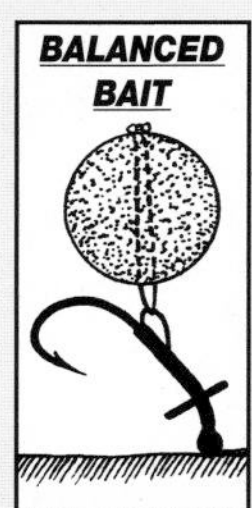

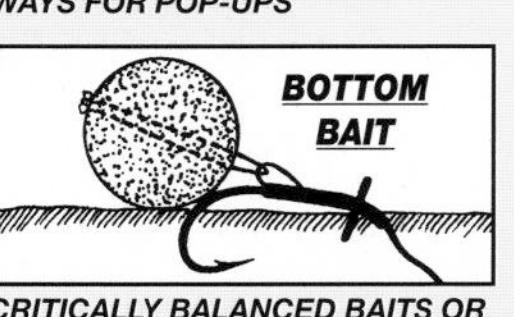

CRITICALLY BALANCED BAITS OR FOR BOTTOM BAITS. BAIT CAN BE ATTACHED WITH A NYLON LOOPED HAIR OR WITH A BAIT BAND OR A NORMAL HAIR (IF SMALL PARTICLES OR SWEETCORN ARE BEING USED).

FRANK WARWICK CRANKED HOOK RIG SIZE 8

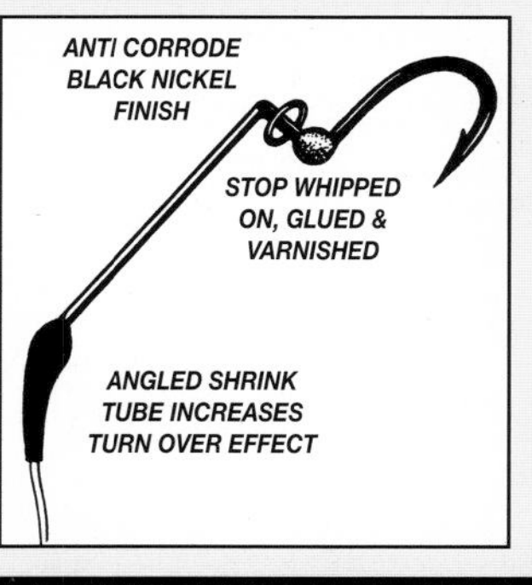

DESIGNED BY FRANK WARWICK AND UTILISIN OUR NEW SIZE 8 CRANKED HOOK THIS R WILL CATCH OUT THE WARIEST CARP. IT MAY BE USED AS A POP-UP RIG WITH A VERY BOUYANT BAIT OR AS A BOTTOM BAIT. THIS HOOK TURNS IN THE MOUTH ON EJECTION AND HOOKS IMMEDIATELY. STRONGL RECOMMENDED BY KE TOWNLEY IN DEC/JAN '9 ADVANCED CARPING.

STRONG HOOKS FOR THOSE EUROPEAN WATERS

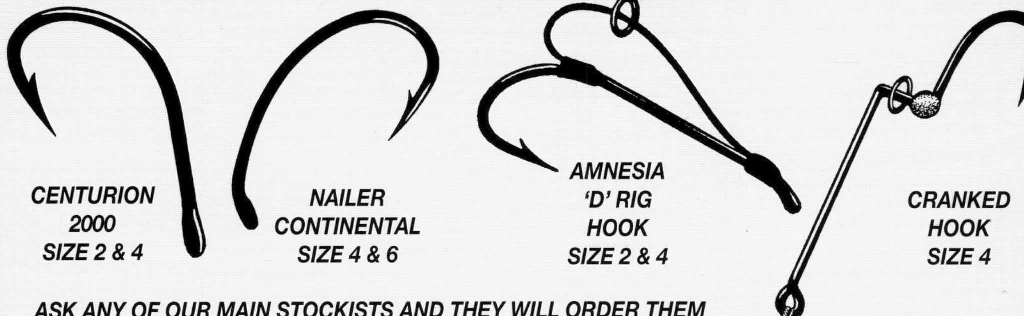

CENTURION 2000 SIZE 2 & 4

NAILER CONTINENTAL SIZE 4 & 6

AMNESIA 'D' RIG HOOK SIZE 2 & 4

CRANKED HOOK SIZE 4

ASK ANY OF OUR MAIN STOCKISTS AND THEY WILL ORDER THEM

CARP 'R' US MAIN STOCKIST

AVON
BRISTOL ANGLING CENTRE, 12-16 DONCASTER ROAD, SOUTHMEAD, BRISTOL, AVON BS10 5PL

BEDFORDSHIRE & BUCKINGHAMSHIRE
LAKE BROS, 26 CHURCH STREET, WOLVERTON, MILTON KEYNES MK12 5JN

LESLIES OF LUTON, 89 PARK STREET, LUTON, BEDS LU1 3HG

PEDDERS, 110 VICTORIA STREET, DUNSTABLE, BEDS LU6 3BA

SANDY ANGLING CENTRE, SHANNON COURT, SANDY BEDS SG19 1DJ

SEAHAWK SUPPLIES, BREWERY HOUSE, 4 CASTLE STREET, BUCKINGHAM MK18 1BS

THE SPORTSMANS LODGE, 3-5 HOWARD STREET, BEDFORD MK40 3HS

BERKSHIRE
READING ANGLING CENTRE, 69 NORTHUMBERLAND AVENUE, READING, BERKS RG2 7PS

WOODLEY SPORTS, 139 CROCKHAMWELL ROAD, WOODLEY, READING, BERKS RG5 2JP

CAMBRIDGESHIRE
STANJAY SPORTS, 7 OLD COURT HALL, GODMANCHESTER, CAMBRIDGE, PE18 8HS

WEBBS FISHING TACKLE, 196 NEWARK AVENUE, DOGSTHORPE, PETERBOROUGH, CAMBS PE1 4NP

DEVON & CORNWALL
CLIVES TACKLE, 152 EXETER STREET, PLYMOUTH, DEVON PL4 ONQ

DRUM SPORTS, 47 COURTNAY STREET, NEWTON ABBOT, DEVON TQ12 2QN

WOOLFYS FISHING TACKLE, 28 BARTHOLOMEWS ARCADE, FORE STREET, EXETER, DEVON EX4 3AN

NEWQUAY FISHING & SHOOTING, 12 FORE STREET, NEWQUAY, CORNWALL TR7 1LW

DORSET & SOMERSET
DORCHESTER ANGLING CENTRE, UNIT 1, NAPPERS COURT, CHARLES ST, DORCHESTER DT1 1EE

BOURNEMOUTH FISHING LODGE, 904 WIMBORNE ROAD, MOORDOWN, BOURNEMOUTH, DORSET BH29 2DW

REVELS COARSE FISHERY, BUCKLAND NEWTON, DORCHESTER DT2 2TW

MICKS TACKLE BOX, 61 PRINCES STREET, YEOVIL BA21 1EE

ESSEX
BEVAN CARP TACKLE, MAIN ROAD, BOREHAM, CHELMSFORD, ESSEX CM3 3HE

BASILDON ANGLING CENTRE, 402 WHITMORE WAY, BASILDON, ESSEX SS14 2HB

COUNTY ANGLING CENTRE, 19 SUTTONS LANE, HORNCHURCH, ESSEX RM12 6RD

BOWLERS ANGLING CENTRE, 2-3 CINEMA PARADE, WHALEBONE LANE SOUTH, DAGENHAM, ESSEX RM8 1AA

CANVEY ISLAND ANGLING CENTRE, 132 FURTHERWICK ROAD, CANVEY ISLAND ESSEX SS8 7AL

CARP UNLIMITED, 16 PEARTREE BUSINESS CENTRE, PEARTREE ROAD, STANWAY, COLCHESTER, ESSEX CO3 5JN

E & J TACKLE, 16 CHURCH STREET, WITHAM, ESSEX CM8 2JL

ESSEX ANGLING & SPORTS, 5 BROADWAY PARADE, ELM PARK AVENUE, ELM PARK, HORNCHURCH, ESSEX RM12 4RS

HOOK, LINE & SINKER, 15/17 KENTS HILL ROAD, SOUTH BENFLEET, ESSEX SS7 5PN

KESWELLS, 618 CHIGWELL ROAD, WOODFORD BRIDGE, ESSEX IG8 8AA

OAK LODGE FISHERY, ARTERIAL WAY, RAYLEIGH, ESSEX

OCKENDEN BAIT & TACKLE, 9 BROXBURN PARADE, BROXBURN DRIVE, SOUTH OCKENDEN, ESSEX RM15 5QZ

PENGE ANGLING SUPPLIES, THE WEIR, ARTERIAL ROAD, RAYLEIGH, ESSEX SS5 7TR

SPECIALIST TACKLE, 93 CHASE CROSS ROAD, COLLIER ROW, ROMFORD, ESSEX RM5 3RP

STANFORD TACKLE CENTRE, 12 WHARF ROAD, STANFORD-LE-HOPE, ESSEX SS17 ODH

THE BAIT BOX, BROADWAY, LOUGHTON, ESSEX IG10 3SY

TRENT TACKLE, 48A TRENT ROAD, CHELMSFORD, ESSEX CM1 2LQ

GLOUCESTERSHIRE
D & J SPORTS, 75 CRICKLADE STREET, CIRENCESTER, GLOS GL7 1HY

MAC'S TACKLE, UNIT 1, THE INDUSTRIAL ESTATE, BOURTON-ON-THE-WATER, CHELTENHAM, GLOS GL54 2EP

THE TACKLE BOX, 82 TENNYSON ROAD, ST MARKS, CHELTENHAM, GLOS GL51 7DB

HUMBERSIDE & NORTH LINCOLNSHIRE
BARRYS OF GOOLE, 25 WESTFIELD AVENUE, GOOLE, HUMBERSIDE DN14 6JY

CHAPMANS TACKLE, 23 BEECH WAY, ASHBY, SCUNTHORPE DN16 2HF

HUMBERSIDE TACKLE EXCHANGE, 95 MARY STREET, SCUNTHORPE, N. LINCS DN16 6LB

HAMPSHIRE
BELL SPORTS, 9-10 NEW ROAD, HYTHE, Nr SOUTHAMPTON, HANTS SO45 6BP

RINGWOOD TACKLE, 5 THE BRIDGES, WEST STREET, RINGWOOD, HANTS BH24 1EA

RODS N REELS, 418 HAVANT ROAD, FARLINGTON ROAD, PORTSMOUTH, HANTS PO8 1NF

TACKLE UP, 155 FLEET ROAD, FLEET, HANTS GU13 8PD

TIGHTLINES ANGLING CENTRE, 1A RUMBRIDGE STREET (BATTS CORNER) TETTON, SOUTHAMPTON, HANTS SO40 4DQ

TWO GUYS ANGLING, 27 BURNABY CLOSE, SOUTH HAM, BASINGSTOKE, HANTS RG22 6UJ

WATERLOOVILLE CAMPING & ANGLING,157A LONDON ROAD, WATERLOOVILLE, HANTS PO7 7RJ

HERTFORDSHIRE
ALAN BROWN COUNTRY SPORTS, 118 NIGHTINGALE ROAD, HITCHIN, HERTS SG5 1RG

COLNEY TACKLE, HIGH STREET, LONDON COLNEY, HERTS

JOHNSON ROSS TACKLE, 3/5 AMWELL STREET, HODDESDON, HERTS EN11 8TP

LAKESIDE TACKLE, STANBOROUGH LAKES, WELWYN GARDEN CITY, HERTS

NORTH HERTS ANGLING CENTRE, 25 LONDON ROAD, BALDOCK, HERTS SG7 6NB

OLD TOWN ANGLING CENTRE, 75 HIGH STREET, HEMEL HEMPSTEAD, HERTS HP1 3AF

OXHEY ANGLING CENTRE, 28 PINNER ROAD, WATFORD, HERTS WD1 4ED

SIMPSONS OF TURNFORD, NUNSBURY DRIVE, TURNFORD, BROXBOURNE, HERTS EN10 6AQ

STORT ANGLING, 40A HOCKERILL STREET, BISHOPS STORTFORD, HERTS CM23 2DW

THE BAIT BOX, 255 HIGH STREET, WALTHAM CROSS, HERTS EN3 7BE

THE TACKLE CARRIER, 157 ST ALBANS ROAD, WATFORD, HERTS WD2 5BD

KENT
A & I ANGLING, 33 HIGH STREET, GREEN ST GREEN, ORPINGTON, KENT BL6 6BG

ASHFORD TACKLE SHOPS, 3B STANHOPE SQUARE, ASHFORD, KENT TN23 2TF

ASHFORD TACKLE SHOPS, 52 ST MARY'S ROAD, FAVERSHAM, KENT ME13 8EM

COUNTRY WAY GUNS & TACKLE, 86 HIGH STREET, WEST MALLING, KENT ME19 6NE

DANSON ANGLING, 159 BLENDON ROAD, BEXLEY, KENT DA5 1BT

DOWNHAM TACKLE, 443 BROMLEY ROAD, DOWNHAM, BROMLEY, KENT BR1 4PH

MARK 2 ANGLING, 224-6 THE HIGH STREET, CRAYFORD, KENT DA1 4HG

MID-KENT TACKLE, 146-148 MILTON STREET, MAIDSTONE, KENT ME16 8LL

PENGE ANGLING SUPPLIES, 309 BECKENHAM ROAD, BECKENHAM, KENT BR3 4RL

THE TACKLE BOX, 198 MAIN ROAD, SUTTON AT HONE, FARNINGHAM, KENT DA4 9HP

LANCASHIRE
MACKS FISHING TACKLE, 33A PARLIAMENT STREET, BURNLEY, LANCS BB11 3JU

NORTH WEST ANGLING CENTRE, CHAPEL STREET, HINDLEY, WIGAN, LANCS WN2 3AD

LEICESTERSHIRE
BENNETTS ANGLING STORES LTD, 9 MARKET PLACE, MOUNTSORREL, LEICS LE12 7BA

LINCOLNSHIRE
CASTAWAY TACKLE, 266 HYKEHAM ROAD, LINCOLN LN6 8BJ

WHEATER FIELDSPORTS, 3-9 TENTERCROFT STREET, LINCOLN LN5 7DB

LONDON
FINE LINE TACKLE, 299 MITCHAM ROAD, TOOTING, LONDON SW17 9JQ

FRAMES OF HENDON, 202 WEST HENDON BROADWAY, HENDON, LONDON NW9 7EE

GERRY'S OF WIMBLEDON, 170-176 THE BROADWAY, WIMBLEDON, LONDON SW19 1RX

JON'S OF STEPNEY, 102 WHITHORSE LANE, LONDON E1 4LR

JOHNS TACKLE BOX, 242-4 WOODHOUSE ROAD, FRIEN BARNET, N12 ORU

OAKWOOD ANGLING, 29 RESERVOIR ROAD, SOUTHGATE, N14 4BB

STABLERS, 350 GARRATT LANE, EARLSFIELD, LONDON SW18 4ES

TOTTENHAM ANGLING CENTRE, 80 WHITE HART LANE, LONDON N17 8HP

MANCHESTER
ROCHDALE ANGLING CENTRE, 204 YORKSHIRE STREET, ROCHDALE OL16 2DW

TRAFFORD ANGLING SUPPLIES, 34 MOSS ROAD, STRETFORD, MANCHESTER M32 OAY

MERSEYSIDE
JOHNSON'S ANGLING CENTRE, 469 RICE LANE, LIVERPOOL L9 8AP

TASKERS SPORT & ANGLING, 29 UTRING AVENUE, ANFIELD, LIVERPOOL L4 7UN

MIDDLESEX
DAVIES ANGLING, 47-49 CHURCH STREET, STAINES, MIDDLESEX TW18 4EN

EXCHANGE TACKLE, 53 FAIRFIELD ROAD, YIEWSLEY, WEST DRAYTON MIDDLESEX

HAREFIELD TACKLE, 2-4 HIGH STREET, HAREFIELD, MIDDLESEX UB9 6BJ

HOUNSLOW ANGLING CENTRE, 265-7 BATH ROAD, HOUNSLOW, MIDDLESEX TW3 3DA

JUDDS OF HILLINGDON, 3 WESTBOURNE PARADE, UXBRIDGE ROAD, HILLINGDON, MIDDLESEX UB10 ONY

JUDDS OF HILLINGDON, 524/6 VICTORIA ROAD, SOUTH RUISLIP, MIDDLESEX HA4 OHE

TACKLE UP, 363 STAINES ROAD WEST, ASHFORD COMMON, ASHFORD, MIDDLESEX TW5 1RP

NORFOLK
BRUNDALL ANGLING, RIVERSIDE, BRUNDALL, NORWICH, NORFOLK NR13 5PY

GORLESTON TACKLE CENTRE, 7-8 PIER WALK, GORLESTON, GREAT YARMOUTH, NORFOLK NR31 6DA

TOM BOULTON, 173 DRAYTON ROAD, NORWICH, NORFOLK NR3 2AA

NORTHAMPTONSHIRE
GILDERS COUNTRY SPORTS, 250-252 WELLINGBOROUGH ROAD, NORTHAMPTON, NN1 4EJ

RUSHDEN ANGLING, 26 CHURCH STREET, RUSHDEN, NORTHANTS NN10 9YT

THE SPORTSMAN'S LODGE, 44 KINGSTHORPE ROAD, KINGSTHORPE HOLLOW, NORTHANTS NN2 6EZ

NORTH WEST
BAILEYS BAIT & TACKLE, 20 PARKSWAY, WOOLSTON, WARRINGTON, CHESHIRE WA1 4BP

BARLOWS OF BOND STREET, 47 BOND STREET, MACCLESFIELD, CHESHIRE SK11 6QS

DAVE'S OF MIDDLEWICH, 67 WHEELOCK STREET, MIDDLEWICH, CHESHIRE CW10 9AB

STAPELEY WATER GARDENS, 92 LONDON ROAD, STAPELEY, NANTWICH, CHESHIRE CW5 7LH

TREV'S TACKLE, 16 ALTRINCHAM ROAD, WILMSLOW, CHESHIRE SK9 5ND

NOTTINGHAM & DERBYSHIRE
EXCHANGE ANGLING NOTTINGHAM, 277 ILKESTON ROAD, NOTTINGHAM NG7 3FY

THE BRIDGE SHOP, 39 HIGH STREET, MEASHAM, SWADLINGCOTE, DERBYSHIRE DE12 7HR

TACKLE BOX, 323 SOMERCOTES HILL, SOMERCOTES, DE55 4JX

OXFORDSHIRE
THE RIGHT ANGLE, WOOTTON ROAD, ABINGDON, OXON OX13 6BH

STAFFORDSHIRE
ALLEN'S OF KINGSBURY, COVENTRY ROAD, KINGSBURY, TAMWORTH, STAFFS B78 2DT

PICKERINGS OF BURSLEM, 4-8 WILLIAM CLOWES STREET, BURSLEM, STOKE ON TRENT, STAFFS ST6 3AP

SUFFOLK
A & P SUPPL[illegible] ESTATE, ELL[illegible]

BIRDS, GIPP[illegible] IPSWICH, SU[illegible]

HOOKED, 12[illegible] SUFFOLK CB8 8LG

SAXMUNDHAM ANGLING CENTRE, REAR OF MARKET PLACE, SAXMUNDHAM, SUFFOLK IP17 1AH

SUDBURY ANGLING, NO1, UNIT2, ACTON SQUARE, SUDBURY, IPSWICH CO10 6HG

TACKLE UP, 49A ST JOHNS STREET, BURY ST EDMUNDS, SUFFOLK IP33 1SP

VISCOUNT FISHING TACKLE, 207 CLAPGATE LANE, IPSWICH, IPS ORF

SURREY
APOLLO ANGLING CENTRE, 79 BRIGHTON ROAD, ADDLESTONE, SURREY KT15 1PT

BANKSIDE FISHING TACKLE, 2 CASTLE PARADE, EWELL BY-PASS, EWELL, SURREY KT17 2PR

COULSDON PET CENTRE, 228 BRIGHTON ROAD, COULSDON, SURREY CR5 2NF

FISHING UNLIMITED, 2-3 HAMPTON COURT ROAD, EAST MOLESEY, SURREY KT8 9HB

GUILFORD ANGLING CENTRE, 92-94 HAYDON PLACE, GUILFORD, SURREY GU1 4LL

SALFORD ANGLING CENTRE, 2 SOUTH PARADE, HORLEY ROW, HORLEY, SURREY RH6 6BH

SURBITON ANGLING CENTRE, 177 HOOK ROAD, SURBITON, SURREY KT6 5AR

YATELEY ANGLING CENTRE, 16 THE PARADE, YATELEY, SURREY GU17 7UN

EAST & WEST SUSSEX
ARUN ANGLING CENTRE, ROUNDSTONE GARDEN CENTRE, ROUNDSTONE BY-PASS, ANGMERING, W. SUSSEX BN16 4BD

CARRINGDALE ANGLING CENTRE, BURY GATE, PULBOROUGH, W. SUSSEX RH20 1NW

CROWBOROUGH TACKLE, WHITEHILL ROAD, CROWBOROUGH, E. SUSSEX TN6 1JS

JACK FROST TACKLE, 54 EWHURST ROAD, WEST GREEN, CRAWLEY SUSSEX RH11 7HE

POLEGATE ANGLING, 101 STATION ROAD, POLEGATE, E. SUSSEX BN26 6EB

SOUTHERN ANGLING SPECIALISTS, 2 STOCKBRIDGE PLACE, STOCKBRIDGE, NR. CHICHESTER, W. SUSSEX PO19 2QH

SUSSEX TACKLE EXCHANGE, WINTONS FARM, FOLDERS LANE, BURGESS HILL, W. SUSSEX RH15 ODR

TIGHTLINES, 31 STATION ROAD, BEXHILL ON SEA, SUSSEX TN40 1RG

UCKFIELD ANGLING CENTRE, 212A HIGH STREET, UCKFIELD, E. SUSSEX TN22 1RD

THE FISHERMAN'S FRIEND, 83 DITCHLING ROAD, BRIGHTON, SUSSEX BN1 4SD

WALES
ANGLER'S SUPPLIES, 172 PENARTH ROAD, GRANGETOWN, CARDIFF CF1 7NL

PILL ANGLING CENTRE, 160 COMMERCIAL ROAD, NEWPORT, GWENT NP9 2PJ

ROGER THOMPSON, LLYN Y GORS, LLANDEGFAN, MENAI BRIDGE, LL59 5PN

WEST MIDLANDS
BIRMINGHAM ANGLING CENTRE, BEECH ROAD, ERDINGTON, W.MIDLANDS B23 5QN

WILTSHIRE
HINDERS BAIT CENTRE, ERMIN STREET, STRATTON ST MARGARET, SWINDON, WILTS SN3 4NJ

REIDS TACKLE, KINGSWAY HOUSE, WARMINSTER ROAD, WILTON, SALISBURY WILTS SB2 OAT

STEVES TACKLE, 26 HIGH STREET, WARMINSTER, WILTS BA12 9AF

YORKSHIRE
BARRY'S OF GOOLE, 25 WESTFIELD AVENUE, GOOLE, HUMBERSIDE, DNJ4 6JY

CALCOTTS TACKLE SHOP, 34-38 THE WICKER, SHEFFIELD S3 8JB

ERICS OF LEEDS, 401 SELBY ROAD, WHITKIRK, LEEDS

GRAHAMS OF DEWSBURY, 9 SUMMERDALE, GOMERSOL, W. YORKS BD19 4AH

PAUL CHAMBERS CYCLES & FISHING, 66/68 STATION ROAD, FEATHERSTONE ROAD, W. YORKS WF7 5BB

THE CARP CABIN, 46 ECKINGTON ROAD, COAL ASTON, SHEFFIELD S18 6AT

Reservoir de la Mouche

Location: East France, near Langres, 60km north of Dijon.
How to Find: From Calais follow autoroute through Reims, past Troyes and onto Langres. Leave the A5/E17 at Langres turn right at Humes to St. Ciergues where the reservoir is situated.
Type & Size: Reservoir of approximately 60 hectares (150 acres).
Carp Stock: Well stocked with carp of 10-20 kg with one or two fish up to 30kg.
Permits: Obtainable locally in bars and tackle shops; may be on the same ticket as Reservoir Charmes and Lac de la Liez.
BK Rating: Easy.
Comments: Some night fishing allowed.

River Auvezere

Location: At Perigueux. One of the best areas is at Le Change about 10 miles upstream of Perigueux
Type and Size: A medium sized river averaging 40 metres in width. Slow flowing
Carp Stock: Reasonably well stocked with carp to at least 40lbs
Permits: Normal French national licence required
BK Rating: Moderate
Comments: Lots of potential. Carp to 40lbs have been caught but much bigger fish are said to exist

River Charente

Location: This excellent carp water is more than 100 miles long and runs into the Atlantic Sea at Rochefort. This river runs through Cognac and Saintes
Type and Size: A medium sized river, slow flowing and very deep in some areas
Carp Stock: Well stocked with big carp to over 45lbs
Other Species: All coarse fish
Permits: French national licence from tackle shops at Rochefort, Saintes or Cognac
BK Rating: Easy to Moderate
Comments: Beautiful carp river in French holiday area, with good places for carp fishing not far away from the Atlantic coast

River Cher

Location: This river is about 70 miles long and runs into the River Loire at Tours
Type and Size: A medium sized river, slow flowing and varying depths
Carp Stock: Heavily stocked with big carp to over 45lbs
Other Species: All coarse fish and big zander to 30lbs
Permits: From tackle shops at Vierzon, Romorantin or Chenonceaux
BK Rating: Easy
Comments: Good results with particle baits

River Dordogne

Location: This big French river is more than 100 miles long and runs through Bort les Orgues, Bergerac and Libourne into the Garonne, about 20 miles north of Bordeaux
Type and Size: The river is dammed in several sections around Bort les Orgues and Argentat, after which it is a beautiful river with considerable depths in some areas
How to Find: Very good areas for carp fishing around Bergerac
Carp Stock: Heavily stocked in some areas with carp to over 40lbs
Other Species: All coarse fish, especially big zander to 30lbs and big pike to 40lbs. Big wels catfish have been caught in some areas
Permits: French national licence required
BK Rating: Moderate

Comments: The possibility to catch a very big carp is real. A French carp angler caught a brace of 51lb and 53lb mirrors in the same day on this river!

River Doubs

Location: This carp water is more than 100 miles long and runs into the River Saône at Verdun sur le Doubs

Type and Size: A medium sized river with considerable depths. Good places in the Besançon area

Carp Stock: Well stocked with big carp to over 55lbs

Other Species: All coarse fish

Permits: French national licence required

BK Rating: Easy to Moderate

Comments: Good places in Besançon area. A big catfish of 150lbs was caught in the 70's

River Garonne

Location: Runs from the border with Spain in a north westerly direction to Bordeaux on the west coast.

How to Find: The river holds many big carp especially in its lower reaches. Some of the best known spots are; the barrage at Cazeres where carp have been caught to 27kg, at its junction with the River Tarn at Moissac and also at its junction with the River Lot at Aiguillon.

Permits: National French licence: Tarn & Garonne dept.

BK Rating: Difficult.

Comments: Enquire locally at tackle shops and with anglers to find best up-to-date spots.

River Garonne

Location: The Garonne runs from the Toulouse area through Moissac, Agen and Marmade, and out to the Gironde about 10 mies north of Bordeaux

Type and Size: A big French river about, 130 miles of good carp fishing, quite fast flowing and slow flowing in other places

Carp Stock: Well stocked with very big carp over 55lbs. One of the best carp rivers in France

Other Species: All coarse fish, especially very big zander and big pike

Permits: French national licence from tackle shops in Moissac, Agen or Marmande

BK Rating: Moderate

Comments: Beautiful river in the south of France. Good places for carp fishing in Agen or Moissac areas

River Lay

Location: In the French département of Vendée (85), on the west French coast

Type and Size: This good carp river is about 30 miles long and runs very slowly into the Atlantic sea on a very touristic French coast

How to Find: From La Roche Sur Yon, take the D746 to Mareuil sur Lay

Carp Stock: Well stocked with a lot of common carp

Permits: French national licence

BK Rating: Easy to Moderate

Comments: Very beautiful common carp

River Loire

Location: The Loire runs from the Lyon area northwards through Roanne and Nevers, and then west through Orleans (60 miles south of Paris), Tours, Angers, and out to the sea at Nantes

Type and Size: A medium-sized river about 400 miles in length, quite fast flowing,

and fairly shallow in places, especially in its upper reaches. There are several power stations on the banks

Carp Stock: Most areas contain carp. The best part of the river is the 150 miles stretch from Decize to Blois. Carp bigger than 30lbs are often caught from the Deciz, Fourchambault, St Laurent and Gien areas

Other Species: Most European species, including catfish to more than 100lbs

Permits: French national licence from tackle shops

BK Rating: Easy - once the fish are located

Comments: The areas near the power stations, especially at Gienan and St Laurent des Eaux, produce a lot of good fish over 30lbs. Unlike most French rivers, boilies are readily acceptable by the Loire carp. It is worth noting that one or two of the lakes alongside the river hold carp of over 40lbs

River Lot

Location: This excellent carp water is more than 100 miles long and runs into the River Garonne about 45 miles south of Bordeaux

Type and Size: The river is dammed in several sections, and water levels vary considerably

How to Find: There are many good areas on this river, but oneof the most popular is near St Geniez d'Olt - follow the signs to Cabanac village

Carp Stock: Very heavily stocked with carp including many big commons.Plenty of doubles, twenties and thirties, and certainly some fish over 50lbs

Permits: French National licence from local tackle shops, such as Serges, 4 Place du Marche, St Geniez

BK Rating: Easy to Moderate

Comments: Often the carp form in large groups so location is important. Large beds of boilies and cooked particles have been very successful. A boat is recommended, and these can be hired in Cabanac. The Lot is featured in two videos: Dave Plummer's 'French Carp Fishing' and Mick Hall's film

River Maine

Location: In the town of Angers

Type and Size: Formed by the junction of three big French rivers: Sarthes, Loire and Mayenne. Only 10 miles long, runs slowly into the river Loire through Angers

Carp Stock: Very well stocked with mirrors and commons

Other Species: All coarse fish

Permits: French national licence from tackle shop at Angers

BK Rating: Easy to Moderate

Comments: A lot of thirties with a good number of forties and fifties. The biggest fish caught in a French competition were caught inthis river in 1990 with a mirror carp of 50lbs (22.8kg). Very hard boilies to beat the small catfish

River Moselle

Location: North east France, flows northwards close to Nancy, through Metz and into Belgium.

Type & Size: Large, natural river.

Carp Stock: Good head of carp but variable according to areas. Most of the bigger fish are caught north of Metz near power station outlets, widening areas and adjoining lakes. Many 15 kilo fish with some to 30 kilos.

Permits: National French licence.

BK Rating: Difficult.

River Rhône

Location: This excellent carp river is more than 200 miles long and runs through Lyon, Valence, Orange and Avignon and out to the Mediterranean Sea about 30 miles west of Marseille
Type and Stock: Big French river with several power stations
Carp Stock: Well stocked with big fish over 55lbs
Other Species: All coarse fish and big catfish to over 150lbs
Permits: French national licence required
BK Rating: Moderate to Easy
Comments: More and more catfish are being caught in this good carp river in the south of France

River Saone

Location: From just north of Dijon to Lyon, at its confluence with the Rhone
Type and Size: River about 100 miles long and 200-400 yards wide; slow flowing with depths of 20-25 feet in the middle
Carp Stock: Good stock of singles, doubles and twenties along the whole length. Carp to over 60lbs have been caught, and it is believed that this river holds a French record
Category: Mixed Fishery
Other Species: Most European coarse fish, including many catfish to 200lbs
Permits: Local tackle shops; French national licence
BK Rating: Moderate
Comments: For big fish, location is vitally important. One of the best areas is in the town of Chalon-sur-Saone, close to the islands and barge moorings. Here many large carp well over 50lbs have been caught. Boilies not successful at first, and you need to bait heavily with sweetcorn and other multiple baits, whilst introducing boilies. Large barges frequent this river, but don't present a problem. Serious approach and commitment needed for success on this river. The Saone was one of the areas fished during the making of the video 'Cat Fever', featuring Kevin Maddocks and Bob Baldock

River Seille

Location: This river is about 40 miles long and runs into the River Saone at Tournus, between Chalon and Macon
Type and Size: A medium sized river which in its lower reaches is some 30 yards wide, with an average depth of about 10 feet
Carp Stock: Heavily stocked with mid-doubles and a good sprinkling of thirties. The river record is supposed to be 59lbs, but the largest authenticated fish we know of is 42lbs
Other Species: Most European species, and catfish to well over 150lbs
BK Rating: Moderate
Comments: One of the best stretches is between the Pont Seille and Ratanelle road bridges especially in the areas of fallen trees. This river is very susceptible to flooding so always have another water you can fish so you don't go all the way there for nothing

River Seine

Location: Runs from Troyes, through Paris, and out ot the sea at Le Havre
Type and Size: Very large river up to a quarter of a mile wide, with varying depths
Carp Stock: Carp are found almost anywhere in the Seine, but certain areas produce the bigger fish. Fish of over 80lbs have been caught, and the French record came from the river, near the River Yonne - a common of 81½lbs!
Permits: French national licence from local tackle shops

BK Rating: Moderate

Comments: For big fish local knowledge must be sought - carp of 50-60lbs are not uncommon in some areas. Heavy baiting with particles at first whilst boilies are introduced is recommended, as many of the fish have never seen boilies; the river carries a lot of boat traffic. A good spot is at Fault Yonne near Monteraux. There are several warm water outlets here, and the winter fishing is quite good

One of a brace of 30's taken by KM on the River Seine - a very prolific carp water.

River Tarn

Location: Northwards from St. Sulpice (30km north east of Toulouse) to junction with River Garonne at Moissac.

How to Find: Spots known to hold big carp are; up river from St. Sulpice, up river from Villemur-s-Tarn and each side of the junction with the Garonne at Moissac.

Type & Size: Varies in width from 10-15 metres.

Carp Stock: Good in certain areas, poor in others, but a good head of 10-20kg fish. Has produced fish to excess of 25kg.

Permits: National French licence: Tarn & Garonne Dept.
BK Rating: Moderate
Comments: A good number of carp are caught from the areas mentioned although it is advisable to obtain local knowledge from tackle shops and anglers.

River Vezere

Location: Runs from Brive westwards
Type and Size: A medium sized river averaging 40 metres in width and slow moving
Carp Stock: Well stocked with carp. Good head of twenties with the chance of fish up to at least 60lbs
Permits: Normal French national licence required
Baits/Methods: Both particles and boilies work well
BK Rating: Difficult
Comments: This river is said to hold huge carp especially in the areas near Terrasson la Villedien and near Larche. Areas of bankside (or fallen) trees most productive

Sandlewood

Location: La Fert Vidame in north France.
How tio Find: Organised trips only through Euro Carp Holidays - 0181 678 1426 or 0181 290 1809.
Type & Size: Lake of 2.4 hectares (6 acres).
Carp Stock: Carp to over 14 kilos (30lbs). Catfish to mid 30's.
Permits: None - only if arranged
Cost: £395 per week.
Restrictions: Three rods only. No groundbait. No fixed leads.
Comments: 7 year old lake never fished prior to 1997.

Sennecey

Location: Between Chalon-sur-Saone and Tournus
Type and Size: The lake is over 40 acres in size, and is the largest of a group of three lakes
How to Find: Turn off the A6/E15 motorway at Chalon. Head south along the N6, which runs parallel to the motorway, to the town of Sennecey. The lakes are clearly signposted in the town
Carp Stock: Lightly stocked with carp to over 40lbs
BK Rating: Difficult
Comments: Became well known some years ago and subsequently received a lot of angling pressure. One English angler had three forties in a weekend, but nowadays it is not much fished. Crayfish and mussels a problem

Tailly

Location: 4 miles south of Beaune, between Dijon and Chalon-sur-Saone
Type and Size: Two gravel pits of about 30 acres and 10 acres
How to Find: Turn off the A6/E15 motorway at Beaune, and head south on the D970. The lakes are either side of the road about 4 miles from Beaune, just past the Meursault turn
Carp Stock: The large lake has a very good head of carp to 47lbs, including many twenties; the smaller lake contains fewer carp to just over 20lbs
Permits: French national licence from Jackie Greset's tackle shop at Chalon-sur-Saone
BK Rating: Moderate
Comments: Local anglers have been moving fish around these lakes to confuse visitors! Hard boilies needed to beat the numerous crayfish. The small lake has many snags. The large lake is shallow at one end, with a small

island at the deeper end, and the island shelf is most productive

Ville Franche A

Location: Near Montpon, 40 miles east of Bordeaux
Type and Size: Two lakes of 30 acres and 5 acres
How to Find: Leave the E70 road, which runs from Bordeaux to Perigueux, at Montpon, then south to Ville Franche. The lakes and camp site are clearly signposted as you enter the village
Carp Stock: The small lake is well stocked with small carp to mid-doubles. The larger lake is lightly stocked with fish up to 40lbs
Permits: Day tickets from the camp site
BK Rating: Small lake - Easy; larger lake - Difficult
Comments: Ideal place to take a family and also enjoy some carp fishing. Boats and swimming allowed on the larger lake, where there is a man-made beach. Very busy at times

Wassy

Location: Wassy, 10km from Lac du Der Chantecoq and 15km from St. Dizier.
How to Find: From Calais take the A26 autoroute through Reims to Chalons-sur-Marne, then the N44/N4 to St. Dizier. From there follow the D384 south for 3 or 4km then take the D2 to Wassy.
Type & Size: Small town lake.
Carp Stock: Heavily stocked with carp to about 20 kilos.
Permits: Enquire locally at tackle shops.
BK Rating: Very easy.
Comments: Night fishing is permitted.

Watermill Lake

Location: Firbeix, Dordogne.
Type & Size: 5 acre lake.
Carp Stock: Heavily stocked.
Other Species: Tench, American perch and black bass.
Permits: Exclusive Angling Holidays, 22 Willen Rd. Newport Pagnell, Bucks, MK16 ODF. Tel/Fax : 01908 616886.
Restrictions: No particle baits.
BK Rating: Easy.
Comments: Bivvy only holiday. Running water and toilet on site. Carp anywhere from 3 - 33lbs; 'designed to catch' water. Very pretty 50 year old mill lake. Open Easter to September 30th. English carp fishing owner.

GERMANY

Ahlbacher Weiher

Location: Westerwald, the Germans call it Mittelgebirge, near the river Rhein and the town Koblenz
Type and Size: Five small lakes and one trout lake with fish to 6lbs
How to Find: From Ahlbach only 12 kilometres to the lakes, follow the signpost from the fishing club
Carp Stock: A lot of carp to 36lb
Other Species: Trout to 18lbs, pike to 24lbs, zander to 15lbs and catfish to 28lbs
Permits: At the car park at the lake, you can buy baits, food and drinks there too

Cost: Not known
Control: Fishing Club
Restrictions: You can only fish on Wednesday and Saturdays from 7am to 5pm
Baits/Methods: Normal baits and methods for carp fishing
BK Rating: Easy
Comments: German national licence essential

Aggerstausee

Location: Near the town of Gummersbach
Type and Size: Big, river dammed lake
How to Find: Take the A4 to Kölm-Olpe and leave the motorway at the town Bergmeustadt
Carp Stock: A few carp to 20lbs
Other Species: Small eels, zanders and pike, a lot of perch, trout and roach
Cost: Two day ticket 90 marks and the week 270 marks
Control: Water Police
Restrictions: No fishing from boat, special fishing permission from tourist department is necessary
Baits/Methods: Boilies and particle
BK Rating: Difficult
Comments: It is not easy to get permission for the water! Geman national licence essential

Altmühlsee

Location: In the south of Gemany, Bavaria, near the towns of Gunrenhausen and Herrieden
Type and Size: Big lake, not very deep
How to Find: The lake is between München and Nürnberg, take the A9 to Munchen, A3 to Nürnberg
Carp Stock: Well stocked with carp to 30lbs
Other Species: Pike, tench, bream and roach
Permits: From the tackle shop in Hervieden, Vogteiplace 1
Cost: 30 marks per day
Control: Water Police
Restrictions: No night fishing. Special German fishing permission is necessary
Baits/Methods: Long range fishing, a lot of baits
BK Rating: Very Easy - small fish to 16lb; Difficult - big fish
Comments: It is necessary to walk long distances with all your gear. Not recommended for lazy anglers! In summer a lot of camping and swimming. German national licence essential

Alt-Rhein

Location: In the Rhein-Main area, near Frankfurt and Damstadt
Type and Size: Small part of the huge river Rhine
How to Find: From Frankfurt take the A5 to Grozs-Gerau, then change to the motorway to Erfelden/Riedstadt
Carp Stock: Well stocked with wild carp to 16lbs, some big mirror carp to 50lb
Other Species: Pike, eel, bream, roach, zander, perch - very big ones to 8lbs. 1992 an angler caught grass carp of 16lbs and the water police have found a dead catfish of 176lbs
Permits: From all tackle shops at the river
Cost: 90 marks for the year
Control: Water Police
Restrictions: Only two rods. Please use the car parks
Baits/Methods: Normal baits and methods, best are boilies at 24mm size, they are big enough to catch only carp

BK Rating: Easy to Moderate
Comments: To many good swims you must walk long distances. You need a lot of baits because there is a lot of ship traffic. The bream cause problems as they like the carp baits. Some swims are very snaggy. Best places are deep holes in the river. German national licence

Bostalsee

Location: Between Hunsruck and Pfalz, in Saarland, south west Germany
Type and Size: Huge gravel pit of 350 acres
Carp Stock: Some carp from 10 to 18lbs
Other Species: Perch, tench, eels, trout, zander and other coarse fish
Permits: German national licence and day and weekly ticket on bank
Cost: £3 per day and £14 per week
BK Rating: Difficult
Comments: Two rods only; no fishing from December 15th to January 31st. Very busy with campers and swimmers

Brombachsee

Location: Near Gunvanhausen, Bavaria, south Germany
Type and Size: Huge lake, only four metres deep
How to Find: The lake is about 10 miles east of Gunvanhausen
Carp Stock: Some carp to 30lbs
Other Species: Pike, trout, perch
Permits: Tackle shop: Baumann-Sonntag, Breitis Angtertreft Am Lindermer 1, 8820 Unterwurmbach
Cost: 30 marks per day ticket
Control: Water Police
Restrictions: No night fishing. Only two rods
Baits/Methods: Bent hook rig, heavy leads
BK Rating: Difficult
Comments: German national licence essential

Dechsendorfer Weiher

Location: Between Nürnberg and Erlangen, in Bavaria, South Germany
Type and Size: Large pit, about three quarters of a mile in length
How to Find: Off the A3 Nürnberg to Wurzburg road
Carp Stock: Well stocked with carp, most of which are under 10lbs
Category: Mixed Fishery
Other Species: Tench and perch
Permits: Sportamt Erlangen, Fahrstree 18, Erlange. Tel: 09131 86590
Cost: £4 per day
Restrictions: Two rods only
BK Rating: Easy
Baits/Methods: Boilies best at present

Diemel -Talsperre

Location: Between Hessen and Nordreihnwestfalen, near the town Korbach
Type and Size: Huge river dam
How to Find: Take the A4 to Olpe, the B55 to Meschede, change to B7 to Messinghausen, then follow the signs 'lake'
Carp Stock: Many carp between 7lbs and 15lbs and some to 30lbs
Other Species: Catfish to 80lbs, eels, pike, zander, roach, trout, tench, bream and perch
Permits: From the tackle shops, Forest office and from some restaurants
Cost: Two day ticket 30 marks; week 75 marks, and year 360 marks
Control: Water Police

Restrictions: Only two rods, no live baits
Baits/Methods: Normal methods, boilies best bait for big carp
BK Rating: Moderate
Comments: No closed season. Difficult to find a good swim, use a boat. Geman national licence

Duisburg Harbour /River Rhein

Location: West Germany, near the Dutch border, the Germans call the area the 'Ruhrgebiet' in the centre of Duisburg
Type and Size: Huge harbour
How to Find: At the A2/A3 take the A2 from Venlo to Duisburg
Carp Stock: Few carp, but very big ones, record carp of 51lbs
Other Species: Pike, zander, eel, roach, bream and perch
Permits: Tackle shop Gervasi, Sternstr. 51, 4150 Krefeld. Tel: 02151 615341
Cost: 30 marks
Control: Water Police
Restrictions: Hard fished water by German carp fishers, modern baits and methods are best at present
BK Rating: Moderate to Difficult
Comments: A difficult water with a chance of a very big fish. German national licence essential

Dümmer

Location: Take the B51 from Osnabruck to Diepholz, near Niedersachen, North Germany
Type and Size: Very big lake, several miles square, and only about five feet deep
Carp Stock: Not many, but some very big ones. Best caught 34 1/2 lbs in 1987
Category: Few Carp
Othe Species: Perch to 6lbs, pike to 36lbs, a few tench and many eels
Permits: The tackle shop Bodeker/Hude, or Friedrich Kemper, Steinstreet 19, 2840 Diepholz. Tel: 05541 3329
Cost: About £5
BK Rating: Super-Difficult
Comments: The best chance is boat fishing and boats can be hired for £3 an hour. Only for the dedicated specialist carp hunter as the fish are few and vary hard to locate

Edertalsperre

Location: Hessen, in the midde of Germany, near the towns Kassel and Korbach
Type and Size: Huge river dam
How to Find: Take the A7 or A44 to Kassel, then change to B251 to Korbach, then take B252 to Herhousen
Carp Stock: Well stocked with small mirrors to 10lbs and some big ones to 40lbs
Other Species: Main fish are pike to 45lbs and zander, bream, roach, tench, eels and perch
Permits: From all tackle shops at the lake
Cost: 30 marks a day, 75 marks a week
Control: Water Police
Restrictions: Only two rods. No night fishing
Baits/Methods: Huge size boilies for carp essential, because the big bream eat the small boilies
BK Rating: Moderate to Difficult, because it's not easy to find the carp (use a boat)
Comments: German national licence essential. Best place to fish for carp is the Niederweber Bucht

Elbe-Havel-Kanal

Location: North east Germany, near Berlin and Brondenburg
Type and Size: Canal
How to Find: Take A2 to Madel
Carp Stock: Some carp
Other Species: Perch, bream, eels and roach
Permits: Tackle shops
Cost: Not known
Control: Water Police
Restrictions: Only two rods. No night fishing
Baits/Methods: Normal baits and methods
BK Rating: Difficult, because there are only a few carp
Comments: German national licence essential

Elchinger Gravel Pits

Location: South Germany, Badenwürttenberg, near to the towns of Unterelchingen and Ulm
Type and Size: Some nice gravel pits
How to Find: Take A7/A8 to Ulm, change at motorway to Ober and Unterelchingen
Carp Stock: Huge carp to 40lbs
Other Species: Pike, eel, zander, perch, roach,bream, chub, tench
Permits: Elchinger Tackle Shop, 7915 Unterelchingen. Tel: 07308/6161
Cost: Day ticket 60 marks
Control: Club
Restrictions: Not known
Baits/Methods: Boilies best bait for the big ones
BK Rating: Moderate
Comments: German national licence essential

Ellertshäuser Reservoir

Location: Unterfranken, between Würzbürg and Schweinfurt
Type and Size: Huge reservoir
Carp Stock: Well stocked with carp to 20lbs
Category: Mixed Fishery
Other Species: Tench, zander and trout
Permits: Bernd Müller, Zum See 10, 8721 Fuchstadt, Unterfranken
Cost: £5 per day
BK Rating: Insufficient information
Comments: The best water in Unterfranken, and a very pleasant area

Erlenholsee

Location: Westerforrest, Mittelgebirge, north of the town Montabaur, West Germany
Type and Size: Small lake
How to Find: Take A3 (Köln-Frankfurt)
Carp Stock: Well stocked with small carp
Other Species: Coarse fish
Permits: Tackle shops in Montabaur
Cost: Not known
Control: Club
Restrictions: Only two rods
Baits/Methods: Bent hook rigs and boilies are the best
BK Rating: Difficult, very hard fished water
Comments: German national licence essential

Falkenhagener See

Location: Near Berlin-Spandau, East Germany
Type and Size: A nice lake in a nice surrounding
How to Find: Take A2 to Berlin
Carp Stock: Carp water, paradise for carp anglers with many fish to 35lbs
Other Species: Pike, tench, rudd, roach, eel and perch
Permits: Tackle shops in Berlin-Spandau
Cost: 24 marks for day tickets; 90 marks for week
Control: Club
Restrictions: Only two rods
Baits/Methods: Hard fished with boilies, a lot of snags
BK Rating: Easy to Difficult
Comments: A lot of lilies and fields. German national licence essential

Gamensee

Location: East Germany, Brandenburg
Type and Size: Big reservoir
How to Find: Take motorway Berlin - Blumberg, then change to B158 to Dannenberg
Carp Stock: Very well stocked with carp to 20lbs
Other Species: Eel, bream, roach, pike, tench and some zander
Permits: Tackle shop
Cost: 30 marks per day
Control: Water Police
Restrictions: Not known
Baits/Methods: Boilies and modern carp fishing rigs are best at present
BK Rating: Difficult, very hard fished water
Comments: The many bream and roach are a problem as they take the baits. German national licence essential

Godelheimer Seen

Location: North of Germany, near the towns of Godelheim and Hoxter
Type and Size: Five gravel pits
Carp Stock: Well stocked with mirror and common carp to 30lbs
Other Species: Catfish to 60lbs, pike to 25lbs, zander to 18lbs, eels to 5lbs and tench to 7lbs
Permits: Tackle shop Müller in Godelheim
Cost: 30 marks
Control: Fishing club and Water Police
Restrictions: Not known
Baits/Methods: Standard rigs, boilies, particle baits and floater fishing
BK Rating: Easy
Comments: The fishing ticket is for all lakes! German national licence essential

Grafenwöhr

Location: Between Amberg and Bayreuth
Type and Size: Some of small river and three lakes
How to Find: Take the motorway B299 to Grafenwöhr
Carp Stock: The lakes are well stocked with carp to 28lbs
Other Species: Pike to 35lbs, bream, roach, eel, barbel, chub, tench, zander and a few catfish
Permits: Tackle shop Weiden, Holunderweg 1,8480 Weiden
Cost: Day ticket 36 marks and the week 120 marks
Control: Club
Restrictions: Only two rods. No night fishing. In lakes only leads to 10gms
Baits/Methods: Particle baits and boiies are very successful because nobody has

fished the water with these baits before
BK Rating: Easy
Comments: German national licence essential

Griebnitzsee

Location: In the middle of Berlin
Type and Size: Large town lake
Carp Stock: Many commons and mirrors to 25lbs
Category: Carp Water
Other Species: Bream, roach, eels and pike
Permits: Tickets from the fishing club Schöneberg, Islandrellistret 56, 1000 Berlin 46
Cost: £15 for 6 months
BK Rating: Easy
Comments: Two rods only;German national licence essential

Griesäcker Gravel Pit

Location: South Germany, near the town Ulm, Baden Württenberg
Type and Size: Small gravel pit
How to Find: Take A7 to Ulm, then change at motorway to Aislingen
Carp Stock: Stocked with carp to 38lbs
Other Species: Big pike and all coarse fish
Permits: Erwin Zaboch, Haupstreet 26, 7983 Königsbronn/Ochsenberg
Cost: Day ticket 60 marks, year 600 marks
Control: Club
Restrictions: No night fishing. Two rods and no live baits
BK Rating: Easy to Moderate
Comments: German national licence essential

Hammerweiher

Location: Near the town of Bodenwöhr, Bavaria, South Gemany
Type and Size: Small lake
Carp Stock: Stocked with carp to 36lbs
Other Species: All coarse fish
Permits: Petrol station Kraus, 8465 Bodenwohr. Tel: 09434/2606
Cost: 150 marks per week; 300 marks per month
Control: Club/Water Police
Restrictions: Not known
Baits/Methods: All advanced baits and rigs, boilies are the best baits. Not hard fished by boilie fishers
BK Rating: Easy to Moderate

Happurger Reservoir

Location: Abbochtal,between Deckersberg, Houbirg and Reicheneck in the Franken area of Bavaria, South Germany
Type and Size: 150 acre reservoir
Carp Stock: A few carp to 18lbs
Category: Few Carp
Other Species: Tench, zander, big trout, roach and eels
Permits: From the Town Hall in Happurg
Cost: £5 per day
BK Rating: Difficult
Comments: Much sailing and windsurfing in summer

Henne-Talsperre

Location: In the industrial area of Ruhr-Gebiet, near the town Meschede
Type and Size: Huge reservoir about 200 hectares
How to Find: Take the motorway 55 to the town Meschede
Carp Stock: Some carp to 25lbs
Other Species: Pike, trout, eel, perch, zander, tench, bream, and roach
Permits: Day ticket water from tackle shop Bischoff, Zeughausstreet 12, 5778 Meschede. Tel:6488
Cost: 24 marks for day
Control: Water Police
Restrictions: Two rods only
Baits/Methods: Worms, particles and boilies. Standard rigs are very successful
BK Rating: Moderate
Comments: The best place to catch carp are Horback-Bucht and Enkhausen. German national licence essential

Hopfensee

Location: Hopfen am See, Bavaria, South Germany
Type and Size: Big lake about half a mile across
Carp Stock: Well stocked with carp to 40lbs
Category: Mixed Fishery
Other Species: Tench, bream, roach, pike, zander, perch and eels
Permits: German fishing permit, and a £3 day ticket from the Hanpt tackle shop nearby
BK Rating: Difficult
Baits/Methods: Most fish are caught by float fishing with sweetcorn
Comments: Very snaggy water with island. Boat needed to catch the carp; a very pleasant lake

Kamneder See

Location: Off the A43 motorway between Witten Herbede and Hattingen, in Nordrheinwestfalen, North Germany
Carp Stock: Not many carp
Category: Few Carp
Other Species: Bream, roach, pike, zander, and perch
Permits: ASV Bochum, Ruhr 1935; the tackle shop Simmerman Bochum, Herner Street 363. Tel: 0234 551679
Cost: £2 per day
BK Rating: Difficult

Kölner Seen-Platte

Location: Off the A4 from Aachen to Köln (Cologne), Nordrheinwestfalen, North Germany
Type and Size: Huge lake
Carp Stock: Well stocked with commons to 18lbs
Category: Mixed Fishery
Other Species: Perch, pike to 33lbs, tench and grass carp
BK Rating: Very Difficult
Comments: You will need to enquire localy how to get permits to fish this lake, as we were not able to find out

Krumme See

Location: East Germany, Brandenburg, near the town of Krummersee
Type and Size: Nice huge gravel pit
How to Find: Drive from Königs-Wustgerhausen to Mittenwold and drive left

	to Schenkendorf, now follow the signs to the lake
Carp Stock:	Well stocked with mirror and common carp to 30lbs
Other Species:	Bream, roach, pike, zander, eel, and perch
Permits:	Tackle shop and town office
Cost:	Not known
Control:	Club/Water Police
Restrictions:	Only two rods
Baits/Methods:	All advanced baits and methods
BK Rating:	Easy
Comments:	German national licence essential

Landgrafenweiher

Location:	Fichtilgebirge, near Warmensteinach
Type and Size:	Large gravel pit
Carp Stock:	Quite well stocked with carp which average 6-8lbs. Some bigger fish to about 20lbs
Category:	Mixed Fishery
Other Species:	Grass carp, pike, zander, bream and catfish
Permits:	From the house at the lake in Warensteinach
BK Rating:	Easy
Restrictions:	No baiting with boilies, fish food or particles

Mahnig - See

Location:	East Germany, district of Brandenburg
Type and Size:	Small lake
How to Find:	From Buchholz to Halbe-Teupitz
Carp Stock:	Carp to 28lbs
Other Species:	All coarse fish
Permits:	Club, tackle shop and forest office
Cost:	Not known
Control:	Club
Restrictions:	Only two rods. No night fishing
Baits/Methods:	Normal carp fishing methods and boilies as bait
BK Rating:	Easy
Comments:	German national licence essential

Mossandl - Weiher

Location:	Between Manning and Dingolfing, near Regensburg in Bavaria, South Germany
Type and Size:	Gravel pit of about 60 acres
Carp Stock:	Well stocked with mirrors and commons to about 20lbs
Category:	Mixed Fishery
Other Species:	Pike and zander
Permits:	Restaurante Fischwirt, 8388 Mamming, and Dingolfing tackle shop, Obere Stadt 52, Dingolfing. Tel: 08731 2404
Cost:	£10 per week
Restrictions:	No night fishing, but boat fishing is allowed
BK Rating:	Moderate

Niedermooser See

Location:	Hessen, in the centre of Germany, between Giessen and Fulda
Type and Size:	90 acre gravel pit
Carp Stock:	Heavily stocked with commons to about 20lbs, and mirrors to 25lbs
Category:	Mixed Fishery
Other Species:	Tench, pike, eels, zander, trout, and most other coarse fish
Permits:	From the Campingrestaurante at the lake

Cost: £4 per day; £24 per week
Control: ASV Lauterbock, Linderstrasse 4, 6420 Lauterbach
BK Rating: Moderate
Comments: A big lake also used for sailing

Niederwaldsee

Location: Near Frankfurt, between Nauheim and Gross Gerau
Type and Size: Big gravel pit
How to Find: Take the A67 from Frankfurt to Darmstadt, then the road to Gross Gerau
Carp Stock: Well stocked with small commons to 15lbs, and mirrors to 30lbs
Category: Mixed Fishery
Other Species: Pike, tench, chub, roach, bream, perch, eels and zander
Permits: Day tickets should be purchsed from the tea shop at the lake. The tickets only cover 12 hours - night fishing not allowed
Cost: £3 per day
Control: Club
BK Rating: Small fish - Easy; big ones - Very Difficult
Baits/Methods: Advanced carp fishing rigs, methods and bait are needed at this lake for the big carp. Boilies and sweetcorn are very successful
Restrictions: No night fishing, two rods only
Comments: Restaurant and disco at the lake; camping in summer; car park

Op Finger See

Location: South Germany, near the town Freiburg
Type and Size: Gravel pit of about 34 acres
How to Find: Take the motorway Basel-Karlsruhe
Carp Stock: Many doubles to 38lbs
Other Species: Perch, pike, zander, tench, eel, roach, bream and a few trout
Permits: From all tackle shops in Freiburg
Cost: Day tickets only, 45 marks
Control: Water Police and Club
Restrictions: Two rods only. Special fishing licence necessary
Baits/Methods: Carp tactics and baits, including sweetcorn and float fishing
Comments: In the hot months a lot of camping and swimming, difficult to get a ticket. German national licence essential

Rappbodetalsperre

Location: Asthorc, near the town of Wernigerode
Type and Size: Huge river dam
Carp Stock: Some carp to 40lbs and a lot of crucian carp
Other Species: Big perch to 7lbs, pike, eel, zander and all coarse fish
Permits: From the fish growing station at the lake
Cost: Day ticket 45 marks and week 90 marks
Control: Water Police
Restrictions: Not known
Baits/Methods: All the most advanced baits, rigs and methods needed for this hard fished water. Some swims are very snaggy and you must use strong line, heavy leads and hooks of between sizes 6 and 2
BK Rating: Moderate to Difficult
Comments: German national licence essential

Rhein-Herne-Canal

Location: Canal between Duisburg, Bochum and Herne, canal flows into the river Rhein
Type and Size: Canal 5 to 8 metres deep and 30 metres wide
How to Find: Near Gelsenkirchen and Duisburg, take A2 from Venlo to Duisberg, change to A59 and in Hamborn change to A42 Herne
Carp Stock: Many carp, the biggest caught weighed 36lbs
Other Species: Eels, roach, bream and zander
Permits: Reko Fishing Tackle, Kahrstreet 71, 430 Essen
Cost: 15 marks day ticket
Restrictions: Two rods only
Baits/Methods: Advanced carp fishing rigs, methods and baits are needed at the lake for the big carp. German carp fishermen use sweetcorn and boilies
BK Rating: Easy to Moderate
Comments: German national licence essential

River Altmühl

Location: South Germany, Bavaria near Nurnberg
Type and Size: Very small river in old mature farm
Carp Stock: Well stocked with wild and common carp to 15lbs
Other Species: Pike, bream, tench and eel
Permits: Tackle shops
Cost: 30 marks per day ticket
Control: Water Police
Restrictions: Only two rods. No night fishing. No lifeboats
Baits/Methods: Sweetcorn and boilies
BK Rating: Moderate to Difficult for the bigger ones
Comments: German national licence essential

River Bille

Location: In the centre of Hamburg, north Germany
Type and Size: Very small river with a lot of fish, not very deep
How to Find: You can find the water on all town maps of Hamburg
Carp Stock: Heavily stocked with small wild carp to 12lbs, some big ones
Other Species: Eel, zander, bream, roach and pike
Permits: From the tackle shops
Cost: Not known
Control: Water Police
Restrictions: Only two rods. No night fishing
BK Rating: Easy
Comments: German national licence essential

River Donau

Location: South Germany, the river flows from Donaueschingen to the Austrian border., Towns on the river: Regensburg, Passau, Ulm
Type and Size: Huge European river
How to Find: Take A8 or A7 to Ulm, then you can drive parallel to the river
Carp Stock: Well stocked with carp to 50lbs possibly
Other Species: Catfish to 150lbs, sturgeon, pike, eels, chub, perch, roach, bream, tench, grass carp, mirror carp, zander
Permits: Tackle shops near the water
Cost: Not known
Control: Water Police
Restrictions: Only two rods. In some areas no night fishing
Baits/Methods: Huge size boilies necessary

BK Rating: Difficult to find the carp
Comments: A water with a lot of species of fish in a nice surrounding. German national licence essential

River Eider

Location: North Germany, near the town of Wrohm
Type and Size: Small river
How to Find: Take the B203 from Heide to Rendsburg
Carp Stock: Well stocked with carp to 30lbs
Other Species: Bream, eel, perch, zander, roach and pike
Permits: Tackle shop Mickan, Hauptstreet 44, 2241 Wrohm
Cost: Not known
Control: Water Police
Restrictions: Not known
Baits/Methods: Normal carp fishing baits and methods
BK Rating: Moderate
Comments: German natonal licence essential

River Fulda

Location: Hessen, near the towns Fulda and Kassel, in the centre of Germany
Type and Size: River
How to Find: Take A7 or A49 to Kassel
Carp Stock: Many carp to 10lbs, but some big ones to 30lbs
Other Species: Bream to 9lbs, chub to 6lbs, eels, trout, barbel, pike to 26lbs and perch
Permits: Tackle shop near the water
Cost: Day ticket 21 marks, week 120 marks and month 130 marks
Control: Water Police
Restrictions: Most fish are caught by float and leger fishing with sweetcorn and boilies
BK Rating: Moderate
Comments: German national licence essential

River Lahn

Location: Middle Germany, Hessen, near the towns of Wetzlar and Limburg
Type and Size: Small river
How to Find: Take A3 to Liburg or A45 to Wetzlar
Carp Stock: Well stocked with carp to 25lbs
Other Species: Pike, trout, barbel, chub, few tench and catfish, perch, eel roach, bream and zander
Permits: Tackle shops and private
Cost: Day ticket 30 marks
Control: Club/Water Police
Restrictions: Not known
Baits/Methods: Normal carp fishing methods and baits
BK Rating: Easy
Comments: German national licence essential

River Leine

Location: Near the town of Hannover, North Germany
Type and Size: Small river which flows into the Aller (flow very fast)
How to Find: Take A2 from Bielefeld to Hannover
Carp Stock: Carp to 24lbs
Other Species: Pike, eel, trout, roach and bream
Permits: FV Hannover, Hildesheimer Street 112,3000 Hannover 1. Tel: 0511 880054
Cost: 60 marks per week; 240 marks per month
Control: FV Hannover

Restrictions: Not known
Baits/Methods: Normal carp fishing baits and methods
BK Rating: Moderate
Comments: German national licence essential

River Main

Location: In the middle of Germany, near the towns of Frankfurst, Hanau, Wümburg and Aschaffenburg
Type and Size: Huge European river with many sluices
Carp Stock: Many carp to 20lbs, some to 40lbs
Other Species: Pike, eel, catfish to 150lbs (German record), zander, roach, bream, barbel
Permits: From all tackle shops near the river
Cost: 90 marks for year
Control: Water Police
Restrictions: Only two rods
Baits/Methods: A lot of bait, strong line, heavy leads. 24mm size boilies are very successful as bream cannot take them
BK Rating: Easy, if you are in the right place
Comments: Some English carp fishermen have fished the river and caught carp to 40lbs

River Mosel

Location: Nordrheinwest Falen, West Germany, between the towns of Koblenz and Trier
Type and Size: River, which flows into the Rhein
How to Find: Take the B416/B49 from Trier to Koblenz
Carp Stock: Well stocked with carp to 44lbs
Other Species: All coarse fish
Permits: From tackle shops at the river
Cost: Not known
Control: Water Police
Restrictions: Only two rods. Do not park your car anywhere
Baits/Methods: Huge size boilies otherwise you will only catch bream, chub and barbel
BK Rating: Easy to Moderate
Comments: German national licence essential

River Naab

Location: South Germany, Bavaria
Type and Size: Small river
Carp Stock: Big mirrors to 30lbs
Other Species: All coarse fish and catfish to more than 100lbs. Jurgen Paul and his friends have this year caught pike and catfish to 26lbs
Permits: Tackle shops
Cost: 180 marks a week
Control: Club/Water Police
Restrictions: Only two rods
Baits/Methods: Snag leader fishing in some swims essential
BK Rating: Easy to Moderate
Comments: A well stocked water in a nice nature area. German national licence essential

River Neckar

Location: Near Heidelberg and Heilbronn
Type and Size: River with a lot of ship traffic and sluices
How to Find: Take the A5 from Frankfurt to Heidelberg, then the motorway parallel

	to the river to the town Mosbach/Heilbronn
Carp Stock:	Heavily stocked with carp to 55lbs, best German carp water
Other Species:	Chub, barbel, roach, bream, eels, some pike, a few zander and catfish to 60lbs
Permits:	From all tackle shops near the river
Cost:	150 marks for the year, no day tickets
Control:	Water Police
Restrictions:	No night fishing. Two rods. No returning of fish
Baits/Methods:	Fish mix. Fixed lead and short hooklength
BK Rating:	Easy
Comments:	Very snaggy, rods to 2 1/2 lbs, sometimes only 1 1/2 lb, leads between 2oz and 4oz, big reels for example Baitrunner 4500 with 15lb line, snagleader very useful. Best fishing before and after a sluice. Not only the carp like boilies so do big barbel and chub. Make 24mm size boilies if you want to catch carp only. A good water to catch your dream carp. A water with a lot of carp between 20lbs and 30lbs. The best times for carp fishing are spring/autumn and sometimes early winter. German national licence essential

River-dam Quitrdorf

Location:	Sachsen,near Dresden, on the Polish border in what used to be East Germany
Type and Size:	Hugh reservoir of about 2,000 acres
Carp Stock:	Well stocked with commons and mirrors; water record is 38lbs
Category:	Mixed Fishery
Other Species:	Grass carp, tench and zander
Permits:	Permits from the camping area in Kollm
Cost:	£4 per day; £12 per week; boat hire £2 per day - two rods only
BK Rating:	Moderate

River Rhein

Location:	West Germany, near the French border
Type and Size:	Huge European river
Carp Stock:	Many carp under 10lbs, but the record is 60lbs
Category:	Mixed Fishery
Other Species:	Pike to 35lbs, zander to 30lbs and big catfish
Permits:	German national rod licence and a weekly permit, bought locally
Cost:	£10 per year
Control:	Water Police
BK Rating:	Easy, if you can locate the fish
Baits/Methods:	Boilies catch the big fish. You need powerful rods, heavy leads, and line of 15lb breaking strain - and at least 200 metres of it, in case you hook one of the big catfish
Comments:	Not a river for beginners to fish

Schnackensee

Location:	Near the town of Gunzenhausen, Bavaria, South Germany
Type and Size:	Eight acre lake
How to Find:	The lake is about 25 miles south of Nürnberg
Carp Stock:	Well stocked with plenty of doubles, and some bigger fish. Lake record is 44lbs
Category:	Mixed Fishery
Other Species:	Many catfish to 150lbs (see Kevin Maddocks' book 'Catfish'), grass carp to 70lbs, pike, zander and 'Mamur Carp' to 70lbs
Permits:	Day ticket on bank
Control:	Private - Werner Vogel

BK Rating: Easy
Cost: £10 for 2 rods; £8 per day for caravans and £4 for tent or bivvy
Baits/Methods: Modern, advanced rigs, methods and baits needed
Comments: A pleasant, heavily stocked water producing hundreds of carp each week; can be very busy at weekends. Night fishing not allowed

River Schwalm

Location: Between Knüllgebirge and Kellerforest, Hessen in the middle of Germany
Type and Size: Small river
Carp Stock: Some carp to 20lbs
Other Species: Pike, perch, chub, trout, tench, bream and a lot of barbel to record size
Permits: From the village office in Schwolmstadt
Cost: Day ticket 30 marks
Control: Water Police
Restrictions: Only two rods. No night fishing
Baits/Methods: Big size boilies, if not you will only catch barbel
BK Rating: Moderate to Difficult
Comments: Not a water for beginners or for big catches. German national licence essential

River Sieg

Location: Between the two towns of Bonn and Siegburg, in the west of Germany on the left side of river Rhein
Type and Size: Small river which flows into the river Rhein
How to Find: Take the A565, A59 or A3 to Bonn
Carp Stock: Well stocked with carp to 30lbs
Other Species: Barbel, pike, trout, chub, small catfish
Permits: Fishing clubs: ASV Obere Sieg, ASV Köln-Nord, ASF Eitdorf, ASF Stein-Stadt Blankenburg
Cost: 35 marks for day ticket
Control: Fishing Clubs
Restrictions: Two rods, sometimes only one rod, no live bait fishing
Baits/Methods: In some areas very snaggy, snag leaders fishing, heavy lead
BK Rating: Moderate
Comments: Not easy to get a licence. German national licence essential

River Spree

Location: In the centre of Berlin
Type and Size: Small river
How to Find: In the middle of Berlin
Carp Stock: Few carp to 24lbs
Other Species: Main fish are zander, roach, bream, pike and eel
Permits: From tackle shops in Berling, day tickets
Cost: Not Known
Control: Water Police and Clubs
Baits/Methods: Modern specimen hunting methods and baits
Comments: A problem to find an angling place because the river is in the centre of the town. German national licence essential

Silbersee

Location: At the town of Neuss and near Dusseldorf
Type and Size: Big gravel pit
How to Find: Take the motorway to Dusseldorf and change to Neuss
Carp Stock: Heavily stocked with a lot of carp to 40lbs
Other Species: Tench, pike, zander, roach, bream

Permits: Tackle shop Holge Menne, Bannerstr. 60, 4040 Neuss/Grimlinghausen
Cost: 18 marks for day tickets
Restrictions: Two rods. Small carp must be returned
Baits/Methods: Boilies and modern rigs
BK Rating: Easy to Moderate
Comments: Crayfish attack the boilies and other baits. One carp fishermen caught 50 carp between 20lbs and 30lbs. German national licence essential

Stichkanal

Location: Off the A2/A39 near Braunschweig
Type and Size: Big canal much used by boats
Carp Stock: Well stocked with carp to 35lbs
Category: Mixed Fishery
Other Species: Most coarse fish,including pike and zander
Permits: In advance only from Restaurant Gerhard Dolsner, Weinberg 8, 3303 Vechelde
Cost: £4 per week - three rods
BK Rating: Moderate
Baits/Methods: Best method is a fixed lead with a pop-up hair rigged bait such as dog food

Storkower See

Location: The lake is south of the motorway Berlin-Frankfurt, near the Berlin Urstromtals, in Berlin
Type and Size: Lake of about 100 acres
How to Find: Take the B248 or the motorway Berlin-Frankfurt
Carp Stock: Well stocked with carp
Other Species: Roach, bream, zander, pike and eel
Permits: From the fishing club Storkow
Cost: Year; for carp fishing 450 marks, for pike fishing 510 marks; per day 30 marks
Control: Fishing Club
Baits/Methods: Nobody has fished with boilies before
BK Rating: Moderate
Comments: Camping area at the lake. German national licence essential

Talsperre-Bautzen

Location: In the middle of Germany, near the town Bautzen
Type and Size: Huge reservoir, which is dammed by the river Spree
Carp Stock: Many carp (up to 60lbs) and tench
Other Species: Zander, eel, perch, roach, bream and grass carp
Permits: Tackle shop Wadewitz in Bautzen
Cost: 30 marks per day; 105 marks per week
Control: Water Police
Restrictions: Two rods only. No live baits for pike fishing
Baits/Methods: Sometimes it is necessary to fish at long range
BK Rating: Easy, if you find the right fishing place
Comments: Around the lake are lots of car parks. Night fishing is permitted. German national licence essential

Twislesee

Location: West Germany, Hessen near the town Arolsen
Type and Size: Huge lake
How to Find: Take A44 to Diemelstadt, change to B252 to Arolsen

Carp Stock: A very well stocked fishery, with some very big carp
Other Species: Pike, trout, roach, bream, chub, perch, zander and eel
Permits: Tackle shop, petrol station, restaurants
Cost: Not known
Control: Water Police
Restrictions: Only two rods
Baits/Methods: Fixed lead, short hook length and boilies. Dutch fishermen have caught carp to 40lbs with two boilies on the hair, pop-up
BK Rating: Difficult, not easy to find the fish
Comments: German national licence

Unteres Oderbruch Kanal

Location: East Germany, near the Polish border
Type and Size: Canal
Carp Stock: A few carp
Other Species: Chub, zander, roach, bream, eels and a lot of perch
Permits: Not known
Control: Water Police
Baits/Methods: Normal rigs and baits
BK Rating: Difficult, because there are only a few carp
Comments: German national licence essential

Successful German carp angler, Andreas Richter, with one of his many carp caught on KM boilies; this one weighed 30 pounds (13.6 kg).

Werbellinsee

Location: East Germany, near the town Neuruppin in Brandenburg
Type and Size: Hugh gravel pit
Carp Stock: Well stocked with carp to 36lbs
Other Species: All coarse fish
Permits: Club and tackle shop
Cost: Not known
Control: Club
Baits/Methods: Nobody has fished the water with boilies
BK Rating: Easy
Comments: German national licence essential

Werrastalsperre

Location: Between the towns of Eschwege, Kassel and Gottingen, in Hessen, central Germany
Type and Size: Huge Gravel pit
How to Find: Take the A7 from Salsgitter to Kassel and then the B7 to Eschwege
Carp Stock: Carp to 20lbs
Category: Mixed Fishery
Other Species: Zander, rudd, bream and roach
Permits: Fremden Vekelswerein (FVV) Eschwege 3440 Eshwege
BK Rating: Moderate
Comments: Float fishing is the best method here

HOLLAND

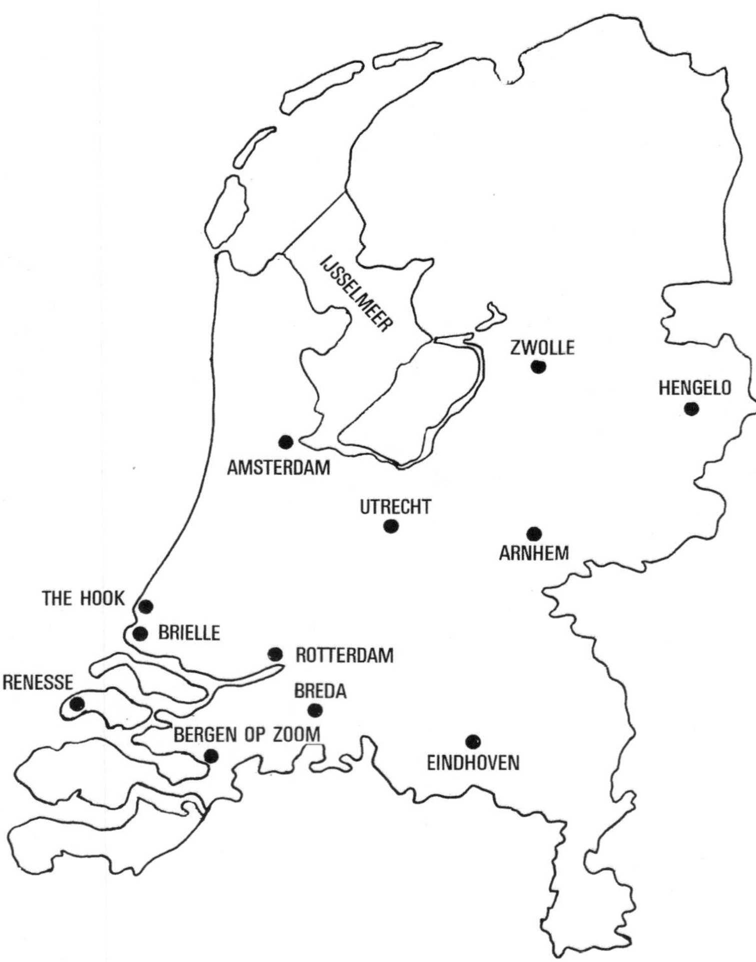

Amstelveense Poel

Location: Near town of Amstelveen
Type and Size: Big lake
Carp Stock: Many carp but not easy
Other Species: Several
Permits: National licence and Licence Amsterdamse Hengelsport Vereniging
Control: Amsterdamse Hengelsport Vereniging
Baits/Methods: Difficult water, so use modern rigs
Comments: Nice place to fish

Barge and Jetty Lake and Complex

Location: Knieuwkoop, about an hour's drive from the Hook of Holland
Type and Size: Barge and Jetty Lakes about 1½ acres each. The main complex is about 150 acres, made up of many small lakes
Carp Stock: Jetty Lake is heavily stocked with carp from 15 - 30lbs, including some big commons.Barge Lake also heavily stocked with carp to mid-twenties
Permits: In advance only from: Carp Fishers Abroad, Rose Cottage, Roddington Heath, Shrewsbury, Shropshire SY4 4RB. Tel: 01952 770771
BK Rating: Easy to Moderate
Comments: Carp Fishers Abroad have a secure clubhouse with washing and toilet facilities. The small lakes immediately adjacent to the clubhouse are heavily stocked with carp to 30lb and are pretty easy. The complex is a mass of natural lakes interconnected by small canals. Access around these is by boat. The lakes are very productive especially in early season. We have a local guide who knows the area very well and will put you straight onto the fish.The Carp Fishers Abroad package includes ferry tickets, local directions, licences, boats, use of the clubhouse and preferential access to the best island swims in the complex (a chance for real isolation!). Night fishing is no problem in the summer months

Binnenbedikjle Maas

Location: Near Gravendal on Oud Beijerland, west of Dordrecht.
Type & Size: Long dammed river.
Carp Stock: Well stocked with carp to upper twenties.
Category: Mixed Fishery.
Other Species: General coarse fish.
Permits: Enquire locally.
BK Rating: Moderate.
Comments: Boat recommended. Not heavily fished.

Brielle Moat

Location: 15 miles west of Rotterdam, very near the coast
Type and Size: Moat around the old town of Brielle
Carp Stock: Quite heavily stocked, including several 20lb commons
Permits: Available from 'local bar' or tackle shops
BK Rating: Moderate
Comments: A very well known fishery, which is heavily fished at times

Damse Vaart

Location: Between Sluis (Holland) and Brugge (Belgium)
Type and Size: Small canal
Carp Stock: Carp up to 30lbs
Other Species: Many
Permits: National licence and a licence from local tackle dealers in Sluis
Restrictions: Night fishing allowed
Baits/Methods: Modern
BK Rating: Very Difficult

De Bosbaan

Location: Not far from Amsterdam
Type and Size: Large lake
Carp Stock: Enormous population of carp with fish up to 50 pounds. Plenty of upper twenties

Permits: Normal 'Sportvisakte' required
Restrictions: No groundbait and no free offerings
Baits/Methods: Good rigs needed as fish only ever encounter hookbaits!
BK Rating: Moderate
Comments: Heavily fished

De Kleiputten of Esbeek

Location: Near the village of Esbeek (Hilvarenbeek) about 5 miles south of Tilburg
Type and Size: Small clay pit, very attractive
How to Find: At the end of a sand track out of the village of Esbeek
Carp Stock: Plenty of doubles and a few twenties
Category: Easy
Permits: Normal 'Sportvisakte' required
Restrictions: No night fishing
Baits/Methods: Standard baits and rigs work well
Comments: A good place for regular runs!

Friesland A

Location: South of Leeuwarden, near Sneek.
Type & Size: Many lakes in the northern province of Friesland, such as the Sneekermeer.
Carp Stock: Heavily stocked with carp.
Permits: Enquire from Willem Zandstra.
BK Rating: Easy.
Comments: The whole of Friesland is one enormous carp water, and is little fished. Accommodation and information from Willem Zandstra's Blikken Plaet's hotel - the Dutch Tel: 0566 689366.

Het Apeldoornskanaal

Location: A channel that goes from Apeldoorn till it ends in the River Ijssel. From the Hoek you drive to Den Haag, take the A12 to Utrecht. Take the A28 to Amersfoort. In Amersfoort you take the A1 to Apeldoorn. Leave the road at Alpeldoorn-zuid, go left and the first right, you'll find it there
Type and Size: 18 miles long
Carp Stock: There is an interesting stock of carp in the channel. Not really very many but up to 34lbs
Category: Mixed Fishery
Other Species: Most European coarse fish
Permits: Government and local permit which you can get at the local tackle shop in Alpeldoorn. Address - Markstraat 5 Apeldoorn
BK Rating: Easy to Moderate
Comments: Night fishing only from 1st June to 31st August

Het Kinselmeer

Location: Near the dam of Ijsselmeer, the huge inland sea in the north of Holland
Type and Size: Huge lake, beautiful and quiet
Carp Stock: A reasonable sprinkling of huge carp
Permits: Normal 'Sportvisakte' required
BK Rating: Difficult
Comments: Location is important. Has produced some huge carp to persistent anglers

Het Nijkerker Nauw/Het Eemmeer

Location: A water next to the N301 between Nijkerk and Zeewolde. From the Hook you drive to Den Haag, take the A12 to Utrecht. In Utrecht you take the A28 to Amersfoort, in Amersfoort you stay on the A28 to Nijkerk. Leave the road at Nikerk/Zeewolde. Now you are on the N301, go in the direction of Zeewolde. After about 1 mile you cross the river
Type and Size: About 8 miles long and an average of half a mile wide
Carp Stock: Not really known, but there are a lot of carp. Professional fishermen have found carp up to 50lbs in their nets
Category: Mixed Fishery
Other Species: Most European coarse fish, very large pike and zander
Permits: Government permit only
BK Rating: Moderate to Difficult
Comments: A lot of day trips and watersports on the water. Night fishing only from 1st June to 31st August

Hoge Vaart

Location: Between Lelystad and Almere
Type and Size: Small river
Carp Stock: Many carp to 20 pounds
Other Species: Big bream
Permits: National Licence and a permit from D G Cornelissen, Archipel 15-27 to Lelystad
Control: Club
Restrictions: Night fishing allowed in June, July and August
BK Rating: Easy
Comments: No close season

Hollands Diep

Location: West of the town of Moerdijk, and south of Dordrecht.
Type & Size: Dammed estuary of the Maas and Rijn rivers.
Carp Stock: Well stocked with carp to 45lbs.
Other Species: General coarse fish.
Permits: Enquire locally.
BK Rating: Easy if you can find the fish.
Comments: Big water needing massive amounts of bait. Former Dutch common record of 45 lbs came from here. Use of boat recommended.

Lage Vaart

Location: Between Lelystad and Almere
Type and Size: Small river
Carp Stock: Many carp to 20 pounds
Other Species: Big bream
Permits: National licence and a permit from D G Cornelissen, Archipel 15-27 te Lelystad
Control: Club
Restrictions: Night fishing allowed in June, July and August
BK Rating: Easy
Comments: No close season

Littie Melanen

Location: Bergen op Zoom, 20 miles west of Breda
Type and Size: Town lake of about 8 acres
How to Find: In the town of Bergen op Zoom
Carp Stock: Very heavily stocked with some twenties
Permits: From the tackle shop in the town, or at the camp site nearby
BK Rating: Very Easy
Comments: An ideal water to take the family; several camp sites nereby

Molengat and Ovensgat Lake

Location: Rossum,near Utrecht
Type and Size: Two lakes of about 7 acres
How to Find: Take the A2 and the N322 to Rossum (between Utrecht and den Bosch)
Carp Stock: Carp to at least 35 pounds
Permits: Available from cafe named 'Waalzicht' in Rossum, cost approximately 5 guilders per day and 60 guilders for a year
BK Rating: Moderate
Comments: Very nice waters with potential of some very big fish. The nearby river also holds carp

Molenwiel

Location: Near Nedarasselt, between Wychen and Druten
Type and Size: 6 acre lake
Carp Stock: Fish to at least 35 pounds, quantity unknown
Permits: Day tickets available from grocer's shop 'Van der Stappen' in Nederasselt, cost: 3 guilders, or 60 guilders per year
BK Rating: Moderate
Comments: A good quality water holding some big carp - full potential unknown

Nieuwkoopse Plassen

Location: About 4 miles north east of Alphen aan de Rin, which is 20 miles north of Rotterdam
Type and Size: A huge complex of shallow lakes
Carp Stock: Fairly well stocked with carp of all sizes, and some big catfish
Permits: Normal 'Sportvisakte' required
Baits/Methods: Simple baits and rigs work
BK Rating: Moderate
Comments: Location is of prime importance on this large water and then holding the fish is sometimes difficult. A boat is essential. Great potential for the serious carp angler

Noord-Hollands Kanaal

Location: Runs from Amsterdam to Den Helder
Type and Size: Big river
Carp Stock: Plenty of carp and other species, up to at least 30lbs
Permits: National licence and from the Amsterdamse Hengelsport Vereniging
Control: Amsterdamse Hengelsport Vereniging
Restrictions: Ask the angling club
Comments: Difficult water to locate the carp but once found, they are easy to catch

Oisterwijkse Vennen

Location: About 5 miles north east of Tilburg
Type and Size: A combinaton of several waters but the only good one is the Belvertsven Lake of about 25 acres. Very deep in the middle
Carp Stock: Some doubles and twenties with a sprinkling of thirties
Permits: Normal 'Sportvisakte' required
Baits/Methods: Advanced rigs and baits required
BK Rating: Moderate
Comments: Spring and summer sees many holidaymakers in the region but very quiet in the autumn

Othense Kreek

Location: In the town of Terneuzen
Type and Size: Very big lake
How to Find: East part of the small town
Carp Stock: Carp to 30lbs, lots of twenties
Other Species: Many
Permits: National licence at any post office
Control: Local eel angler
Restrictions: No close season. No night fishing
BK Rating: Very Easy
Comments: A good place to fish

Renesse

Location: 30 miles south west of Rotterdam, on the coast
Type and Size: 5 acre lake
Carp Stock: Well stocked with carp, and lots of twenties
Permits: Available at £6 per year from local - WV tourist office
BK Rating: Moderate
Comments: A good place to take the family; many camp sites close by. Heavily fished in summer

Rijnkanaal

Location: Amsterdam area, where there are many other canals, all containing carp
Type and Size: If you thought the Twente was big, you ought to see this one!
Carp Stock: Heavily stocked with plenty of big carp
Category: Mixed Fishery
Other Species: Most coarse fish
Permits: Compulsory Sportvisakte, the national licence obtainable from Post Offices; you MUST NOT fish in Holland without this licence - no other permit required. Covers two rods for a year at low cost
BK Rating: Difficult, unless the fish can be located when it is quite easy
Comments: No close season. Many big fish lost when line is cut on freshwater mussels, so you need line heavy enough and of the right type to combat this problem.
NB. The new Dutch record of 52lbs was caught from a river, and most of the biggest carp are found in rivers and canals; for this reason we strongly recommend anglers to fish these and not the lakes, which often are private and do not contain the biggest carp. Night fishing only allowed in June, July and August

River De Eem

Location: A not very long river. The most interesting part for carp fishermen is the part from highway A1 to the end of the Eemmeer. From the Hook you drive to Den Haag, take the A12 to Utrecht. In Utrecht you take the A27 to Hilversum, stay on this road till you can take the A1 to Amersfoot. Leave the road at Baarn. The road you come on now is next to the river
Type and Size: 14 miles long
Carp Stock: You won't catch 10 carp a day, but there are plenty of nice fish up to 35lbs
Category: Mixed Fishery
Permits: Government and at most parts you need a local permit too
BK Rating: Moderate to Difficult
Comments: Night fishing only from 1st June to 31st August

River Ijssel

Location: Runs through Zwolle which is about 50 miles east of Amsterdam
Type and Size: A medium sized river with not too much flow
Carp Stock: Heavily stocked with many twenties and thirties
Permits: Normal 'Sportvisakte' and local permits are required
Cost: About £15 a year
Baits/Methods: Advanced rigs and baits very effective
BK Rating: Moderate
Comments: The stretch near Kampen has produced several huge commons. Lots of potential for the serious carp fisher

River Maas

Location: Runs from Liege heading north to Nijmegen, then west and out to sea below Rotterdam
Type and Size: A large river with considerable flow at times and regularly used by boats
Carp Stock: This river yielded the latest Dutch record of 53lbs in 1993. Tremendous potential
Permits: Normal 'Sportvisakte'. A permit from a local tackle shop at a cost of about £15 a year is required to fish one of the attached sand pits
BK Rating: Difficult
Comments: There are numerous sand pits connected to this river and the ones near the towns of Roermond and Echt are prolific carp venues

Sloterplas

Location: Amsterdam
Type and Size: Big lake
How to Find: East part of Amsterdam
Carp Stock: Many carp up to well over 30lbs
Other Species: Many
Permits: National licence at any post office. Licence from Amsterdamse Hengelsport Vereniging
Control: Members Amsterdamse Hengelsport Vereniging
BK Rating: Difficult/Moderate
Comments: A very well known fishery. Quality baits best; responds to heavy baiting

Surfkolk or Zwenkolk

Location: Highway A28 between Amersfoort and Zwolle.
Type & Size: 20 acre lake.
Carp Stock: Good head of twenties, with a few thirties.
Category: Mixed Fishery.
Other Species: Pike, roach, zander, bream, chub and eels.
Permits: Wezep local tackle shop - Fred Wolf.
Control: Private.
Restrictions: Two rods only.
BK Rating: Moderate.
Comments: Wilco Fredriks, Molenhamweg 45, Heende. Tel: 5702 2631.

The Ijsselmeer

Location: North Holland, north of Amsterdam
Type and Size: Huge inland sea, once salt water, 40 miles long and about 25 miles across and separated from the sea only by the Afsluitdijk, a 12 mile dam built by the Dutch and one of the world's greatest engineering feats
Carp Stock: Very well stocked with carp, most of which are huge and immensely long wildies which go to over 20lbs
Category: Mixed Fishery
Other Species: Most European coarse fish
Permits: You must have the official Government licence, the Sportvisakte, obtained from Post Offices at low cost, and valid for two rods for a year. No other permits needed
BK Rating: Very Difficult, though some huge catches have been made when the fish are located
Comments: No close season. Best areas are around Amsterdam and Flevoland. Try to get help from someone who knows the area, and may know where carp are caught. When I stood at the middle of the dam, two years ago, the waves on this 'lake' were several feet high, with spray breaking over my head. Heavy baiting required to hold the 'nomadic' fish on the spot

The Lakes van het Gooi

Location: Ankeveense plassen; Loenerveense plas; Loosdrechtse plassen; Breukeleveense plassen; Maarseveense plassen; Vinkeveese plassen. These are the waters you find in the square Amsterdam-Hilversum-Utrecht-Amstelveen

Carp Stock: There have been catches over 50lbs and there are plenty of carp in the lakes, but the lakes are big

Category: Mixed Fishery

Permits: Government and there are a few places you need a local permit, but you better ask around

BK Rating: Difficult

Comments: Night fishing is not allowed everywhere and not on every place the year round. These water are heavily controlled so best behaviour is a must

T Luytelaar

Location: Mariahout, near Eindhoven

Type and Size: Lake of about 3 acres

How to Find: Take the N266 and N272 to Lieshout and from there to Mariahout

Carp Stock: Heavily stocked with carp to 30 pounds, mainly commons

Other Species: Big grass carp

Permits: Day tickets availabe in the village of Mariahout and the address and directions are explained on a signpost at the lake

BK Rating: Easy

Comments: A very peaceful and quiet place to fish

Twentekanaal

Location: Hengelo area, by the warm water outlet

Type and Size: Huge canal, about 80 metres across

Carp Stock: Heavily stocked with many big carp to nearly 40lbs

Category: Mixed Fishery

Other Species: Most coarse fish

Permits: You will need a Sportvisakte, which is a national licence - you must not fish in Holland without this licence, which can be bought at all Post Offices and most tackle shops. The licence is annual, covers two rods and costs only about £6 for a year - there is no close season in Holland. You can fish most other Dutch waters with this licence,and no other permits, the exceptions being where a club has the rights, which is usually indicated by the sign 'Verpacht Viswater'

BK Rating: Difficult

Comments: This is one of the most famous and pressurised fisheries in Europe especially as it fishes so well in the winter, due to the warm water. It is wide and very deep, and the boats are of ocean-going size, and will disturb your swim for half an hour after they pass. Best fishing is at night, and the most sophisticated methods and rigs are needed - PM had a blank here too - though nothing at all was caught during the day whilst he was there, although a number of good fish were taken during the night.....after he had left for England! Night fishing only allowed in June, July and August. Steam rises from the water in winter!

Wilhelminakanaal

Location: Tilburg
Type and Size: A long canal which eventually runs out into the sea below Rotterdam
Carp Stock: Sparsely stocked with carp of a good average size
Permits: Normal 'Sportvisakte' required
Baits/Methods: Advanced rigs and baits an advantage
BK Rating: Moderate
Comments: Once one of Holland's top carp waters but not so good nowadays

Zeumerse Plas

Location: A water next to the A1 highway between Amersfoort and Apeldoorn. From the Hook you drive to Den Haag, take the A1 to Utrecht. In Utrecht you take the A28 to Amersfoort. In Amersfoort you take the A1 to Apeldoorn. Leave the road at Voorthuizen,turn left and immediately to the right, now you drive straight to the water
Type and Size: 15 acres
Carp Stock: A lot of commons up to 18lbs
Category: Mixed Fishery
Other Species: Most European coarse fish except zander
Permits: Government and local permit, information from: Zevenbergjesweg 27, 3781 NV Voorthuizen
BK Rating: Easy to Moderate
Comments: No baiting, night fishing only from 1st June to 31st August. Very deep water, not under 20 feet, good plumbing necessary. Control every day so keep the place clean

The Dutch record common of 53 pounds (24.1kg) caught by Mark Adams on a Cream RM30 KM Boilie.

Zuid Willemsvaart

Location: Between the town of Eindhoven and Weert.
Type & Size: Canalised river.
Carp Stock: Very well stocked with carp to 40 lbs.
Other Species: General coarse fish.
Permits: Enquire locally.
BK Rating: Difficult to Moderate.
Comments: Heavily fished, heavy baiting needed.

Zuiderdiep

Location: Near the town of Stellendam on the west coast about 15 miles south of the Hook of Holland
Type and Size: A dammed stretch of canal with a soft bottom
Carp Stock: Well stocked with upper doubles and twenties with the occasional thirty pounder
Permits: Normal 'Sportvisakte' and a local permit
Cost: About £15 year
BK Rating: Moderate
Comments: A magnificent water offering high class fishing and only a few minutes drive from the nearest ferry port. Heavy fishing pressure during school holidays

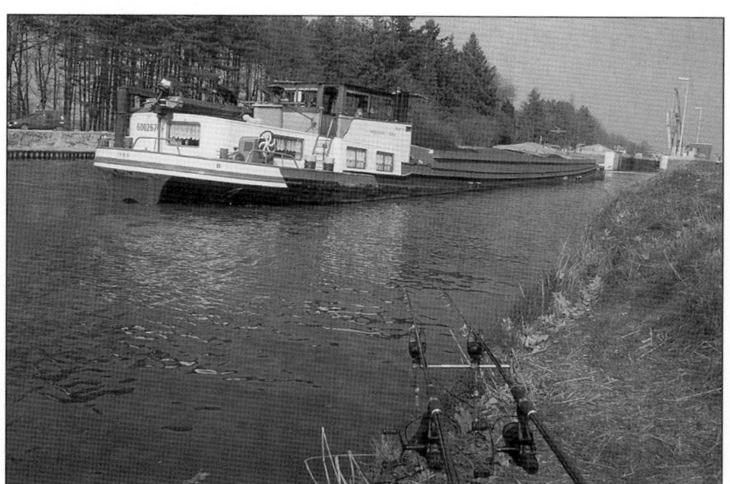

Even the small canals of Holland and Belgium carry considerable barge traffic!

ITALY

Accesa Lake

Location: Along the Aurelia way, close to Follonica. Exit Bagni di Gavorrano to Lago dell' Accesa

Type and Size: Small immaculate lake in beautiful surroundings

Carp Stock: Almost unknown. Already caught fish over 36 lbs (grass carp) but commons and mirrors over 40 lbs are in the lake

Other Species: Black bass and a few trout

Permits: Government licence

Restrictions: Night fishing allowed but no fire or camping tents. Take your litter home!

BK Rating: Difficult

Comments: Needs accurate fish location due to deep water. No snags. This fantastic lake (you can drink the water) is almost unknown and has been closed for twenty years. Today it is one of the most beautiful waters in Central Italy (Tuscany Region) and the real potential is not known. Carp over 20 kg have been caught with paste baits (and released) in the past. Heavy maize and hemp prebaiting to stop some big shoals of carp cruising. No nuisance fish or crays.Fish location is very difficult. Not many facilities apart from a small food shop 3 km from the lake

Albano Lake

Location: South of Rome. Also called Lake of Castelgandolfo where the Pope spends his holidays. It is 30 minutes driving from Rome along the road to Genzano.

Type and Size: Big volcanic lake with depths in excess of 50 mt.

Carp Stock: Very big mirrors and commons. Grass carp over 25 kg

Other Species: Coarse fish and pike

Permits: Government licence and local permission

Restrictions: Night fishing allowed with extra permission available by local shops.
BK Rating: Very Difficult
Comments: Several well known anglers including British have had blanks. Weeds and snags are the main problem. Food and drink available. Do not argue with local anglers!. Boats are essential for good fish location. Heavy prebaiting with mixed particles is suggested. Needs heavy tackle.

Alviano Lake

Location: Along the A1 highway Milano - Rome, exit Orvieto is 10 km south of Corbara lake
Type and Size: Big lake with hundreds of good venues. Shallow water.
Carp Stock: Almost unknown. Many fish over 20 and several 30's. I had two 40's in a day during a memorable session in 1993 but no more.
Other Species: Coarse fish and zander. Few pike.
Permits: Government licence
BKRating: Easy (if location is right)
Comments: Due to the wildness of the lake, very few fishing checks are made at night. No food and drinks available near the lake. GSM coverage medium /poor. A secret unfished, unpressured carp water.

Avigliana Lake

Location: West of Turin along the E13 road exit Avigliana
Type and Size: Small lake. Different depths
Carp Stock: Well stocked with 20's and 30's. Several fish over 40 lbs and more.
Other Species: Coarse fish, pike and perch
Permits: Government and FIPSAS required
Restrictions: No night fishing
BK Rating: Moderate but needs a good location
Comments: Good carp water with several big fish. Restaurants and food shops along the bank Nice water with good potential. Many fish over 30lbs have been caught in the past. Nice surroundings.

Biferno Lake

Location: Along the E2 highway Pescara/ Foggia, take the exit to Campomarino, drive to the opposite side.Use an accurate map for location of dam.
Type and Size: Big dam along the river Biferno
Carp Stock: Well stocked with carp over 20 lbs. Few bigger fish
Other Species: Coarse fish and a few trout
Permits: Government licence
Restrictions: No night fishing but lack of controls
BK Rating: Moderate to easy
Comments: This big dam is almost unfished with boilies and hair rigs. Potential is unknown but we had fish over 30 lbs a few years ago. Very good along the bridge. Food and drink available within 20 km. Credit cards not accepted. GSM coverage medium / poor.

Bracciano Lake

Location: 40 km from Rome along the SS2 Cassia, exit Anguillara
Type and Size: Huge volcanic lake
Carp Stock: Almost unknown but fish over 20 kg caught by perch anglers with nets. No carp fishing pressure at all
Other Species: Coarse fish, pike, perch and mullet
Permits: Government licence
Restrictions: No night fishing but lack of controls
BK Rating: Difficult fish location due to lake size.

Comments: Boats are necessary. Many weeds in warmer months. Highly recommended in winter and autumn for big catches. One of the biggest lakes around Rome. Potential almost unknown but several sessions gave us screaming runs with several 20's and 30's. Fish over 20 kg. 3 rods allowed. Food and drinks available in local villages. Restaurants cheap with high quality food. GSM coverage good. Tackle and bait at the Andrea De Matteis shop in Rome

Brian Canal

Location: East of Venice, exit 'San Stino di Livenza / Motta di Livenza'
Type and Size: Medium canal with slow current. Many different good venues.
Carp Stock: Some big carp (mirror and common) with fish over 22/23 kg.
Other Species: Pike, black bass and coarse fish
Permits: Government and local weekly permission
Restrictions: Night fishing tolerated but no tents close to the water because of rising water risks
BK Rating: Moderate in warmer months, excellent in winter.
Comments: Record carp water where fishmeals are recommended. Good catches with crab and shellfish flavours. Small town and villages close to bank to buy food. Permission (10,000lt.) requested along the canal and available at Caorle tackle shops.

Calcione Dam

Location: South East of Siena along the Siena / Arezzo way. Rapolano exit
Type and Size: Big lake dam with many snags
Carp Stock: Many carp over 20 and 30 lbs. Several 40's with many 40 lb grass carp
Other Species: Pike
Permits: Government licence
Restrictions: Night fishing not allowed but very few checks made by local rangers. No fires for safety reasons
BK Rating: Difficult
Comments: This water needs heavy prebaiting. Fish finders and small boats are suggested. No engine allowed. Snags and fish location difficult. Food and drink available at the nearest village. GSM coverage poor. This is a good carp water with huge grass carp. Location is important and 'rotten bottom' techniques are suggested for many snags on the bottom.

Canal Bianco

Location: From Governolo (Mantova) to Rovigo's road to Adria.
Type and Size: Medium canal
Carp Stock: Many 30's and few 40's. Excellent water for good fishing
Other Species: Many big catfish (silurus)
Permits: Government licence. 3 rods allowed
Restrictions: Night fishing tolerated
BK Rating: Easy (if location is good)
Comments: GSM coverage medium / good. Great unknown water. Grass carp over 45 lbs reported by top anglers. Many good venues so just have a look.

Canterno Lake

Location: 60 km from Rome along the A 1 Rome-Napoli highway exit Fiuggi. Once in the Fiuggi take the way to Alatri (SS156)
Type and Size: Small natural lake
Carp Stock: Mostly commons with an average size of 20 lbs. Lots of smaller fish.
Other Species: Coarse fish
Permits: Government and FIPSAS licences

Restrictions: No night fishing with checks made by Park Rangers (Guardia Forestale)
BK Rating: Moderate
Comments: Attractive lake. Good for short sessions. Food and drink available at Fuiggi town.

Capacciotti Lake

Location: South of Italy, Puglia region, near Cerignola (Foggia)
Type and Size: Big dam
Carp Stock: Well stocked with 20's and 30 lb commons and mirrors
Other Species: Coarse fish, perch and tench
Permits: Government licence
Restrictions: Night fishing allowed
BK Rating: Moderate
Comments: Not a safe area for single foreign anglers, your gear can be stolen! Boat needed for extra long range baiting. Food and drink available within 20 km. GSM coverage poor. Credit cards not accepted. Do not argue with local anglers and take your litter home.

Casale Gravel Pit

Location: Along the A4 highway Venezia - Udine exit at Quarto, then to Marcon. Once in the village ask for 'Cave di Casale'
Type and Size: Big gravel pits
Carp Stock: Many fish over 25 lbs plus several 30's.
Other Species: Black bass and pike
Permits: Government 3 rods allowed
Restrictions: Night fishing allowed
BK Rating: Moderate
Comments: Food and drinks available at Marcon, just 3 km from the water For best venues contact local top angler Stefano Bonazza or Daniele Campello. Few chances in daylight but several fish in night time. Moderate water but small boat necessary for long range fishing (at least 200 m.) Few fish in the margins.

Caverni Lakes

Location: West of Pisa town along the way to Marina di Pisa
Type and Size: Three small lakes (gravel pits)
Carp Stock: Many doubles and 20's. Few big grass carp and huge silver carp
Other Species: Nuisance fish
Permits: Government and FIPSAS licences
Restrictions: Night fishing not allowed with heavy checks made by FIPSAS rangers. Action in daylight.
BK Rating: Easy

Chiusi Lake

Location: Along the A1 highway from Florence to Rome at exit Chiusi, exit Moltepulciano to Lago di Chiusi
Type and Size: Big lake
Carp Stock: Well stocked with 20's and 30's. Good stock of carp over 40lbs. Few grass carp over 40 lbs
Other Species: Coarse fish
Permits: Government and FIPSAS licences
Restrictions: No night fishing
BK Rating: Difficult (due to the limited number of venues available)
Comments: Good restaurants close to the bank. Food and drinks available at the closest villlages. Few locals are always in the 2/3 good venues for

very long sessions. They catch a lot of 20 pound fish at extra long distance. Boat is always needed for prebaiting and fish location.

Coghinas Lake (Sardinia)

Location: North east of Sardinia along the Olbia - Sassari SS527 exit Oschiri
Type and Size: Big dam in autumn and springtime. Big water level changes
Carp Stock: Stocked with medium size fish. Many double figure fish.
Other Species: Perch
Permits: Government licence
Restrictions: No night fishing but lack of controls
BK Rating: Moderate (difficult fish location)
Comments: Big Sardinian lake almost unfished for carp. Needs a boat for fish location. Please avoid any spring month for spawning fish everywhere. Food and drink available at Oschiri. No GSM coverage. No carp tackle available.

Corbara Lake

Location: Along the A1 highway exit Orvieto.
Type and Size: Immense dam on Tevere river. One of the best Italian waters in the past
Carp Stock: Full of 4 lb carp..It was an incredible carp fishing lake just 5 years ago. Duncan Kay did his Italian carp video for national TV here with a common over 20 kg. Although professionals are destroying this water there are many fish around the 10 kg mark with far less above
Other Species: Zander, pike and perch. Coarse fish
Permits: Government and FIPSAS licences
Restrictions: Night fishing not allowed with checks made by Police and Carabinieri. No fires allowed
BK Rating: Easy (small carp). More difficult to land decent fish (over 20 lb)
Comments: Several carp anglers here and many takes during daylight hours. No problem for food, drink or telephone. No camping allowed. GSA cover age medium.

Dese River

Location: Along the A4 highway Venezia - Udine at the final exit to Mestre, drive along the road to Marcon. Then go to San Liberale and take Via Zuccarello. You will find the river 4 km. later
Type and Size: Small river
Carp Stock: Many fish over 30 lbs, few 40's
Other Species: Coarse fish
Permits: Government. 3 rods allowed
Restrictions: Night fishing tolerated but high presence of rats! Daylight fishing very good
BK Rating: Easy to Medium
Comments: Food and drink available at the local 'Pizzeria' 100 metres from the bank Good winter water with lots of carp. Fishmeal baits highly recommended

Endine Lake

Location: 25 km. north of Bergamo along the SS42 highway Milano Bergamo A4
Type and Size: Big lake
Carp Stock: Commons and mirrors over 25 Kg. and grass carp over 27 Kg. already caught
Other Species: Pike, perch, zander and coarse fish
Permits: Extra permits required for night fishing and controls by local Rangers
Restrictions: Night fishing allowed with permission

BK Rating: Medium to Difficult
Comments: Very poor winter fishing but excellent during warmer months.Good chances to land fish over 40 lbs.

Fiastra Lake

Location: Way SS77 'Cofiortro' from Perugia (Macerata) then turn to Fiastra.
Type and Size: Small /medium lake from a dam
Carp Stock: Several fish over 20 lbs, lake record is 35 lb
Other Species: Perch and coarse fish
Permits: Government and FIPSAS licences
Restrictions: No night fishing
BK Rating: Difficult
Comments: This is a small mountain lake stocked with big fish. 2 rods allowed, Beautiful surroundings and good autumn fishing. Camping not allowed.

Isola Liri Lake

Location: Along the A1 highway at San Giovanni in Carico exit, then to Pico, ask for the lake. Use an accurate map
Type and Size: Small lakes formed by the dam on river Liri
Carp Stock: Well populated with double figure carp! 95% commons.
Other Species: Coarse fish
Restrictions: Night fishing is allowed but extra permission is needed
BK Rating: Easy
Comments: Some problems in the dark if using 3 rods. An average of 15/20 runs per night if your prebaiting is heavy. Shoals of carp are looking for your boilies. No way if you want to relax. Your bite indicators will be a nightmare! Food and drink at nearest village 'San Giovanni in Carico' Drop your marker and cast out at least 5/10 kg of boilies mixed with particles to beat your record of runs in one single night.

Lago di Viverona

Location: Along the highway A5 Vercelli - Ivrea exit at Cavaglia to the lake
Type and Size: Medium lake
Carp Stock: Well stocked with all sizes of fish. Many carp over 20 lbs. Big grass carp reported
Permits: Government and FIPSAS licences
Restrictions: No night fishing
BK Rating: Difficult
Comments: Not many facilities. Some food and drink available at Cavaglia village. Some good restaurants.Small rowing boat recommended for fish location. Not an angler in sight

Lake Di Mezzo and Inferiore

Location: Mantova town
Type and Size: Medium lake with 4.5 metre depth (average)
Carp Stock: Many carp around the 20 lb mark, several 30's
Other Species: Catfish, zander, perch and coarse fish
Restrictions: Night fishing allowed
BK Rating: Easy
Comments: Along the town edge. 'La Mincio' shops (0376 / 604856) for licences and tackle. Boat not needed.

Lake San Pietro

Location: 3 km south of Goito along the SP 236 Mantova Brescia
Type and Size: Medium gravel pit
Carp Stock: Many doubles; several 20's; very few 30's. Many grass carp over 45 lbs
Other Species: Pike
Permits: Private permission (day or week ticket available)
Restrictions: Night fishing allowed
BK Rating: Easy
Comments: Private water with restaurant and facilities. Good for a comfortable session. Great chances for record grass carp in autumn. As this is a private water, request permission to 'La Mincio' tackle shops (0376 / 604856)

Livenza River

Location: Along the highway Venezia - Udine exit San Stino di Livenza / Motta di Livenza
Type and Size: Big river unpolluted. Crystal clear water
Carp Stock: Almost unknown with fish over 25 kg and specimen carp over 30 kg netted in the past. Giant commons over 25 kg with uncaught mirrors. One of the best rivers in Italy
Other Species: Coarse fish, pike and trout (northern part)

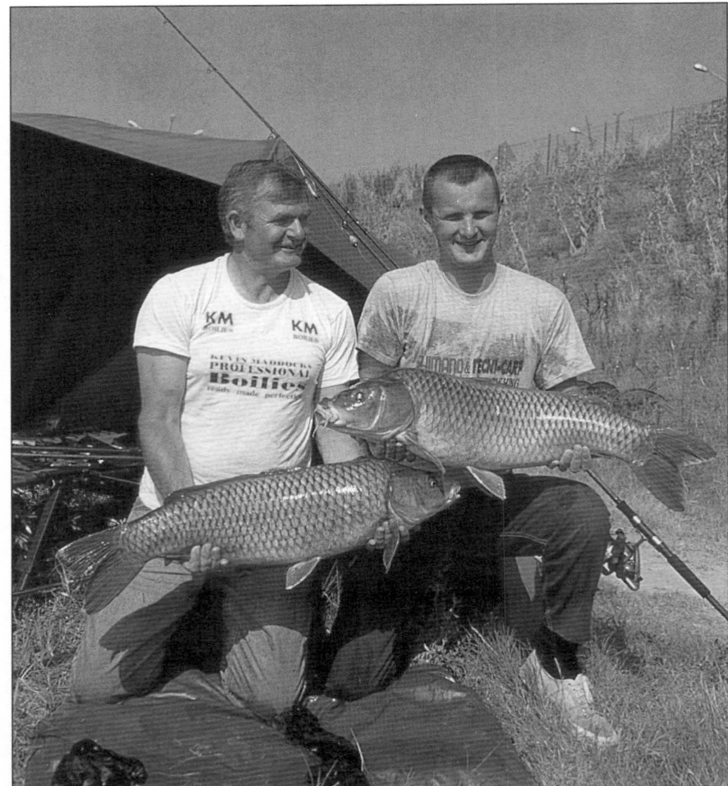

Kevin Maddocks and Paul Guggi with typical commons from the prolific lakes, Di Mezzo and Inferiore, at Mantova.

Permits: Government and FIPSAS
Restrictions: Night fishing not allowed but due to lack of control, not dangerous for your tackle. Please avoid any fire
BK Rating: Difficult due to depth and current.
Comments: Fish location is important with very heavy prebaiting. Heavy tackle suggested (3 lb rod with 20lb b.s. line) Food and drink easily available close to the river. Great food at every restaurant

Mantova Lakes. Lake Superiore

Location: North of Mantova town exit along the A1 highway or Brescia - Milano highway
Type and Size: Big lake with lots of reeds. Boats are highly recommended
Carp Stock: Potential almost unknown but many good catches of 30 + lb commons and several 40 + mirrors. We had over 15 thirties in one night
Other Species: Pike and coarse fish. No catfish here.
Permits: Government and FIPSAS licences (available at La Mincio shop)
Restrictions: Night fishing allowed
Comments: For further information and licences contact 'La Mincio' shops 0376 / 604856 (English spoken)

Martignano Lake

Location: 3 km from Bracciano lake, take the SS2 Cassia to Bracciano lake and exit at Anguillara / Trevignano. Please buy an accurate map for location because there is just a path to the lake
Type and Size: Medium volcanic lake almost unknown by anglers
Carp Stock: Several commons and mirrors about 30lb. Bigger fish caught by nets
Other Species: Coarse fish
Permits: Government licence. 2 rods allowed
Restrictions: Night fishing not allowed but lack of controls.
BK Rating: Easy (if location right)
Comments: Needs heavy prebaiting. This is an unknown water for the majority of carp anglers. We had very few fish in the past but the average size was over 30 lb. A beautiful extra long range water. No food and drink available close to the water but just 5/10 km from the lake. Just a path to the lake

Merse River

Location: Along the Senese from Grosseto to Siena (Tuscany)
Type and Size: Medium / small river
Carp Stock: Several 30's (commons) with few mirrors. Few fish over 40 lbs
Other Species: Pike and barbel
Permits: Government licence
Restrictions: Night fishing allowed for lack of control
BK Rating: Difficult
Comments: Hard fish location. (Suggested the Rice Fields zone) A nice river almost unfished with good potential. Not an angler in sight for miles! Best venues are 10/15 km from food shops and telephones. GSM coverage very poor. Tackle: Misterfish 0564 / 457406 (fax and tel)

Mincio River

Location: Outlet of Mantova's lakes to Po river. At least 20 different venues so it needs pages to show all the good chances. Excellent winter fishing river. Fantastic from Mantova to the Po river
Type and Size: Medium river with 6 metres of depth
Carp Stock: Many carp with lots of 30's and several 40's. Fish over 60 lbs.

Other Species: Great catfishing river. Perch, zander and pike. Coarse fish
Permits: Government and FIPSAS licences. 3 rods allowed
Restrictions: Night fishing not allowed but tolerated for catfishing and those who return fish
BK Rating: Moderate to Easy
Comments: FIPSAS permission mandatory. Please contact 'La Mincio' at (0376 / 604856)

Narni Lake

Location: Along the highway A1 exit Terni, then to Narni scalo.
Type and Size: Medium dam with crystal clear water
Carp Stock: Many double figure carp with few 20's
Other Species: Coarse fish
Permits: Government licence. 2 rods allowed
Restrictions: No night fishing
BK Rating: Easy (shallow water with many takes in daylight)
Comments: Food and drink available at the nearest village (2 km) GSM coverage poor. Weeds and reeds in warmer months. Very good in winter

Occhitto Lake

Location: Along the road Campobasso Foggia, South East of Italy (Puglia Region) Approx. 35 km from Campobasso
Type and Size: One of the largest dams in Europe, a huge lake
Carp Stock: Very well stocked with medium and small size carp. Few fish over 30 lbs
Other Species: Tench, black bass and perch
Permits: Campobasso (Government and FIPSAS) while Foggia's bank is just Government licence
Restrictions: Night fishing not allowed on Campobasso bank (north), allowed due to lack of controls along the Foggia bank (south)
BK Rating: Moderate to easy for medium fish (20 lbs), difficult for larger fish
Comments: Boats recommended GSM coverage poor. 2 rods allowed on Campobasso bank while 4 allowed on Foggias. No facilities within 30 km.

Omodeo Lake (Sardinia)

Location: Middle of Sardinia along the SS131 Way Cagliari - Sassari exit Ghilarza
Type and Size: Biggest lake in Sardinia
Carp Stock: Well stocked with commons and mirrors. Average size 15 - 20 lbs. Record carp is 20 kg (44lb).
Other Species: Coarse fish and black bass
Restrictions: Night fishing tolerated
BK Rating: Moderate to difficult (due to hard fish location)
Comments: Uncontaminated water with an amazing potential for carp. Almost unknown by 99% of carp lovers due to the distance from Italy. Very nice place for a week or two.

Ombrone River

Location: Grosseto town (Tuscany). Along the Senese way to Siena. Good venues on Ischia d'Ombrone, Paganico, Batignano.
Type and Size: Small river but almost unfished and unpressured.
Carp Stock: Mostly long thin powerful commons. Several doubles, few 20's and 30's
Other Species: Coarse fish
Permits: Government licence
Restrictions: Night fishing allowed in summer. Lack of controls
BK Rating: Easy (but not big catches)
Comments: All the river is almost unfished with boilies, a small boat is suggested

because many good venues are quite uncomfortable. Some poisonous snakes such as vipers on the bank. Grosseto or Istia d'Ombrone for food and drinks. For further contact R.Ripamonti at 0564/493506. Tackle shop is Misterfish at 0564/457406 (fax and tel). GSM coverage medium. Tigers and fishmeal are the best bait.

Pelagone Pond

Location: Along the Livorno - Grosseto (Aurelia) way, exit Bagni di Gavorrano
Type and Size: 3 acre gravel pit
Carp Stock: Commons and mirrors over 13 kg. Many grass carp over 15 kg
Other Species: Nuisance fish.
Permits: Private water. Local club permission required (lt 20,000 per day) at 0564/457406
Restrictions: Night fishing allowed
BK Rating: Medium to Easy
Comments: Private water, no carp sacks; unhooking mats mandatory. 2 rods allowed GSM coverage good. Closest town is Bagni di Gavorrano at 8 km.

Penne Lake

Location: Reach Pescara then Loreto Aprutino. In 20 km this beautiful lake
Type and Size: Big dam
Carp Stock: Almost unknown but many double figure carp and 20`s. Fish over 30 lbs reported but not confirmed
Other Species: Coarse fish
Permits: Government licence
Restrictions: Few checks when night fishing
BK Rating: Moderate to easy
Comments: Nice venue for a relaxing session. Ask John Llewellyn. No facilities

Po River in Turin

Location: Town of Turin
Type and Size: Biggest Italian river
Carp Stock: Very well stocked with all sizes of carp and catfish
Other Species: All freshwater species including trout and grayling
Permits: Government licence
Restrictions: No night fishing but no controls
BK Rating: Easy
Comments: You can have everything in Turin. This huge river is full of carp, fish well over 70lbs have been caught in the past with paste baits. Just find a comfortable venue and wait for fish

Polverina Lake

Location: Along the SS77 'Colfiorito' way from Perugia to Recanati. On the right side of the road you will find the first lake (dam)
Type and Size: Medium dam
Carp Stock: Well stocked with 20's and 30's
Other Species: Coarse fish and a few catfish (silurus)
Permits: Government licence
Restrictions: No night fishing
BK Rating: Moderate
Comments: Severe checks made by Rangers in night time. 2 rods allowed. For any help please contact Fish Eye Italia shops (see details). Food and drinks available at the nearest village (3 km). GSM coverage poor / medium

Salto Lake

Location: Along the highway A24 Roma - L'Aquila, exit 'Salto' then to Fiumata

Type and Size: Huge dam with crystal clear water

Carp Stock: Number one carp water in Italy and one of the best in Europe. Commons over 25 kg already landed several times, mirrors over 27/29 kg. Grass carp over 30 kg. This is the heaven of carp fishing!. Fishing pressure poor due to difficult fish location

Other Species: Black bass, perch and coarse fish

Permits: Government licence. 3 rods allowed

Restrictions: Night fishing not allowed from October to June. Permitted during summer months

BK Rating: Fantastic water but needs good fish location. Really a carp record lake.

Comments: You can hire a boat and have a free guide by a local angler called 'Franco' (no English spoken) or by a top angler Sandro Di Cesare. Just reach Fiumata and ask for those two carp stars and everyone

Roberto Ripamonti with a 25 pounder (11.5 kg) from the fabulous Salto Lake.

in the place will tell you where and when. Food and drinks available at Fiumata. This unpressured water is strongly checked by National Park Rangers, so avoid any fires, take your litter home and help us to have more night fishing in the future!

Sile River

Location: Treviso town to Casale sul Sile
Type and Size: Medium river with strong current and weeds. Many good venues for carp anglers. Nice surroundings.
Carp Stock: Many fish over 30 lbs, several 40's with fish over 55 lbs
Other Species: Trout, barbel, pike and coarse fish
Permits: Government and FIPSAS (is a trout and grayling water)
Restrictions: Night fishing not allowed
BK Rating: Medium
Comments: Beautiful river with nice surroundings. Several good venues with lots of chances to land hard fighting carp. Use of heavy tackle 20/25 lb line

Tevere River

Location: From Corbara lake to Rome, Tevere river is along the A1 highway. Literally there are thousands of good venues; you can spend years having good catches everywhere. Very famous underneath the Nazzano dam. You can spend many hours within Rome, only 250m. from St. Peter's square. Many commons in daylight with an average of 18/20 lb. Easy fishing! I also suggest the 'Aeroporto dell'Urbe' area at the Aniene river junction, along the Salaria way, the 'Banco di Roma' area.
Type and Size: Tevere river is today one of the main carp rivers in Italy. It's almost unfished mostly with traditional methods.
Carp Stock: Really a terrific potential with commons over 25 kg.
Other Species: Terrific zander river; coarse fish
Permits: Government licence.
Restrictions: Night fishing allowed due to lack of controls
BK Rating: Moderate
Comments: Needs accurate fish location and good prebaiting. Good in winter, excellent in autumn. Facilities depend on chosen venue. Average food and drinks available. GSM coverage good. Boats with powerful engine (20 hp) are suggested to check the river. Really a carp heaven if you have a boat!

Trasimeno Lake

Location: Biggest lake in the centre of Italy. Close to the beautiful Perugia. Take the A1 highway to Rome then exit to Perugia and follow the SS75 until you see this huge lake

Type and Size: Immense lake with plenty of venues. Ask for Isola Maggiore and Minore, Castiglione del Lago

Carp Stock: Literally billions of 5 kg carp. Fish over 20 kg but some problems due to professional fishermen. Grass carp over 45 kg (100 lb) but uncaught!

Other Species: All you need apart from catfish

Permits: Government and FIPSAS

Restrictions: Night fishing not allowed but tolerated for carp anglers.

BK Rating: Difficult

Comments: Fish location difficult and some problems with professionals after your prebaiting. They drop their nets where you've baited. Good in winter, poor in full summer because of sun bathers and holiday makers. No problem for food , drink and GSM telephone coverage.

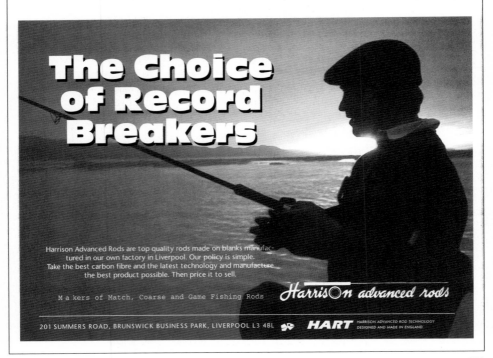

Turano Lake

Location: A24 highway Roma - L'Aquila exit 'Carsoli'
Type and Size: Huge dam with clear water
Carp Stock: Commons over 28 kg and big mirrors (lake record is 28 kg)
Other Species: Coarse fish and perch
Permits: Government licence
Restrictions: No night fishing
BK Rating: Difficult (needs good fish location but really big catches)
Comments: All available in local villages. GSM coverage medium. One step behind Salto lake but another great carp water. Really there are fish over 30 kg caught by nets in the past but many are still there!

Turano Lake produced this fine brace of carp for top Italian carp specialist Roberto Ripamonti.

SPAIN
by Norman Smith

Agrio - Aznalcollar (Embalse)

Location: 36km north of Sevilla on the N630 turn west towards Aznalcollar.
Type & Size: Reservoir of about 700 acres.
Carp Stock: Known to exist.
Category: Mixed Fishery.
Other Species: Black bass.
Permits: Licence from any branch of Caja Rural bank or the I.A.R.A office in Sevilla at Avda. Ramon y Cajal,1.
BK Rating: Insufficient information.
Restrictions: Two rods, no night fishing.
Comments: Difficult access.

Alagon (Rio)

Location: Joins the Tajo just above the Embalse de Alcantara.
Type & Size: Moderate sized river.
Carp Stock: Good head of sizable fish.
Category: Mixed Fishery.
Other Species: Huge barbel, black bass, pike and boga.
Permits: Comunidad de Extremadura licence required available form almost any bank.
BK Rating: Moderate.
Restrictions: Three rods, no night fishing.

Almochuel (Embalse).

Location: 64km from Zaragoza on the N232 turn west towards Belchite.
Type & Size: Small reservoir of about 60 acres.
Carp Stock: Known to exist.
Category: Mixed Fishery.

Other Species: Black bass and barbel.
Permits: Licences from I.C.O.N.A office in Zaragoza at Vazquez de Melia, 6 not far from the football ground.
BK Rating: Insufficient information.
Restrictions: Two rods, no night fishing.
Comments: Difficult access.

Norman Smith proving that English methods work well in Spain, with one of his many 20 pound plus (9 kg plus) carp.

Almodovar (Embalse).

Location: Turn east off the N340 highway 20km west of Tarifa.
Type & Size: Reservoir of about 150 acres.
Carp Stock: Known to exist.
Category: Mixed Fishery.
Other Species: Barbel.
Permits: I.A.R.A licence required. Available form any branch of the Cajal Rural bank.
BK Rating: Insufficient information.
Restrictions: Two rods, no night fishing.
Comments: Rather open and muddy.

Amposta (Rio Ebro).

Location: The river is crossed by the main N340 highway at Amposta which is half way between Tarragona and Castellon de la Plana.
Type & Size: A large deep river which is fast running at times.
Carp Stock: A very large head of carp (mainly commons) to 30lbs.
Category: Mixed Fishery.
Other Species: Barbel, mullet, black bass, rudd, occasional chub, zander and catfish.
Permits: Licences from the Generalitat de Catalunya, Department d, Agricultura, Ramaderia i Pesca. Which is next to the tourist office on the town wharf.
BK Rating: Very easy.
Restrictions: Two rods, no night fishing.

Comments: This venue was first made popular by the late Billy Lane back in the 1960's and enormous catches are possible.

Arquillo de San Blas

Location: 7km west of the city of Teruel.
Type & Size: Drinking water reservoir of about 200 acres.
Carp Stock: Uncertain as rarely fished by non-Spanish anglers.
Category: Mixed Fishery.
Other Species: Barbel, trout.
Permits: Only 35 permits issued by the I.C.O.N.A office in Turuel at San Francisco, 29.
BK Rating: Insufficient information.
Restrictions: Two rods, no night fishing, no swimming, no motor boats.
Comments: Worth a try but getting one of the few permits on offer may prove difficult.

Baragem do Arade.

Location: Take the Silves road out of Portimao. (PORTUGAL)
Type & Size: A very large reservoir.
Carp Stock: A big head of smallish commons with the occasional mirror to double figures.
Category: Carp Water.
Other Species: Black bass.
Permits: Licences from local Forestry Office.
BK Rating: Easy.
Comments: The large head of turtles can make fishing very difficult in the summer.

Baragem de Bravura.

Location: Turn north off the Lagos - Portimao road at Udiaxere. (PORTUGAL)
Type & Size: Very large deep reservoir.
Carp Stock: Heavy stock of rather small commons.
Category: Carp Water.
Permits: Licences from local forestry office.
BK Rating: Easy.
Comments: Larger fish few and far between.

Barragem de Idhana-a-Nova **A**

Location: Take the north bound N233 from Castelo Branco. After 20km turn right on to the N353 for 12 kms. (PORTUGAL)
Type & Size: Smallish reservoir built in 1935.
Carp Stock: Plenty of small carp but no reports of large fish.
Category: Carp Water.
Other Species: Barbel, black bass.
Permits: Uncertain.
BK Rating: Easy.
Comments: A well appointed modern campsite close to the lakeside.

Barragem de Santa Clara **A**

Location: About 70kms north of Portimao on the N266 road (PORTUGAL)
Type and Size: Huge attractive reservoir
Carp Stock: Reputed to hold carp to very large size
Category: Mixed Fishery
Other Species: Black bass, barbel, very large catfish
Permits: Enquire at Tourist Office in Portimao
BK Rating: Insufficient information
Comments: Has a Pousada or state run hotel on its banks

Barragem do Montagil.

Location: North east of Lisbon on the N2 raod to Ponte do Sor. (PORTUGAL)
Type & Size: Large reservoir (20km long).
Carp Stock: Good head of carp to 25lbs plus.
Category: Carp Water.
Other Species: Black bass.
Permits: Enquire locally.
BK Rating: Moderate.
Restrictions: No night fishing.
Comments: Little fished by non Portuguese anglers.

Maureen Smith with a lovely Spanish common of 23 pounds (10.5 kg).

Barcena (Embalse)

Location: 108km west of Leon just north of the N120 road east of Ponferrada.
Type & Size: Reservoir of about 2400 acres.
Carp Stock: Known to exist.
Category: Mixed Fishery.
Other Species: Pike, black bass.
Permits: Uncertain, enquire locally.
BK Rating: Insufficient information.
Restrictions: Two rods, no night fishing.
Comments: Large variations in water level.

Cantera Coceinma.

Location: Almost within Malaga city limits, just four kilometers north of the Carlos Haya Hospital. Behind the brick works.
Type & Size: Clay pit of about two acres.
Carp Stock: Small head of carp to about 20lbs.
Category: Mixed Fishery.
Other Species: Very large black bass, eels, goldfish.
Permits: Licence from I.A.R.A office in Malaga at Edificio de Uso Multiples, Avda de Andalucia or any branch of the Caja Rural bank.
BK Rating: Moderate.

Restrictions: Two rods, no night fishing.
Comments: This water is very deep with no marginal shallows. Floating baits made difficult due to many ducks and coots. This water is private property but no objections seem to be raised to anglers who behave themselves.

Castrejon (Canal de).

Location: Runs from El Embalse de Castrejon in Toledo.
Type & Size: Canal 25km long and about 30 metres wide.
Carp Stock: Heavy stock of mainly commons.
Category: Mixed Fishery.
Other Species: Barbel, boga, black bullhead.
Permits: Licence from I.C.O.N.A office in Toledo.
BK Rating: Easy.
Restrictions: Two rods, no night fishing.
Comments: Much used for matches.

Celemin (Embalse)

Location: 46km east of Cadiz near Casas Viejas.
Type & Size: Irrigation water reservoir of about 1200 acres.
Carp Stock: Good head of fish with good ones reported.
Category: Mixed Fishery.
Other Species: Barbel, black bass.
Permits: I.A.R.A licence required. Available from any branch of the Caja Rural bank.
BK Rating: Moderate.
Restrictions: Two rods, no night fishing.
Comments: Limited access.

Charco Redondo-Palomones (Embalse).

Location: 132km from Cadiz on 440 Road. north of Algeciras.
Type & Size: Drinking water reservoir of about 1200 acres.
Carp Stock: Modest head of good fish before the drought.
Category: Mixed Fishery.
Other Species: Barbel, black bass, boga.
Permits: I.A.R.A licence required. Available from any branch of the Caja Rural bank.
BK Rating: Moderate.
Restrictions: Two rods, no night fishing.
Comments: Suffered badly in the drought of 1995. Limited access. Beware of fighting bulls.

Conde de Guadalhorce A

Location: 62 kms north of Malaga,near the villageof Ardales
Type and Size: Reservoir for irrigation water. Approximately 1350 acres
Carp Stock: Many carp to double figures. Best fish reported was 25 kilos but bigger fish very few and far between
Category: Mixed Fishery
Other Species: Barbel, black bass. Unusually for a southern Spanish fishery, there are also a few pike
Permits: Licence from IARA office in Malaga - Edificio de Usos Multiples, Avenida de Andalucia
Restrictions: No night fishng.Two rods. Strictly speaking no boats or swimming allowed but pedaloes at campsite and swimming does take place
BK Rating: Easy, except for the few very big fish

Comments: 2000 place municipal campsite on bank. Very popular picnic spot at weekends and on Fiesta days

El Pantano de la Cuerda del Pozo.

Location: A few kilometers west of Soria to the north of the N234 highway.
Type & Size: A very large reservoir built in 1941.
Carp Stock: A good head of carp to large size.
Category: Mixed Fishery.
Other Species: Boga, barbel, black bass.
Permits: Licences from the I.C.O.N.A office in Soria at Alfonso VII 1 and 6. Tel. 975 211975.
BK Rating: Moderate.
Restrictions: Two rods, no night fishing.
Comments: Little fished by non - Spanish anglers.

Embalse Alcantara 2 Jose Maria de Oriol

Location: 48 kms north of Caceres on the N630 road
Type and Size: Largest capacity reservoir in Spain at nearly 30,000 acres
Carp Stock: Large stock of carp, mainly commons to unknown size
Category: Mixed Fishery
Other Species: Barbel, black bass and tench
Restrictions: Two rods. No night fishing
BK Rating: Insufficient information
Comments: Made difficult due to its size, it would take a lifetime to explore it

Embalse de Aliaga.

Location: North of Teruel on the N420 highway and then east on minor road at Mezquita de Jarque.
Type & Size: Reservoir of about 125 acres.
Carp Stock: Uncertain but reports of some good fish.
Category: Run as a trout fishery.
Other Species: Brown trout, rainbow trout, barbel, black bass, madrilla.
Permits: Licenses from Servicio Provincial de Agricultura Ganaderia y Montes, San Francisco, 27 Teruel. Permits from either Bar Alfonso (Aliaga) or Bar Carretera (Ejulve).
BK Rating: Insufficient information.
Comments: Forty permits issued on weekdays and sixty on weekends and fiestas.

Embalse el Becerril.

Location: 8km south of Avila. East of the 403 road.
Type & Size: Reservoir of about 55 acres.
Carp Stock: Known to exist.
Category: Trout Fishery.
Other Species: Trout.
Permits: 8 permits issued daily; try the I.C.O.N.A office in Avila at Mendez Vigo, 6.
BK Rating: Insufficient information.
Restrictions: No swimming or motor boats.
Comments: Very little known about this water.

Embalse de Anzalcollar.

Location: Leave Sevilla on the N431 towards Huelva and turn off just past Sanlucar la Mayor.
Type & Size: A very attractive looking reservoir.
Carp Stock: Some very large carp reported.

Category: Mixed Fishery.
Other Species: Black bass, barbel.
Permits: Licences from the I.A.R.A office in Sevilla at Avda. Ramon y Cajal, 1. Tel: 954 638904.
BK Rating: Moderate.
Restrictions: Two rods, no night fishing.
Comments: Rarely fished by non Spaniards but the locals are now using hair rigged boilies.

Norman Smith with a fine Spanish carp of 36 pounds (16.4 kg).

Embalse de Arcos

Location: 35 kms east of Jerez on the N342
Type and Size: Small reservoir of approximately 80 acres
Carp Stock: Heavily stocked but carp rather small
Category: Mixed Fishery
Other Species: Barbel and black bass
Restrictions: Two rods. No night fishing
BK Rating: Easy
Comments: Fun fishing

Embalse de Atazar.

Type & Size: Reservoir of about 3000 acres.
Location: About 100km north of Madrid to east of N1 highway.
Carp Stock: Known to exist.
Category: Mixed Fishery.
Other Species: Barbel, black bass, pike.
Permits: Licence from I.C.O.N.A office in Madrid at Jorge Juan, 39.
BK Rating: Moderate.
Restrictions: No night fishing, two rods, no motor boats, no swimming.
Comments: It is possible that an extra permit is required.

Embalse de Azutan

Location: Turn off the N5 Madrid-Badajoz highway at Talavera de la Reina
Type and Size: Reservoir of approximately 3000 acres
Carp Stock: Heavily stocked with mainly wild carp
Category: Mixed Fishery
Other Species: Barbel, tench and black bullhead catfish
Permits: Licences from ICONA office in Toledo
Restrictions: Two rods. No night fishing
BK Rating: Easy
Comments: Fished very little by non-Spanish anglers

Embalse de Beniarres.

Location: Just north of the 3311 minor road which runs west from Denia.
Type & Size: An irrigation reservoir of about 700 acres.
Carp Stock: A good head of carp to double figures.
Category: Mixed Fishery.
Other Species: Barbel, black bass.
Permits: Licences from La Conselleria de Medio Ambiente, Calle Profesor Manuel Sala 2, Alicante.
B.K. Rating: Easy.
Restrictions: No night fishing, two rods.
Comments: Water quality reported to be poor.

Embalse de Bornos

Location: 50 kms east of Jerez de la Frontera to the south of the N342 highway
Type and Size: Reservoir of more than 6000 acres
Carp Stock: Heavily stocked with carp, maximum size not known
Category: Mixed Fishery
Other Species: Barbel, black bass
Restrictions: Two rods. No night fishing
BK Rating: Easy
Comments: Little fished by non-Spanish anglers

Embalse de Buendia

Location: East of Madrid. To the south of the N320 Guadalajara - Cuenca road
Type and Size: Fourth largest reservoir in Spain. More than 20,000 acres
Carp Stock: Carp to 60lbs and more reported
Category: Mixed Fishery
Other Species: Barbel, black bass, pike
Restrictions: Two rods. No night fishing
BK Rating: Difficult, due to size of water

Embalse de Calanda.

Location: Take the minor road to the east at Calanda on the N420 Alcaniz - Teruel main road.
Type & Size: Reservoir of about 750 acres.
Carp Stock: Uncertain but reports of some good fish.
Category: Run as trout fishery.
Other Species: Brown trout, rainbow trout, barbel, black bass, madrilla.
Permits: Licences from Servicio Provincial de Agricultura, Ganaderia y Montes, San Fransisco 27, Teruel. Permits from Bar Hoya (Calanda)
BK Rating: Insufficient information.
Restrictions: Two rods, no night fishing.
Comments: Two hundred permits issued on weekdays and 400 on weekends and fiesta days.

Embalse de Camarasa. A

Type & Size: Drinking water reservoir of about 1500 acres.
Location: About 40km north east of Lerida on the 147 road.
Carp Stock: Modest head of both common and mirror carp.
Category: Mixed Fishery.
Other Species: Barbel, black bass, chub, brown trout, zander, pike.
Permits: Day tickets available from Bar Mirador del Llac and at Camping La Noguera both in San Lorenzo de Montgay. Licences from the I.C.O.N.A office in Lerida at General Yague, 37.
BK Rating: Moderate.
Restrictions: No night fishing, two rods.
Comments: There are several campsites in the area along with at least two hotels. Due to the difficult access to the water's edge the use of a boat is recomended.

Embalse de Campanario.

Location: Turn off the N435 in the province of Huelva between San Juan del Puerto and Valverde del Camino.
Type & Size: Old mature reservoir with a lot of vegetation both in the water and on the banks.
Carp Stock: Good head of mainly common carp well into double figures.
Category: Mixed Fishery.
Other Species: Large black bass, large barbel.
Permits: Licences from the I.A.R.A office in Huelva at General Mola, 20.
BK Rating: Moderate.
Restrictions: No night fishing, two rods.
Comments: Little fished as it is rather difficult to locate.

Embalse de Castrejon

Location: 45 kms south west of Toledo
Type and Size: Large reservoir, dammed section of River Tajo. Approximately 1900 acres
Carp Stock: Very large 90% commons
Category: Mixed Fishery
Other Species: Barbel, tench and black bullhead catfish
Permits: Licences avalable in ICONA office in Toledo
Restrictions: Two rods. No night fishing
BK Rating: Very Easy for fish up to double figures
Comments: Potential unknown. Very lightly fished

Embalse de Cedillo.

Type & Size: A very pretty well wooded hydro-electric reservoir of about 3500 acres.
Location: Forms part of the Spanish/Portuguese border north west of Badajoz.
Carp Stock: Commons and mirrors but no reports of very large fish.
Category: Mixed Fishery.
Other Species: Barbel, black bass, pike.
Permits: An Extremadura licence is required which is available from most banks.
B.K. Rating: Easy.
Restrictions: No night fishing, two rods, fishing from boats not permitted between Jan 1st and 31st of July.
Comments: A boat is recommended due to the limited access to the bankside (see above). A large head of barbel which are often taken on lures by the black bass anglers.

Embalse de Cerro Alarcon

Location: 45 kms west of Madrid
Type and Size: Small reservoir approximately 60 acres
Carp Stock: Heavily stocked with fish of modest size
Category: Mixed Fishery
Other Species: Barbel and black bass
Permits: Licences from ICONA office in Madrid at Calle de Jorge Juan 39
Restrictions: Two rods. No night fishing
BK Rating: Very Easy
Comments: Water reported to be good for fishing and swimming. Lake's prime purpose is recreation. Will get very crowded weekends and fiesta days

Embalse de Chira (Canary Islands)

Location: South of the centre of the island of Gran Canaria 58 kms from Las Palmas
Type and Size: Small irrigation water reservoir of approximately 28 acres
Carp Stock: Good stock of carp to 50lbs plus
Category: Carp Fishery
Permits: ICONA office in Las Palmas
Restrictions: Two rods. No night fishing
BK Rating: Moderate
Comments: Access by difficult mountain roads

Embalse de Cornalbo

Location: 60 kms east of Badajoz
Type and Size: Reservoir of approximately 100 acres
Carp Stock: Holds carp but stock uncertain
Category: Mixed Fishery
Other Species: Not known, but probably barbel and black bass
Permits: This is a special fishing preserve or Coto and an additional permit may be required
Restrictions: Two rods. No night fishing
BK Rating: Easy

Embalse de Crevillente.

Location: To the north of the N340 highway just outside Elche in the direction of Murcia.
Type & Size: Irrigation reservoir of about 250 acres.
Carp Stock: Good stock of modest carp.
Category: Mixed Fishery.
Other Species: Barbel, black bass.
Permits: Licences from La Conselleria de Medio Ambiente, Calle Profesor Manuel Sala 2, Alicante.
BKRating: Easy.
Restrictions: No night fishing, two rods.
Comments: Sometimes suffers from very low water levels.

Embalse de Cubillas A

Location: 7 kms north of Granada on N323 Madrid road
Type and Size: Irrigation water reservoir approximately 500 acres
Carp Stock: Very many small to medium sized carp and a few bigger ones to about 20lbs
Category: Mixed Fishery
Other Species: Barbel, black bass and a few pike
Permits: From campsite office or bar San Isidro in nearby village of El Chapparal

Restrictions: Two rods. No night fishing
BK Rating: Very Easy for smaller carp, bigger fish difficult to find
Comments: Very friendly family run campsite at waters edge. Yacht club and wind surf club on opposite bank to campsite

Embalse de Cuevas de Almanzora

Location: To the east of the N340 road just north of the town of Vera
Type and Size: Reservoir of approximately 1400 acres
Carp Stock: Plenty of carp up to double figures
Category: Mixed Fishery
Other Species: Barbel and black bass
Permits: Licence from IARA office in Almeria
Restrictions: Two rods. No night fishing
BK Rating: Moderate
Comments: The driest area of Spain. Water level often low

Embalse de Ebro

Location: 65 kms south of Santander on N623
Type and Size: Huge reservoir of approximately 16,000 acres
Carp Stock: Heavily stocked with carp to 20lb, potential for large fish not yet explored
Restrictions: Two rods. No night fishing
BK Rating: Insufficient information
Comments: This water boasts an Olympic rowing course

Embalse de El Limonero.

Location: Just north of Malaga to the west of the N321 highway.
Type & Size: Reservoir of about 250 acres.
Carp Stock: Large head of mainly small carp with a few larger fish up to 20lbs.
Category: Mixed Fishery.
Other Species: Barbel, black bass, pike, goldfish.
Permits: Licence from I.A.R.A office in Malaga at Edificlo de Uso Multiples, Avda de Andalucia or any branch of the Caja Rural bank.
BK Rating: Easy.
Restrictions: Two rods, no night fishing.
Comments: Access road is locked between 8pm and 9am. Banks are very steep and dangerous, the only easy access is close to the dam. This reservoir is used by Malaga official rescue team to practice scuba diving.

Embalse de Encinarejo

Location: 30 kms north of Andujar in the province of Jaen. Turn off the NIV main Madrid-Cadiz highway
Type and Size: Reservoir of approximately 400 acres
Carp Stock: Some good fish to 35lbs plus
Category: Mixed Fishery
Other Species: Many black bass to good size, also barbel and gudgeon
Restrictions: Two rods. No night fishing
BK Rating: Insufficient information
Comments: Few places where access to water possible due to very steep sides

Embalse de Entrepeñas.

Location: North of N420 road, 48km east of Guadalajara.
Type & Size: Huge reservoir of about 8,500 acres.
Carp Stock: Known to exist.

Category: Mixed Fishery.
Other Species: Black bass, barbel.
Permits: Licence from I.C.O.N.A office in Guadalajara at Marques de Villaverde, 2.
BK Rating: Insufficient information.
Restrictions: No night fishing, two rods.
Comments: Considerable variation in water level.

Embalse de Foix.

Type & Size: Reservoir of about 150 acres.
Location: 60km south of Barcelona just north of N340 highway.
Carp Stock: Many medium - sized carp.
Category: Mixed Fishery.
Other Species: Barbel.
Permits: Licences from I.C.O.N.A offices in either Barcelona or Tarragona.
BK Rating: Easy.
Restrictions: No night fishing, two rods.
Comments: Water reported to be polluted. Many matches held here.

Embalse de Gabriel y Galan.

Location: Lies to the north of the 513 road that runs from the Portugese boarder to Bejar.
Type & Size: The tenth largest reservoir in Spain at about 14,000 acres.
Carp Stock: A good head of large carp.
Category: Mixed Fishery.
Other Species: Pike, barbel, black bass, tench.
Permits: A Comunidad de Extremadura licence required. Available from any bank.
BK Rating: Moderate, made difficult due to its size.
Restrictions: No night fishing, two rods.
Comments: Rarely fished by non - Spanish anglers but some very large fish reported.

Embalse de Garcia de Sola.

Location: Take the minor road that is the extension of the N430 to the east of Merida.
Type & Size: Reservoir of more that 1000 acres.
Carp Stock: Heavily stock of large carp.
Category: Mixed Fishery.
Other Species: Large black bass, pike, tench.
Permits: A Comunidad de Extremadura licence required, available from any bank in Merida.
BK Rating: Easy.
Restrictions: Two rods, no night fishing.
Comments: A water little known by foreign anglers but has an enormous potential. Whilst camping is strictly speaking illegal it seems to be tolerated in this area.

Embalse de Grena

Location: 50 kms north west of Caceres.Not far from border with Portugal
Type and Size: Small reservoir of about 30 acres
Carp Stock: Holds carp but size and numbers uncertain
Category: Mixed Fishery
Other Species: Barbel and black bass
Restrictions: Two rods. No night fishing
BK Rating: Easy
Comments: Water reported to be rather coloured but providing good fishig. Rarely fished by non -Spanish anglers

Embalse de Guadalcacin.

Type & Size: Reservoir of about 2000 acres.
Location: South off the N342 at Acos de la Frontera.
Carp Stock: Mainly smallish fish.
Category: Mixed Fishery.
Other Species: Barbel, black bass.
Permits: I.A.R.A licence required. Available from any branch of the Caja Rural bank.
BK Rating: Easy.
Restrictions: No night fishing, two rods.
Comments: Used for matches. Too much litter.

Embalse de Guadalest.

Location: Just north of the Alcoy - Callosa road north west of Benidorm.
Type & Size: Drinking water reservoir of more than 200 acres.
Carp Stock: Good numbers of modest sized carp.
Category: Mixed Fishery.
Other Species: Barbel, black bass.
Permits: Licences from La Conselleria de Medio Ambiente, Calle Profesor Manuel Sala 2, Alicante.
BK Rating: Easy.
Restrictions: No night fishing, two rods, no swimming, no motor boats.

Embalse de Guadalhorce

Location: 74 kms north of Malaga on the Campanillas/Alora road
Type and Size: Irrigation water reservoir of approximately 1800 acres
Carp Stock: Good stock of carp to double figures, better fish hard to find
Category: Mixed Fishery
Other Species: Barbel and black bass
Permits: From IARA office in Malaga, Edificios de Usos Multiples, AVenida de Andalucia
Restrictions: No swimming. No motor boats. Two rods. No night fishing
BK Rating: Easy for fish to double figures. Difficult to find bigger fish
Comments: Carp respond well to floating crust

Embalse de Guadalmellato.

Location: Turn off the N4 highway near Cordoba at Alcotes.
Type & Size: Drinking water reservoir of about 2000 acres.
Carp Stock: Large head of big carp.
Category: Mixed Fishery.
Other Species: Barbel, black bass.
Permits: Licences from the I.A.R.A office in Cordoba.
BK Rating: Easy.
Restrictions: No motor boats, two rods, no night fishing.
Comments: Often suffers from very low water levels. A 45lb carp taken in 1993.

Embalse de Guadalmena.

Location: To the west of the N322 main road about halfway between Linares and Albacete.
Type & Size: Reservoir of about 3000 acres.
Carp Stock: Good head of carp with fish to 35lb + reported.
Category: Mixed Fishery.
Other Species: Barbel, black bass.
Permits: Licences from the I.C.O.N.A office at Avda. Madrid, 25, Jaen or from any branch of the Caja Rural bank.

BK Rating: Insufficient information.
Restrictions: Two rods, no night fishing.
Comments: A water that appears to have a lot of potential but has received very little attention so far.

Embalse de Guadalteba

Location: 74 kms north of Malaga on the Campanillas-Alora road
Type and Size: Irrigation water reservoir of approximately 2000 acres
Carp Stock: Good head of carp to double figures, larger fish hard to find
Category: Mixed Fishery
Other Species: Barbel and black bass
Permits: From IARA office in Malaga, Edificios de Usos Multiples, Avenida de Andalucia
Restrictions: No swimming. No motor boats. Two rods. No night fishing
BK Rating: Easy for smaller fish. Large carp hard to find
Comments: Carp respond well to floating crust

Embalse de Guadlen.

Location: About 25km along the minor road number 3210 out of Linares in the province of Jaen.
Type & Size: Irrigation reservoir of about 350 acres.
Carp Stock: Uncertain.
Category: Mixed Fishery.
Other Species: Barbel, gudgeon, black bass.
Permits: Licences from I.A.R.A office in Jaen at Avda de Madrid, 25 or from any branch of the Caja Rural bank.
BK Rating: Insufficient information.
Restrictions: Two rods, no night fishing.
Comments: Very rarely fished by non - Spanish anglers.

Embalse de Guajaraz.

Location: 11km S.W. of Toledo, off the N401 road.
Type & Size: A drinking water reservoir of about 400 acres.
Carp Stock: Lots of carp, mainly commons to low doubles.
Category: Mixed Fishery.
Other Species: Barbel, tench, American bullheads, pike.
Permits: The I.C.O.N.A office in Toledo issues 10,000 permits per year at Plaza de San Vincente, 6.
BK Rating: Easy.
Restrictions: Two rods, no night fishing, no swimming, no motor boats.

Embalse de Gulmets.

Location: Lies to the south of the N420 highway about 65km west of Tarragona.
Type & Size: Irrigation reservoir of 100 acres.
Carp Stock: Good stock of carp to uncertain size.
Category: Mixed Fishery.
Other Species: Black bass, barbel, pike.
Permits: Licence from I.C.O.N.A office at Avda, Cantaluna 50, Tarragona. 100 permits issued daily.
BK Rating: Insufficient information.
Restrictions: Two rods, no night fishing.

Embalse de Iznajar

Location: Turn off N342 Malaga - Granada road on to C334 to Rute
Type and Size: Ninth largest reservoir in Spain at approximately 7000 acres

Carp Stock: Large number of fish large size
Category: Mixed Fishery
Other Species: Barbel and black bass
Permits: IARA office in Granada
Restrictions: Two rods. No night fishing
BK Rating: Easy for smaller fish. Big fish very difficult to locate

Embalse de Jandula

Location: 35 kms north of Andujar in the province of Jaen. Turn north off the N4 highway
Type and Size: Large reservoir of 2,250 acres
Carp Stock: Number uncertain but fish to 30lbs plus
Category: Mixed Fishery
Other Species: Large numbers of black bass plus barbel and gudgeon
Restrictions: Two rods. No night fishing
BK Rating: Insufficient information, but good potential

Embalse de la Concepcion

Location: To the west of Marbella, turn north off the N340 towards Istan
Type and Size: Drinking water reservoir
Carp Stock: Carp to double figures
Category: Mixed Fishery
Other Species: Barbel
Permits: Licence from IARA office in Malaga - Edificio de Usos Multiples, Avenida de Andalucia
Restrictions: No swimming. No motor boats. Two rods.No night fishing
BK Rating: Easy
Comments: Access to water difficult due to very steep sides

Embalse de la Pedrera.

Location: Less than 20km to the east of the city of Murcia. Easy access as secondary roads go round the reservoir.
Type & Size: Irrigation reservoir of about 3500 acres.
Carp Stock: Heavily stocked with carp.
Category: Mixed Fishery.
Other Species: Barbel, black bass.
Permits: Licences from La Conselleria de Medio Ambiente, Calle Profesor Manuel Sala 2, Alicante.
BK Rating: Easy.
Restrictions: No night fishing, two rods, no swimming, no motor boats.
Comments: Some good carp have been reported from this water.

Embalse de la Torre de Abraham.

Location: Take the NIV highway from Cuidad Real to Piedrabuena then turn towards Porzuna and straight on to Torno y Bullaque.
Type & Size: Reservoir of about 5000 acres.
Carp Stock: Good head of carp to double figures.
Category: Mixed Fishery.
Other Species: Barbel, black bass, boga, a few trout.
Permits: Permits from Centro de Recepcion Pueblonuevo del Bullaque together with licences from Delegacion de Agricultura, Calle Alarcos 21, Cluidad Real.
BK Rating: Easy.
Restrictions: No ground baiting allowed except in matches.
Comments: Heavy policing of this fishery ensures compliance with the regulations. Many matches held here.

Embalse de la Vinuela

Location: North of Velez Malaga to the west of the C335 road
Type and Size: Reservoir of approximately 1500 acres
Carp Stock: Plenty of small carp, potential for bigger fish unexplored
Category: Mixed Fishery
Other Species: Barbel and black bass
Permits: Licence from IARA office in Malaga, Edificio de Usos Multiples, Avenida de Andalucia
Restrictions: Two rods. No night fishig
BK Rating: Easy

Embalse de las Medranas.

Location: About one kilometer north of San Pedro de Alcantara (Costa del Sol).
Type & Size: Natural looking reservoir of about 12 acres.
Carp Stock: Reputed to hold some good size fish.
Category: Mixed Fishery.
Other Species: Barbel and goldfish.
Permits: Licence from I.A.R.A office in Malaga at Edificio de Usos, Multiples, Avda, de Andalucia or any branch of the Caja Rural bank.
BK Rating: Difficult.
Restrictions: No night fishing. Two rods.
Comments: This lake is fenced off and is used for cable skiing during the season so it is only available for fishing during the winter months. In addition it is over-run with turtles which can make things very difficult indeed.

Embalse de los Bermejales

Location: 44 kms south west of Granada, turn south off N342 towards Alhama de Granada
Type and Size: Reservoir, approximately 175 acres
Carp Stock: Plenty of carp to double figures. Otherwise unknown
Category: Mixed Fishery
Other Species: Barbel and black bass
Permits: Licences availabe from IARA office in Granada
Restrictions: Two rods.No night fishing
BK Rating: Easy for smaller fish
Comments: Potential unknown. Little fished

Embalse de los Hurones A

Location: 100 kms east of Jerez on the C344
Type and Size: Drinking water reservoir of approximately 2250 acres
Carp Stock: Many carp up to 5lbs or so, larger fish difficult to find
Category: Mixed Fishery
Other Species: Barbel and black bass
Restrictions: No swimming, No motor boats. Two rods. No night fishing
BK Rating: Easy
Comments: This fishery has a Parador (government run luxury hotel) close by

Embalse de los Morales.

Location: 82km west of Madrid.
Type & Size: Small reservoir of about 100 acres.
Carp Stock: Known to exist.
Category: Mixed Fishery.
Other Species: Black bass, barbel.
Permits: Licences from I.C.O.N.A office in Madrid at Jorge Juan, 39.

BK Rating: Insufficient information.
Restrictions: No swimming, motor boats or night fishing, two rods.
Comments: An additional permit may be required.

Embalse de Marmolejo.

Location: About 4km west of Andujar in the province of Jaen.
Type & Size: Reservoir of about 650 acres.
Carp Stock: Good stock of carp but maximum size unknown.
Category: Mixed Fishery.
Other Species: Barbel, black bass, chub.
Permits: Licences from I.A.R.A office in Jaen at Avda. de Madrid, 25.
BK Rating: Easy.
Restrictions: Two rods, no night fishing.
Comments: Access to this reservoir and to the water's edge is rather difficult.

Embalse de Mequinenza

Location: 45kms south west of Lerida
Type & Size: Fifth largest resevoir in Spain, nearly 20,000 acres
Carp Stock: Good stock of fish to 40lbs, although the average is less than 10lbs
Category: Mixed Fishery.
Other Species: Catfish to 200lbs plus, large black bass and barbel
Restrictions: Two rods, no night fishing.
BK Rating: Moderate for good fish
Comments: A water with enormous potential for anyone with the time to explore it. This water boasts an Olympic rowing course. Most of the larger carp caught have taken a dead fish

Embalse de Negratin. A

Location: North of Baza off N342 highway.
Type & Size: Large reservoir of about 5,000 acres.
Carp Stock: Known to exist.
Category: Mixed Fishery.
Other Species: Barbel, black bass, chub.
Permits: I.A.R.A licence required. Available from any branch of the Caja Rural bank.
BK Rating: Insufficient information.
Restrictions: Two rods, no night fishing.
Comments: Campsite close by.

Embalse de Oliana. A

Location: 92km north of Lerida on the C1313 road to Andorra.
Type & Size: Reservoir of about 1000 acres.
Carp Stock: Both commons and mirrors to double figures.
Category: Mixed Fishery.
Other Species: Black bass, barbel, zander, brown and rainbow trout.
Permits: Licences from the I.C.O.N.A office in Lerida at General Yague,37.
BK Rating: Moderate.
Restrictions: Two rods, no night fishing.
Comments: Water reported to be cold but the carp stock is growing well. Two campsites and several hotels nearby.

Embalse de Orellana. A

Location: Turn south off the N430 road about 70km east of Merida.
Type & Size: Reservoir of more than 3000 acres.
Carp Stock: Heavy stock of large carp to 50lb + mainly commons.

Category: Mixed Fishery.
Other Species: Very large black bass, pike, tench.
Permits: A Comunidad de Extremadura licence required. Available from any bank in Merida.
BK Rating: Easy.
Restrictions: Two rods, no night fishing.
Comments: A water little known by foreign anglers but it has an enormous potential. Whilst camping is strictly illegal it seems to be tolerated in this area. There is a Parador or state run hotel in the village of Orellana.

Embalse de Penarroya.

Location: Turn off the N4 highway at Manzanares on the N430 towards Ruidera.
Type & Size: A drinking water reservoir of about 1000 acres.
Carp Stock: A heavy stock of very large carp. A mirror of 53 lbs was taken in 1993.
Category: Mixed Fishery.
Other Species: Barbel, pike, black bass.
Permits: Licences from the I.C.O.N.A office in Cuidad Real or Albacete.
BK Rating: Easy.
Restrictions: No swimming, no motor boats, no night fishing, two rods.
Comments: Little fished by non - Spanish anglers but a water with a lot of potential.

Embalse el Pintado.

Location: 89km north of Sevilla on N433 then turn west at Cazalla de la Sierra.
Type & Size: Reservoir of about 2600 acres.
Carp Stock: Good head of carp to unknown size.
Category: Mixed Fishery.
Other Species: Black bass, barbel, pike, boga.
Permits: Licences from the I.C.O.N.A office in Sevilla at Avda. Ramon y Cajal, 1.
BK Rating: Easy.
Restrictions: Two rods, no night fishing.
Comments: Access rather difficult.

Emblase de Proserpina

Location: 5 kms north of Merida just off the N630 road
Type and Size: Small, very old reservoir of about 20 acres
Carp Stock: Uncertain but known to exist
Category: Mixed Fishery
Other Species: Barbel
Permits: Additional permit may be required as this is a special fishing preserve or Coto
Restrictions: Two rods. No night fishing
BK Rating: Easy
Comments: Fishing reported to be very good but used as a recreation area so best avoided at weekends

Embalse de Rosarito.

Location: 30km from Arenas de San Pedro (Avila).
Type & Size: Reservoir of about 3600 acres.
Carp Stock: Known to exist.
Category: Mixed Fishery.
Other Species: Black bass, barbel, boga.
Permits: Both Castilla de Leon and Castilla la Mancha licences required as this water is on the border.
BK Rating: Moderate.

Restrictions: No night fishing, two rods.
Comments: Water reported to be cold.

Embalse de Rumblar.

Location: 10km north of Bailen at Baños de la Encina in the province of Jaen.
Type & Size: Irrigation water reservoir of about 1700 acres.
Carp Stock: Good stock of carp but maximum size unknown.
Category: Mixed Fishery.
Other Species: Barbel, black bass.
Permits: Licences from the I.A.R.A office in Jaen at Avda de Madrid, 25.
BK Rating: Easy.
Restrictions: Two rods, no night fishing.
Comments: Sometimes made difficult due to very large variations in water level.

Embalse de San Jose.

Location: Turn off the N620 Valladolid - Salamanca highway north on the minor road no.112.
Type & Size: Irrigation reservoir of about 650 acres.
Carp Stock: Heavy stock of carp to good size.
Category: Carp Fishery.
Other Species: Crucian carp, barbel, black bass.
Permits: This is a "coto" or fishing preserve and requires an additional permit. Enquire locally.
BK Rating: Easy.
Restrictions: Two rods, no night fishing.
Comments: Large fishing matches are held here from time to time. Access to part of this reservoir is restricted as a game reserve.

Embalse de San Juan.

Type & Size: Reservoir of about 1750 acres.
Location: 70km west of Madrid on N501 Road.
Carp Stock: Known to exist.
Category: Mixed Fishery.
Other Species: Barbel, black bass.
Permits: Licence from I.C.O.N.A office in Madrid at Jorge Juan, 39.
BK Rating: Insufficient information.
Restrictions: No night fishing, two rods.
Comments: Water reported to be very cold.

Embalse de Santa Ana.

Location: About 20km due north of Lerida off the N230 road.
Type & Size: Reservoir of about 2000 acres.
Carp Stock: Good head of large fish.
Category: Mixed Fishery.
Other Species: Very large pike, black bass, trout, zander, barbel.
Permits: Permits cost 1000 pesetas. Licences from the I.C.O.N.A office in Lerida at Avda. Blondel, 1.
BK Rating: Moderate.
Restrictions: Two rods, no night fishing and no trolling permitted.
Comments: Camping on banks is permitted but permission must be obtained from The Ayuntamiento de Baldellou in writing in advance. The carp fishing has been neglected by the locals in favour of the very large predators that are present.

Embalse de Santillana

Location: 48 kms north of Madrid turn off N1 highway to Colmenar Viejo
Type & Size: Irrigation water resevoir approximately 2400 acres
Carp Stock: Good stock of carp to huge sizes, fish of 60lbs plus reported and even bigger fish seen. Mainly commons
Category: Carp Fishery.
Permits: This is a nature reserve and permits are difficult to come by. They are issued together with the licences from the ICONA office at Calle de Jorge Juan 39, Madrid
Restrictions: Two rods. No night fishing
BK Rating: Moderate.
Comments: A major fish kill was reported from this area in 1991. It is not known how this has affected the stock

Embalse de Santolea.

Location: Take one of the minor roads to the west of the N232 Alcaniz - Vinaroz main road.
Type & Size: Reservoir of about 1000 acres.
Carp Stock: Uncertain but reports of some good fish.
Category: Run as a trout fishery.
Other Species: Brown trout, rainbow trout, barbel, black bass, madrilla.
Permits: Licences from Servicio Provincial de Agricultura Ganaderia y Montes, San Francisco, 27, Teruel. Permits from Bar Como tu (Castellote).
BK Rating: Insufficient information.
Restrictions: Two rods, no night fishing.
Comments: Two hundred permits issued on weekdays and 400 on weekends and fiesta days.

Embalse de Sau

Location: 28 kms west of Gerona
Type and Size: Drinking water reservoir of approximately 1850 acres
Carp Stock: Reputed to hold very big carp
Permits: From ICONA office Gerona
Restrictions: No swimming. No motor boats. Two rods. No night fishing
BK Rating: Insufficient information
Comments: Water reported to be dirty looking

Embalse de Soria (Canary Islands)

Location: To the south of the centre of the island of Gran Canaria. 58 kms from Las Palmas
Type and Size: Modest sized reservoir approximately 170 acres
Carp Stock: Plenty of good sized fish to 50lbs plus
Category: Carp Fishery
Permits: From the ICONA office in Las Palmas
Restrictions: Two rods. No night fishing
BK Rating: Moderate
Comments: Approached by difficult mountain roads

Embalse de Susqueda

Location: 29 kms west of Gerona
Type and Size: Drinking water reservoir of approximately 1300 acres
Carp Stock: Reputed to hold very large carp
Permits: From the ICONA office in Gerona
Restrictions: No swimming. No motor boats. Possible other restrictions regarding angling. Enquire when buying licence. Two rods. No night fishing

BK Rating: Insufficient information

Embalse de Tozo.

Type & Size: Reservoir of about 9 acres.
Location: To east of NV highway 70km east of Caceres.
Carp Stock: Double figure mirrors.
Category: Mixed Fishery.
Other Species: Barbel, black bass.
Permits: Communidad de Extremadura licence required. Available from almost any bank.
BK Rating: Insufficient information.
Restrictions: No night fishing, two rods.
Comments: Difficult access.

Embalse de Utchesa.

Location: About 27km south west of Lerida.
Type & Size: Reservoir of about 190 acres.
Carp Stock: Uncertain.
Category: Mixed Fishery.
Other Species: Barbel, black bass.
Permits: 1500 permits available from the I.C.O.N.A office in Lerida at General Yague, 37.
BK Rating: Insufficient information.
Restrictions: Two rods, no night fishing.
Comments: Little fished by non - Spanish anglers.

Embalse de Valdajos

Location: Turn north off the N400 Ocana - Taracon road at St Cruz de la Zarza
Type and Size: Small irrigation water reservoir of approximately 10 acres. Dam constructed 1530
Carp Stock: Large head of carp to 5lbs; bigger fish exist but hard to find
Category: Barbel and tench
Permits: ICONA office in Toledo
Restrictions: Two rods. No night fishing
BK Rating: Easy

Embalse de Valdecañas

Location: Just south of Navalmoral de la Mata on the NV highway west of Talavera de la Reina.
Type & Size: Large reservoir about 20,000 acres.
Carp Stock: Many carp to large size.
Category: Mixed Fishery.
Other Species: Barbel, pike, black bass.
Permits: Enquire at any bank for licences.
BK Rating: Easy.
Restrictions: Two rods, no night fishing.
Comments: Used for match fishing, the sixth largest reservoir in Spain.

Embalse de Valmayor

Location: 29 kms west of Madrid
Type and Size: Drinking water reservoir of approxiately 1900 acres
Carp Stock: Good stock of carp to 20lbs plus
Category: Mixed Fishery
Other Species: Pike, barbel and sun bass
Permits: From ICONA office in Madrid, Calle Jorge Juan 39

Restrictions: No swimming. No motor boats. Two rods. No night fishing
BK Rating: Moderate
Comments: Very popular water with the locals. Heavily bailiffed. It is possible that extra permits are required. Enquire when buying licence

Embalse de Vellon

Location: 45 kms north of Madrid, turn off N1 highway towards Guadalix de la Sierra
Type and Size: Irrigation water reservoir of approximately 1000 acres
Carp Stock: Heavily stocked with mainly common carp to 40lbs plus. Fish of 60lbs reported by Spanish press
Category: Pike and tench
Permits: Licence from ICONA Calle de Jorge Juan 39, Madrid
Restrictions: Two rods. No night fishing
BK Rating: Easy for carp to 20lbs; Moderate to 35lbs
Comments: Yacht club and windsurf club . Banks very busy weekends and fiesta days. Stocks now rather uncertain since partial draining in 1989

Embalse de Yesa. A

Location: Lies to the south of the N420 highway about 70km south east of Pamplona.
Type & Size: Large reservoir of about 5000 acres.
Carp Stock: Many carp to good size.
Category: Mixed Fishery.
Other Species: Black bass, barbel, pike, tench.
Permits: Licences from Arrieta, 11 bis, Navarra.
BK Rating: Insufficient information.
Restrictions: Two rods, no night fishing.
Comments: A second category campsite on its banks. Very considerable variations in water levels.

Embalse de Zujar.

Type & Size: Reservoir of about 1200 acres.
Location: South of the N430 towards the village of Orellana.
Carp Stock: Uncertain but very large fish reported.
Category: Mixed Fishery.
Other Species: Barbel, black bass, pike.
Permits: A Comunidad de Extremadura licence is required. Available from almost any bank.
BK Rating: Insufficient information.
Restrictions: No night fishing, two rods.
Comments: Being extended to 50,000 acres. Great potential.

Embalse del Amadorio.

Location: A short distance inland from Villajoyesa just off the N332 highway south of Benidorm.
Type & Size: Irrigation reservoir of about 200 acres.
Carp Stock: Good stock of modest carp.
Category: Mixed Fishery.
Other Species: Barbel, black bass.
Permits: Licences from La Conselleria de Madio Ambiente, Calle Profesor Manuel Sala 2, Alicante.
BK Rating: Easy.
Restrictions: No night fishing, two rods.
Comments: Considerable variation of water levels.

Embalse del Sichar.

Location: Directly west of the town of Castellon.
Type & Size: Small reservoir of just 120 acres built in 1960.
Carp Stock: Some big carp reported.
Category: Mixed Fishery.
Other Species: Barbel, eels, black bass, trout.
Permits: Licences from the I.C.O.N.A office in Castellon at Herrero, 1. Tel. 964 224100.
BK Rating: Insufficient information.
Restrictions: Two rods, no night fishing.
Comments: Little fished by non Spanish anglers.

Embalse el Becerril.

Location: 8km south of Avila. East of the 403 road.
Type & Size: Reservoir of about 55 acres.
Carp Stock: Known to exist.
Category: Trout Fishery.
Other Species: Trout.
Permits: 8 permits issued daily; try the I.C.O.N.A office in Avila at Mendez Vigo, 6.
BK Rating: Insufficient information.
Restrictions: No swimming or motor boats.
Comments: Very little known about this water.

Embalse el Pintado.

Location: 89km north of Sevilla on N433 then turn west at Cazalla de la Sierra.
Type & Size: Reservoir of about 2600 acres.
Carp Stock: Good head of carp to unknown size.
Category: Mixed Fishery.
Other Species: Black bass, barbel, pike, boga.
Permits: Licences from the I.C.O.N.A office in Sevilla at Avda. Ramon y Cajal, 1.
BK Rating: Easy.
Restrictions: Two rods, no night fishing.
Comments: Access rather difficult.

Embalse el Vicario.

Location: A few kilometers north of Culdad Real on the N401 highway.
Type & Size: A reservoir of about 1000 acres.
Carp Stock: Uncertain due to few reports but some very large carp rumoured.
Category: Mixed Fishery.
Other Species: Black bass, pike, tench, barbel.
Permits: Licences from the I.C.O.N.A office in Cuildad Real at Avda. de los Martires, 31.
BK Rating: Insufficient information.
Restrictions: Two rods, no night fishing.
Comments: A water little known by foreign anglers but heavily fished by locals. Reported to suffer from periodic pollution problems.

Embalse el Villar.

Location: 70km north of Madrid just east of the N1 highway.
Type & Size: Reservoir of 410 acres.
Carp Stock: Known to exist.
Category: Trout fishery.
Other Species: Trout.
Permits: Only four permits issued daily. Licences from the I.C.O.N.A office in Madrid at Jorge Juan, 39.

BK Rating: Insufficient information.
Restrictions: No swimming or motor boats.
Comments: It may prove difficult to get one of the only four permits issued daily.

Embalse la Baells.

Location: The extreme north eastern corner of Spain not far from Andorra.
Type & Size: A drinking water reservoir of about 1000 acres.
Carp Stock: Holds mirrors and commons but size unknown, rumours of good fish.
Category: Mixed Fishery.
Other Species: Barbel, black bass.
Permits: Licences from the I.C.O.N.A office in Barcelona at Roberto Bassas, 22. Tel. 3309397.
BK Rating: Insufficient information.
Restrictions: No swimming or motor boats, no night fishing, two rods.

Embalse La Cijara.

Location: Take the minor road to the north off the N430 to Villarta de los Montes.
Type & Size: The third largest reservoir in Spain at more than 5000 acres.
Carp Stock: Heavy stock of large carp.
Category: Mixed Fishery.
Other Species: Large black bass, pike, tench.
Permits: A Comunidad de Extremadura licence required available from any bank in Merida.
BK Rating: Easy.
Restrictions: Two rods, no night fishing.
Comments: A water little known by foreign anglers but it has enormous potential. Whilst camping is strictly speaking illegal it seems to be tolerated in this area. Very considerable variation in water levels.

Embalse Las Picadas.

Location: About 70km west of Madrid, lies to the south of the N501 road.
Type & Size: Drinking water reservoir of about 240 acres.
Carp Stock: Good head of carp but maximum size unknown.
Category: Mixed Fishery.
Other Species: Barbel, black bass.
Permits: Licences from the I.C.O.N.A office in Madrid al Jorge Juan, 39.
BK Rating: Easy.
Restrictions: No swimming, no motor boats, two rods, no night fishing.

Embalse San Rafael de Navallana.

Location: North of NIV just east of Cordoba.
Type & Size: Reservoir of about 2400 acres.
Carp Stock: Known to exist.
Category: Mixed Fishery.
Other Species: Black bass, barbel.
Permits: Licence from I.A.R.A office in Cordoba at Sto.Tomas de Aquino, 14th floor.
BK Rating: Insufficient information.
Restrictions: No night fishing, two rods.
Comments: Recently constructed.

Estepona Golf.

Location: A few kilometers out of Estepona town in the direction of Gibraltar, take the unmade road nearly opposite Costa Natura.
Type & Size: Totally artifical lake of about four acres used to irrigate the golf course.

Carp Stock: Stocked with mainly mirror carp to 3lbs or so in 1990.
Category: Carp Fishery.
Other Species: Goldfish.
Permits: 500 peseta day ticket available on site plus licence from I.A.R.A office in Malaga at Edificio de Usos Multiples, Avda de Andalucia or any branch of the Caja Rural bank.
BK Rating: Easy.
Restrictions: No night fishing, two rods.
Comments: It is very rare to find a golf course that allows one to fish in its lakes and this is the only one that I know of.

Flix (Embalse de).

Location: 98km from Tarragona on the 230 road.
Type & Size: Reservoir of about 800 acres.
Carp Stock: Heavy stock of good fish.
Category: Mixed Fishery.
Other Species: Black bass, zander, catfish, pike all to large sizes + rudd.
Permits: Licences from the I.C.O.N.A office in Lerida at General Yague, 37.
BK Rating: Easy.
Restrictions: Two rods, no night fishing.
Comments: Much fished by Spanish anglers.

Guadalhorce (Rio).

Location: Close to Malaga airport.
Type & Size: Small.
Carp Stock: Mainly commons to 8lb.
Category: Mixed Fishery.
Other Species: Barbel, boga.
Permits: Licence from I.A.R.A.
BK Rating: Easy.
Restrictions: No night fishing, two rods.
Comments: Very badly affected by drought in 1995.

Guadarranque (Embalse).

Location: To west of 3331 road, to the north of Gibraltar.
Type & Size: Drinking water reservoir of about 1000 acres.
Carp Stock: Mainly modest sized fish.
Category: Mixed Fishery.
Other Species: Barbel, boga, black bass.
Permits: I.A.R.A licence required. Available from any branch of the Caja Rural bank.
BK Rating: Easy.
Restrictions: No swimming, motor boats, no night fishing, two rods.
Comments: Suffered badly in the drought of 1995.

Jesus y Maria.

Location: Down stream of the main N340 road bridge at Amposta.
Type & Size: River Ebro, tidal and very wide and deep in this area.
Carp Stock: Large head of mainly commons to 30lb plus.
Category: Mixed Fishery.
Other Species: Barbel, mullet, eels, roach.
Permits: From the Generalitat de Catalunya, Department d, Agricultura Ramaderia i Pesca, which is next to the tourist office on the town wharf at Amposta.
BK Rating: Easy.

Comments: Access to waterside rather difficult and bank tends to be 10 - 15 feet above water level and rather snaggy.

La Laguna.

Location: North of Malaga just off the Cartama Coin road at 9.9km.
Type & Size: A small private lake of less that one acre.
Carp Stock: Good head of carp to low doubles.
Category: Mixed Fishery.
Other Species: Tench, koi, rudd, goldfish, barbel, tropical oatfish.
Permits: Licence from I.A.R.A office in Malaga at Edificio de Uso Multiples, Avda Anadalucia or any branch of the Caja Rural bank. Plus a 1000 pesata day ticket available from the owner John Mitchell on the bank.
BK Rating: Usually very easy but sometimes the fish just 'turn off' and become impossible.
Restrictions: Whilst night fishing is strictly speaking illegal, Mr. Mitchell sometimes allows it on request.
Comments: The geese, ducks and other birds sometimes are a nuisance.

Lago Casa de Campo.

Location: Within Madrid city limits.
Type & Size: Large park lake.
Carp Stock: Very large head of carp to double figures.
Category: Carp water.
Other Species: Not known.
Permits: Licences from I.C.O.N.A office at Jorge Juan, 39.
BK Rating: Easy.
Restrictions: Two rods, no night fishing.
Comments: Very popular fishery used for matches at weekends.

Lake Caspe. A

Location: Turn south off the N11 (Zaragoza/Lerida) highway at Bujaraloz to Caspe, then take the Mequinenza road; the campsite is on the left.
Type & Size: Upper end of the Mequinenza reservoir.
Carp Stock: Good stock of carp to over 30lbs.
Category: Mixed Fishery.
Other Species: Very large black bass, pike, barbel, zander, catfish.
Permits: Licences from the Servicio Provincial de Agricultura Ganaderia y Montes, at Vazquez de Mella 10, Zaragoza. (Not far from the football ground).
BK Rating: Moderate.
Restrictions: Two rods, no night fishing.
Comments: The campsite on the lake holds regular national and international black bass fishing competitions.

Las Lagunas de Ruidera. A

Location: Turn off the N4 highway at Manzanares on the N430 to Ruidera.
Type & Size: A series of lakes called in turn, Cenagal, Cololadilla, Cueva del Langua, Rendorilla, San Pedro, Tinaja, Tomilla, Conceja and Blanca.
Carp Stock: A huge head of carp to very large size.
Category: Mixed Fishery.
Other Species: Pike to 40lb +, barbel - one of 33lb + taken in 1993, black bass.
Permits: Uncertain but probably the I.C.O.N.A office in Albacete.
BK Rating: Easy.
Restrictions: Two rods, no night fishing.
Comments: Possibly the fishery with the most potential in the whole of Spain but

hardly ever fished by non-Spanish anglers. Access to the water's edge can prove difficult in places due to the large number of private roads and estates. As this area is a national park it is subject to heavy control. Several campsites in the area.

Los Arroyos (Embalse).

Location: 50km west from Madrid turn off 505 road to Galapagar.
Type & Size: Reservoir of about 32 acres.
Carp Stock: Carp to 20lb +.
Category: Carp Fishery.
Other Species: Tench.
Permits: Licence from I.C.O.N.A office in Madrid at Jorge Juan, 39.
BK Rating: Moderate.
Restrictions: Two rods, no night fishing.
Comments: Water reported to smell.

Lozoya (Rio)

Location: North of Madrid on N1 turn off to Rascafria.
Type & Size: Moderate sized river.
Carp Stock: Some carp.
Category: Moderate.
Other Species: Trout, barbel, boga, chub, tench.
Permits: Licence from Madrid I.C.O.N.A office at Jorge Juan, 39.
BK Rating: Moderate.
Restrictions: Some special trout reserves.
Comments: Enquire about additional permits required.

Maria Cristina (Embalse de)

Location: 19km west of Castellon, south of 232 road.
Type & Size: Reservoir of about 650 acres.
Carp Stock: Mainly smallish fish.
Category: Mixed Fishery.
Other Species: Black bass, barbel.
Permits: Licence from I.C.O.N.A office in Castellon at Herrero, 31.
BK Rating: Easy.
Restrictions: Two rods, no night fishing.
Comments: Badly affected by the drought in 1995.

Matarranas (Rio).

Location: Runs into river Ebro above Ribarroja.
Type & Size: Medium sized river.
Carp Stock: Carp to 30lb +.
Category: Mixed Fishery.
Other Species: Large black bass, pike, chub, barbel.
Permits: Campsite or bars in Mequinenza or I.C.O.N.A at Vazquez de Melia, 6 Zaragoza.
BK Rating: Easy.
Restrictions: Two rods, no night fishing.
Comments: Only the lower reaches worth bothering with.

Moneva (Embalse de).

Location: To the west of the N222 road, 80km south of Zaragoza.
Type & Size: Reservoir of about 240 acres.
Carp Stock: Know to exist.
Category: Mixed Fishery.

Other Species: Large black bass, barbel.
Permits: Licences from the I.C.O.N.A office in Zaragoza at Vazquez de Melia 6, not far from the football ground.
BK Rating: Insufficient information.
Restrictions: Two rods, no night fishing.
Comments: Often suffers very low water levels.

Monte la Torre.

Location: A few kilometers south of Los Barrios which is to the west of Gibraltar.
Type & Size: A smallish reservoir of about 40 acres.
Carp Stock: A modest head of mainly mirrors to low doubles.
Category: Mixed Fishery.
Other Species: Barbel, black bass, eels.
Permits: Licences from the I.A.R.A office in Cadiz at Avda, Ana de Viya, 3 or from any branch of the Caja Rural bank.
BK Rating: Easy.
Restrictions: Two rods, no night fishing.
Comments: When the water level is high access to the water is limited to a very few swims. Access to the lake is via unpaved country lanes in a very poor state, not recommended in bad weather conditions.

Navalperal de Pinares (Embalse).

Location: About 40km east of Avila on the N600 turn south onto minor road towards Cebreros.
Type & Size: Small reservoir of about 21 acres.
Carp Stock: Known to exist.
Category: Basically a trout fishery.
Other Species: Trout.
Permits: Licences and permits (10 daily) from the I.C.O.N.A office in Avila al Alfonso de Montalvo, 2.
BK Rating: Insufficient information.
Restrictions: No swimming or motor boats.

Pantanao de Almoguera.

Location: Off the N200 road, 57km south east of Guadalajara.
Type & Size: Reservoir of about 600 acres.
Carp Stock: Known to exist.
Category: Mixed Fishery.
Other Species: Barbel, black bass.
Permits: Licence from I.C.O.N.A office in Guadalajara at Marques de Villaverde, 2.
BK Rating: Insufficient information.
Restrictions: Two rods, no night fishing.

Pantanillo Castrejon el Carpio.

Location: 52km west of Toledo just south of the 502 road.
Type & Size: Small reservoir of about 10 acres.
Carp Stock: Mainly small commons.
Category: Mixed Fishery.
Other Species: Barbel.
Permits: Licence from I.C.O.N.A office in Toledo.
BK Rating: Easy.
Restrictions: Two rods, no night fishing.
Comments: Little fished by non-Spanish anglers.

Pantano de Agujero.

Location: Just north of Malaga on the N331 highway.
Type & Size: Long narrow reservoir formed by damming a steep sided valley. About 150 acres.
Carp Stock: Mirrors and commons up to double figures.
Category: Mixed Fishery.
Other Species: Black bass, barbel, eels and goldfish to a surprising size.
Permits: Licence from I.A.R.A office in Malaga at Edificio de Uso Multiples, Avda de Andalucia or any branch of the Caja Rural bank.
BK Rating: Moderate.
Restrictions: Two rods, no night fishing.
Comments: Being so close to Malaga it is a popular fishing and picnicking spot as the amount of litter bears witness. Bank access is very limited. Not recommended for weekends or fiesta days.

Pantano de Canelles.

Location: Due north of Lerida to the east of the N230 road.
Type & Size: Reservoir of about 4,500 acres.
Carp Stock: Double figure mirrors.
Category: Mixed Fishery.
Other Species: Black bass, pike, barbel.
Permits: Licences from the I.C.O.N.A office in Lerida at Avda. Blondel, 1.
BK Rating: Moderate.
Restrictions: No night fishing, two rods.

Ribeira de Arade (Portugal)

Location: Town of Silves, about 38kms inland from Portimao
Type and Size: Small attractive river, looks almost like a chalk stream
Carp Stock: Large numbers of carp to double figures
Category: Mixed Fishery
Other Species: Large numbers of grey mullet to good size
Permits: Enquire at Tourist Office in Portimao
BK Rating: Easy
Comments: Bottom baits only due to the mullet taking anything presented on the surface or mid - water

Rio Cinca

Location: River runs through Monzon, Fraga, Zaidin, Osso Beliver and a number of other villages in the province of Huesca.
Type & Size: Modest sized mainly shallow river.
Carp Stock: Common carp to 20lb +.
Category: Mixed Fishery.
Other Species: Large barbel, many pike, black bass, chub, rainbow trout.
Permits: Permits required for sections holding trout may be obtained from the Hotel Vianetto. Tel. 974 40 19 00.
BK Rating: Moderate.
Restrictions: Two rods, no night fishing, with further controls on trout holding reserves.
Comments: Fished mainly for its good trout, pike and black bass, but the carp are well worth trying for.

Rio Ebro

Location: Countless good fishing areas including Amposta, Tivenys,Tortosa, Mesquinenza etc, almost anywhere on this river will fish well
Type and Size: Huge river that runs right across Spain and empties into the Mediterranean about halfway between Tarragona and Castellon

Carp Stock: Enormous numbers of small common carp but some of a very large size especialy in the river's many reservoirs
Category: Mixed Fishery
Other Species: Catfish to 100lbs plus, barbel, black bass, chub, dace and pike
Permits: This river flows through many different licensing areas
Restrictions: Two rods.No night fishing
BK Rating: Easy
Comments: It would take a lifetime just to visit all the fishing areas on this river and a book the size of the Bible to detail them all

Rio Fluvia

Location: Flows/west/east about 40kms north of Gerona
Type and Size: Smallish river
Carp Stock: Mainly wildies with a few mirrors
Category: Mixed Fishery
Other Species: Barbel, rudd and borgue
Restrictions: Two rods. No night fishing
Comments: Due to improvements now flows underground in places

Rio Fuengirola.

Location: Runs under the main N340 highway to the west of Fuengirola (Costa del Sol).
Type & Size: Small rather polluted river.
Carp Stock: Modest head of small carp to about 5lbs.
Category: Mixed Fishery.
Other Species: Barbel, mullet.
Permits: Licence from I.A.R.A office in Malaga at Edificio de Uso Multiples, Avda de Andalucia or any branch of the Caja Rural bank.
BK Rating: Very easy.
Restrictions: Two rods, no night fishing.
Comments: Not worth a special trip but alright for the odd morning whilst on holiday in the area. There is a very popular picnic area up stream of the road bridge.

Rio Guadalquivir.

Type & Size: Major river.
Location: Rises in La Cazorla National Park (Jaen) and runs through Cordoba and Sevilla.
Carp Stock: Many medium sized fish.
Category: Mixed Fishery.
Other Species: Barbel, black bass.
Permits: I.A.R.A licence required from any Branch of the Caja Rural bank.
BK Rating: Easy.
Restrictions: No night fishing, two rods.
Comments: Heavilly polluted by olive oil producers.

Rio Llobregat.

Location: Empties into the sea just south of Barcelona.
Type & Size: Large and shallow.
Carp Stock: Commons to double figures.
Category: Mixed Fishery.
Other Species: Black bass, barbel, chub, eels, crucians, bullhead catfish, trout.
Permits: Licence from the I.C.O.N.A office in Barcelona at Roberto Bassas,22. Also local permits required on some stretches.
BK Rating: Easy.

Restrictions: Two rods, no night fishing. Some stretches are preserved trout fisheries.

Comments: Very popular fishery with the locals.

Rio Segre.

Type & Size: A longish river runs through the city of Lerida and empties into the river Ebro at Mequinenza.

Carp Stock: Some very good carp reported despite average size being small,

Category: Mixed Fishery.

Other Species: Huge catfish, barbel, pike, zander, black bass.

Permits: Licences can be obtained from the campsite or many of the bars in Mequinenza and also from the I.C.O.N.A office in Lerida at General Yague, 37. Tel. 973 235643.

BK Rating: Moderate.

Restrictions: Two rods and no night fishing except for catfish which is permitted up until midnight and can restart at 6am. NB. An extra permit is required for fishing from a boat.

Comments: The lower reaches of this river have produced many huge catfish.

Rio Tajo

Location: Flows round three sides of the city of Toledo

Type and Size: Huge river. Flows right across Spain and empties into the sea in Portugal

Carp Stock: Almost paved with carp up to double figures

Category: Carp Fishery

Other Species: Barbel, tench, and black bullead catfish

Permits: Licences from ICONA office in Toledo

Restrictions: Two rods. No night fishing

BK Rating: Very Easy

Comments: Carp respond well to floating crust

Rio Teba

Location: Turn off the C341 Ronda Campillos road at Teba,signposted to Ardales

Type and Size: Very small, rather muddy river

Carp Stock: Small head of carp to low double figures

Category: Carp Fishery

Permits: Licence from IARA office in Malaga, Edificio de Usos Multiples, Avenida de Andalucia

Restrictions: Two rods. No night fishing

BK Rating: Easy

Comments: Not worth a special trip as access is limited to area either side of the roadbridge but if you are in the area fishing one of the reservoirs it is worth a try for an hour or two. It is often possible to take one or even two decent fish

Rio Ter

Location: Rises inland and flows through Gerona into the sea near Torroella de Montgri

Type and Size: Good sized river; the flow varies a lot, not only with the season but due to various improvements

Carp Stock: Mainly wilde carp to 7lb plus

Category: Mixed Fishery

Other Species: Barbel, rudd and borgue

Restrictions: Two rods. No night fishing

BK Rating: Easy

Comments: Polluted in region of Gerona

River Guadiana.

Location: Runs halfway across Spain and through Portugal forming the border between the two countries in its lower reaches.
Type & Size: Major river 744km long.
Carp Stock: Very heavily stocked with mainly common carp to very large size, especially in the many reservoirs along its course.
Category: Mixed Fishery.
Other Species: Barbel, black bass, pike, tench.
Permits: Different licences required according to area, enquire locally.
BK Rating: Varies from area to area but mainly easy.
Restrictions: Two rods, no night fishing.
Comments: Match fishing results include very heavy bags of carp in the 2 - 5lb bracket.

San Bartolome (Embalse).

Location: About 40km west of Zaragoza on the N232. Turn north on the 127 to Elea de los Caballeros then north about 15km on a minor road.
Type & Size: Small reservoir of about 24 acres.
Carp Stock: Known to exist.
Category. Mixed Fishery.
Other Species: Black bass, barbel, pike, trout.
Permits: Licences from the I.C.O.N.A office in Zaragoza at Vazquez de Melia, 6 (not far from the football ground).
BK Rating: Insufficient information.
Restrictions: No night fishing, 6 fish limit for trout.
Comments: Built in 1908. Pike to 20lb +.

San Lorenzo de Montgay.

Location: 40km NE of Lerida on the river Segre.
Type & Size: Reservoir of about 350 acres.
Carp Stock: Common carp to 20lb +.
Category: Mixed Fishery.
Other Species: Black bass, barbel.
Permits: Licences from the I.C.O.N.A office in Lerida at General Yague, 37. Tel. 973 235643.

San Pons (Embalse de).

Location: North west of Barcelona off the 149 road.
Type & Size: Modest reservoir of about 300 acres.
Carp Stock: Commons to double figures.
Category: Mixed Fishery.
Other Species: Large black bass.
Permits: Licences from the I.C.O.N.A office in Barcelona at Roberto Bassas, 22.
BK Rating: Easy.
Restrictions: Two rods, no night fishing.

Serena (Embalse la).

Location: East of Merida on NV, then N430 turn south east towards Oreliana.
Type & Size: Huge reservoir of about 35,000 acres.
Carp Stock: Very large carp reported.
Category: Mixed Fishery.
Other Species: Very large black bass, pike and barbel.
Permits: Communidad de Extremadura licence required available from almost

any bank.
BK Rating: Moderate.
Restrictions: No night fishing, no motor boats.
Comments: Newly constructed. When full this will be the largest reservoir in Spain.

Tiveneys (Rio Ebro).

Location: North of Tortosa on the 235 road.
Type & Size: Large deep river with very varied features including a weir and several islands.
Carp Stock: Large head of carp (Mainly commons) to 30lbs +.
Category: Mixed Fishery.
Other Species: Barbel, mullet, black bass, rudd.
Permits: Licences from the Generalitat de Catalunya, Department d, Agricultura Ramaderia i Pesca, which is next to the tourist office on the town wharf.
BK Rating: Easy.
Restrictions: Two rods, no night fishing.
Comments: Featured in John Wilson's Go Fishing series. Other access points on this same road are all the towns of Tortosa, Xerta and Miravel, parking and access to the river bank is rather limited.

Tortosa (Rio Ebro).

Location: About 20km upstream from Amposta.
Type & Size: A large deep river which is fast running at times.
Carp Stock: A very large head of carp (mainly commons) to 30lbs +.
Category: Mixed Fishery.
Other Species: Barbel, mullet, black bass, rudd.
Permits: Licences from the Generalitat de Catalunya, Department d, Agricultura Ramaderia i Pesca, which is next to the tourist office on the town wharf.
BK Rating: Very Easy.
Restrictions: Two rods, no night fishing.
Comments: Access to the water here is the easiest on the whole river Ebro. Easy banks right within town limits.

Tranco de Beas

Location: Within the National Park of La Cazorla (Jaen)
Type and Size: Reservoir of approximately 4500 acres
Carp Stock: Many carp to unkown size, possibly quite large
Category: Mixed Fishery
Other Species: Barbel and black bass
Permits: Enquire at control points at entrance to park
Restrictions: Two rods. No night fishing
BK Rating: Easy
Comments: Many hostels and campsite within park limits

ADVERTISING - NEXT EDITION

If you would like to be contacted in time to consider advertising in our next edition please complete this form, photocopy it and return it to us at:

Graphic Solutions
Dave Watson
7 Eastgate
Banstead
Surrey SM7 IRN.

Company Name: ______________________

Contact: ______________________

Tel: ______________________

Fax: ______________________

Address: ______________________

____

____

Post Code: ______________________

Space required (half, or full page) ______________ col - b/w

Preferred position in guide. ______________________

INDEX

EUROPEAN INDEX

LIST OF BRITISH WATERS THAT CONTAIN CATFISH

BEDFORDSHIRE

Arlesey Lake
Arlesey, Bedfordshire
Blue Circle Pit
Houghton Regis, Bedfordshire
Airman Pit
Near Shefford, Bedfordshire
Hunters Moon
Bedfordshire
Jones Pit
Heath and Reach, Bedfordshire
Little Jones Pit
Heath and Reach, Bedfordshire
Withy Pool,
Henlow Camp, Bedfordshire
Little Withy
Henlow Camp, Bedfordshire
Husborne Crawley Lake
Husborne Crawley,
Bedfordshire
Ledburn Pit
Leighton Buzzard, Bedfordshire
Rackley Hills Pit
Leighton Buzzard, Bedfordshire
Tiddenfoot Pit,
Leighton Buzzard, Bedfordshire
Wrest Park
Silsoe, Bedfordshire
Snowberry Lake,
Bedfordshire
Woburn Estate Lakes
Woburn Park, Bedfordshire
Offley Village Pond
Near Hitchin, Bedfordshire
Westminster Pool
Near Ampthill, Bedfordshire
Tingrith Manor
Near Woburn, Bedfordshire
Tingrith Coarse Fishery
Near Luton, Bedfordshire
Ivel Valley Fishery
Near Broome, Bedfordshire
Broome Pits
Near Broome, Bedfordshire
Vauxhall Pits
Woburn Sands,
Bedfordshire

BERKSHIRE

Horton Boat Pool
Horton, Berkshire
Horton Church Pool
Horton, Berkshire
Metropolitan Police Lake
Slough, Berkshire
Long Moor Farm
Finchamstead, Berkshire

BUCKINGHAMSHIRE

Western Turville Reservoir
Aylesbury, Buckinghamshire
Grand Union Canal
Aylesbury Arm,
Buckinghamshire
Mount Farm Lake
Bletchley,
Buckinghamshire
Hyde Lane Lakes
Buckinghamshire
London Brick Pit
Calvert, Buckinghamshire
**Lower and Middle
Claydon Lakes**
Claydon, Buckinghamshire
Church Pool
Lillingstone Dayrell,
Buckinghamshire
Arboretum Lake
Linford, Milton Keynes,
Buckinghamshire
Lodge Lake
Milton Keynes,
Buckinghamshire
Furzton Lake
Milton Keynes,
Buckinghamshire
Blackhorse Lake
Great Linford Lakes, Milton
Keynes, Buckinghamshire
Grebe Lake
Near Calvert, Buckinghamshire
River Ouzel
Milton Keynes,
Buckinghamshire
Teardrop Lake
Milton Keynes,
Buckinghamshire
Willen Lake
Milton Keynes,
Buckinghamshire
Len Gurd's Pit
Near Woburn Sands,
Buckinghamshire

CAMBRIDGESHIRE

Barnwell Pit
Near Cambridge,
Cambridgeshire
Barway Pit
Near Soham, Cambridgeshire

LIST OF BRITISH WATERS THAT CONTAIN CATFISH cont.

River Cam
Cambridge, Cambridgeshire
Houchins Reservoir
Coggeshall, Cambridgeshire
River Great Ouse
Littleport, Cambridgeshire
Werrington Lakes
Peterborough, Cambridgeshire
Maxey Pit No.4
Maxey, near Peterborough, Cambridgeshire
Bluebell Lakes
Near Tansor, Peterborough, Cambridgeshire
Hertford Marina
Cambridgeshire
Eggetts Lake
Cambridgeshire
Northey Park
Peterborough, Cambridgeshire

CHESHIRE

Founders Pool
Near Antrobus, Cheshire
Lakemore
Cheshire
Shackerley Mere
Middlewich, Cheshire
Dukes Pool
Sandbach, Chesire
Whitley Pool
Whitley, Cheshire
Grimsditch Mill Pool
Near Whitley, Cheshire
Crabmill Flash
Cheshire
Plex Flash
Cheshire
Spring and New Pool
Near Runcorn, Cheshire

CORNWALL

Whiteacres Country Park
Near Newquay, Cornwall

DEVON

Anglers Eldorado
Beaworthy, Devon
Anglers Paradise
Beaworthy, Devon
Southreed Fisheries
Oakhampton, Devon

DORSET

Revels Fishery
Dorchester, Dorset

ESSEX

Berwick Ponds
Rainham, Essex
Bulphan Park Fishery
Bulphan, Essex
Churchwood Fisheries
Brentwood, Essex
Cobblers Mead
Corringham, Essex
Jimmy's Lake
Corringham, Essex
Mollands Lane Lake
South Ockenden, Essex
Slough House Lake
Bulphan, Essex
Burrows Farm
Bulphan, Essex
Gloucester Park
Near Basildon, Essex
Donylands Lake (Snake Pit)
Near Colchester, Essex
Crown Netherall Fishery
Near Nazeing, Essex
Chigboro Fisheries
Maldon, Essex

HEREFORD AND WORCESTER

Shatterford Lakes
Kidderminster, Hereford and Worcester
Arrow Valley Lake
Redditch, Hereford and Worcester

HERTFORDSHIRE

Friday Lake
Cheshunt, Hertfordshire
Aldenham Reservoir
Elstree, Hertfordshire
Riverside Road Fishery
St. Albans, Hertfordshire
Marsworth, Startops and Wilstone Reservoirs
Tring, Hertfordshire
Abbey Cross A.C. Pit
Turnford, Hertfordshire
Marsh Pit
Turnford, Hertfordshire
Wormleybury Lake
Wormley, Hertfordshire

Claverhambury Lakes
Claverhambury, Hertfordshire

LIST OF BRITISH WATERS THAT CONTAIN CATFISH cont.

HUMBERSIDE

Barton Broad
North Humberside
Gull Pond
South Humberside
Holme Fishery
Scunthorpe, Humberside
Lakeside
Cleethorpes, Humberside
Leven Park Lake
Leven, Humberside
Greaves End Pond
Humberside

KENT

Chilham Mill
Kent
Darenth Long Lake
Darenth, Kent
Barden Park
Near Tonbridge, Kent
Somerhill Fishery
Near Tonbridge, Kent
Wishing Tree Lake
Near Hastings, Kent

LANCASHIRE

Bailrigg Lake
Lancaster, Lancashire
Rawcliffe Fisheries
Near Blackpool, Lancashire
Star Mount Lake
Bradley Fold, Lancashire

LINCOLNSHIRE

Wagtail Lodge Fishery
Grantham, Lincolnshire

MANCHESTER

Giants Seat Fishery
Greater Manchester
Debdale Reservoir
Manchester,
Greater Manchester
Chorlton Marina
Sale, Greater Manchester
Sale Marina
Sale, Greater Manchester

MIDDLESEX

Mayfields Lake
West Drayton, Middlesex
Old Slade Lane Lake
West Drayton, Middlesex
Little Britain Lake
Uxbridge, Middlesex
Savay Lake
Near Uxbridge, Middlesex

MERSEYSIDE

Lymm Dam
Warrington, Merseyside
Lymm Vale
Warrington, Merseyside
Burton Mere
Wirral

NORFOLK

Swangey Lake
Near Attleborough, Norfolk
John Wilson's Lake
Great Witchingham, Norfolk
Denver Mill Ponds
Norfolk
Taverham Mills Lake
Taverham, Norfolk
Upper River Thurne
Norfolk
River Bure
Wroxham, Norfolk
Pentney Carp Lakes
Pentney, Norfolk
Little Dunham Carp Lakes
Near Swaffham, Norfolk

NORTHAMPTONSHIRE

Mid-Northants Carp Fishery
Ringstead, Northamptonshire
Mill Pool
Barby, Northamptonshire
Naseby Reservoir
Naseby, Northamptonshire

OXFORDSHIRE

Stoneacres Lake
Linch Hill Fishery
Stanton Harcourt, Oxfordshire
Willow Lake,
Linch Hill Fishery
Stanton Harcourt, Oxfordshire
Vauxhall Pit
Stanton Harcourt, Oxfordshire
Orchid Lake (the Creek)
Dorchester, Oxfordshire

SHROPSHIRE

Withy Pool
Dawley, Shropshire
Apley Pool
Leegomery, Shropshire
Baylis Pools
Shifnal, Shropshire

LIST OF BRITISH WATERS THAT CONTAIN CATFISH cont.

Alma Lake
Telford, Shropshire
Blue Pool
Telford, Shropshire
Homer Lake
Telford, Shropshire
Middle Pool
Telford, Shropshire
Radley Pool
Telford, Shropshire
Trench Pool
Telford, Shropshire
Rob Hales Syndicate Lake
Acton Burnell, Shropshire

STAFFORDSHIRE

Chase Water
Cannock, Staffordshire

SUFFOLK

Yew Tree Lake
Wortwell, Suffolk
Homersfield Lake
Near Wortwell, Suffolk
Holten Pit
Halesworth, Suffolk

SURREY

Lakeside
Stowmarker, Suffolk
Brittens Pond
Guildford, Surrey
Beaver Farm Fishery
Near Lingfield, Surrey
Newdigate
Dorking, Surrey
Badshot Lea Large Pond
Near Farnham, Surrey
River Thames
Kingston, Surrey
Sandersons Lakes
Woking, Surrey
Match Lake
Yateley, Surrey
Split Lake
Yateley, Surrey

Mill Lane Pit
Yateley, Surrey

SUSSEX

Kingfisher Lake,
Wintons Fishery
Burgess Hill, Sussex

Mallard Lake,
Wintons Fishery
Burgess Hill, Sussex

WALES

Sontley Pools
Wrexham, North Wales
Llyn Pentre Bach
Pwhelli, West Wales
Pwil Ruddbysg
Near Caernafon, West Wales
Pwil Helyg
Near Caernafon, West Wales
Lyn-y-Gors
Llandegfan, Anglesey,
North Wales

WARWICKSHIRE

Adam's Pool (C.C.G.Lake)
Alcester, Warwickshire
Tunnel Barn Farm
Shrewley, Warwickshire

WEST MIDLANDS

Himley Lake
Wolverhampton, West Midlands
Earlswood Lakes
Earlswood, West Midlands

YORKSHIRE

Tyram Hall Fisheries
Lindholme, South Yorkshire
Grafton Mere
Boroughbridge, West Yorkshire
Knotford Lagoon
Otley, West Yorkshire
Pasture Farm Lake
Kirton in Lindsey
South Yorkshire

Reproduced by kind permission of the Catfish Conservation Group.

Waters Questionnaire

Please insert name of contact..

Tel: (...................) ....who can verify details

Name: ....

Location: ....

Type and Size: ....

How to Find: ....

Carp Stock: ....

Other Species: ....

Permits: ....

Control: ....

Cost: ....

Restrictions: ....

Baits/Methods: ....

Comments: ....

Please insert name of contact..

Tel: (...................) ....who can verify details

Name: ....

Location: ....

Type and Size: ....

How to Find: ....

Carp Stock: ....

Other Species: ....

Permits: ....

Control: ....

Cost: ....

Restrictions: ....

Baits/Methods: ....

Comments: ....

Please return to:

Beekay Publishers, Withy Pool, Henlow Camp, Bedfordshire SG16 6EA

KM Donkey Chokers™

Want to catch the bigger fish? Then KM Donkey Chokers™ could be the answer to your dreams. Each pack contains 40 hand-made, specially hardened 25mm hookbaits. If you are fishing heavily stocked waters where the smaller fish get to the bait first, these Donkey Chokers™ will put off 'nuisance' fish and the smaller carp. They are also the perfect bait for french carp fishing. Available in packs of floaters (pop-ups) or sinkers.

Price: £4.99 a pack.

For full range of flavours see Boilie Flavours list.

KM Snowman™

The Snowman™ hookbait presentation is the latest alternative to standard boilie fishing and works extremely well on most waters. The new KM Snowman™ packs contain 50 specially-made boilies, half of which are floaters and half sinkers. One of each are fished on a hair, the sinker being nearest the hook. The buoyancy of the floating boilie takes the weight of the sinker so that they gently rest on the bottom. No shot or putty is required. The weightless Snowman™ is easily sucked in and is often taken before any free offerings are picked up. Available in 15mm or 20mm.

Price: £3.99 a pack.

For full range of flavours see Boilie Flavours list.

KM Boilie Flavours

Strawberry Oil Palatant
Honey Necta
Peach Oil Palatant
Ultra Birdspice
Rosehip XL
Tutti Frutti
Indian Spice
Cream RM30
Monster Mussel
Neutral (No flavour)
Squidmeal X Mix

New flavours in the KM boilie range this year are: Rosehip XL, Indian Spice, Monster Mussel, and Peach Oil Palatant. The very successful Wild Strawberry has now been blended with our new liquid palatant and is re-named: Strawberry Oil Palatant. Squidmeal has been further improved with our liquid smell and is now re-named: Squidmeal X Mix.

Following the success of our neutral pop-ups, the complete KM boilie range is now available in neutral (no flavour). You can simply soak, spray or glug them with your favourite flavour; your own exclusive bait without the hassle of making boilies!